1995

Yearbook of Science and the Future

1995

Yearbook of Science and the Future

Encyclopædia
Britannica, Inc.

Chicago
Auckland
London
Madrid
Manila
Paris
Rome
Seoul
Sydney
Tokyo
Toronto

1995

Yearbook of Science and the Future

Library of Congress Catalog Card Number: 69-12349
International Standard Book Number: 0-85229-602-9
International Standard Serial Number: 0096-3291

Encyclopædia Britannica, Inc.

President and Chief Executive Officer
Peter B. Norton

President, Encyclopædia Britannica North America
Joseph J. Esposito

Executive Vice President, Operations
Karen M. Barch

Editor
David Calhoun

Associate Editor
Charles Cegielski

Editorial Staff
Arthur Latham, Karen Sparks

Senior Picture Editor
Kathy Nakamura

Picture Editors
Julie Kunkler Stevens, Amy Zweig

Layout Artists and Illustrators
Kathryn Diffley, John L. Draves,
Jon Hensley, Steven Kapusta

Art Production Supervisor
Stephanie Motz

Art Staff
Diana M. Pitstick

Manager, Cartography
Barbra A. Vogel

Cartography Staff
Steven Bogdan, Dione E. Fortin, Michael D. Nutter

Manager, Copy Department
Sylvia Wallace

Copy Supervisors
Julian Ronning, Barbara Whitney

Copy Staff
Madolynn Cronk, Letricia Dixon,
Anthony L. Green, John Mathews,
Maria Ottolino, Beverly Sorkin,
Jeffrey Wallenfeldt, Lee Anne Wiggins

Manager, Production Control
Mary C. Srodon

Production Control Staff
Marilyn L. Barton, Stephanie A. Green

Contents

16

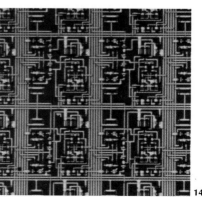

69

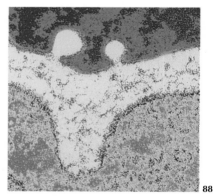

88

143

171

193

238

Encyclopædia Britannica Science Update

The Science Year in Review

A Science Classic

Institutions of Science

481

The New Submersibles

by Barrie B. Walden

New manned and unmanned vehicles are being developed to explore the deep-ocean environment and the seafloor.

During the late 1960s there was a popular belief that ocean exploration and exploitation would provide a major opportunity for United States industry. Many viewed the ocean as the frontier of the future, possibly able to surpass the opportunities envisioned for the exploration of space. A number of major U.S. corporations prepared for this eventuality by constructing deep-diving manned submersible vehicles. Many of these companies intended to operate their submersibles on a profit-making basis in support of the expected scientific and industrial activities in the deep ocean. During this period more than a dozen submersibles were designed and constructed. Additionally, a myriad of manned and unmanned vehicles with shallower depth capabilities were produced, both in the United States and in other nations. These tended to be designed for specific tasks and frequently were intended to be sold to companies that were providing support services to the growing offshore oil and gas industry. The late 1960s and early 1970s witnessed the heyday of undersea vehicle development.

By the late 1970s the reality of attempting to operate complicated electromechanical devices in the hostile ocean environment had taken its toll on the available vehicles, and many of the original developers moved on to other pursuits. There remained, however, a small number

Deep Submergence Vehicle Alvin *is lowered into the ocean from its support vessel. The best known of the early submersibles,* Alvin *was placed in service in 1964. Among its many achievements were its discovery of deep-sea hydrothermal vents and its help in the search for and recovery of a hydrogen bomb accidentally lost off the coast of Spain.*

of successes—vehicles that, for a variety of reasons, remained operational and played an important role in scientific and industrial ocean activities. Additionally, the experiences with these submersibles, both successes and failures, resulted in a substantial increase in the body of knowledge associated with ocean engineering.

Early manned vehicles

The best known of the manned submersibles of that time is unquestionably the Deep Submergence Vehicle (DSV) *Alvin*. This vehicle was originally constructed by Litton Industries for operation by the Woods Hole (Massachusetts) Oceanographic Institution, with funding provided by the U.S. Navy. The intended purpose was to support deep-ocean research by allowing scientists to make direct observations and manipulations in the deep sea. *Alvin* could go as deep as 1,828 meters (6,000 feet), and the vehicle routinely carried two scientists and a pilot on dives that lasted from 6 to 10 hours. *Alvin* was placed in service in 1964 and almost immediately proved its worth by assisting in the search and recovery of a hydrogen bomb accidently lost in 780 meters (2,550 feet) of water off the coast of Spain in January 1966. From then until the early 1970s, *Alvin* made 60 to 80 dives per year from its catamaran support vessel, *Lulu,* in support of science programs. Its success caused it to be used as a model for the *Sea Cliff* and *Turtle* submersibles, vehicles that could dive as deep as 2,000 meters (6,500 feet) and constructed by General Dynamics Corp. for U.S. Navy deep-water search-and-retrieval tasks.

In 1974 *Alvin* participated in Project FAMOUS (French-American Mid-Oceanic Undersea Survey) along with the French submersibles *Cyana* and *Archimède*. During this expedition scientists were able to obtain information confirming the theory of seafloor spreading. Following that success utilization of *Alvin* steadily increased, accompanied by continuous technological improvements to the craft. In 1993 *Alvin* could achieve an operational depth of 4,000 meters (13,000 feet) and routinely made between 150 and 200 dives per year.

During the 1960s Canada, the U.K., France, Japan, and the Soviet Union, in addition to the U.S., developed manned submersible vehicles. As with *Alvin,* many of those that survived were devoted to research activities. Examples included France's *Cyana* (launched in 1970), the Soviet Union's *Sever 1* and *2,* and Canada's *P2.* In contrast to those developed in the United States, the early vehicles of other countries were frequently used as stepping-stones in the development and construction of newer, more capable submersibles. In 1985 the French launched *Nautile,* a vehicle capable of diving 6,000 meters (19,700 feet). Japan's *Shinkai 2000,* rated for a depth of 2,000 meters, and *Shinkai 6500,* rated for 6,500 meters (21,300 feet), were launched in 1981 and 1989, respectively. The Soviet submersibles *Mir 1* and *2,* with operational depths of 6,000 meters, were constructed by Rauma Repola in Finland and launched in 1987. *Sea Cliff, Turtle,* and *Alvin* continued to operate in the United States, and each was upgraded in depth capability—*Sea Cliff* to 6,000 meters, *Turtle* to 3,000 meters (9,850 feet), and *Alvin* to

BARRIE B. WALDEN is Manager of Submersible Engineering and Operations at the Woods Hole Oceanographic Institution, Woods Hole, Massachusetts.

Photograph on page 9 by Emory Kristof, © *National Geographic Society*

11

French submersible Cyana, *launched in 1970, could dive as deep as 3,000 meters (9,800 feet) and housed a crew of three. In 1974 it participated in Project FAMOUS (French-American Mid-Ocean Undersea Study), during which scientists collected data that confirmed the theory of seafloor spreading.*

4,000 meters (13,120 feet)—but no new deep-diving submersibles with capabilities greater than 2,000 meters have been constructed in the United States since the 1960s.

A similar situation exists for manned submersibles designed for shallower operations. During the 1960s many vehicles were designed and constructed for the purpose of supporting the offshore oil and gas industry. They were intended to provide the means for conducting the surveys and inspections associated with offshore drilling and production platforms. By the end of the decade, there were nearly 50 such submersibles in existence but, as with their deeper-diving cousins, many proved uneconomical to operate and served primarily as prototypes for improved vehicles constructed in the 1970s.

The need for direct human observation and participation in undersea industrial activities continued into the 1970s, and two submersible manufacturers distinguished themselves with the design and construction of a large number of "offshore workboats": Perry Submarine Builders of Riviera Beach, Florida, and HYCO Ltd. of North Vancouver, British Columbia. Between the two of them, they constructed almost 50 submersibles, many of which remained operational in 1994. In addition, Harbor Branch Oceanographic Institution of Fort Pierce, Florida, con-

Soviet submersible Mir 1, with pilot Andrey Andreyev standing astride the hatch (left), is hoisted by crane with a single cable to the support vessel Akademic Mstislav Keldysh. Below, Anatoly Sagalevitch (left), director of the Soviet manned submersible program, pilots Mir 1, with U.S. photographer Emory Kristof at his side. Along with its twin, Mir 2, the submersible could descend as deep as 6,100 meters (20,000 feet) and, therefore, cover 95% of the ocean floor.

Johnson-Sea-Link I explores the waters of the Bahama Islands. One of a pair of submersibles built in the 1970s for scientific research by Harbor Branch Oceanographic Institution of Fort Pierce, Florida, it remained operational in 1994.

structed the *Johnson-Sea-Link I* and *II* vehicles, which were operating in 1994 for scientific research applications. Many others were built by various organizations on the basis of the lessons learned by the pioneers of the 1960s, but by the end of the 1970s most had been removed from service as the costs of their operation increased and less expensive alternatives were developed.

Remotely operated vehicles

Manned submersibles were not the only undersea vehicles developed during the 1960s and 1970s. Unmanned remotely operated vehicles (ROVs), controlled via electromechanical cable connections with their support ships, were constructed. Initially, vehicles of this type consisted of little more than video cameras in pressure-resistant housings with attached propellers to allow some degree of maneuverability. As time progressed, however, the tasks for these vehicles increased in complexity, as did their sophistication and cost. At first, ROVs were constructed for inspection and survey tasks, where they had the advantage of inexpensive operational costs in comparison with manned submersibles. In addition, they were easily transported between work sites and could be deployed for long periods without concern for the well-being of human occupants. However, they could not accomplish the tasks possible with a manned vehicle, particularly those requiring manipulation. As a result,

14

ROVs were frequently used in conjunction with manned submersibles. The unmanned vehicles conducted inspections and identified tasks to be undertaken with the help of manned vehicles. While the work was in progress, an ROV's cable connection to the surface allowed video monitoring by supervisory and coordinating personnel.

This combination of submersibles seemed to be an ideal situation, capitalizing on the strong points of both devices. However, operating two types of vehicles with different manpower and support requirements proved expensive, and increasingly capable ROVs were developed. The hope was that the need for manned submersibles could be eliminated by the provision of imaging sensors and manipulators sufficient to allow ROVs to duplicate the capabilities of the manned vehicles. To some extent this was successful; during the late 1970s the use of manned submersibles in support of offshore industrial activities declined, and the majority of the vehicles designed for that purpose ceased operation. ROVs were constructed with specific support tasks in mind and, in some cases, the equipment they were intended to service was tailored for their use. However, as the ROVs' capabilities progressed, so did their complexity and expense.

The 1980s began with few operational deep-diving submersibles, most of which were employed in support of ocean research. Many of the world's shallow-depth submersibles, previously utilized in industrial activities, had been replaced with unmanned, remotely controlled devices. Those that continued to operate were frequently engaged in scientific research. Hundreds of ROVs of every size and description were in routine use, principally for industrial and military applications. Most were of the tethered, free-swimming variety with a depth capability of less than 1,000 meters (3,300 feet), but others were designed to walk or crawl along the seafloor, and some had depth capabilities equal to those of the deep-diving, untethered submersibles. In 1985 a drop in the price of oil forced the oil and gas industry to cut costs in every possible manner, including the discontinuation of much of the offshore production activities. Consequently, the undersea service industry's operations were severely reduced, and development of new vehicles and equipment sharply declined. Only the few vehicles utilized for military and research purposes continued to operate as usual, and the entire ocean engineering support industry looked for other opportunities to market their skills. Two such opportunities emerged in the realm of undersea vehicles: tourist submersibles and low-cost ROVs.

Tourist submersibles

In the early 1960s Jacques Piccard developed the submersible *Auguste Piccard* for use in carrying up to 40 passengers to depths of 820 meters (2,500 feet) in Lake Geneva during the 1964–65 Swiss National Exposition. During its year of service at the fair, it made 1,112 dives, carrying more than 32,000 passengers. The success of this entertainment-oriented submersible may well have spawned an industry in the 1980s. With the demise of submersible operations for the oil and gas industry, many

15

vehicles became available, and seven were purchased by Research Submersibles Ltd. (RSL) of Grand Cayman, British West Indies. Beginning in 1983, RSL began passenger operations by offering dives to a depth of 250 meters (820 feet) on the Grand Cayman Wall.

RSL's submersibles, originally constructed for undersea work tasks, had space for only two passengers, which proved to be far below demand during peak tourist seasons. Consequently, SUB Aquatics Development Corp. (SADC) of Vancouver was formed in 1983 to design and construct the first modern built-for-the-purpose tourist submersible. Their *Atlantis I* submarine, designed to carry 28 passengers to depths of 45 meters (148 feet), began operations at Grand Cayman Island in 1986. Soon afterward, SADC constructed more vehicles of the *Atlantis* series and was joined

Atlantis Submarines International, Vancouver, British Columbia

by three other manufacturers: Fluid Energy Ltd. of Scotland, Wartsila of Finland, and Mitsubishi Heavy Industries of Japan. Between them, 14 multipassenger (28–48) shallow-diving submarines were constructed during the 1980s, for use throughout the world in the tourist industry.

Despite initial success, of the three manufacturers only SADC remained in the business during the 1990s, with continued construction of *Atlantis* vehicles. However, other companies entered the field with new designs, construction materials, and techniques, and there appeared to be a developing trend toward deeper-diving capabilities. Industry consultants estimated that there is a worldwide market for between 50 and 100 vehicles of this nature.

Atlantis submersibles, built in the 1980s by SUB Aquatics Development Corp. of Vancouver, British Columbia, take tourists on underwater explorations in the Caribbean Sea. On the opposite page, the 15.25-meter (50-foot)-long Atlantis I was designed to carry 28 passengers to depths of 45 meters (150 feet). A later model (above), measuring 19.8 meters (65 feet) in length, accommodates 46 passengers.

Low-cost ROVs

A second major trend in submersible vehicles in the 1980s was begun by *MiniRover*, a small, inexpensive ROV developed by Deep Sea Systems International and manufactured by Benthos, Inc., both of the United States. This vehicle was a breakthrough in ROV technology not because of increased capability but because its price was one-tenth of that for similar devices. This ROV was small, was easily transported and deployed, and required little maintenance and support equipment, yet it provided both sonar and video search capabilities to depths of more than 260 meters (850 feet) and had a limited ability to manipulate tools.

17

MiniRover MKII, *a small, remotely operated submersible, cost only one-tenth as much as similar vehicles. Easily transported and deployed and requiring little maintenance, it provided both sonar and video search capabilities to depths of more than 260 meters (850 feet).*

The concept of an inexpensive underwater vehicle was extremely popular, and many manufacturers joined in the production of these devices. Twenty to thirty different models were designed, and hundreds of individual units produced. Noteworthy was the *Phantom* series, begun in 1985 by Deep Ocean Engineering; by 1993, more than 200 had been sold.

Research activities

Deep-diving undersea vehicles received a much-needed boost in 1977 when geologists utilizing *Alvin* to study the Galapagos Rift in the eastern Pacific discovered hydrothermal vents. These are areas in the seafloor where water warmed by subsurface volcanic activity percolates upward, rich in dissolved minerals. Astonishingly, these areas were found to be teeming with a variety of undersea life existing as an ecosystem based on chemical synthesis. This discovery overturned the conventional belief that sunlight is the basic source of energy for all life cycles.

The science community reacted to these discoveries with enthusiasm and planned further expeditions to study these areas. The French submersible *Cyana* explored the East Pacific Rise off the mouth of the Gulf of California in 1978 and found evidence of past vent activity, including dead animals of the types discovered the previous year. In 1979 *Alvin* returned to the Pacific for dives on both the Galapagos Rift at latitude 9° N and the East Pacific Rise (latitude 21° N). This time hydrothermal vents having water temperatures estimated at 350° C (660° F) were discovered. These vents were termed "black smokers," and they resembled

18

miniature versions of steel-mill chimneys in full production. When this extremely hot water, saturated with dissolved minerals, contacts the surrounding 2° C (35.6° F) water, much of the mineral content precipitates out, turning the water inky black and forming a tall column surrounding the hot water.

Again, there was an abundance of unexpected life, including clams 30 centimeters (12 inches) long, red-tipped tube worms 300 centimeters (120 inches) long, vast beds of mussels, and free roving crabs. Although the life forms were perhaps the most spectacular of the discoveries, geologists, geochemists, volcanologists, and others found research in these "spreading center" areas to be extremely rewarding. As a result, the deep-diving submersible became a valued and respected workhorse of the oceanographic research community.

John Edmond

"Black smokers," deep-sea hydrothermal vents with water temperatures of about 350° C (660° F), were discovered by Alvin in the Pacific Ocean in 1979. When the hot water, saturated with dissolved minerals, contacts the surrounding 2° C (35.6° F) water, much of the mineral content precipitates out, turning the water black.

At the time of the hydrothermal vent discovery, there were two manned deep submergence vehicles in common use for oceanographic research: *Alvin* in the United States and *Cyana* in France. In 1981 the Japan Marine Science Center in Yokosuka began operating the *Shinkai 2000*, a submersible constructed by Mitsubishi Heavy Industries. France launched *Nautile* in 1985, and in 1987 the Russian Institute of Oceanology began operating *Mir 1* and *Mir 2*, constructed by Rauma Repola of Finland. In 1989 Mitsubishi Heavy Industries launched *Shinkai 6500;* it was the deepest-diving manned submersible in the world. This upswing in construction was the result of the interesting discoveries made by the few remaining deep-diving submarines operating in the late 1970s. All of the new vehicles were constructed for oceanographic research purposes.

The research projects assisted by these vehicles required first-hand observations, controlled sampling, and detailed manipulation of experimental equipment. The dive sites were usually chosen after extensive analysis of data obtained by other means, such as towed mapping sonar, ship-mounted multibeam echo sounders, and, occasionally, towed "sniffers"—instruments designed to report specific anomalies such as high-temperature water or concentrations of telltale chemicals. Submersibles use rechargeable batteries, and their dives are thus power-limited. Even if they were not, the personnel compartments of these vehicles are small, and so the length of a normal dive is frequently limited by human comfort factors. As a result, submersibles are rarely used for search and

A fresh fissure on the seaward slope of the Japan Trench in the Pacific Ocean, at a depth of 6,200 meters (20,335 feet), was photographed in 1991 by the Japanese submersible Shinkai 6500. *At the time of its launch in 1989, the 9.5-meter (31-foot)-long craft was the world's deepest-diving manned submersible.*

survey purposes, which, to be done efficiently, require lengthy, sustained horizontal transits beyond an untethered vehicle's capacity. Instead, manned vehicles spend the majority of their time working on or near the seafloor in a limited area. Exceptions occur, such as a sampling and imaging transect in which the vehicle travels over the bottom obtaining film and video images plus geologic and biological samples. However, investigations of this type can cover only limited distances and usually involve some amount of the manipulation tasks for which the DSV is ideally suited.

The common theme of submersible utilization for oceanographic research is that of direct human observation, on the part of either the scientists or the pilot. A human occupant, looking out through a viewport and feeling the motion of the submersible, is able to obtain a clearer understanding of size and spatial relationships than is possible by any other means. The pilot's three-dimensional perception, obtained by use of both eyes through the forward viewport, allows him or her to operate the exterior manipulators with an ease not possible with remote, monocular vision. For this reason, manned submersibles remain the tool of choice for many seafloor research activities. Unfortunately, they are expensive both to build and to operate, frequently requiring a specially trained maintenance and operations crew of more than 10 persons, plus those associated with the support vessel. The safety aspects related to the fact that human occupants are involved in the dives adds another degree of complexity and expense.

Unmanned remotely operated vehicles have some advantages over manned submersibles; their tethers to the surface can provide them with unlimited power, and when their crews get tired, they can be replaced without disrupting the dive. In theory an ROV can make dives lasting weeks and can cover hundreds of kilometers in a search-and-survey mode. Initially, ROVs were designed for operations in a manner similar to manned submersibles; they were intended for tasks at specific sites and thus required only limited horizontal-transit capability. Search-and-survey work was done either with ship-mounted sensors or by towed vehicles distinguished from ROVs by their limited maneuvering ability. As with submersibles, ROVs were used for science activities after other techniques had located interesting research sites.

Combined unmanned missions

As the technology of the 1980s progressed, the sensors available for deployment on all types of deep-submergence vehicles became capable of gathering increasing amounts of data. In the case of remotely controlled vehicles, the ability of the tether to deliver the collected data to the surface became a major operational hurdle, solved by employment of fiber-optic data-transmission techniques. New cables were developed, along with specialized winches to handle them. It became possible to transmit real-time video imagery to the surface from multiple sources, allowing an ROV pilot a view of the work area rivaling that of the submersible pilot. The available video equipment was not equal to the human eye,

21

but ROVs had power and dive time on their side. Additionally, ROVs were operated with a cable and winch on the surface support ship, the same cable and winch required by the more sophisticated towed survey vehicles. This fact enabled a single ship to carry and deploy both types of vehicle. The technology of each type was similar and, therefore, a single crew could be responsible for operations, thus minimizing costs.

The first attempt to utilize this concept was made by the Deep Submergence Laboratory of the Woods Hole Oceanographic Institution. This group, under the guidance of Robert Ballard, constructed the *Argo* and *Jason* vehicles, which were intended to be used simultaneously from the same support ship. *Argo* was a towed survey vehicle equipped with two types of sonar—down-looking and side-looking—plus a specially developed high-altitude "snap shot" video system. Additionally, *Argo* served as the "garage" for *Jason*, a smaller, fully maneuverable ROV with sonar, film, and video imaging systems designed for close-up, detailed work. The concept was to survey vast areas of the seafloor by using *Argo*, with stops for deployment of *Jason* whenever something warranting closer scrutiny was located.

Development of these vehicles was a difficult and expensive task extending over many years. *Argo* was the first system to be developed fully

Robert D. Ballard and Martin Bowen, © Woods Hole Oceanographic Institution

enough for an actual deep-sea test to be practical and warranted. The Deep Submergence Laboratory needed a site with a bottom terrain that provided sufficient imaging targets but was uncluttered enough to allow for testing *Argo*'s search capabilities. Many areas in the northern Atlantic were suitable, but to make the test more interesting, Ballard chose the site believed to be the resting place of the *Titanic*. On Sept. 1, 1985, *Argo* obtained images of the *Titanic* resting on the bottom at a depth of almost 4,000 meters (13,100 feet); thus, the first of the new ROVs had been successful.

Jason's development presented a considerably more complex undertaking because the data link to the surface needed to be fast enough to allow real-time control of the vehicle by its surface pilots while at the same time transmitting the large volume of data produced by an array of sophisticated imaging sensors. As a first step a small vehicle originally constructed for the U.S. Navy was modified to incorporate some of the features intended for use with *Jason*. This vehicle was dubbed *Jason Jr.,* and it was mated with *Alvin* for testing purposes. This arrangement allowed the ROV pilot to observe the ROV from within *Alvin* as he attempted to control its activities in deep water. Again the test site was that of the *Titanic*. In 1986 *Alvin* carried *Jason Jr.* to the wreckage 12 times,

Opposite page, the small submersible Jason Jr., controlled by the crew aboard Alvin, looks into the sunken ocean liner Titanic. Inside the ship, Jason Jr. obtained many images, including a brass-and-crystal light fixture from which a feathery sea pen was sprouting (above).

23

where its maneuverability enabled it to obtain video and film images not previously possible.

The real *Jason* was not ready for testing with *Argo* until 1989, when both systems were taken to the Mediterranean Sea for a search-and-survey test. Unfortunately, *Jason* had become larger than originally expected in order to accommodate a greater number of sensors. The size of *Argo* thus had to be increased to allow *Jason* to fit inside. The increased size and weight of the combination proved to be too much for the support ship's winch and cable; the latter parted during a launch, and both vehicles fell to the seafloor. They were recovered without difficulty, but the idea of operating them together was abandoned; instead it became common practice to deploy the wide-area search vehicles and the close-look vehicles independently. However, the concept of two vehicles operating together was not lost entirely; for control purposes *Jason* had been designed to be attached to a larger, heavier submersible. The heavy vehicle was termed the "depressor" because it provided the mass needed to control the end of the long cable leading to the surface. This cable could not be allowed to pull on *Jason* directly because it would make control of the craft almost impossible. *Argo* was to be the "depressor," and when it proved to be too large, it was replaced by *Medea*, a smaller vehicle but one having similar imaging sensors. The end result was a

The submersible Jason *is lifted out of the water onto the deck of its support ship. A fully maneuverable ROV,* Jason *was equipped with sonar, film, and video imaging systems designed for close-up, detailed work.*

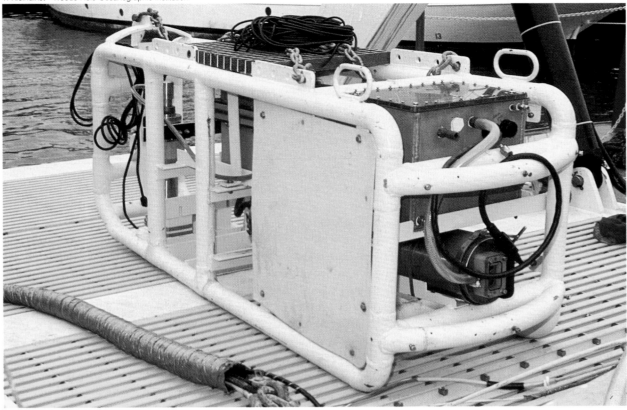

system in which *Jason* accomplished detailed tasks in close proximity to the seafloor, while *Medea* remained 10–20 meters (30–65 feet) above, providing wide-area imaging coverage. The views from both vehicles were available in real time to the pilot located on the surface support ship.

The remotely operated Medea *took part in joint missions with* Jason. *While* Jason *provided close-up views near the ocean floor,* Medea *remained 10–20 meters (30–65 feet) above it to achieve wide-area-imaging coverage.*

Advantages of manned vehicles

The *Argo/Jason/Medea* combination would seem to be an ideal deep-ocean research tool, possibly replacing manned submersibles. For a number of reasons, however, a comparison of the two is difficult. ROVs of these vehicles' sophistication require a support ship with capabilities similar to those that support manned submersibles. Of particular importance for *Jason*-type operations is the requirement for a dynamic positioning system that allows the ship to remain stationary with a high degree of accuracy, despite changing sea conditions. This is needed to ensure that the ship does not pull on the ROV tether at inappropriate moments. ROV operations do not involve the safety issues that result from human occupants, but the expense of these vehicles warrants a similar degree of expensive operational safeguards.

Despite advancing technology, remote imaging sensors do not provide the same "feel" that is obtained from firsthand observations through a viewport, and a vehicle without the mass of the average manned submersible does not have the leverage to perform many manipulative tasks

25

with the same ease. On the other hand, ROVs deliver their data to scientists working in the relative comfort of the support ship rather than in the close quarters of a submersible's personnel sphere. And, by utilizing satellite communications technology, it becomes unnecessary for them even to be on the ship; they can effectively work at communications consoles in their laboratories. This concept was demonstrated in the spring of 1993 when scientists at multiple sites in the United States were able to take an active part in a *Jason/Medea* cruise conducted in Guaymas Basin, off the coast of Guaymas, Mexico.

When operational costs are compared on the basis of time spent on the seafloor, it is reasonable to expect ROVs to outperform manned submersibles. This is primarily due to the cost of the surface support ship, however, and assumes that nothing useful is being done when the manned submersible is not diving. The manpower requirements for operating the vehicles themselves are quite similar when one considers that ROVs require three complete personnel exchanges while conducting 24-hour-per-day operations. Other expenses such as those for expendable supplies are also similar.

All things considered, ROVs and manned submersibles do not have the same capabilities and cannot be directly compared. The advancement of technology has allowed ROVs to make considerable inroads into manned submersible territory, and this will continue; however, at the present time, "remote presence" and "real presence" are not equivalent. The availability of deep-diving manned submersibles and the proliferation of ROVs provide the oceanographic research community with the opportunity to determine the relative benefits of these highly capable research tools.

Future prospects
The question of the relative merits of manned submersibles versus remotely controlled vehicles is probably best answered with the recognition that they are complementary. Another possible outcome, however, is for both to be eclipsed by the latest deep-sea technological development, Untethered or Autonomous Unmanned Vehicles (UUVs or AUVs). These devices combine some of the best features of the previously discussed vehicles and frequently have the added advantage of lower operational costs. They are true undersea robots, designed and programmed to accomplish predetermined tasks. Once deployed, they have little or no contact with the surface until their mission is complete; consequently, surface-ship and personnel requirements are minimal.

Vehicles of this type are not new, and some have considerable operational history. The French UUV *Epaulard* was launched in 1983, as was the U.S. Navy's Advanced Underwater Search System (AUSS). Recently, however, technological advances facilitated by microprocessors, increased capacity low-power data-storage devices, improved materials for long-term seawater service, general miniaturization of electronic components, increased capacities for energy-storage devices, and improvements in remote sensor systems have combined to enable the development of UUVs with unprecedented capabilities. Continued advances in this area

The Autonomous Benthic Explorer (ABE) *is lowered into the ocean on a test dive. An Untethered Unmanned Vehicle (UUV), it is a true undersea robot, designed and programmed to undertake predetermined missions. It has little contact with the surface until the task has been completed; therefore, surface-ship and personnel requirements are minimal, and costs are reduced.*

will undoubtedly result in research vehicles tailored to accomplishing many of the tasks presently achieved by manned submersibles and ROVs. Examples include wide-area-imaging surveys, where the maneuverability of these devices will provide a clear advantage over towed systems, and local-area monitoring, where their lengthy unattended deployment periods provide a cost-effectiveness superior to either of the other vehicle types. Representative UUVs designed for each of these tasks, respectively, are *Odyssey,* constructed by the Sea Grant College Program at the Massachusetts Institute of Technology, and the *Autonomous Benthic Explorer (ABE),* constructed by researchers at the Woods Hole Oceanographic Institution. Both vehicles have been successfully deployed and will soon be available for general research purposes.

27

Calling Nature's Bluff

The Secret World of Cliffs

by D.W. Larson, P.E. Kelly, and U. Matthes-Sears

Home to a surprising variety of plants and animals, the edges and faces of cliffs are unique ecosystems that are offering scientists new evidence of the impact of industry and technology on natural habitats.

In the 60 years since Sir Arthur Tansley first coined the word *ecosystem*, an enormous amount of ecological research has been carried out in every imaginable habitat. Verdant deciduous forests, productive grasslands, Antarctic polar deserts, tropical rain forests, and deep-sea hydrothermal vents have all yielded their secrets to ecological researchers. Until recently, however, vertical cliff ecosystems were completely overlooked by ecologists because they appeared to be hostile, lifeless, and seemingly impossible to sample. Indeed they do not even show up on the most detailed aerial photographs. While cliffs such as Gibraltar or Dover are very conspicuous from the ground and in many instances instantly recognizable, they have attracted no scientific inquiry.

The following article attempts to rectify this situation by presenting a discussion of recent ecological research on a cliff ecosystem known as the Niagara Escarpment that snakes its way across the landscape of southern Ontario. In the course of their work, the researchers came to two unrelated conclusions. First, cliff ecosystems may represent some of the most biologically interesting and significant habitats on the Earth. Second, significant scientific breakthroughs can be made in relatively short periods of time if one works in areas neglected by others.

Cliffs and the Niagara Escarpment

A slope becomes a cliff only when the slope is parallel to the force of gravity—when objects fall off rather than roll down. This distinction may sound trivial, but the practical differences are enormous; one cannot conduct research on cliffs unless one uses ropes and other rock-climbing equipment, and mistakes on cliffs can kill or cause serious injury. Cliffs need not be continuous vertical drops, however, and all of the cliffs discussed below have ledges, crevices, and cracks that represent locally horizontal (or at least nonvertical) ground within the cliff proper. These

(Overleaf) Cliff ecologist Cal Clark descends the cliff face of the Niagara Escarpment. These cliffs support an old-growth forest characterized by a diverse assemblage of plant and animal species including eastern white cedar trees that reach ages exceeding 1,500 years.
Photograph, Peter Kelly

Among the world's best-known cliffs are Gibraltar (left) and Dover (below). Although they are likely to be biologically interesting habitats, they have as yet attracted no scientific inquiry.

Photos, A.G.E. Fotostock

D.W. LARSON is a Professor of Botany, and **P.E. KELLY** and **U. MATTHES-SEARS** are research associates at the Cliff Ecology Research Group at the University of Guelph, Ontario.

small microhabitats within the cliff turn out to be very important to the ecology of the organisms that occupy them.

The cliffs of the Niagara Escarpment are the exposed edge of an ancient seabed called the Michigan Basin that was formed more than 450 million years ago. Roughly 800 kilometers (500 miles) in diameter and centered near Lansing, Michigan, it extended from what is now central Ontario to eastern Wisconsin and from Sault Sainte Marie, Michigan, to northern Ohio. Over the next 400 million years the seabed became a concave basin. Then, during the past one million years, four episodes of

30

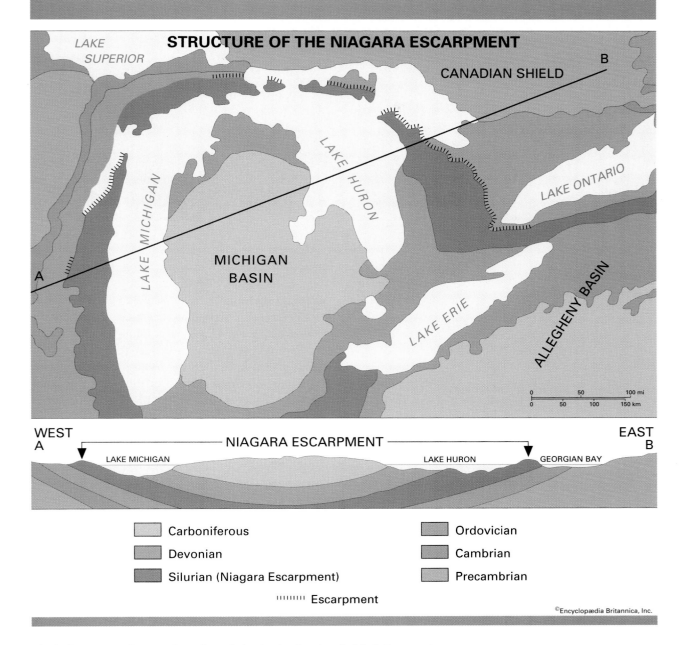

STRUCTURE OF THE NIAGARA ESCARPMENT

LAKE SUPERIOR

CANADIAN SHIELD

B

LAKE MICHIGAN

LAKE HURON

LAKE ONTARIO

MICHIGAN BASIN

ALLEGHENY BASIN

LAKE ERIE

A

| 0 | 50 | 100 mi |
| 0 | 50 | 100 | 150 km |

WEST
A

NIAGARA ESCARPMENT

EAST
B

LAKE MICHIGAN

LAKE HURON

GEORGIAN BAY

Carboniferous

Devonian

Silurian (Niagara Escarpment)

Ordovician

Cambrian

Precambrian

Escarpment

©Encyclopædia Britannica, Inc.

glaciation scoured away the edge of the basin, leaving behind the most wear-resistant rocks—the Silurian dolomitic limestones. While much of this exposed limestone was subsequently buried by glacial till and outwash deposits, some 160 kilometers (100 miles) of sinuous exposed cliff edge in Ontario and somewhat less in Wisconsin and Michigan remained exposed.

The cliff is nearly vertical along the entire length of the escarpment because of the erosion of the weaker Ordovician shales and limestones that lie underneath the Silurian dolomite. Often this erosion is repeated

The structure of the Niagara Escarpment is shown within the context of the surficial geology of the Michigan Basin. The cross-sectional layering of geological strata along the line joining A and B is shown in the bottom panel.

31

The Niagara Escarpment was formed by differences in the rates of erosion of the overlying limestone and dolomite and the underlying shales at the edge of an ancient seabed. While most of the rim is buried under glacial overburden, 160 kilometers (100 miles) of cliff face are exposed as in this section near Wiarton, Ontario.

over the centuries, precipitated by the weathering and undercutting of the cliff face, the subsequent production of overhanging table rocks, and their ultimate collapse, restoring the cliff to its original vertical orientation. The most famous of these table rock collapses was recorded at Niagara Falls in the 1850s, when a horse-drawn carriage was reportedly carried into the canyon as the foolhardy passenger jumped for his life.

The Niagara Escarpment now appears as a slender rock outcrop that extends from the familiar Niagara Falls in the south to the tip of Ontario's Bruce Peninsula and Manitoulin Island in the north and then across the top of the Great Lakes near Sault Sainte Marie and down to Door County, Wisconsin. It finally disappears under glacial till near Chicago. While no special designation is made of this landform in the United States, an agency of the Ontario government, called the Niagara Escarpment Commission (NEC), exists to control the use and abuse of all lands adjacent to the escarpment. Though the NEC was established more than 20 years ago to regulate economic exploitation of escarpment lands, it had no mandate to conduct scientific research.

The first look at cliffs

Prior to 1986 the white exposed limestone cliffs of the Niagara Escarpment were considered barren and lifeless. To graduate student Steven Spring, however, they represented something quite different. Being both a naturalist and a rock climber, he had experienced sparse forests of stunted trees and other organisms such as ferns and lichens that were hard to see on cliffs at distances of more than 15 meters (50 feet). He also had recognized that the cliff, in addition to harboring this rich botanical biodiversity, was actually a mosaic of rock faces, cracks, crevices, and ledges that formed microhabitats and runways for a wide variety of animals such as bobcats, chipmunks, and snakes.

Despite these interesting aspects of the structure and function of the cliff habitat, what Spring really wanted to ask was, How can trees grow from bare rock? What neither he nor anyone else in the laboratory realized at the time was that by asking that simple question, he was

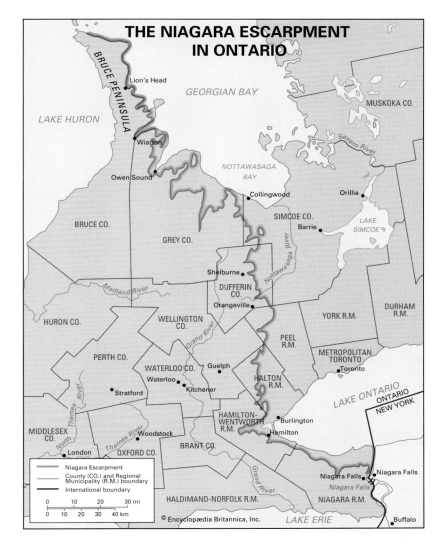

THE NIAGARA ESCARPMENT IN ONTARIO

Niagara Escarpment
County (CO.) and Regional
Municipality (R.M.) boundary
International boundary

0   10   20   30 mi
0 10 20 30 40 km
© Encyclopædia Britannica, Inc.

An eastern white cedar clings tenuously to a Niagara Escarpment cliff face. Questioning how trees grow out of bare rock sparked a line of scientific inquiry related to cliff ecology and the factors that control the form and function of a cliff ecosystem.

Doug Larson

going to open a window on what turned out to be an ecosystem full of superlatives, one containing some of the oldest trees in Canada, the oldest coarse woody debris in any forest in eastern North America, and some of the slowest-growing trees in the world.

The apparently simple question How do trees grow from bare rock? actually has several more critically important questions built into it. First, has anyone else ever studied such a question? Second, are the trees there really growing any differently from trees in the surrounding forest? Third, is the cliff forest really different in structure and function from the rest of the forested landscape? These three questions are really all facets of an additional question—Is the cliff a distinctive place in the landscape, or is it part of a larger place? This question is not as difficult to answer as one might think. If the larger surrounding ecosystem changes in space and time without there being corresponding changes in the cliff ecosystem, then the cliff is a distinctive place somewhat separate from its surroundings.

Determining the age structure of a cliff-face forest involved sampling every tree within measured transects (vertical strips) at several sites (above). Old fire hoses painted black and white in one-meter intervals serve as both scale markers and boundaries between transects. Cliff ecologist Steven Spring (right) places a quadrant at a predetermined location on a Niagara Escarpment cliff face and records the existence, frequency, and species name of individual plants that occur within it.

After discovering that no one had ever investigated the biological structure of communities on cliffs, the authors and their colleagues set out to sample directly the biophysical conditions along the gradient from plateau to cliff face and talus slope (the rock debris at the base of a cliff). They carried out the sampling by using many transects, narrow strips of neighboring plots running from the top to the bottom of the cliff. The use of multiple transects within sites allowed for statistical replication, and ultimately such replication allowed the researchers to decide how much of the variance in the biophysical data was attributable to geographic location, how much to the location of transects within sites, and how much to random error. What they discovered was that a predictable group of species and an equally predictable array of environmental conditions existed at each location along the gradient from plateau to cliff face to rocky talus slope at the bottom. These structural characteristics were the same for all cliff faces despite the fact that each cliff was in a slightly different geographic region. Recent studies have revealed that cliffs as far south as Virginia, as far east as the Gaspé Peninsula in Quebec, as far north as Sault Sainte Marie, and as far west as the Door Peninsula in Wisconsin have biophysical structures similar to one another and to the Niagara Escarpment cliffs, even though the surrounding landscapes are vastly different.

34

Characteristics of the cliff ecosystem

The results of this first survey revealed some amazing things about the environment at the edge of a cliff. About 20 meters (66 feet) back from the edge, there would be a forest typical of that particular region. For example, in Virginia it would be a rich deciduous forest with towering oak, hickory, and maple. In Ontario and Wisconsin it would be part of the Great Lakes deciduous forest of maple, ash, cherry, and beech. On the islands in Lake Huron between the Bruce Peninsula and Manitoulin Island, it would be a mixed forest of hemlock, spruce, and poplar. All of these forests would have a tall canopy, a dense multilayered understory, abundant seedlings, a wide diversity of plant and animal life, and moderate physical environmental conditions—thick organic soils (perhaps 50 centimeters [20 inches] or more), gently fluctuating soil temperature and water content, and abundant soil nutrients. Wildflowers would be abundant in the spring.

These conditions remain constant up to 10 meters (33 feet) from the cliff edge. Soils begin to thin at that point, and by 5 meters (16 feet) the canopy becomes much shorter although the species composition does not change. At about 2 meters (6.5 feet) from the edge, there will often be a trail made by large animals or humans. Between the trail and the edge, there is a completely different community of plants compared with the adjacent forest, comprising just a few wildflowers but abundant ferns and shrubs such as dogwood and serviceberry. Grasses and plants tolerant of dry conditions, such as the rock polypody fern, are commonly found. The upper branches of cliff-face trees (usually *Thuja occidentalis,* also known as eastern white cedar, or *Juniperus virginiana,* also known as eastern red cedar) are visible there, and while their crowns may appear straight, a close examination reveals that they are grossly twisted and deformed where they enter the rock. In the last two meters to the cliff edge, the benign environment gives way to more hostile conditions. Soils are thin or absent, there are wild fluctuations in temperature and water availability, and there is no protecting snow cover in winter. In fact, the conditions on the cliff edge resemble those of the Arctic/Alpine tundra rather than those of the nearby temperate forest.

From the edge of the cliff to the bottom of the face, gravity becomes the major organizing force in the forest. All organisms are subject to its effects and to the friability (tendency to crumble) of the rocky substrate. Some organisms that colonize the cliff are those that can lodge themselves and complete their life cycle without ever exposing themselves to the outside world; these include the algae, fungi, and lichens that live in the rock itself. Others, such as the canopy-forming cedar trees and their neighboring ferns, bend with the nagging and destructive force of gravity and persist, exposed to searing heat and numbing cold, even after their rocky substrate has partially fallen away. Still others such as birds of prey actually use the cliff as enemy-free space in which to rear their young.

At the bottom of the cliff on the talus slope, conditions rapidly change once again. There the environmental conditions become more moderate. Rich organic soil, fed by an endless rain of organic debris, accumulates

Cliff faces along the New River in Virginia are populated by eastern red cedars up to 400 years old. Cliff faces throughout the world may support some of the last remaining old-growth stands. The trees have persisted because the cliffs are not readily accessible to humans, fire cannot spread in the low-density stands, and the complex structures of these trees render them useless as forestry products.

Cliff edges are regions of transition from one ecosystem to another, including (clockwise from top left) deciduous forest to cedars, a deciduous stand 20 meters from the edge, a fern restricted to cliff-edge sites, and a sharp change from deciduous forest to a tundralike cliff face.

Photos, Doug Larson

between scattered rocks and fallen tree trunks, all victims of the effects of gravity on the cliff face. The talus is a bizarre and inhospitable place with lush rock gardens of dogwood, impatiens, raspberries, and poison ivy separated by large expanses of bare, loose, jagged rock and tree limbs. Not surprisingly, snakes are frequently encountered there. As one moves down the talus slope and its gradient becomes more gradual, habitat conditions revert to conditions very much like those of the rich forest at the top of the cliff on the plateau.

Formation of the cliff community

The striking distribution patterns described above led naturally to questions about how they were formed. The most obvious answer was that the species on the cliff face were specifically adapted for the harsh conditions found there and that the plants and animals found on the talus slopes and on the plateau simply could not live on the face. This is the physiological preference hypothesis. The senior author and his colleagues suspected that there was more to the story than that, however, because *T. occidentalis* and several of the other species on the cliff were also found in swamps. Therefore, an extensive series of experiments was started to try to compare the performance of cliff species in noncliff habitats with that of noncliff species in cliff habitats. What the researchers found was that the cliff is hostile to all organisms—even the ones that are dominant there. Though eastern white cedar forms the bulk of the biomass on the cliff, it performs very poorly there and grows much better if transplanted to noncliff habitats. White cedar seedlings planted at the cliff edge die off completely by the end of the summer but survive for years if planted in the neighboring deciduous forest. The question thus arises as to how cedar gets established on the cliff face at all.

Three possible explanations were discussed for the genesis of these patterns: one was that the cedars had been present on the cliff face only since extensive forest clearing at the end of the 1800s; a second was that human trampling was killing off saplings that occasionally got started on

Effects of gravity on cliff-edge vegetation can be seen in the twisted, inverted old trees (right) and the cedar trying to grow toward sunlight (below).

Photos, Mitch Epstein

Large mammals such as raccoons make dens in snags and hollow cedar logs and stumps in the talus at the base of a cliff (left), while small rodents flee to the cliff face in times of danger. Bobcats have been seen on the cliff face itself. A millipede feeds on lichen on the cliff face (above). A host of invertebrate species, some of which have never been described, lives on the Niagara Escarpment. Newts are commonly found among the rocks in the talus (below left).

the cliff edge; a third was that there were multiple pulses of recruitment (periods of time when large numbers of seedlings grew), but at time scales much longer than normally considered likely for temperate North America. The one common feature of all these hypotheses was that they could be addressed by examination of the age structure of the populations of trees on cliff edges and faces. If forest clearing at the end of the last century was responsible for the observed patterns, the oldest trees on the cliff face would be between 65 and 100 years old. If trampling disturbance was responsible for eliminating seedlings, then there should be very different rates of new growth in trampled and nontrampled cliff edges. And finally, if there were recruitment pulses at odd time intervals,

Mitch Epstein

A stunted eastern white cedar growing out of a cliff is about 30 years old. Some eastern white cedars on the Niagara Escarpment do not grow higher than about half a meter and live in that dwarfed form for as long as 600 years.

the age structure would reveal this. Therefore, a careful study was carried out to determine the age structure of *Thuja* in two very different areas, one untrampled and the other heavily trampled.

The results were clear and showed something completely unexpected about the sparse forest of stunted trees on the Niagara Escarpment. First, the mean age of the trees on the cliffs and cliff edges exceeded the end-of-century forest clearing by 60 years or so. Second, there were large differences in the number of saplings in the trampled and the untrampled cliff edges, but even in untrampled cliff edges the rate of new growth was low. Third, the age structure of the undisturbed cliff-edge forest showed several pulses of recruitment separated by periods of time of about 60 years. This last point hints at the most interesting result of all. The age structure of the cliff-edge population showed a heavily pulsed curve with ages extending to more than 500 years. Other trees sampled outside of the sample plots had ages in excess of 700 years. At first these numbers were so surprising that the researchers employed radiocarbon dating to assure themselves that the trees were actually producing annual rings (they were).

Such an age structure helps to explain the existence of the vegetational patterns on the cliffs; annual recruitment rates need not be high if recruitment can occur over hundreds rather than dozens of years. At this time there was a significant reorientation of research priorities. If the results were correct, then at one site within view of downtown Toronto and surrounded by approximately six million people and the most heavily industrialized part of Canada, there existed at least one stand of presettlement (old-growth) forest.

A heavily trampled cliff-edge forest (top) reveals almost no new growth on the forest floor. By contrast, a cliff-edge forest not exposed to heavy pedestrian traffic (bottom) features an abundance of young plants.

Presettlement stand or presettlement forest?

To try to determine if these results were applicable to the entire Niagara Escarpment, researchers examined more than 30 cliff sites along the 700-kilometer (435-mile) length of the escarpment in Ontario and carried out random sampling of the age structure of the trees at nine of these, more or less evenly spaced from south to north. Again, multiple transects were established and, where possible, trees were nondestructively sampled for their age, diameter, and height. Tree age proved to be the most difficult component to measure but, by use of a small drill-like tool (called an increment borer), a small pencil-sized piece of wood could be taken from each tree and the number and size of the rings counted in that piece. The results demonstrated that virtually all exposed limestone cliffs of the Niagara Escarpment support the same kind of presettlement forest that had been found at the first site. Trees at all sites showed the same diameter and height-class distributions, but there was a tendency for greater longevity in northern sites. Maximum tree age was found to be 1,032 years for a specimen sampled in Fathom Five National Marine Park at the northern tip of the escarpment. More recently, stems up to 1,654 years of age have been located. The oldest trees are usually no more than 3 meters (10 feet) in height and less than 30 centimeters (12 inches) in diameter.

Each site had a different rate of seedling recruitment, but active colonization of cliffs by seedlings was seen everywhere. The researchers found no evidence of fire or human disturbance in any of the sites that were quantitatively sampled. Though some cliffs had been exposed to fire and to damage from recreational rock climbing, the damage was confined to specific sections of cliff face.

The results of this work were then compared with data published from other parts of North America, and an astonishing conclusion was reached. The exposed cliffs of the Niagara Escarpment—the cliffs thought by some people to be "barren" or "lifeless"—actually supported the oldest and most undisturbed forest ecosystem in eastern North America. The diversity of plants that had been sampled by Steven Spring represented the plants growing in an ecosystem free of almost any human and even natural disturbance. Rockfall events certainly happen, but the time scale of these events turned out to be low for any given section of cliff. So, for all practical purposes, the ecosystem was in a steady-state condition despite its close proximity to six million people and intense agricultural and industrial activity.

Putting the presettlement forest to work

Other scientists studying old-growth forests have pointed out that trees record in their rings a long history of annually resolvable events. The vigorous growth of youth, the slow growth of old age, the damage caused by pests and fungi, the accelerated growth caused by forest clearing, and, most important, the climate during the tree's lifetime are all revealed in tree rings. The formal study of tree growth over time is called dendrochronology, and its objective is to assign a precise date to events recorded in the rings of trees (the procedure by which this is done is called cross dating). When the researchers realized that the exposed cliffs of the escarpment had a complete, intact, and undisturbed forest ecosystem with individual trees up to 1,500 years of age, they immediately began to find out if those particular trees could be cross-dated. But there were several characteristics of the trees that suggested this could not be accomplished.

Peter Kelly

While perched on the trunk of a 253-year-old cliff-face cedar, cliff ecologist Cal Clark removes a thin cylindrical tree core from a drill-like instrument called an increment borer. Increment borers allow researchers to obtain physical records of the variations in tree-ring widths without harming the tree. These ring-width patterns hold the key to reconstructing past environmental changes in the region.

41

Cliff ecologist Jeff Matheson sits next to a dead 1,555-year-old cliff-face cedar that was found at the base of the Niagara Escarpment in 1993. Despite its overall length of only 3.2 meters, it was the third oldest tree ever documented in Canada.

Ed Cook of the Lamont-Doherty Earth Observatory, who had been searching for old climate-sensitive trees in eastern North America for more than a decade, began to collaborate with the research team in the attempt to cross-date the trees. He pointed out that all of the trees growing on the cliff were grossly deformed in their cross sections. The pith (or the central point of the tree) was on one side of the cross section, and all of the growth of the stem was on one side of the stem's axis in a form known as strip-bark growth. Worried that such extreme strip-bark growth would completely erase any climate signal, the researchers addressed this problem directly by trying to determine how many trees showed the slowest rates of growth and by finding out whether different asymmetrical trees from the same site would reveal a common growth signal driven by climate. As it turned out, there were abundant trees with the necessary growth rates to allow for the development of dendrochronology. Also, it was found that even the most grossly deformed trees had growth-rate fluctuations that were comparable to neighboring trees that had different deformities.

Quite accidentally, the research team also discovered that the processes responsible for stem deformations in *Thuja* were similar to those in another tree used by dendrochronologists—bristlecone pine, the tree species with the oldest living individuals in the world. They also found out that the trees growing on the cliffs were not dependent on fluctuations in water and nutrients during the growing season, and this made it much more likely that the tree-growth rates would reflect fluctuations in temperature.

The search for the old, the dead, and the ugly

After determining that *T. occidentalis* was going to be a useful species to exploit dendrochronologically, the researchers began an all-out search

42

for the oldest, most deformed, and best-preserved woody material derived from the Niagara Escarpment cliffs. They already knew that tree-growth rates (when alive) and decomposition rates (when dead) were low in the northern part of the escarpment, and so the most extensive search for new material was initiated there. After two summers of sampling, they had collected core samples from approximately 500 grossly deformed but living trees and cores or cross sections from another 500 deformed dead trees. The best of this material was retained for cross dating, and the researchers were able to piece together the past 1,397 years of tree growth common to the population as a whole. A statistical comparison of the tree-ring fluctuations with the last 114 years' worth of real climate data revealed that the growth of cedar trees on cliffs responds negatively to high temperatures in summer and positively to low temperatures.

The next challenge for the researchers was to use the 1,397 years of tree-ring data to reconstruct the past 1,397 years of summer temperatures. Beyond that, the researchers had found abundant samples of *Thuja* that revealed radiocarbon dates extending back 3,250 years. By early 1994 enough material had been collected that should allow them to determine tree-growth patterns and, by correlation, summer temperature patterns back to 1300 BC. In the summer of 1993, additional samples of cedar were collected from the edge of an underwater cliff drowned during the postglacial refilling of the Great Lakes. This material was radiocarbon-dated to 7,660 years ago. Thus, the dendrochonological potential of this ancient forest ecosystem was not yet exhausted. Work can now be done to evaluate how much of what is perceived as "global warming" is a phenomenon rarely seen in nature or has occurred in a similar fashion in the distant past.

The tree-ring record can also be used to determine the effect on the ecosystem of such human disturbances as atmospheric pollution and acid rain. Trees are known to bind heavy metals such as lead and mercury in their cell walls, so the tree-ring record can be used to look at the pattern of natural versus man-made heavy metal contamination in the environment. All of these studies are likely to succeed because this ancient forest is completely surrounded by industrial and agricultural development. If pollution effects are occurring, they should appear in the tree-ring record of the cliff-face cedars.

Back to basic science
Until recently researchers did not understand why the grossly deformed trees cross-dated so well. The obvious external structural distortion characteristic of those trees was not reflected in their internal tree-ring structures. In a careful study of what happens to produce the stem asymmetry, the authors found what appeared to be the explanation: individual cedar trees are rooted at several places on the rock surface of the cliff, but each root is connected to just one particular part of the stem. When a rockfall exposes and kills one root, the rest of the tree carries on as though nothing has changed. The individual tree is actually behaving as a population of independent parts rather than as an integrated being.

Cross section of a 1,032-year-old cliff-face eastern white cedar reveals the deformation experienced by the tree during its long lifetime. The "P" marks the location of the pith, or center of the tree, while the "S" indicates the location of the last growth rings added before the tree died in 1876.

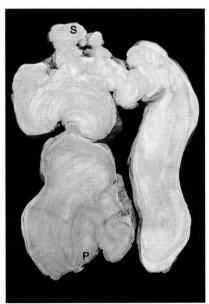

Peter Kelly

43

The patterns of tree rings in the dead woody debris at the base of the escarpment can be cross-dated with the same patterns of tree rings in the cedar trees still growing on the cliff face. A mean growth index can be calculated for every year of growth represented in the tree-ring record to produce a tree-ring chronology. The longer the material has been lying at the base of the cliff, the farther back in time the chronology can be extended and thus the farther back in time the climate can be reconstructed.

Another discovery that was puzzling until recently was that the stunted trees on the cliff were not nutrient- and water-deprived. This was especially surprising because they were not receiving any water from the level-ground woodland at the cliff top. Then two separate studies accidentally provided a likely answer for this question; trees harvested from cliff faces were found to be heavily colonized by mycorrhizal fungi, which are known to supply trees with phosphorus and water. The spores of these fungi are probably dispersed in the feces of the mammals and birds that hunt from the cliffs. In addition, a rich community of algae and fungi was found actually living inside the solid limestone cliffs of the escarpment. Such a community had previously been found in Antarctica but never in southern Ontario. Since many of the algae are nitrogen-

44

Cliff ecologist Ceddy Nash stands beside a typical member of the Niagara Escarpment ancient cedar forest. These trees are rooted directly into cracks on the cliff face where there is little or no soil accumulation. Despite these conditions, the cedars are not severely deprived of water and nutrients.

fixing cyanobacteria, they are very likely contributing significant amounts of nitrogen compounds to the cliff ecosystem and are probably indirectly fertilizing the trees at a rate just high enough to keep them and the whole ecosystem alive.

Finally, an intense research effort was under way to try to determine how sensitive the cliff ecosystem is to the pressures of an increasingly urban environment; nonconsumptive pursuits such as hiking and rock climbing as well as consumptive activities such as quarry operations and real-estate development were threatening parts of the Niagara Escarpment. Through observation of the impact of these human disturbances, it should be possible to advise ecosystem managers how best to ensure the integrity of the cliff ecosystem for all time.

45

The thin green band in this cross section of a limestone slab defines the diverse assemblage of algae and fungi known as a cryptoendolithic community. These organisms live within the crystalline structure of the rock on the exposed cliff faces of the Niagara Escarpment. More than 20 different species of endolithic organisms have been documented in these communities.

Providing a stark contrast to the surrounding landscape of southern Ontario, the Niagara Escarpment was declared a UNESCO Biosphere Reserve in 1991 (opposite page, top). A 275-year-old cedar survives on a cliff edge despite the harsh environment (opposite page, bottom). Most of its secondary branches have broken off or have been eroded away, a common growth form in these trees.

Significance of the ecosystem

The authors have found a previously unknown vertical forest ecosystem that is growing at a rate so slow that its appearance does not change from century to century. It is a forest of small, stunted, marvelously twisted trees excluded from the fertile habitat nearby because they never did evolve to fight, just to persist. They and their neighbors grow very slowly and by almost any measure of performance are not very successful, but this community has been putting up with these poor conditions since deglaciation and has seen countless other productive and more "successful" forest ecosystems dominated by spruce, pine, oak, maple, and hemlock come and go without a trace.

The cliff ecosystem is rich not only in the microhabitats that are contained within it but also in the opportunities it offers scientists to examine the impact of technology and industry on natural ecosystems. It can be viewed as a great teacher whose presence was not detected and whose importance was not revealed until all of the other teachers had been given their pink slips. For example, the impact of global warming on forest ecosystem structure has been studied in many second- or third-growth forests in the Northern Hemisphere, but the lack of a time scale of sufficient length in those areas limited researchers' ability to discriminate natural climatic fluctuations from ones imposed by human activities. The cliff forest, by contrast, offers evidence of climate change over an enormously greater period of time and therefore increases the ability of scientists to discriminate between natural and human-generated influences on climate.

What is most significant, however, is that by studying a place and by asking questions that have been ignored or avoided by others, researchers can make discoveries that are both globally important and exciting. Similar opportunities exist everywhere in the scientific landscape.

46

New Eyes on the Gamma-Ray Sky

by Kenneth Brecher

From the nuclear reactions that power the stars to the blazing hearts of the enigmatic quasars, the universe teems with gamma rays. Detection of this invisible radiation is now providing astronomers with a unique probe of the most violent and energetic phenomena in nature.

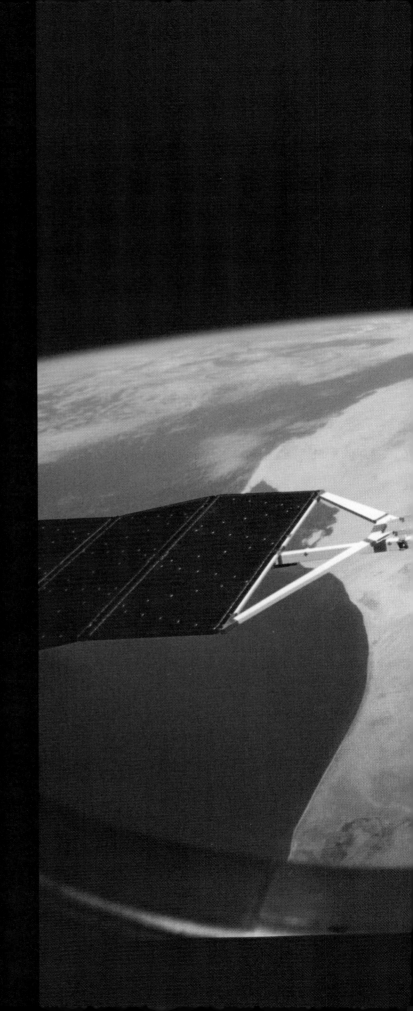

When we look out at night, we are struck by several things: the dark of the night sky, its occasional punctuation by dots of starlight, and the constancy of the stars themselves. The stars we see with our eyes shine primarily in visible light. But deep beneath their surfaces, high temperatures and pressures promote a continuous process called nucleosynthesis. In this process nuclei of the lightest elements, beginning with hydrogen and helium, fuse to form increasingly heavy elements while giving off enormous amounts of energy. The fusion reactions in these nuclear furnaces release their energy primarily in the form of radiation that cannot be seen with the human eye—highly energetic photons, or packets of electromagnetic energy, called gamma rays. As the gamma-ray photons travel the hundreds of thousands of kilometers or more to the stellar surfaces, they collide with particles of matter many times, lose energy, and ultimately leave the stars in the form of visible light.

That the universe may be seething with gamma rays, from sources other than ordinary stars, had been suggested near the dawn of the nuclear age. Yet their study is becoming a major tool of astronomical research only in the 1990s. In the past few years gamma-ray astronomers have begun to explore the energetic, violent, wildly varying properties of pulsars, supernovas, quasars, and perhaps even more exotic objects. Observing the sky in various kinds of invisible radiation—from radio waves beginning in the 1950s and X-rays in the 1960s to infrared light in the 1980s—has deepened our understanding of the cosmos. Now gamma-ray astronomy is also expanding our cosmic horizon.

Gamma rays: the most energetic radiation

Gamma rays were named by the British physicist Ernest Rutherford in 1903. Early nuclear experiments showed that they differed qualitatively from the alpha rays (which are nuclei of helium) and beta rays (which are electrons) that were observed in the radioactive decay of unstable atomic nuclei. Unlike alpha and beta rays, gamma rays are high-energy quantum packets of electromagnetic radiation. Nevertheless, they are so energetic that they can sometimes act as if they are particles. In particular, when a high-energy gamma ray hits an electron, it can make the electron recoil as if it had been struck with a particle of matter. That phenomenon was discovered in 1923 by the U.S. physicist Arthur Holly Compton. For his discovery and subsequent explanation of what is now called Compton scattering, Compton was awarded the 1927 Nobel Prize for Physics. By the late 1930s the U.S. theoretical physicist Hans Bethe had explained the origin of the energy of stars as resulting from gamma-ray-releasing fusion reactions taking place deep within their interiors, an idea for which he, too, was later awarded the Nobel physics prize.

Gamma rays made in the stellar cores cannot be detected directly owing to the thick opacity of the stars. After World War II, however, scientists began to realize that other processes elsewhere in the universe could produce gamma rays, for example, in more diffuse regions of space by the interaction of fast-moving cosmic-ray particles with thin gas and magnetic fields. In 1958 physicist Philip Morrison, then at Cornell

KENNETH BRECHER is Professor of Astronomy and Physics and Director of the Science and Mathematics Education Center at Boston University.

(Overleaf) The Compton Gamma Ray Observatory (GRO) is deployed from the space shuttle Atlantis on April 7, 1991. Photograph, NASA

50

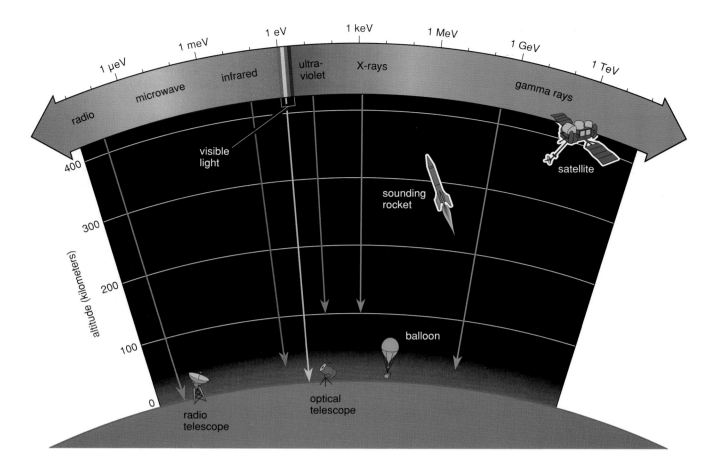

The electromagnetic spectrum extends from the lowest energy radio photons through the increasingly energetic microwave, infrared, visible, ultraviolet, and X-ray photons to the highest energy gamma-ray photons. With the major exception of radio and visible-light radiation, radiation in most other regions of the spectrum, including gamma rays, is strongly absorbed in the Earth's atmosphere. In order to conduct observations in these regions, astronomers send their instruments above most of the atmosphere in high-altitude balloons, sounding rockets, or orbiting spacecraft.

University, Ithaca, New York, wrote the seminal paper "On Gamma-Ray Astronomy," outlining how gamma rays could be used to probe the nature of high-energy phenomena in the universe.

Understanding the value of gamma rays to astronomy requires some knowledge of their basic properties. Electromagnetic radiation can behave either as waves having a frequency and a wavelength or as particle-like photons possessing a discrete, or individually distinct, energy. The spectrum of electromagnetic energy extends from the lowest energy radio photons to the increasingly energetic microwave, infrared, visible, ultraviolet, X-ray, and finally gamma-ray photons. While radio photons have energies of less than a millionth of an electron volt (microelectron volt; μeV), visible-light photons have energies of about 1 eV, and X-rays range in energy from about 1,000 eV (1 kiloelectron volt; 1 keV) to a few hundred keV.

Gamma rays are the most energetic form of electromagnetic radiation. Though no sharp boundary exists between X-rays and gamma rays, photons are called gamma rays if they have energies starting at about 50–100 keV, continuing through energies of 1 million eV (1 megaelectron volt; 1 MeV) and 1 billion eV (1 gigaelectron volt; 1 GeV), to energies in the trillions of electron volts (teraelectron volts; TeV). The most energetic gamma rays of astronomical origin reported to date have an energy per photon of about 10,000 TeV (10^{16} eV). To put such extraordinary energies in perspective, a single 1-TeV gamma ray carries about as much energy

51

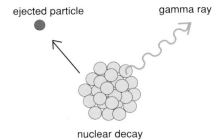

ejected particle   gamma ray

nuclear decay

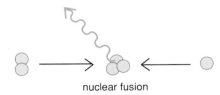

nuclear fusion

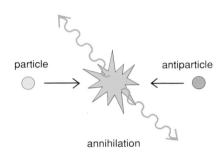

particle   antiparticle

annihilation

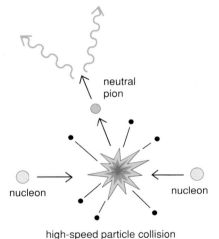

neutral
pion

nucleon   nucleon

high-speed particle collision

magnetic field

charged
particle

synchrotron radiation

as is contained in the kinetic energy of a pea-sized marble (containing about 10^{23} atoms) rolling slowly across a table.

Gamma rays can be produced by a variety of mechanisms. Some are associated with ordinary stars, while others are believed to be created in the extreme conditions of temperature, pressure, strong magnetic fields, and high radiation energy densities found in and around supernovas, pulsars, black holes, and quasars. Gamma rays are therefore a valuable diagnostic tool for studying the many kinds of physical processes thought to occur in the most violent and energetic objects in the cosmos. To better understand those objects it will help to look at some of the physical processes associated with them.

As noted above, gamma rays were first discovered in the decay of radioactive nuclei. Gamma rays emitted in this way have energies specific to the emitting nuclei. For example, the decay of cobalt-56, a radioactive isotope of the element cobalt, releases gamma-ray photons with characteristic energies of 0.85 and 1.24 MeV. Gamma rays can also be emitted in nucleosynthesis—whether in the hot interior of stars, where many of the lighter elements are created; in supernova explosions, where heavier elements are created; or in the interactions of individual cosmic rays (fast-moving protons, neutrons, or more massive nuclei) with atoms. For example, when a proton combines with a neutron to form a deuteron (a nucleus of hydrogen-2, or deuterium), it is accompanied by the release of a gamma-ray photon with a characteristic energy of about 2.2 MeV.

For every kind of particle of matter, there is also an antimatter counterpart, usually of opposite electric charge but always having the same mass. Corresponding to the negatively charged electron, which at rest (*i.e.*, with no kinetic energy) has a mass equivalent to an energy of 0.511 MeV, there exists an antielectron, or positron, having a positive electric charge but the same rest energy of 0.511 MeV. When an electron and a positron meet, they annihilate, transforming completely into energy. This energy usually takes the form of two gamma-ray photons, each having an energy of 0.511 MeV. However, an electron and a positron can combine temporarily to form an exotic atom called positronium, which subsequently annihilates, leading to the release of either two or three photons. Similarly, when a proton and an antiproton annihilate, gamma-ray photons each having an energy of 938 MeV are released. One of the great mysteries of science is why there seems to be so little antimatter in the universe. Detection of these annihilation gamma rays is one way to show the presence of antimatter in the cosmos.

Collisions of protons with one another (or of any nuclei with other nuclei) at sufficiently high speeds—that is, at sufficiently high kinetic energies, typically greater than about 1,000 MeV per particle—can lead to the production of a variety of subatomic particles. Particularly interesting is the production of pi mesons, or pions. Being unstable particles, pions decay in flight while emitting gamma-ray photons with characteristic energies of about 70 MeV. In astronomical situations pions are usually produced by protons having a range of high kinetic energies. Thus, the resulting pion-decay gamma rays ordinarily possess a continuous spread, or spectrum, of energies rather than the characteristic rest energy of pions.

Gamma rays can also be produced by such processes as synchrotron emission, bremsstrahlung, and inverse Compton scattering. Synchrotron emission is radiation produced by fast-moving charged particles such as electrons when their paths are deflected by strong magnetic fields. Bremsstrahlung (German for "braking radiation") results from the deceleration of fast-moving electrons passing through matter and being scattered by the electric fields of atomic nuclei. Inverse Compton scattering produces gamma rays when electrons that are moving very fast (usually near the speed of light) encounter relatively low-energy photons and transfer some energy to the photons, thus boosting their energy to gamma-ray levels.

Early days of gamma-ray astronomy

Although gamma rays are a highly penetrating form of radiation, after traveling essentially unimpeded through the low-density gases that fill space, they are readily absorbed in Earth's thick atmosphere. Thus, in order to study gamma rays, scientists must send their detectors up in high-altitude balloons, sounding rockets, or spacecraft. Only the most energetic gamma rays, those with energies greater than about 1 TeV, can be detected at ground level by means of very large arrays of detectors that search for the effects of these extremely energetic photons on the atoms of the atmosphere.

Because celestial sources of gamma rays radiate relatively few (but very energetic) photons, the instruments that have been sent into space have had to carry very large detectors to look for sources of MeV gamma rays. Although a number of early spacecraft designed primarily to observe the Sun contained detectors to look for characteristic solar gamma-ray energies, the first high-energy gamma-ray detector was flown in 1961 aboard the U.S. Explorer 11 spacecraft. This was followed in 1967 by OSO 3, which observed gamma rays coming from the vicinity of the center of our galaxy, the Milky Way. SAS 2 was launched in 1972, to be followed by the European Space Agency's COS B satellite in 1975. Three more spacecraft carried major astronomical gamma-ray telescopes: HEAO 3 launched in 1979, the Solar Maximum Mission (Solar Max) launched in 1980, and the French-Soviet GRANAT launched in 1990.

Together with instruments aboard about a dozen spacecraft designed primarily for different purposes, the early missions provided a rather sketchy yet tantalizing glimpse of the gamma-ray sky. Along with a general flux of gamma rays over a broad range of energies coming from the plane of the Milky Way, they also detected gamma-ray photons characteristic of nuclear emissions from several celestial sources. They saw the 0.511-MeV gamma rays (sometimes called 511-keV gamma rays) of electron-positron annihilation coming from somewhere near the galactic center. However, of the roughly two dozen sources detected in those studies, only a few could be identified with any known type of celestial object: two with well-known young supernova remnants (Crab and Vela) that

(Opposite page and below) Gamma rays are produced by a variety of mechanisms that include nuclear decay, nuclear fusion, and processes involving the interaction of subatomic particles with other particles or with magnetic fields, matter, or photons. Some of these mechanisms are associated with ordinary stars, while others are believed to exist in the extreme conditions found in and around supernovas, black holes, pulsars, and quasars. Details of each are discussed in text.

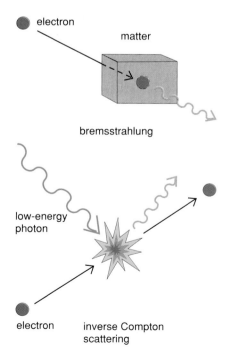

electron

matter

bremsstrahlung

low-energy photon

electron   inverse Compton scattering

53

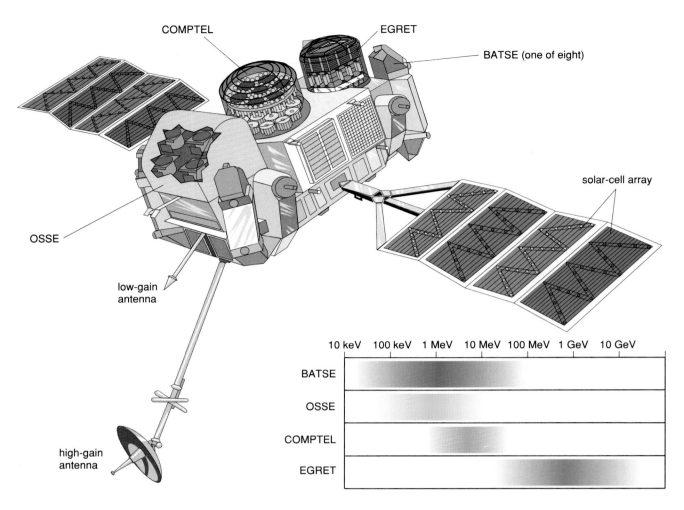

COMPTEL   EGRET   BATSE (one of eight)

solar-cell array

OSSE

low-gain
antenna

high-gain
antenna

	10 keV	100 keV	1 MeV	10 MeV	100 MeV	1 GeV	10 GeV
BATSE							
OSSE							
COMPTEL							
EGRET							

GRO is the first space observatory to have diverse gamma-ray capabilities and, with a mass of more than 16 tons, is the heaviest scientific satellite deployed from a space shuttle. Each of its four separate instruments—BATSE, OSSE, COMPTEL, and EGRET—is the largest and most sensitive of its type ever sent aloft. Together the instruments cover an enormous range of photon energies, from about 20 keV to 30 GeV.

contain pulsars, one with a giant molecular cloud called Rho Ophiuci, and another with one of the nearer quasars to Earth, 3C 273.

The Compton Gamma Ray Observatory

In order to make gamma-ray astronomy a major a tool for exploring the universe, astronomers as early as 1975 proposed development of a spacecraft observatory having diverse gamma-ray capabilities. Finally, after 15 years of work by hundreds of scientists and engineers, the Gamma Ray Observatory (GRO) was successfully deployed from the U.S. space shuttle *Atlantis* on April 7, 1991, into a nearly circular orbit 457 kilometers (284 miles) high. As it revolves about the Earth every 92 minutes, it has an unobstructed view of the half of the sky not blocked by the planet. Subsequently renamed the Arthur Holly Compton Gamma Ray Observatory after the American physicist, the spacecraft has operated almost flawlessly during the first three years since its launch.

Weighing more than 16 tons, GRO is the largest scientific payload ever deployed from a space shuttle. It carries four separate experiments for observing celestial sources of hard (higher energy) X-rays and gamma rays. Overall it contains instruments that are some 10 times more sensitive to gamma rays than those on board earlier gamma-ray satellites.

54

These instruments also cover an enormous range of photon energies from about 0.02 MeV (20 keV) to about 30,000 MeV (30 GeV).

The Burst and Transient Source Experiment (BATSE) is an all-sky detector system that is sensitive in the lowest energy range, from about 20 keV to 100 MeV. It consists of a set of eight detectors, one positioned at each upper and lower corner of the roughly rectangular spacecraft. BATSE's primary task is to detect changes in gamma-ray intensity due to sudden bursts and transient emissions. It can also provide data on pulsars, other spatially discrete high-energy sources, and solar flares. As gamma rays enter BATSE's detectors, they excite crystals of sodium iodide to emit pulses of light, which are then recorded. The detectors are uncollimated—*i.e.,* they have an unrestricted field of view—making them sensitive to gamma rays from any direction.

The Imaging Compton Telescope (COMPTEL) is sensitive to medium-energy gamma rays from about 0.8 to 30 MeV. Gamma-ray photons in this range enter an upper array of liquid detectors, where they undergo Compton scattering and emit light, which is recorded. The scattered photons then pass into a lower array of sodium iodide detectors and are absorbed, again emitting recordable light pulses. COMPTEL can produce images of both discrete objects and diffuse sources over a field of view covering about 10% of the sky with an angular resolution of 1°–2°, depending on gamma-ray energy. Though it possesses poorer angular resolution than optical telescopes, COMPTEL is the first imaging telescope to explore the sky in MeV gamma rays.

The Oriented Scintillation Spectrometer Experiment (OSSE) comprises four identical sodium iodide detectors, each collimated for a 4° by 11° field of view and sensitive to gamma rays in a 50-keV–10-MeV range. OSSE's design enables it to derive intensity and spectrum information about the sources of the gamma rays it detects. Its main task is to find low-energy nuclear gamma rays from energetic celestial objects, although it can also detect gamma rays from more extended sources such as the plane of the Milky Way Galaxy.

The Energetic Gamma Ray Experiment Telescope (EGRET) uses a device called a spark chamber to detect gamma rays in the highest energy range, from 20 to 30,000 MeV. When such a high-energy photon enters the chamber, it produces an electron-positron pair whose tracks are recorded, providing information on the direction and energy of the gamma ray. EGRET, like COMPTEL, can produce images; it has a field of view covering about 4% of the sky and is capable of locating a strong gamma-ray source to roughly 0.1°.

In GRO's initial phase of operation, the two wide-field instruments, COMPTEL and EGRET, completed a full sky survey. OSSE, with its smaller field of view, studied specific targets in depth. BATSE, with its all-sky coverage, continuously monitored the sky, a job that would continue throughout the spacecraft's lifetime. In its first three years in orbit, GRO provided the most detailed view of the gamma-ray sky to date.

As described above, the various ways that gamma rays are produced make them a good probe of astronomical sources—for example, pulsars

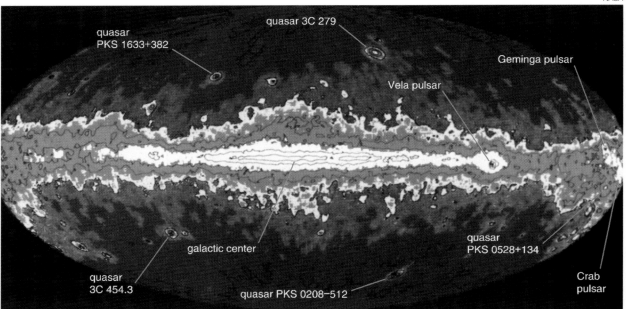

quasar
PKS 1633+382

quasar 3C 279

Geminga pulsar

Vela pulsar

galactic center

quasar
PKS 0528+134

quasar
3C 454.3

quasar PKS 0208−512

Crab
pulsar

This false-color, all-sky map is synthesized from observations made by GRO's EGRET wide-field instrument at energies above 100 MeV. White areas represent the highest gamma-ray intensities, dark blue the lowest. Diffuse gamma-ray emissions from the plane of the Milky Way Galaxy account for most of the horizontal band, while a number of discrete sources of strong emission lie within and outside the plane of the galaxy. The brightest discrete sources within the galaxy are pulsars.

and quasars, where particles are being accelerated to high energies; supernova explosions, where nuclei are being synthesized outside the matter-shrouded cores of stars; and solar flares, where nuclei that have been forced into excited states shed their excitation energy as gamma rays. What follows is a short tour of the gamma-ray universe, proceeding from the neighboring Sun to the remotest reaches of the universe.

The Sun

The Sun is not generally considered to be a high-energy astronomical object. As with other stars, its interior gamma rays are degraded into lower energy photons as they move to the surface. Nonetheless, during solar flares, high-energy particles in the form of electrons, protons, and heavy nuclei, as well as gamma-ray photons, are produced. The OSSE instrument aboard GRO observed several solar flares, showing evidence for the presence of neutrons for the first time and finding characteristic gamma-ray emissions from deuterium, carbon, and oxygen. The COMPTEL instrument detected major solar flares on June 9 and 11, 1991. Gamma-ray photons with energies specific for the formation of deuterium were present in both events. The June 9 event presented a clear gamma-ray signal for neutrons. The telltale 0.511-MeV gamma-ray signal for electron-positron annihilation was also detected in the solar flares. Although the detailed mechanism by which charged particles are accelerated in solar flares is not well understood, GRO measurements are helping to shape the latest theories.

Neutron stars and pulsars

Astronomers believe that when a star within a certain mass range reaches the end of its nuclear-burning life, its center collapses so violently as to compress the constituent matter into a tiny, dense core of neutrons. Whereas the outer layers of the star are blown into space by the ensuing supernova explosion, the core remains behind as a rapidly spinning, highly magnetized remnant called a neutron star. It is thought that, at least in some cases, the intense magnetic field that surrounds a neutron star gives rise to a narrow beam of electromagnetic radiation, which sweeps around the star like a beam of light from a lighthouse. When Earth happens to lie in the path of the beam, observers detect brief, precisely timed signals from the star, which then is labeled a pulsar. The time between pulses corresponds to the pulsar's period of rotation.

Pulsars first came to the attention of astronomers as pulsating sources of radio emission, but of the 500 or so pulsars detected to date, several pulsate at visible, infrared, and X-ray wavelengths as well. As of 1994, six of these pulsars were known to emit gamma rays. One is the famous pulsar at the center of the supernova remnant known as the Crab Nebula. It pulsates at radio, visible, X-ray, and gamma-ray energies with a period of 33 milliseconds. Another, somewhat slower (89-millisecond) pulsar in the constellation Vela also radiates at all of these wavelengths. OSSE detected pulsed gamma rays from the Crab pulsar, coincident with ground-based observations of giant radio pulses from the pulsar. COMPTEL also detected the Crab pulsar, measuring its 1–10-MeV radiation curve with unprecedented accuracy. Although theories exist for particle acceleration in the strong magnetic fields and rapid rotation of pulsars, a detailed understanding of gamma-ray emission from pulsars is still missing.

In the early 1970s the SAS 2 spacecraft detected a bright gamma-ray source with no obvious visible counterpart. It remained the most perplex-

A period of intense flare activity on the Sun in June 1991 gave GRO an opportunity to observe several large flare events. The gamma-ray spectrum of a flare that occurred on June 4 (left) was recorded by the OSSE instrument. The peaks in intensity at discrete photon energies come from nuclei of deuterium, carbon, oxygen, and a number of other elements. (Right) Gamma-ray emission from a major solar flare on June 11 is shown in an image made by COMPTEL.

(Left) Adapted from information obtained from James Kurfess of the Naval Research Laboratory and the OSSE team; (right) COMPTEL team

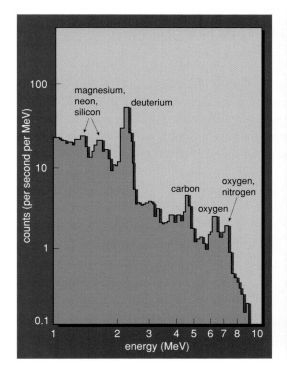

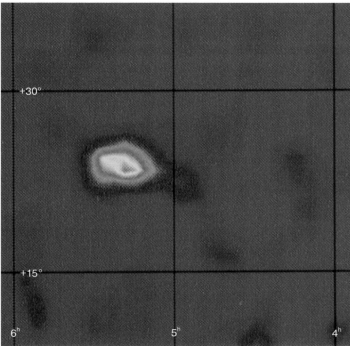

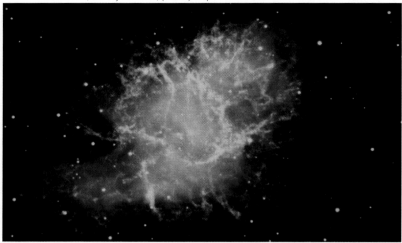

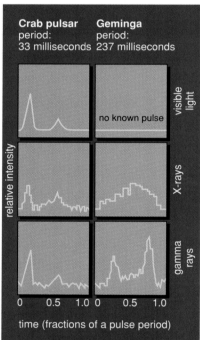

Crab pulsar
period:
33 milliseconds

Geminga
period:
237 milliseconds

no known pulse

visible light

X-rays

gamma rays

relative intensity

time (fractions of a pulse period)

ing discovery in the succeeding two decades of gamma-ray astronomy. Although it is the second brightest source of gamma rays in the sky, it was initially undetectable at any other wavelength. It was therefore dubbed Geminga by its discoverers, which in Milanese Italian dialect means "it's not there." Finally in 1992 GRO and the X-ray-detecting satellite ROSAT settled part of the puzzle. Both satellites detected pulsations from Geminga with a period of 237 milliseconds, demonstrating that it is in fact a pulsar. Why it emits so much of its radiation in the form of gamma rays, a property very different from all other pulsars, is still unclear.

In February 1992 astronomers reported that they had measured the proper motion of the object, from which they concluded that Geminga was the nearest pulsar to Earth found to date. More recent observations support its identification with a very dim (25th-magnitude) star. It now seems that Geminga is both comparatively young (about 350,000 years old) and nearby (300 light-years). The solar system is known to reside within a hot, rarefied region of interstellar space called the Local Bubble. The supernova that produced Geminga may have formed the bubble, heating and thinning out matter in Earth's local region. X-rays and gamma rays emitted during the supernova explosion would have hit the Earth's atmosphere, possibly resulting in effects on Earth's biosphere.

Supernovas

Supernova 1987A (SN 1987A) was the brightest supernova seen on Earth since the one observed by Johannes Kepler in AD 1604. This spectacular event, first noticed on the night of Feb. 23–24, 1987, represented the death of a massive blue supergiant star in the nearby Large Magellanic Cloud, one of the Milky Way's companion galaxies. It has been fading from view as a visible object since the spring of 1987. Throughout 1988, X-rays and gamma rays were observed from the supernova. Scientists used the Solar Max spacecraft to search for gamma-ray photons of discrete energies that might result from the decay of short-lived radioactive elements produced in the supernova explosion. Indeed, gamma rays of

0.85 MeV and 1.24 MeV were found, corresponding to the energies characteristic of the decay gamma rays from cobalt-56. The detected intensity was in good agreement with theories suggesting that the decay of such products of nucleosynthesis powers the visible-light emission from supernovas in the months following the initial explosion.

Six years later GRO's OSSE instrument detected the 0.122-MeV gamma rays characteristic of another nucleosynthesis product thought to be produced in SN 1987A, cobalt-57. Through comparison of the ratios of the intensities of the cobalt-56 and cobalt-57 emissions, the ratio of the abundances of these nuclei could be found. The value turned out to be in good agreement with the abundance ratio found in the Sun, adding further strength to current models of nucleosynthesis in stars. Together these gamma-ray observations represent the first direct evidence for the hitherto theorized synthesis and dispersion of heavy elements in stellar explosions.

In addition to the gamma rays from SN 1987A seen by Solar Max and GRO, the latter spacecraft found evidence for nucleosynthesis in many supernovas throughout the Milky Way. Besides cobalt, supernova explosions should produce, among other elements, aluminum. One of its radioactive isotopes, aluminum-26, takes millions of years to decay away completely and so should be present even in comparatively old supernovas. When the isotope decays, it emits gamma rays with an energy of 1.8 MeV. In addition, 0.511-MeV emission is produced from the annihilation of positrons given off in the decay process. In its recent sky survey the COMPTEL instrument mapped the Milky Way at these gamma-ray energies, again confirming the general picture of nucleosynthesis in supernovas and the dispersal of elements throughout the galaxy.

The Great Annihilator

Beginning in 1970 and throughout the ensuing decade, gamma-ray astronomers reported detecting the 0.511-MeV signature of electron-positron annihilation from the direction of the galactic center. In the mid-1980s, however, balloon-borne instruments having narrow angular fields of view ceased detecting the radiation, suggesting that some discrete object responsible for the positrons had suddenly "turned off." On the other hand, 0.511-MeV emission continued to be seen throughout the period by the wide-angle gamma-ray detectors aboard Solar Max. These results indicated the existence of both pointlike and diffuse sources of positrons in the direction of the galactic center.

In 1989 scientists reported the reappearance of the discrete source. Using a gamma-ray imaging spectrometer carried on balloon flights in early and late 1988, they detected the 0.511-MeV radiation with roughly the same strength as had been seen throughout the '70s. Most recently GRO's COMPTEL instrument also detected the electron-positron annihilation emission from the direction of the galactic center. Some of the emission is presumably due to the positrons produced by aluminum-26 decay in the many supernova remnants that lie in the galactic plane toward the center. Part of the emission, however, seems to come from a

(Opposite page) Both the famous Crab pulsar and the perplexing object Geminga, a bright gamma-ray source that was initially undetectable at other wavelengths, appear in a gamma-ray image (top left) made by the EGRET instrument. The Crab pulsar is the rotating neutron star at the heart of the Crab Nebula (top right, shown in a visible-light image), the remains of a star whose explosion was witnessed on Earth nearly 950 years ago. The detection of 237-millisecond pulsations from Geminga by GRO and the X-ray-detecting satellite ROSAT established that Geminga is also a pulsar. Graphs (bottom left) contrast the differences in the variations in brightness of the Crab and Geminga pulsars as seen in the visible-light, X-ray, and gamma-ray regions of the electromagnetic spectrum. Why Geminga radiates so much of its energy in the form of gamma rays remains a mystery.

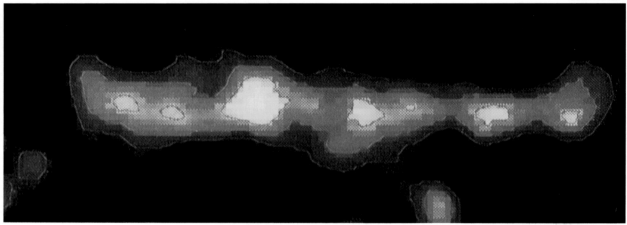

This wide view toward the center of the Milky Way consists of a false-color map made from COMPTEL observations of characteristic gamma rays that are produced in the decay of radioactive aluminum-26 nuclei. Much of the emission is thought to come from the aluminum-26 present in the many supernova remnants that lie in the plane of the galaxy. The bright spots scattered along the plane, representing intense areas of emission, were not expected and remain unexplained. COMPTEL's mapping of aluminum-26 confirmed astronomers' general understanding of nucleosynthesis in supernovas and the dispersal of elements throughout the galaxy.

discrete source, dubbed by some the Great Annihilator. If one assumes that the source is indeed at the distance of the galactic center, its luminosity at this one gamma-ray energy value is about 10,000 times the total luminosity of the Sun.

The intensity of the emission, narrow energy width, and short time scale of variability have inspired a variety of candidate sources for the positrons. Most popular have been models involving black holes with masses ranging from a hundred to a million times that of the Sun. Black holes are hypothetical gravitationally collapsed objects of extremely intense gravity from which nothing, not even light, can escape. Energetic positrons, however, could come from matter surrounding a black hole. Sources for the positrons involving less massive objects have also been proposed, ranging from single young pulsars to supernovas.

What now appears to be the most likely explanation involves an X-ray-emitting binary star system; that is, two stars locked in orbit around a common center of gravity. In the system in question, one member is a neutron star that is gravitationally accreting matter from a more conventional companion star, giving off X-rays in the accretion process. In a clever piece of detective work, X-ray astronomers showed that an X-ray binary system lying toward the galactic center falls within the positional error box for the location of the discrete 0.511-MeV source. They found that the intensity of the binary X-ray source, called GX 1 + 4, and that of the 0.511-MeV source had varied since the 1970s in a strikingly similar manner, both being "on" in the '70s, "off" for part of the '80s, and back "on" at present. This correlation strongly suggests that the two sources are one and the same. Just how the system, if it is indeed the Great Annihilator, produces so many positrons remains a mystery. So also does the reason why it should do so when other equally luminous X-ray binaries do not.

Quasars and active galactic nuclei

Quasars, short for quasi-stellar objects, were discovered in the 1960s. Most appear starlike in photographs made in visible light, hence their name. They are the brightest objects in the universe, radiating as much as 10,000 times the visible luminosity of our own galaxy. Some quasars have jets emanating from them; others are strong radio sources with giant double lobes of radio-emitting material, one on either side of the object. No quasar shows the characteristic light spectrum indicative of galaxies containing billions of normal nuclear-burning stars. Though the nature of quasars is still enigmatic, the current working hypothesis is that the central engine consists of a massive (perhaps billion-solar-mass) black hole surrounded by a disk of accreting matter, leading to the formation of energetic jets perpendicular to the accretion disk.

In 1992 the EGRET instrument aboard GRO detected energetic gamma rays from the quasars 3C 273 and 3C 279. The former, one of the nearest quasars, is about a billion light-years from Earth. The more distant quasar, 3C 279, lies about 4.6 billion light-years away. The latter object is the most distant and by far the most luminous celestial gamma-ray source ever observed. If it radiates the same in all directions, its gamma-ray luminosity is about 100 million times that of the entire Milky Way and several times larger than the radiation emitted at all wavelengths by our galaxy. It is probably variable on a time scale of years, since if it had been as luminous in the 1970s as it was in 1992, the SAS 2 and COS B satellites would likely have seen it. To the astonishment of gamma-ray astronomers, EGRET observed the gamma-ray intensity of 3C 279 to vary by a factor of four on a time scale of only two days. Because no physical object can move faster than the speed of light, the time of variation means that the object producing the gamma rays must be smaller than about two light-days across.

Normal galaxies get their luminosity mostly from the combined visible-light emission of their component stars. By contrast, a peculiar and intriguing assortment of galaxies called active galaxies are brightest in radio, infrared, X-ray, or gamma-ray energies, and most of that output comes from their centers. Astronomers speculate that, like quasars, active galaxies have massive central black holes and accretion disks that serve as the source of their tremendous energy output. (In fact, some astronomers consider quasars to be active galaxies whose intensely luminous cores are all that appear in photographs.) It is thought that the gamma rays coming from quasars and active galaxies arise from collisions between cosmic rays and lower energy radiation in the jets emanating from the centers of these objects. In the first three years of observation, EGRET detected more than two dozen gamma-ray-emitting quasars and active galaxies.

Background radiation

Our own galactic disk has been identified as a diffuse source of gamma rays, which mainly arise from cosmic-ray collisions with interstellar gas. Gamma rays also appear to come from all over the sky, not just from the plane of the Milky Way or from identifiable sources. Unlike microwave background radiation, which is also observed uniformly across the sky and which is well understood as radiation left over from the big bang,

The quasars 3C 273 and 3C 279 are among objects of that class imaged by EGRET. The latter quasar, lying at a distance of about 4.6 billion light-years from Earth, is the most distant and by far the most luminous celestial gamma-ray source observed to date.

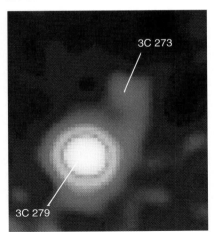

Carl E. Fichtel and the EGRET team

the origin of the spatially uniform part of the gamma-ray background radiation is currently a subject of active investigation.

Gamma-ray bursts

Finally, perhaps the most exciting and perplexing topic in gamma-ray astronomy comprises the mysterious flashes of gamma rays called gamma-ray bursts. For more than two decades, these events, which last from milliseconds to hundreds of seconds, have been detected occasionally (daily or weekly) from the sky. They were first reported in 1973 by scientists from the Los Alamos (New Mexico) National Laboratory who were looking for clandestine nuclear weapons testing around the world by means of orbiting detectors designed to spot the telltale gamma rays associated with nuclear explosions. They soon realized that the gamma-ray bursts that they had been detecting were of a nonterrestrial origin, although they could not connect the events with any known astronomical source. Subsequently a number of other gamma-ray satellites detected gamma-ray bursts.

After the launch of GRO, the BATSE instrument began detecting gamma-ray bursts at a rate of about one per day. EGRET also detected several burst events with energies as high as 10 GeV. Analysis of the arrival times of bursts detected in coincidence by GRO's instruments and those aboard one or both of two other spacecraft—Ulysses, which is on a mission to pass over the Sun's poles, and Pioneer Venus orbiter, which was circling the planet Venus—has allowed precise determinations of the positions of some gamma-ray-burst sources. Despite the determinations, however, the bursts have resisted being conclusively associated with any known type of astronomical object. In other words, after the burst position is found, no detectable object seems to be there.

Nonetheless, since the discovery of the bursts, it had been widely hypothesized that most of them are somehow produced by neutron stars lying within our own galaxy. According to one model, comets or aster-

A plot of the positions of 921 gamma-ray bursts observed by GRO's BATSE instrument as of early 1994 reveals a strikingly uniform distribution over the sky, with no concentration toward the plane of the Milky Way or its center. Such a distribution can be accounted for if the sources of the bursts lie at cosmological distances, billions of light-years from Earth.

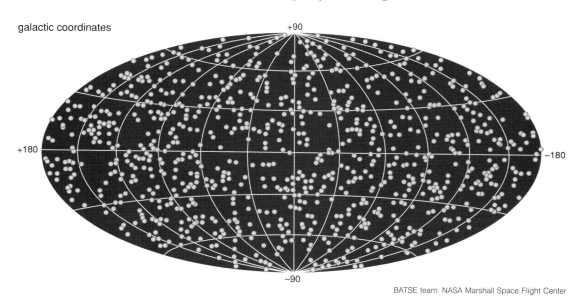

galactic coordinates

BATSE team, NASA Marshall Space Flight Center

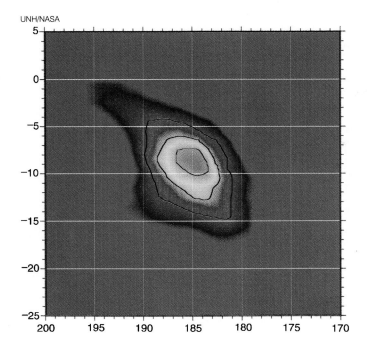

oids falling into neutron stars might produce brief flashes of gamma rays. Another model associates the events with pulsar phenomena called glitches—sudden changes in pulse period, which might be accompanied by a brief burst of gamma-ray energy. And since a neutron star is only a few kilometers across, if it were distant enough from Earth, it would be too dim to be seen in visible light after the gamma-ray burst was over.

In the past three years, BATSE has been steadily detecting gamma-ray bursts, with more than 900 events reported by early 1994. It now appears that there are really two classes of event: those lasting only tenths of a second and those lasting tens or hundreds of seconds. The bursts also have a tremendous range of relative brightnesses. One event on Jan. 31, 1993 (dubbed the Super Bowl burst for its coincidence with the football event), was, while it lasted, 100 times brighter than the steady Geminga pulsar. The weakest are thousands of times dimmer. The distribution of burst intensities can be used to tell something statistically about the distances from Earth of their sources. For example, if the sources are sprinkled uniformly throughout the volume of space around us, one should see more dim bursts than bright ones. Though this has been found to be the case, there are not as many very dim bursts as expected, suggesting that BATSE is seeing out to the edge of the distribution of sources.

In the most popular neutron star models, most of the bursts should be coming from the plane of the Milky Way, where most stars are found. Therefore, even if individual bursts cannot be associated with specific objects, their spatial distribution should reflect the distribution of stars within the Milky Way. However, from a look at the arrival directions of the hundreds of gamma-ray-burst positions determined by BATSE, it is clear that there are no more gamma-ray bursts coming from one direction than from any other. By combining the results of the distribution in

A false-color image created from COMPTEL observations depicts the especially powerful gamma-ray burst of Jan. 31, 1993. Dubbed the Super Bowl burst, the event was, while it lasted, 100 times brighter than the Geminga pulsar. The EGRET instrument, GRO's high-energy telescope, recorded photons from the burst having energies as great as 1,000 MeV.

63

Adapted from information obtained from the BATSE team, NASA Marshall Space Flight Center

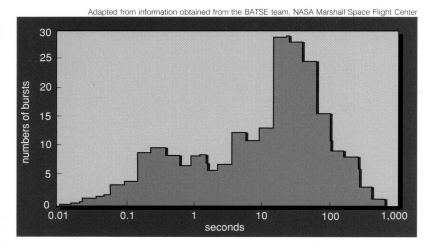

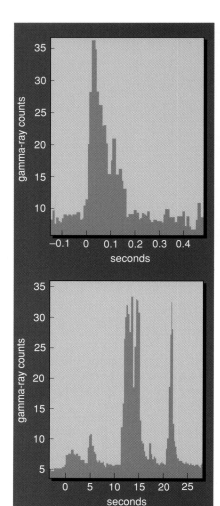

A plot of the distribution of the durations of 222 gamma-ray bursts detected by BATSE (top right) shows two clusterings separated roughly at two seconds. The distribution pattern suggests the existence of two classes of burst: short-duration bursts that typically last tenths of a second and long-duration bursts that last at least several seconds and as long as hundreds of seconds. Time profiles for a short-duration event (top left) and a long-duration event (above) reveal differences in the way the intensities of the bursts vary with time.

intensity and in angle, astronomers are left with three possibilities: the sources are very close, filling a spherical region not much larger than the solar system; they lie in a large halo about the Milky Way; or they are mainly at the farthest reaches of the universe.

Each of these possibilities has its drawbacks. If the bursts are produced near the solar system—say, by colliding comets, as some astronomers have speculated—the question remains as to just how such hypothetical collisions could produce gamma rays at all. If the bursts come from objects filling a halo around the Milky Way, then where is the evidence for the objects, presumably neutron stars, that produce the bursts? Perhaps most intriguing is the suggestion that gamma-ray bursts come from cosmological distances. That possibility garnered support in early 1994 from a new analysis of the BATSE detections, which revealed that, on average, dim bursts last longer than bright bursts. Such a result is consistent with cosmologists' present idea of the expanding universe, specifically that objects at great distances from us are receding faster than comparatively close ones. Because of a relativity effect called time dilation, the duration of a burst will appear stretched out as a consequence of the motion of its source away from Earth, becoming longer and longer as recession speed increases. The stretching seen in the dimmer bursts suggests that they originate billions of light-years from Earth.

If most gamma-ray bursts do come from far beyond the Milky Way, then each burst contains the amount of energy that would be released by conversion of several percent of the mass of a star into gamma rays. How could this come about? The most plausible explanation to date is that the bursts arise from high-speed collisions between two neutron stars, resulting in the obliteration of both stars—or perhaps from collisions between neutron stars and black holes, accompanied by the release of a prodigious burst of gamma rays. Even these scenarios have problems, since none of the bursts has been associated with a distant galaxy, in which such neutron stars or black holes presumably would reside. As of early 1994, there was still no definitive identification of any gamma-ray burst (with the possible exception of an event in 1979 in the direction of a young supernova remnant in the Large Magellanic Cloud) with a star, galaxy, quasar, or other known type of astronomical object.

Now and tomorrow

What has gamma-ray astronomy revealed so far? The detection of gamma-ray photons with discrete, characteristic energies has helped astronomers confirm that the chemical elements are formed in fusion reactions in the centers of stars and in the fiery explosions of supernovas. The observation of electron-positron annihilation gamma rays shows that objects capable of making prodigious amounts of antimatter lie somewhere near the center of the Milky Way. The ubiquity of variable gamma-ray emission from objects ranging from the nearby Sun to the distant quasars has shown that the universe is a more violent and energetic place than had been previously believed. And, perhaps most exciting, gamma-ray astronomy has provided a mystery as intriguing as has ever confronted astronomy: the ultimate source or sources of the enigmatic gamma-ray bursts.

The future of gamma-ray astronomy is bright. In the years ahead an international collaboration between the European Space Agency, the Russian Institute for Space Research, and the National Aeronautics and Space Administration plans to launch an even more sensitive gamma-ray facility called the International Gamma Ray Astrophysics Laboratory (Integral). With 10–50 times more sensitivity than earlier missions, higher spatial resolution, and longer proposed observing times, Integral will very likely contribute more exciting discoveries well into the next millennium.

See also *1989 Yearbook of Science and the Future* Feature Article: SUPERSTAR 1987; *1992 Yearbook of Science and the Future* Feature Articles: COLORS FOR A COSMIC CANVAS; BALLOONING FOR SCIENCE.

FOR ADDITIONAL READING

Gerald J. Fishman, "Gamma Ray Astronomy, Space Missions"; Thomas L. Cline, "Gamma Ray Bursts, Observed Properties and Sources"; and Giovanni F. Bignami, "Gamma Ray Sources, Galactic Distribution," in Stephen P. Maran (ed.), *The Astronomy and Astrophysics Encyclopedia* (Van Nostrand Reinhold, 1992).

Michael Friedlander, Neil Gehrels, and Daryl J. Macomb (eds.), *Compton Gamma Ray Observatory* (American Institute of Physics, 1993).

Neil Gehrels *et al.*, "The Compton Gamma Ray Observatory," *Scientific American* (December 1993, pp. 68–77).

Kevin Hurley, "Probing the Gamma-Ray Sky," *Sky and Telescope* (December 1992, pp. 631–636).

Donald A. Kniffen, "The Gamma-Ray Universe," *American Scientist* (July–August 1993, pp. 342–349).

Poolla V. Rama Murthy and Arnold W. Wolfendale, *Gamma-Ray Astronomy* (Cambridge University Press, 1993).

Art, Science, and the Renaissance Way of Seeing

by Samuel Y. Edgerton, Jr.

The recovery of Euclidean geometry and the rediscovery of linear perspective gave Renaissance Europe a way of looking at physical reality that was unique among the world's cultures. This change in perception played a critical role in the subsequent revolutions in Western art and science.

The Renaissance was that profound historical period in Western Europe, roughly between AD 1300 and 1600, when the "spiritual" Middle Ages gave way to "secular" modernism. It was the age when art changed from stylized abstraction to perspective realism and when science evolved from empirical speculation to mathematical quantification. Today, with several centuries behind us, we can discern in detail these dramatic shifts in the evolution of art and science. But if we had been living when and where we now know the Renaissance began, would we have noticed any differences between that age and a time only two or three generations earlier? If so, what clues might we have found that there would soon emerge geniuses of art and science like Leonardo da Vinci and Galileo Galilei? Moreover, if we had been able to visit such far-off places as China or the Islamic sultanates, would we have seen similar clues there? Or would we have concluded that the Renaissance was, in fact, unique not only in time but also in place—localized to Western Europe and even, in the first years, to central Italy between Rome and Florence?

Indeed, why was Western Europe in the wake of the Renaissance the first of all the world's civilizations to develop what is commonly understood as modern science, moving rapidly ahead of the previously more sophisticated cultures of the East? Why were some of the most spectacular achievements of both the Western artistic and scientific revolutions conceived in the very same place, the Italian city of Florence?

At least one answer to these questions begins to emerge on examination of some of the differences between the pictorial arts of Renaissance Europe and those of its Oriental contemporaries. As a start one can compare ordinary Western Renaissance-style scientific illustrations with examples from traditional China and Islam. Take, for instance, the engraving of a blue fly published in the English microscopist Robert Hooke's monumental *Micrographia* of 1665 (*see* Figure 1) and a similar subject depicted in a detail of a Yüan dynasty Chinese painting, "Early Autumn," attributed to the 13th-century artist Ch'ien Hsüan (*see* Figure 2).

SAMUEL Y. EDGERTON, JR., *is Professor in the Department of Art, Williams College, Williamstown, Maryland.*

This article is adapted from passages appearing in The Heritage of Giotto's Geometry: Art and Science on the Eve of the Scientific Revolution, *by Samuel Y. Edgerton, Jr. Copyright © 1991 by Cornell University. Reprinted by permission of the publisher, Cornell University Press.*

It is immediately apparent how the Chinese painter sought with rare sensitivity to reveal the gossamer lightness of flying insects, whereas Hooke, who probably made only the preparatory drawing for the engraving, stressed just the fixed geometric structure of the fly's wings and gave no indication of how they actually move in flight. Hooke, of course, was examining a dead fly. In the West people take it for granted that if they are to understand the structure of an object, be it organic or inorganic, they must first envisage it as *nature morte,* with all constituent parts translated into impartial, static geometric relationships. In such pictures, as someone once wryly remarked, "Pontius Pilate and a coffeepot are both upright cylindrical masses." To the traditional Chinese this approach was both scientifically and aesthetically absurd.

Geometrizing space

No educated modern person would deny that the geometrization of three-dimensional space is a conceptual condition fundamental to modern science. All scientists, even if they cannot artistically express what they see, can nonetheless picture in their mind's eye a set of geometric shapes in uniform space regulated by horizontal and vertical axes. The Swiss psychologist Jean Piaget even tried to prove that this ability is innate, coming as a natural "logico-mathematical" stage in early child development.

On the other hand, the historical record of human accomplishment in both art and science would seem to argue that such reasoning owes as much to nurture as to nature. In their ability to visualize geometrically regulated space, the traditional Chinese, for instance, were less logico-mathematical than Renaissance Europeans; that is, until after the 17th century, when Jesuit missionaries introduced the 13 books of the *Elements,* Euclid's treatise on geometry. Before the Renaissance, Western Europeans were likewise lacking in logico-mathematical comprehension, as seems clear from most examples of early medieval art.

What scientists since the 17th century have come to mean when they speak of *geometrized* (or more often *Cartesian*) *space* is the capacity to envision it—both in the mind's eye and in graphic projection—as

Figure 3: A painting by an Islamic artist depicts the siege of Vienna by the Ottoman sultan Suleyman I in 1529. Solid forms in the work are shown in a nonperspective "squashed" view, a mode of representation shared by some of the most sophisticated and beautiful art ever created.

infinitely extending in three dimensions. The ancient Greeks, the first to address the problem quantitatively, were working to define an appropriate graphic system when their civilization was subsumed by Rome. The new conquerors, unfortunately, were interested more in practice than in theory and appreciated Euclidean geometry only when it could be applied to military technology. Furthermore, as Roman rule decayed in Europe, theoretical geometry all but disappeared. By the 12th century AD there no longer existed any shared pictorial language by which people could communicate the precise shapes and relative positions of three-dimensional bodies in space.

Medieval scribes were continually frustrated by their inability to depict geometric volumes in their illustrations. In most cases they tried to signify such solid forms by representing them "squashed"; that is, flattened out with all aspects of the object incongruously showing at once. Interestingly enough, this squashed method may be truly innate, as it is recognized universally in the drawings of children. This is not to say that pictorial representations based on the nonperspective squashed view are necessarily childlike or even naive (as modern Western perceptual psychologists use the term). Indeed, some of the most sophisticated and beautiful art ever created is in this mode. Witness medieval Irish and Persian manuscript painting, to give but two examples (*see* Figure 3).

Recovery of Euclidean geometry and optics

What changed the art of Western Europe from this more or less "natural" course—one shared by all cultures of the world in early medieval times—was the recovery of Euclidean geometry after the retreat of Islam from Sicily during the 12th century. The Arabs, who in the 7th century came into possession of many great works of classical Greek scholarship, had managed to translate most into their own language. In the rich residue of such manuscripts left behind after the Arabs retired, Christian scholars discovered and eagerly read works of ancient Greek philosophy and mathematics heretofore only vaguely remembered or altogether unknown in the West. Among these were the complete 13 books of Euclid's *Elements,* his *Optics,* and the incomplete *Optica* of Ptolemy. Within a century these works had been translated from Arabic into Latin, and readable copies slowly began to disseminate to the various learning centers of Western Europe.

Of Euclid's works, second only to the *Elements* in importance to subsequent Western thought was the *Optics,* which in Latin became translated as *Perspectiva,* the science of "seeing through." What the Greeks achieved by this geometrically related study was the realization that light, because it appeared to move in the form of rectilinear rays, could be diagrammed on paper as straight lines. The physical act of seeing, the Greeks believed, occurred when these linear rays framed the observed object as if the object were the base of a cone or pyramid with the eye as the apex (*see* Figure 4). Consequently, the theorems of Euclid's *Elements* as applied to cones and pyramids must also govern the way one sees in the real world. All the classical rules of geometric

70

optics, including those worked out by Ptolemy on mirror reflection and refraction, assumed the viewer to be detached at a fixed distance from the object seen. These same rules could now explain such mysterious optical effects as the apparent diminution in the size of an object when it is seen at distance.

Perhaps the earliest Western commentator to grasp the metaphysical significance of this newly arrived science was the early-13th-century English scholar Robert Grosseteste, chancellor of the recently founded University of Oxford and later bishop of Lincoln. Grosseteste realized that the hypothetical space in which Euclid imagined his figures and drew his textual diagrams was completely homogeneous and isotropic—the same everywhere and in every direction. Grosseteste then had the brilliant idea that light, all pervading in the universe, propagates in exactly the same homogeneous and isotropic way. By no coincidence, God created light on the first day, as the essential medium through which to dispatch his divine grace, according to the geometric laws of *perspectiva*.

It is to the 13th-century Franciscan Roger Bacon, Grosseteste's student, that one turns for the most interesting theoretical link between the renascence of geometry and *perspectiva* before the Renaissance of art and science. Bacon was the precursor of a whole group of Oxford and Paris schoolmen whose studies during the 14th century on the quantification of force and the structure of substance began inadvertently to undermine traditional Aristotelianism and open the way for wholly new conceptions of space and volume.

Following his mentor, Bacon was convinced that *perspectiva* provides the model for understanding how God spreads his divine grace to the world. Since classical optics taught that luminous bodies like the Sun propagate light in rectilinear rays in all directions without loss of substance, Bacon concluded that every physical and spiritual object in the universe also gives off a similar force. He termed the force in Latin *species*, meaning "likeness." *Species* then "multiply" invisibly throughout the spatial medium, interacting with other *species*, those coming from a stronger source forcing a qualitative change upon the weaker—as fire consumes wood, for example.

71

Figure 5: Three scenes from the life of St. Francis of Assisi are detailed in a row of frescoes painted on an inner wall of the Church of San Francesco, Assisi, Italy. Superposed lines reconstruct the way in which the blocklike elements of the painted frame over the frescoes were laid out geometrically to enhance the sense of visual immediacy conveyed by the paintings.

A revolutionary change in perception

No one knows if Roger Bacon ever visited Assisi, the lovely Italian hill town where his Franciscan order was based and where, during his own lifetime, a great basilica honoring St. Francis was under construction. There is evidence, however, that Bacon's ideas on *perspectiva* were being paid attention to by the patrons of the new building, especially when it came time, about 1290, to embellish the inner walls of the vast nave with frescoes detailing the atavistic life of the charismatic founder.

Art historians have never agreed on just who the artists were that the church patrons hired, but one thing does seem certain. The 28 scenes of the life of St. Francis decorating the upper church all show an unprecedented sense of visual immediacy, breaking the established tradition of medieval art in which figures stand flat, static, and remote from the living space of the here-and-now world. In the Assisi frescoes the viewer is given the sense of being an eyewitness to St. Francis's true "likeness." Such a feeling of experiencing the saint's miracles as they happened is especially enhanced by the painted picture frames, which were designed to present the holy stories as if positioned at the base of a Euclidean-Ptolemaic visual pyramid with the viewer implied at the apex (*see* Figure 5).

In considering the change in perception that began after the 12th century in the West, one should regard the year 1425 as among the most decisive in human history, for in that year linear perspective first (at least since classical antiquity) came into painters' practice. Within a century this geometric system, which is based on the apparent shrinking of objects and the apparent convergence of parallel lines and planes as they recede from the viewer, spread throughout Christian Europe and then during the age of imperialism to the rest of the world. No other idea before or since has done more to shape the psychological outlook of the West—or to undermine the traditional outlooks of all other cultures with which the West has come into contact. From that time until the advent of Einsteinian relativity in the early 20th century, Western peoples and all their dominions believed that visual "reality" and geometric linear perspective were one and the same thing.

The Renaissance rediscovery of geometric perspective, how it was foreshadowed by 14th-century painters like the Assisi masters, and how the Florentine architect Filippo Brunelleschi first worked it out in relation to Euclidean-Ptolemaic optical principles can be found amply discussed in other writings. It suffices to add only that what Brunelleschi did in his famous painting (*see* Figure 6; original now lost) of Florence's baptistery was to bestow a mathematical imprimatur on the tentative achievements of the Assisi masters and their followers. In other words, by adjusting those painters' empirical perspective to the "natural law" of optical geometry, Brunelleschi appeared to have fulfilled Roger Bacon's Christian plea:

"Oh, how the ineffable beauty of the divine wisdom would shine and infinite benefit would overflow, if these matters relating to geometry, which are contained in Scripture, should be placed before our eyes in their corporeal figurations!"

Linear perspective and the artisan-engineer

As is known, Brunelleschi's linear perspective geometry revolutionized Renaissance art, first in Italy and then the rest of Western Europe. It also had considerable influence on a peculiar Renaissance profession commonly called the artisan-engineer. The practitioners of this unique trade proclaimed themselves expert in the designing of weapons and fortifications, palaces and public monuments, and any other kind of machinery useful in war or peace. All kept notebooks that were filled with pictures of their special inventions, drawn more or less according to the rules of geometric perspective, and that they hoped would impress a princely patron to grant them a court position with a lifetime sinecure. Two of the most important late-15th-century Italian artisan-

Figure 6: A photograph of Florence's baptistery, taken in a mirror positioned in front of the central door of the city's main cathedral, the Duomo, re-creates what is most likely the scene that Filippo Brunelleschi painted in 1425 to show how realistic perspective could be achieved. Standing in the doorway with his back to the baptistery, Brunelleschi set up a mirror and a small wood panel side by side on an easel and used the reflection of the baptistery as a model for the painting, which he rendered on the panel. The dot on the image of the camera in the photo marks the center of the camera lens, which is positioned at the approximate eyepoint of the artist, and it lies on a horizon line that also includes vanishing points (traced with lines) for the two oblique sides of the octagonal baptistery. A tracing adds the top of the baptistery, which was included in Brunelleschi's painting but is cut off by the camera's rectangular format.

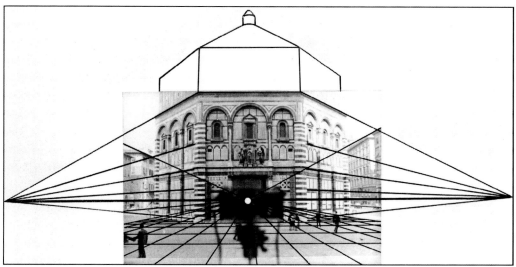

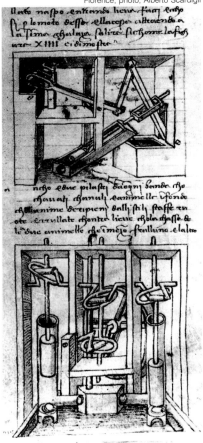

*Figure 7: Detail from folio 42v of the
artisan-engineer Francesco di Giorgio's
Tratatto ("Treatise"), written in the 1470s,
shows two of his designs for crank-driven
pumping devices.*

engineers were Francesco di Giorgio of Siena and, of course, Leonardo da Vinci of Florence.

One can see, for instance, Francesco's creative use of the cutaway-view convention in various pages of his drawings. Many of them show screw- and crank-driven pump devices, which he drew as being set into little open-ended, boxlike, perspective "rooms" with carefully placed wall and floor partitions so that the observer would understand exactly how the various machine parts had to be supported and at what point in three-dimensional space they connected to each other and to the outside power source (*see* Figure 7). Francesco drew so many variations of pumping devices in this manner (there are pages and pages of them) that it seems quite unlikely he ever had the time or the capital to turn more than a few into actual working machines. In all probability most are "thought experiments" worked out solely on paper. Each sketch not only recorded a particular device but revealed otherwise hidden problems that he then corrected in further drawings. Francesco was quite aware of the power of perspective drawing, even advising the would-be architect to learn the skill, especially how to make clear the internal details of structures in relation to the exterior parts that cover them.

Not until after the second decade of the 16th century did the burgeoning European printing industry manage to turn out scientific and technical treatises with illustrations that approached in subtlety those of Francesco and Leonardo. Engravers and wood-block cutters simply did not have the requisite skills. It took nearly a half century for them to learn the perspective conventions already commonplace in Renaissance painting and drawing. The great Italian artisan-engineers had good reason, then, for not subjecting their work to the new medium of printing.

"Technology illustrated" for the 16th century

In truth, however, as the Renaissance matured, the evolving postfeudal upper social classes of Western Europe began to think that they needed to know something of the mechanical arts. Not that nouveau riche aristocrats should actually indulge in the manual trades, but their new sense of noblesse oblige (reinforced by the Christian belief that everyone, especially the privileged elite, was responsible for overseeing God's natural law) demanded an understanding of how things work in the physical world. One thinks of Francis Bacon in England or Thomas Jefferson in America in this regard. There was no parallel to this peculiar Western attitude among the mandarin gentry of any other civilization in the world at the time.

In any case, after about 1520 an unprecedented number of handsome books on applied geometry, architecture, mining and metallurgy, pyrotechnics, ballistics, hydraulics, mechanics, and other such subject matter, not to mention human anatomy, botany, and zoology, issued from European presses. Most of these volumes would be called coffee-table books if published today. Though they were filled with detailed text and explanatory diagrams, their appeal for the most part was to an upper-class audience more interested in the idea of scientific technology than its actual practice. Finally, during the 18th century such books did undergo a reverse metamorphosis into cheap, how-to handicraft manuals expressly directed to the workshop artisan.

Whatever the intended readership, these treatises came to be illustrated with woodcuts and engravings of the highest quality, in which the pictorial conventions of linear perspective were at last assumed to be universally understandable. Also notable was how well the illustrations accorded informationally with the message of the words. Generally, during earlier periods, authors and publishers thought of pictures more or less as impressionistic accompaniment, mere decorative relief from the monotonous columns of text. In the new printed works, however, word and image were to function in unison as never before in the annals of human communication.

Who were the illustrators who caused this sea change in "visual thinking," eventually influencing the education of Galileo, William Harvey,

Figure 8: A woodcut from Georgius Agricola's De re metallica *("On the Subject of Metals"), published in 1556, illustrates the workings of a reciprocal suction pump installed in a mine shaft.*

René Descartes, and Sir Isaac Newton? If Francesco's and Leonardo's seminal drawing conventions remained unpublished, then it was left to other less well-known names both north and south of the Alps to disseminate and popularize their ideas through the medium of the printed, illustrated textbook.

Perhaps the genre of printed illustrated books instigated by the 16th-century perceptual revolution that most set the stage for the coming scientific and industrial revolutions was that which catered to an ever increasing demand for knowledge of practical mechanics. Their authors were often skilled technologists who, while never possessing the drawing talent of a Francesco or a Leonardo, had at least the foresight to have their ideas adequately depicted by competent artists connected with the printing trade.

One outstanding example is *De re metallica* ("On the Subject of Metals") by Georg Bauer, latinized as Georgius Agricola, published posthumously in Basel, Switzerland, in 1556. The author was born in Germany but educated in the early 1500s in Italy, where he received a degree in medicine. While serving as town physician in the Bohemian mining center of Joachimsthal, he applied his *artes liberales* education to the problems, both technical and health-related, of that dangerous industry and composed what quickly was recognized as a classic on matters of metallurgy. Moreover, his book remains a masterpiece of the German wood-block artist's skill.

One of Agricola's illustrations shows a reciprocal suction pump deployed in a mine shaft (*see* Figure 8). While not following Francesco's mechanical modifications, Agricola's artist clearly depended on the drawing conventions established under Francesco's influence; namely, the cutaway, transparent, and exploded view for displaying in scale the whole and the parts of the machine. The viewer sees, as if through a hole torn in the Earth, the pump operating deep in a mine. Moreover, on the adjacent ground surface the same pump is shown dismantled, each of its pieces accompanied by an alphabetic letter referring to its description in the text. Furthermore, the box labeled "D," enclosing the internal workings of the machine, is indicated twice more, once as if transparent, so the viewer can tell how the pistons function as attached to the crank, and again broken apart to reveal the holes through which the pistons and waterspout pass.

A new reality for science

What happened when those same European illustrated books on technology were studied by a trained Western scientist already well-schooled in linear perspective? Galileo Galilei of Florence offers a paradigmatic case study. While everyone knows about Galileo's extraordinary contributions to astronomy, few historians have taken seriously that the famous Florentine was also interested in the fine arts. As his contemporaries often remarked, he knew something of painting and was particularly skilled in the specialized Florentine practice of *disegno,* "perspective drawing." This peculiar skill, which Galileo learned in his native city, was crucial

76

to at least one of his revolutionary astronomical discoveries, the true physical appearance of the surface of the Moon.

Europeans at the start of the 17th century still had no reason to doubt Aristotle's definition of the Moon as a perfect sphere, the prototypical form of all planets and stars in the cosmos. Christian dogma added to this euphoric image by having the Moon symbolize the Immaculate Conception of the virgin mother of Jesus. "Pure as the Moon" became a commonplace expression for Mary, implying that the universe, like herself, was incorruptible, that God would not have created the Moon or any heavenly body in another shape.

In Padua, near Venice, where Galileo was living and teaching, the Florentine scientist first learned of the recent Flemish invention of the telescope in May 1609. Immediately he sent for instructions. With remarkable ingenuity, not to say alacrity, he applied his considerable experience with perspective geometry to the optical problems and managed by the end of the year to build a number of the instruments with such improvements as aperture stops and a magnification increased to 20 power. There is no reason to believe that Galileo waited until he had perfected his most powerful instrument before turning it on the Moon. His long familiarity with the geometry of shadow casting may have allowed him to perceive the irregular topography of the lunar surface even

Figure 9: Sepia-wash studies of Galileo's early observations of the Moon are the work of an experienced artist and are believed to have been done by the scientist himself.

Biblioteca Nazionale, Florence; photo, Scala/Art Resource, New York

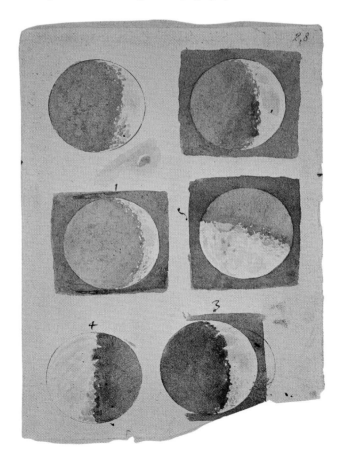

from images he saw through one of his earlier telescopes. Even when only weakly magnified, the Moon does indeed look like a black-and-white study of light and shading.

Perhaps Galileo made some illustrations from the beginning, there on the spot as he stared at the Moon from the bell tower of the Venetian church of San Giorgio Maggiore. While none of these has survived, there exist seven finished sepia studies, obviously done later but probably based on firsthand ad hoc sketches. Clearly these small wash drawings, four of the waxing and three of the waning Moon, were done by someone well-practiced in the manipulation of ink washes, especially the rendering of light-and-shade effects. They are by an experienced artist, and there is no reason to believe by anyone other than Galileo himself (*see* Figure 9). The astronomer no doubt prepared these washes as models for the engraver who would illustrate his book *Sidereus Nuncius* ("The Starry Messenger"), which he rushed to publication in March 1610, barely five months after he began looking at the skies through his telescope.

Galileo's accompanying matter-of-fact textual description of these engravings belies both his own excitement and the stupendous impression they made upon an unsuspecting world:

I have been led to the opinion and conviction that the surface of the Moon is not smooth, uniform, and precisely spherical as a great number of philosophers believe it (and the other heavenly bodies) to be, but is uneven, rough, and full of cavities and prominences, being not unlike the face of the Earth, relieved by chains of mountains and deep valleys.

Did ever a Baroque painter express the new spirit of landscape art better than this? Was ever an artist's eye better prepared to recognize the universal geometric principles of *perspectiva* at work even on the Moon? Moreover, after thus having marveled at the picturesque lunar terrain, Galileo quickly reverted to his scientific self and made another amazing perspective-related discovery. He noticed that some of the lunar peaks were tipped with light within the shadow side even as the terminator boundary lay a long way off. At the same time, he was able to convert this phenomenon into a geometric diagram for solving a shadow-casting problem, perhaps one similar to a drawing exercise from his student days in Florence, and thus to calculate the height of the lunar mountains.

West and East: critical differences

In the first decade of the 17th century, at the same time Galileo was pursuing science in Europe, a Christian Jesuit mission was being established in Beijing (Peking), led by yet another gifted Italian mathematician, Matteo Ricci. Ricci was convinced that the European Renaissance style of drawing and painting as exemplified in the illustrated books of his time obeyed the same rational scientific principles as those he wished to teach the Chinese about the Christian religion. Accordingly, he persuaded the Chinese emperor to allow a special library to be set up in Beijing that would contain not only Christian tracts but the latest published treatises on Western science and technology.

78

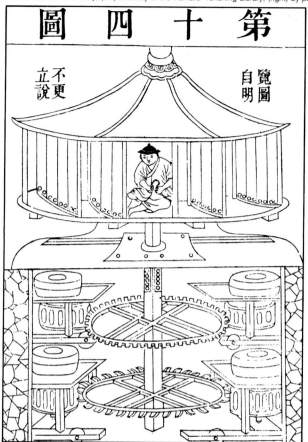 

These books not only attracted the curiosity of the Chinese but also inspired a Chinese-language anthology with numerous illustrations by Chinese woodcut artists after the original European prints. It was entitled *Yüan-hsi ch'i-ch'i t'u-shuo* ("Diagrams and Explanations of Curious Machines from the Far West"), published in Beijing in 1627 and prepared by a Christian convert named Philip Wang Cheng. The work is often cited by modern historians as the earliest import of Renaissance European engineering ideas done up in Chinese dress. It remained popular in China for generations, its woodcut images being republished again and again down to the 20th century.

What is fascinating is the manner in which printed illustrations from the 16th- and 17-century European "theater-of-machines" treatises (as these technical books came to be generally known) were copied into woodcuts for the Chinese edition by indigenous artists, who apparently could neither read the original captions nor understand Western drawing conventions. One such example (*see* Figure 10), copied directly from Plate 11 of Faustus Verantius' *Machinae Novae*, published in Venice around 1615 (*see* Figure 11), depicts a horizontal turbine driving four millstones on two floors of a circular stone windmill tower. No Chinese-language explanation follows, however, save a few characters stating

Figure 10 (left): Woodcut by an anonymous Chinese artist, from Johann Schreck and Philip Wang Cheng's Yüan-hsi ch'i-ch'i t'u-shuo *("Diagrams and Explanations of Curious Machines from the Far West"), published in Beijing (Peking) in 1627, is copied directly from the illustration shown at right.*

Figure 11 (right): Engraving of a two-story windmill tower comes from Faustus Verantius' treatise Machinae Novae, *published in Venice about 1615.*

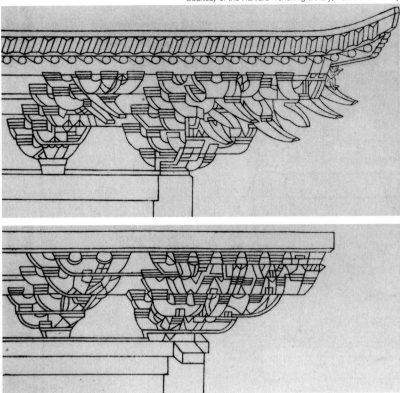

Figure 12: Woodcuts by an anonymous Chinese artist, from Li Chieh's Ying-tsao fa-shih *("[Manual of] Architectural Practice"), published in a second version in 1145, illustrate two variations of bracket-arm sets used as cornice supports in Chinese architecture.*

"Illustration 14" and a brief message: "Looking at this picture one sees that it is self-explanatory; there is no need to say more about it."

Nothing could be farther from the truth. The Chinese picture is quite confusing since the drawing system in China had not yet developed commonly understood conventions for showing depth by means of shading or scale relationships through geometric perspective. Not only could the Chinese artist not "read" the European diagram, he also had no means of his own to indicate, for example, where the vanes of the turbine connected to the driveshaft or how the gearing of the millstones engaged that of the driveshaft in the two-story building.

To be sure, illustrated books on technology had been published in China long before anything similar was produced in the West. Printing, after all, had been a traditional Chinese craft since the 9th century. In 1103, while Western Europeans were still laboriously copying and illuminating manuscripts by hand, Li Chieh, assistant to the Sung dynasty imperial department of building construction, published a thick book on building standards, *Ying-tsao fa-shih*, ("[Manual of] Architectural Practice"), consisting of more than a thousand printed pages with numerous illustrations. A second version, prepared in 1145, has been repeatedly reprinted down to the 20th century. One figure from the work depicts two variations of bracket-arm sets used as cornice supports in traditional Chinese architecture (*see* Figure 12). Like all indigenous Chinese technical and scientific diagrams published before the 18th century, neither of the pictures is drawn to scale. That is to say, they were never meant to be used as actual working drawings from which measurements could be taken or proportioned templates prepared for constructing a three-dimensional replica of the depicted object. Such illustrations were never intended for working craftsmen, who knew perfectly well how to build houses without needing detailed plans. *Ying-tsao fa-shih* was intended instead as a scholarly reference book for a mandarin supervisor.

Unlike the confused illustrators of *Yüan-hsi ch'i-ch'i t'u-shuo*, the artist of *Ying-tsao fa-shih* clearly understood the device he was depicting. Even so, there is no way that a craftsman unfamiliar with the trade in question could replicate a three-dimensional bracket-arm set just by looking at these Escherlike designs. The Chinese aristocrats for whom these books were written could only show them to experienced craftsmen, who, after studying the images briefly, would return to their workshops and, with no further recourse to the models, turn out similar, but hardly identical, functional objects.

Knowing the mind of God

It is true that Western Renaissance treatises on technology were illustrated and printed, just as in China, with an upper-class clientele in mind. Most were designed as deluxe reference books for patrons who, like the Chinese mandarins, would never themselves do manual labor. Nonetheless, a fundamental difference existed between Renaissance Europe and Ming-dynasty China in this respect—not only China but all non-Western cultures everywhere in the world at that time. As was discussed above, a unique tradition rooted in medieval Christian doctrine was growing in the West; it was becoming de rigueur for the privileged gentry to know Euclidean geometry. Even before the 12th century, the early church fathers suspected that they might discover in Euclidean geometry God's very thinking process. In other words, geometry, along with arithmetic, astronomy, and music, sister arts of the ancient quadrivium, was believed to speak the language by which God first inscribed his natural laws of the universe.

Since the mechanical crafts in medieval times were regarded as practical manifestations on Earth of this divine message, the ruling elite, both in Western Europe and in newly colonized America after the 17th century, believed it their Christian duty to sponsor public projects involving applied mathematics, especially geometry. The illustrated architecture and theater-of-machines books in the Renaissance were thus understood as having an almost Gospel-like purpose, to propagate God's works. Ownership of such books demonstrated both to the Creator and to the general public that the upper class was indeed fulfilling its natural mandate as designated caretaker of God's master plan.

Geometric linear perspective was quickly accepted in Western Europe after the 15th century because Christians wanted to believe that when they contemplated a work of art laid out in this fashion, they were seeing a replica of the same underlying structure of reality that God had conceived at the moment of creation. By the 17th century, as the "natural

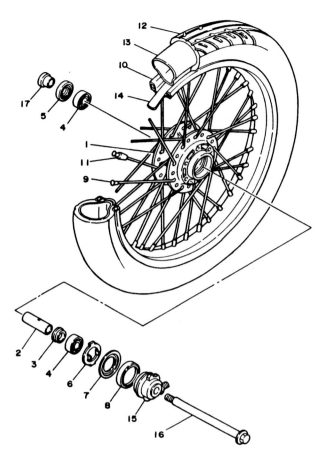

philosophers" like Galileo, Descartes, and Newton came more and more to realize that linear perspective does in fact conform to the optical and physiological process of human vision, not only was perspective's Christian imprimatur upheld, but it now also served to reinforce Western science's increasingly optimistic and democratic belief that God's conceptual process had at last been penetrated and that control of nature lay potentially within the grasp of any living human being.

If in subsequent Western art the perspective underdrawing seemed implicitly to endow the finished picture with the ideal higher reality found in the Platonic otherworld of pure forms, then perhaps one can pinpoint at least one reason why Western artisan-engineers, particularly during the 16th and 17th centuries, came to depend more and more on preparatory measured drawings to scale. By demonstrating that they could draw such geometric plans on paper, craftsmen in effect joined their patrons as divinely anointed administrators of God's works, obviously enhancing their own social position.

Whatever one may say about the poor-quality, formulaic art that this kind of standardized procedure encouraged, there is no question that a fundamental difference arose after the Renaissance between the West and the rest of the world with respect to the way one not only looked at pictures but also conceived of physical reality. In the long run, philoso-

Figure 13: Exploded, cutaway illustration of the front wheel assembly of a modern motorcycle, taken from a service manual, follows the conventions of perspective drawing laid down during the Italian Renaissance.

82

phers will have to judge just how beneficial or dangerous to humankind has been the unique Western way of seeing. In the short run, however, there is no doubt that every literate, educated person in the world who desires to succeed in technology or science (or, for that matter, to maintain a motorcycle), whatever his or her philosophy, gender, race, or ethnic origin, must be able to read a modern working drawing to scale and to comprehend instantly those peculiar conventions of perspective invented during the Italian Renaissance (*see* Figure 13).

FOR ADDITIONAL READING

I. Bernard Cohen, *From Leonardo to Lavoisier, 1450–1800* (Scribner, 1980).

Alister C. Crombie, *Robert Grosseteste and the Origins of Experimental Science, 1100–1700* (Clarendon Press, 1953).

Samuel Y. Edgerton, Jr., *The Renaissance Rediscovery of Linear Perspective* (Basic Books, 1975).

Samuel Y. Edgerton, Jr., *The Heritage of Giotto's Geometry: Art and Science on the Eve of the Scientific Revolution* (Cornell University Press, 1991).

Eugene S. Ferguson, "The Mind's Eye: Nonverbal Thought in Technology," *Science* (Aug. 26, 1977, pp. 827–836).

Margaret A. Hagen (ed.), *The Perception of Pictures,* 2 vol. (Academic Press, 1980).

Martin Kemp, *The Science of Art: Optical Themes in Western Art from Brunelleschi to Seurat* (Yale University Press, 1990).

Michael Kubovy, *The Psychology of Perspective and Renaissance Art* (Cambridge University Press, 1986).

David C. Lindberg, *Theories of Vision from al-Kindi to Kepler* (University of Chicago Press, 1976).

John E. Murdoch, *Antiquity and the Middle Ages* (Scribner, 1984).

Joseph Needham, *The Grand Titration: Science and Society in East and West* (University of Toronto Press, 1969).

Erwin Panofsky, *Galileo as a Critic of the Arts* (Martinus Nijhoff, 1954). Reprinted (updated but abridged) in *Isis* (vol. 47, 1956, pp. 1–18).

Ladislao Reti, "Francesco di Giorgio Martini's Treatise on Engineering and Its Plagiarists," *Technology and Culture* (vol. 4, 1963, pp. 287–298).

Ewen A. Whitaker, "Galileo's Lunar Observations and the Dating of the Composition of *Sidereus Nuncius,*" *Journal for the History of Astronomy* (vol. 9, 1978, pp. 155–169).

NO and CO:
The Body's Unprecedented Signaling Molecules

by Solomon H. Snyder

The noxious gases nitric oxide and carbon monoxide have been found, unexpectedly, to play vital communications roles in the human brain and elsewhere in the body. Their significance extends to such diverse phenomena as memory, breathing, digestion, and the brain damage resulting from stroke.

The human brain comprises about 10 billion nerve cells, or neurons. Like other cells in the body, neurons have a nucleus, a cytoplasm, and a surrounding cell membrane. They are unique, however, in that they send out fiberlike processes, enabling them to communicate with literally thousands of other neurons. Incoming signals are received by processes called dendrites, several thousand of which may extend from a given neuron. Neurons project information via a long process called an axon, which can branch into as many as 10,000 different nerve endings. The nerve endings in turn make contact with the dendrites of other neurons or with other parts of neuronal cells. The site of contact between nerve endings and other neurons is called the synapse. Because each neuron has so many ways of making synaptic contact with other neurons, the possible interactions among all the brain's neurons is in the trillions.

How do neurons talk to each other so that the brain can process information? The language of neurons is chemical. Each nerve ending releases one or more distinct chemical messenger molecules called neurotransmitters. Neurotransmitters diffuse across the synapse to adjacent neurons and either excite them or inhibit them. In principle, the brain could function with only two kinds of neurotransmitter, one excitatory and one inhibitory. In order for subtle messages to be conveyed, however, nature has evolved a large number of distinct chemical neurotransmitters. The exact number is not known but is thought to range between 50 and 100. A single nerve ending usually contains and releases one, two, or maybe three distinct neurotransmitters. Since the nuances of the response elicited by each of the many different neurotransmitters remain to be worked out, scientists have yet to understand exactly why a particular group of neurons uses one or another neurotransmitter.

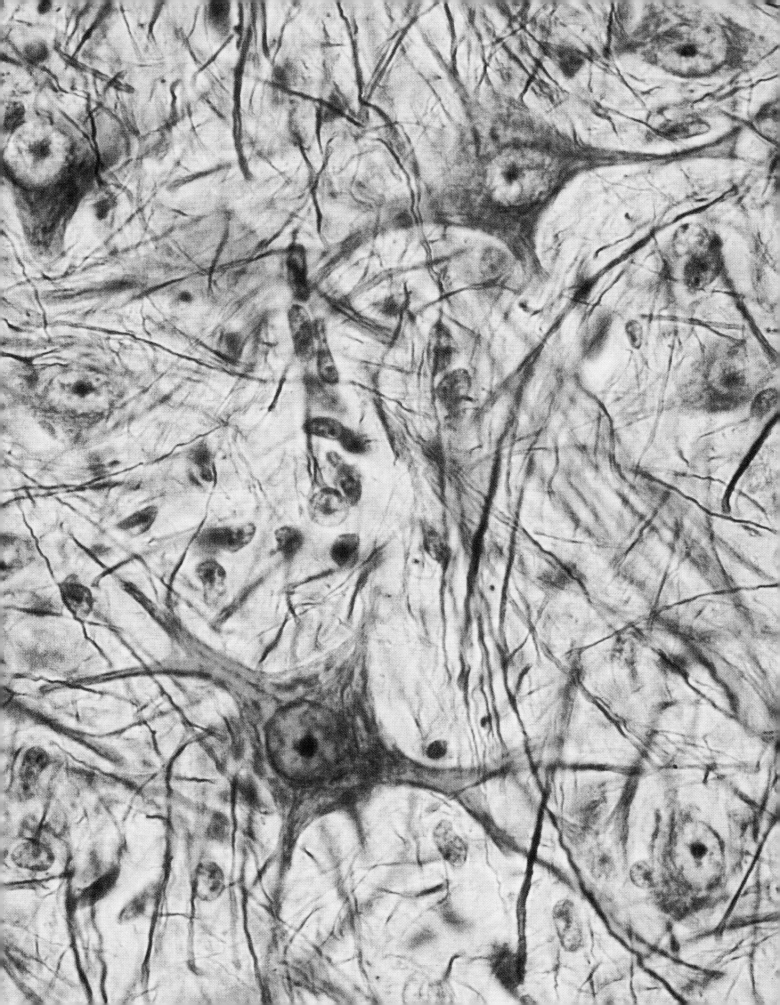

Neurotransmitters fall into different chemical classes. The first known neurotransmitters, which were discovered between 1930 and 1960, are all amines, organic molecules based on the structure of ammonia (NH$_3$), with a nitrogen group as their major signaling mechanism. In the 1960s researchers began to appreciate that amino acids are also neurotransmitters. Amino acids are best known as the building blocks of proteins. However, certain amino acids such as glutamic acid, aspartic acid, and glycine also serve as neurotransmitters. In terms of sheer quantity, amino acids are the major neurotransmitters in the brain. Glutamic acid, usually referred to simply as glutamate, is the principal excitatory neurotransmitter in the brain and is employed by 30–45% of neurons, depending on the particular brain region. By contrast, most of the amines are neurotransmitters for only 1–5% of neurons.

The third class of neurotransmitters to be identified comprises peptides. Peptides consist of amino acids hooked to each other by the same types of chemical bonds that are employed in constructing proteins. In essence, peptides are simply small proteins. Peptides that function as neurotransmitters may contain as few as 3 or as many as 50 amino acids, whereas most proteins contain 100–1,000 amino acids.

Great interest in peptides as neurotransmitters arose in the mid-1970s following the discovery of opiate (or opioid) receptors, specific sites on the surface of brain neurons that bind to and mediate the actions of opiate drugs like morphine and heroin. The properties of opiate receptors so closely resembled those of receptors for neurotransmitters that scientists wondered why the body made opiate receptors. Because humans were not born with morphine in them, it was reasonable to ask if there might not be a naturally occurring neurotransmitter with morphinelike properties. Research in the laboratories of John Hughes and Hans Kosterlitz in Scotland and then by Rabi Simantov and me in the U.S. resulted in the identification of the enkephalins, peptides that are naturally occurring morphinelike neurotransmitters. From the mid-1970s until the early 1990s, it was assumed that amines, amino acids, and peptides "filled out" all the possibilities for neurotransmitters in the brain and that no other classes were likely to be discovered. That assumption, it turned out, was quite wrong.

A class apart

Over the past few years, work in various laboratories has led to the recognition of a fourth, remarkable class of neurotransmitters. The two known members of the class are simple molecules that are already well recognized as noxious environmental pollutants; namely, nitric oxide (NO) and carbon monoxide (CO). Nitric oxide and carbon monoxide, both of which are gases at ordinary temperatures, violate many of the classic "laws" of the neurotransmitter field. The classic neurotransmitters are stored within nerve endings inside small, round packages called synaptic vesicles. They are released by a unique process in which the synaptic vesicle fuses with the membrane of the nerve ending, releasing its chemical contents into the synapse. The neurotransmitter then diffuses across

SOLOMON H. SNYDER is Director of the Department of Neuroscience, Johns Hopkins University School of Medicine, Baltimore, Maryland.

(Overleaf) Brown-stained neurons stand out against blue-counterstained surrounding tissue in a photomicrograph of central gray matter of the human spinal cord.
© Biophoto Associates—Science Source/ Photo Researchers, Inc.

Some prominent neurotransmitters in the brain

amines

acetylcholine

The first known neurotransmitter, discovered in the 1920s. It is the neurotransmitter at nerve-muscle connections for all the voluntary muscles of the body as well as at many of the involuntary (autonomic) nervous system synapses. Despite its long history, the exact role of acetylcholine neurons in the brain is unclear.

norepinephrine

One of the two major catecholamine neurotransmitters and the second known transmitter, having been characterized in the 1930s. It was discovered as the transmitter of the sympathetic nerves of the autonomic nervous system that mediate emergency responses, such as acceleration of the heart, dilatation of the bronchi (major airways of the lungs), and elevation of blood pressure.

dopamine

Another catecholamine neurotransmitter, discovered in 1958 as a major transmitter in the corpus striatum, a part of the brain regulating motor behavior. Destruction of the dopamine neurons in the corpus striatum is responsible for the symptoms of Parkinson's disease, such as rigidity and tremor. Blockade of the actions of dopamine in other brain regions accounts for the therapeutic activities of antischizophrenic drugs.

serotonin

The transmitter of a discrete group of neurons that all have cell bodies located in the raphe nuclei of the brain stem. Changes in its concentration are associated with several mood disorders, including some kinds of depression.

histamine

In addition to its roles in allergic conditions and in regulating acid secretion by the stomach, histamine is a neurotransmitter in the brain. It is most highly concentrated in areas of the brain that regulate emotional behavior, and its localization is roughly similiar to that of norepinephrine. It is unclear whether certain effects of antihistamine drugs, such as sleepiness, relate to actions at brain histamine receptors.

amino acids

GABA (gamma-aminobutyric acid)

One of the amino acid transmitters in the brain. It has no known function other than serving as a neurotransmitter and occurs almost exclusively in the brain. GABA reduces the firing of neurons and so is an inhibitory neurotransmitter. It is the transmitter at 25–40% of all synapses in the brain.

glycine

In addition to its roles as a conventional amino acid in protein synthesis and general metabolism, glycine serves as an inhibitory neurotransmitter in small neurons in the spinal cord and brain stem. Here it is a transmitter at 30–40% of synapses and quantitatively is more prominent than GABA.

glutamate (glutamic acid)

One of the major amino acids in general metabolism and protein synthesis, glutamate is also a neurotransmitter. It stimulates neurons to fire and is probably the principal excitatory neurotransmitter in the brain. Glutamate appears to be the neurotransmitter of the major neuronal pathway that connects the cerebral cortex and the corpus striatum. It is also the transmitter of the granule cells, which are the most numerous neurons in the cerebellum. There is some evidence that glutamate is the principal neurotransmitter of the visual pathway. No drugs are yet known to exert their effects via interactions with glutamate.

peptides

enkephalins

Composed of two peptides, each containing five amino acids. The enkephalins were discovered as the normally occurring substances that act upon opiate receptors. Thus, enkephalins can mimic the effects of opiates. Enkephalin neurons are localized to areas of the brain that regulate functions that are influenced by opiate drugs.

substance P

A peptide containing 11 amino acids. It is a major transmitter of sensory neurons that convey pain sensation from the periphery of the body, especially the skin, into the spinal cord. Opiates relieve pain in part by blocking the release of substance P. Substance P is also found in numerous brain regions.

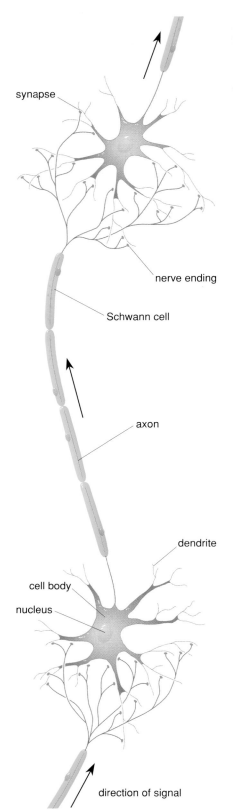

synapse

nerve ending

Schwann cell

axon

dendrite

cell body

nucleus

direction of signal

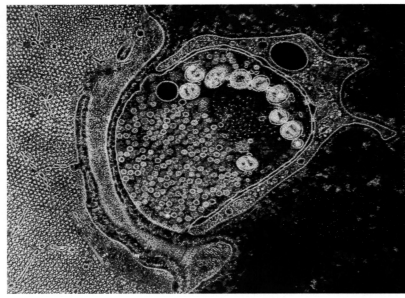

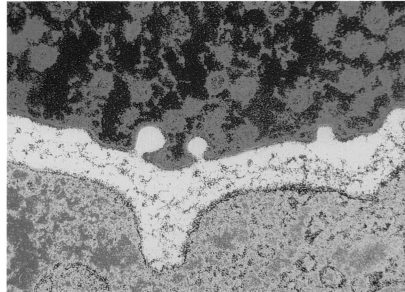

the synapse and binds to specific receptor sites on adjacent neuronal membranes. The receptor is sculpted to fit the neurotransmitter precisely as a lock fits a key. Binding of the neurotransmitter to its receptor had long been thought to be the crucial element in synaptic transmission, accounting for the specificity of information processing among neurons.

The chemical features of NO and CO preclude their functioning like other neurotransmitters. As gases, they cannot be fixed for storage in synaptic vesicles. Instead, they are synthesized by enzymes (proteins that promote specific chemical reactions) on demand, as the body needs them. Their release amounts simply to their diffusing through the cell membrane and out of the neuron. When they reach adjacent neurons, rather than binding to specific protein receptors on the neuronal membranes, they merely diffuse into the neurons, where they bind to a variety of proteins.

The first reasonably strong evidence that NO could be a neurotransmitter dates from 1989, while comparable information for CO emerged three years later. Yet by 1993 the number of roles established or suspected for NO and CO in the brain already equaled or exceeded that for neurotransmitters that had been well characterized for dozens of years. Nitric oxide is now well established as a neurotransmitter in the brain and in nerves of the involuntary, or autonomic, nervous system throughout the body. NO has been shown to be the neurotransmitter of the nerves that cause the relaxation of the intestine during peristalsis, the waves of muscular movement that convey food through the digestive tract. NO is the neurotransmitter of nerves that regulate erection of the penis and appears to be fully responsible for the erectile process. Excessive release of NO following stroke seems to account for a major portion of the brain damage of stroke victims. For its part, carbon monoxide may play a prominent role in specific neuronal systems that regulate learning and memory. CO may also function as a neurotransmitter to control breathing, especially in response to low levels of oxygen in the blood.

Identifying nitric oxide and its enzyme

Scientists first appreciated a role for nitric oxide not in the brain but in bodily functions associated with the inflammatory process and with responses seen in blood vessels. In the early 1980s numerous researchers were studying nitrosamines, organic compounds containing both oxygen and nitrogen, as cancer-causing agents. Nitrosamines are converted in the body to nitrates, inorganic compounds that also contain nitrogen and oxygen. It was first assumed that nitrates that were being detected in samples of human urine came from nitrosamines in the diet. Researchers discovered, however, that nitrates in the urine derive from the body's own metabolic activities and that nitrate formation increases markedly during inflammation.

Soon it was appreciated that macrophages, white blood cells that are active in inflammation, are a source of nitric oxide in the body. Macrophages engulf and kill tumor cells and bacteria. Researchers showed that these functions of the macrophages derive from their ability to form NO, which in turn is converted to the nitrates that turn up in the urine in increased amounts during inflammation. NO is formed from the amino acid arginine by an enzyme called NO synthase, which takes one of the nitrogen atoms from arginine and adds an oxygen atom to it. Drugs that block the function of NO synthase thus also interfere with the normal defensive abilities of macrophages. For example, simple derivatives of arginine that chemically tie up NO synthase and keep it from making NO completely prevent macrophage function.

About the same time that the macrophage research was taking place, NO was discovered to be a major regulator in blood vessels. Nitro-

The general features of a neuron constituting part of a pathway for nerve signals are diagrammed on the opposite page. Neurons communicate by means of chemical neurotransmitters that are released from the nerve endings of the sending neuron. The neurotransmitters travel across the synapse, the point of contact between neurons, to receptors on adjacent receiving neurons. The classic neurotransmitters are stored in nerve endings in small, round packages called synaptic vesicles. They are released by a process in which the vesicles fuse with the membrane of the nerve ending and empty their contents into the synaptic space between the neurons. A photomicrograph (opposite page, top right) shows a vesicle-filled nerve ending in contact with the membrane of an adjacent cell, while a more magnified view (opposite page, bottom right) shows several vesicles discharging their contents into the synaptic space.

Photos, Science Source/Photo Researchers, Inc.; (top) © Fawcett and Reese; (bottom) © Fawcett, Heuser, and Reese

H
|
$H_2N—C—COOH$
|
CH_2
|
CH_2
|
CH_2
|
NH
|
C＝NH
|
NH_2

arginine

|

NO synthase

↓

NO nitric oxide

+

H
|
$H_2N—C—COOH$
|
CH_2
|
CH_2
|
CH_2
|
NH
|
C＝O
|
NH_2

citrulline

(Top) Nitric oxide (NO) is formed in the body from the amino acid arginine by the catalytic action of the enzyme NO synthase. (Right) Neurotransmitters that dilate blood vessels act on the endothelium, the blood vessel's inner cellular lining. In response to stimulation by the neurotransmitter, the endothelial cells make a messenger molecule that diffuses to the overlying muscle cells, causing them to relax. This messenger molecule, dubbed ERDF upon its discovery, was later found to be NO.

glycerin and other nitrates have been employed in clinical medicine for almost 100 years to dilate blood vessels and so relieve angina pectoris, the intermittent chest pain caused by atherosclerotic narrowing of the coronary arteries of the heart. But it was only in the 1970s and early 1980s that researchers began to understand the reason for the drugs' effectiveness—nitroglycerin and related drugs act by being transformed by enzymes into NO. In 1980 Robert Furchgott of the State University of New York at Brooklyn discovered that neurotransmitters that dilate blood vessels act on the cell layer, called the endothelium, that lines the inside of the blood vessel. In response to stimulation by the neurotransmitter, the endothelium fabricates a biological messenger molecule that diffuses to the overlying muscle cells, which then relax. Furchgott dubbed the mystery molecule endothelium-derived relaxing factor (EDRF).

Numerous scientists tried to isolate EDRF but were unsuccessful, as it was extremely labile, disintegrating in only a few seconds. Several researchers noticed that the properties of EDRF closely resembled those of NO. Salvador Moncada of the Wellcome Research Laboratories, Beckenham, England, and Louis Ignarro of the University of California at Los Angeles obtained direct experimental evidence that NO is EDRF. It now appears that NO is the major normal regulator of blood-vessel diameter and, consequently, of blood pressure. As might be expected, arginine derivatives that inhibit NO synthase cause blood vessels to constrict and elicit a marked elevation in blood pressure.

Nitric oxide was first suspected to exist in the brain when John Garthwaite at the University of Liverpool, England, noticed that rat brain cells in culture form a substance having the properties of NO. About the same time David Bredt, an M.D.-Ph.D. student in my laboratory at Johns Hopkins University, and I became interested in a possible role for NO

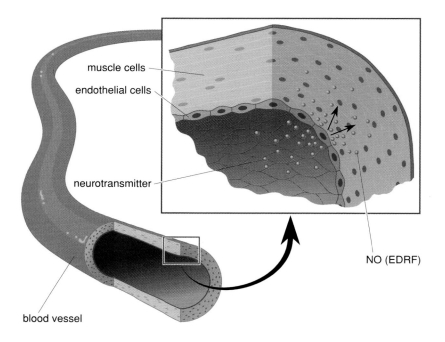

muscle cells

endothelial cells

neurotransmitter

NO (EDRF)

blood vessel

in brain function. How could we discover such a function? Because NO is so labile, it was difficult to study the molecule directly. We decided instead to explore the biochemical effects of NO release.

When neurotransmitters act upon neurons, they often stimulate the formation of molecules called second messengers, which then pass on the neuronal signal inside the cell. Cyclic adenosine monophosphate (AMP) and cyclic guanosine monophosphate (GMP) are well-known second messengers. We knew from previous research that NO relaxes blood vessels by stimulating the formation of cyclic GMP. We also were aware that glutamate, the brain's major excitatory neurotransmitter, greatly increases levels of cyclic GMP in various brain regions. When we applied glutamate to slices of rat brain prepared in the laboratory, we were surprised to see a rapid tripling of the enzymatic activity of NO synthase. We wondered whether NO formed from the enzymatic activity was responsible for the ability of glutamate to stimulate cyclic GMP levels. To test the idea, we treated the brain slices with chemical inhibitors of NO synthase, which indeed blocked the stimulation of cyclic GMP levels. Independently, Garthwaite and Moncada observed similar results. That NO mediates one of the actions of the major excitatory neurotransmitter in the brain indicated to us that NO is certainly of importance and worth exploring in detail.

In the brain the best way to understand the function of a chemical is visualization. If one can observe at a microscopic level the exact neuronal structures that contain a chemical, then one often can surmise its function. Because the lability of NO would make it difficult to pinpoint, we decided instead to visualize the NO synthase protein. To do this, one employs antibodies that bind selectively to the protein in tissue slices on microscope slides. The antibodies in turn can be stained, causing the tissues in which they are present to stand out visually. This procedure, called immunohistochemistry, has enabled researchers to visualize the location of many different proteins at a microscopic level. Accordingly, Bredt proceeded to purify the NO synthase protein so that he could develop antibodies against it.

When Bredt tried to purify NO synthase, he was thwarted at the very first purification steps. No matter what he did, the enzyme seemed to lose activity. Bredt then realized that the purification procedure was removing from the enzyme a crucial chemical, a cofactor, that was important for enzyme function. He showed that the cofactor was the calcium-binding protein calmodulin. This discovery enabled him to stabilize NO synthase and proceed with its purification. Perhaps just as important, it explained how glutamate stimulates NO synthase during synaptic transmission. Glutamate can bind to a number of different kinds, or subtypes, of neuronal receptors for it. One of them, called the NMDA receptor, is named for N-methyl-D-aspartate, a synthetic amino acid that has been found to act at the receptor in the same way as does glutamate. When glutamate binds to the NMDA receptor, it opens channels that are permeable to calcium so that calcium rushes into the cell. The calcium then binds to calmodulin, which in turn associates with and activates NO synthase. In this way the neurotransmitter glutamate can stimulate NO formation in a fraction of a second to convey synaptic signals.

Bredt raised antibodies to the purified NO synthase by injecting the enzyme into rabbits, whose immune system responded by making an antibody that specifically recognized and bound to the enzyme. The antibody was then employed in immunohistochemical staining in order to locate where the enzyme was concentrated. In most of the brain, a strikingly limited number of neurons stained for NO synthase. In the cerebral cortex and many other brain regions, only 1–2% of neurons contained NO synthase. Each of these neurons was found to give rise to large numbers of axon processes. The branching of these processes is so dense that it appears likely that virtually every neuron in the brain receives input from NO-releasing neurons. In some parts of the brain, however—for example, the cerebellum, which regulates motor activity— all neurons of certain classes contained NO synthase. Why the distribution of neurons that release NO is different throughout the brain is an intriguing question that remains to be clarified.

NO in stroke and AIDS dementia

As discussed above, in a normally functioning brain the neurotransmitter glutamate excites neurons by binding to its receptors. The best-known glutamate receptor is the NMDA subtype, which triggers an opening of channels in neurons that allow passage of calcium. In the mid-1980s researchers began to realize that the release of excessive glutamate may damage neurons, especially in vascular stroke, the kind caused by blood clots. Strokes are caused either by blood clots in the brain or by cerebral hemorrhages. Clots account for the most common types of stroke. Typi-

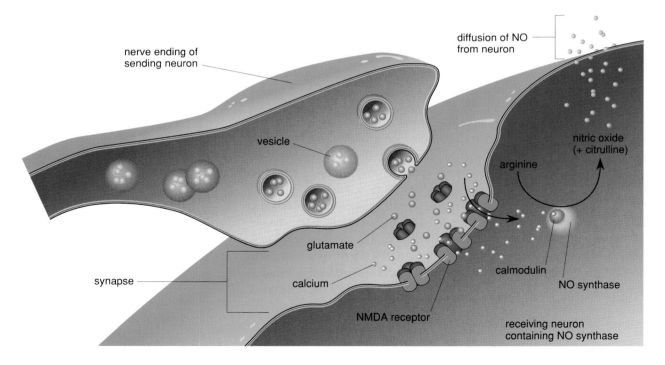

nerve ending of sending neuron

diffusion of NO from neuron

vesicle

arginine

nitric oxide (+ citrulline)

glutamate

calmodulin

synapse

calcium

NO synthase

NMDA receptor

receiving neuron containing NO synthase

From "Mechanisms of Nitric Oxide–mediated Neurotoxicity in Primary Brain Cultures," V.L. Dawson, *et al.*, *The Journal of Neuroscience*, June 1993, vol. 13(6), pp. 2651–2661; copyright © 1993 Society for Neuroscience

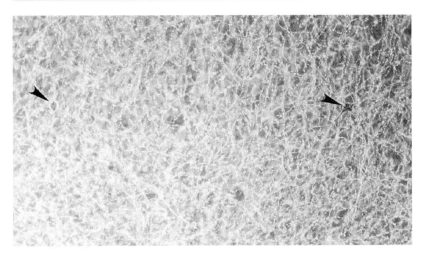

A photomicrograph of a section of cerebral cortex from a rat brain that has been immunohistochemically stained for NO synthase (top) illustrates the strikingly limited number of NO-releasing neurons (arrowheads) in the cortex—only one or two out of every hundred neurons. On the other hand, photographed in a different kind of illumination, the same section (bottom) reveals the dense network of axon processes that branch from the NO-releasing neurons. The branching is so dense that it appears likely that virtually every neuron in the brain receives input from NO-releasing neurons.

cally, a clot will form in the large middle cerebral artery, depriving much of the cerebral cortex of adequate supplies of blood.

It was once thought that the death of brain neurons from stroke is simply the result of their being starved of blood. Abundant recent evidence shows, however, that outright death from blood and oxygen deprivation accounts only for a small amount of neuronal damage in strokes. Instead, various processes associated with the stroke event trigger a massive release of glutamate from neurons. For about 24 hours following the stroke, this glutamate damages cells that were only partially deprived of their blood supply and that otherwise would have survived. Evidence of a role for glutamate in stroke damage comes from studies using drugs that block glutamate receptors. In laboratory animals in which researchers have modeled stroke by tying off the middle cerebral artery to simulate a blood clot, these drugs can prevent more than 50% of neuronal damage even if they are administered several hours after the stroke is induced. Drugs that block the NMDA subtype of glutamate receptor are most effective. Indeed, numerous pharmaceutical companies are presently developing similar drugs for the possible therapy of stroke damage in human beings.

Because NO had been shown to mediate other activities of glutamate at NMDA receptors, we wondered whether NO also plays a role in neuronal damage from excess glutamate. Ted and Valina Dawson in our research group used cultures of cerebral-cortex neurons treated with glutamate or NMDA to explore this question. They discovered that the neuronal damage caused by stimulation of NMDA receptors could be prevented by treatment of the cultures with NO synthase inhibitors. Moreover, simply deleting arginine, the chemical that NO synthase needs to make NO, from the incubation medium prevented neuronal damage. When the two researchers stained NMDA-treated cultures for NO synthase in order to visualize NO-releasing neurons, they found that the neurons that had been killed by the NMDA treatment always lay closely adjacent to the processes of NO-releasing neurons. Thus, NO is responsible for glutamate-induced neuronal damage.

Numerous laboratories have extended these findings to middle-cerebral-artery stroke induced in laboratory animals. Intravenous injec-

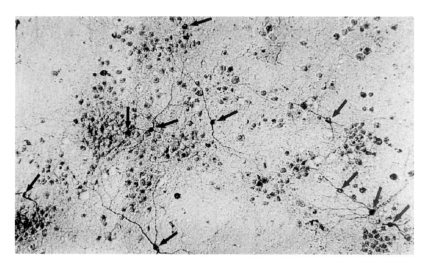

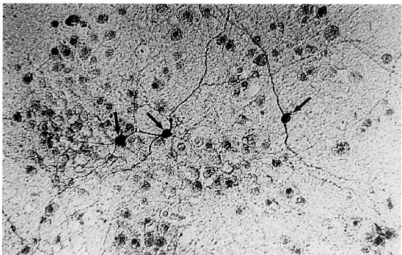

Cultures of cerebral-cortex neurons treated with NMDA to stimulate the NMDA subtype of glutamate receptor have helped reveal the role of NO in damage to neurons caused by excess glutamate, as is seen in stroke. In the photomicrographs at right (the lower image is a detail of the upper one at higher magnification) arrows locate neurons that have stained for the presence of NO synthase, while neurons that have died after NMDA treatment appear as clusters of dark round spots. The micrographs show that neurons killed by NMDA treatment invariably lie close to NO-releasing neurons or their processes.

From "Mechanisms of Nitric Oxide–mediated Neurotoxicity in Primary Brain Cultures," V.L. Dawson, *et al., The Journal of Neuroscience,* June 1993, vol. 13(6), pp. 2651–2661; copyright © 1993 Society for Neuroscience

tions of the NO synthase inhibitor nitroarginine in small doses dramatically alleviate stroke damage in these animal models. Thus, NO synthase inhibitors may afford a novel means for treating stroke damage in humans.

AIDS dementia has long been a puzzle. Many AIDS patients develop severe confusion and memory loss early in the disease process, yet researchers rarely find particles of the human immunodeficiency virus, the cause of AIDS, in neurons in the brain. Instead, the major protein in the outer coat of the virus, called the gp120 protein, dissociates from the virus and itself causes neuronal damage. In cultures of brain cells, extremely low concentrations of gp120 cause neuronal death. Stuart Lipton of Harvard University discovered that gp120 has this neuron-damaging ability only if the culture medium contains glutamate. Moreover, the actions of glutamate in this case were found, once again, to involve the NMDA subtype of glutamate receptor. This suggested to us that the neuron-damaging ability of gp120, like that of stroke, could involve NO. The Dawsons were able to duplicate Lipton's observations. They then showed that the damage to nerves caused by gp120 could be blocked by NO synthase inhibitors as well as by omission of arginine from the incubation medium. Their findings suggest that NO synthase inhibitors may be of therapeutic utility in AIDS dementia.

NO as a regulator of digestion
Neurons that release nitric oxide are not restricted to the brain. In Bredt's initial research he observed NO-releasing neurons in many locations throughout the body. For instance, he discovered neurons that stained for NO synthase in networks throughout the gastrointestinal tract. These networks, together called the myenteric plexus, contain NO-releasing neurons in the esophagus, stomach, small intestine, and large intestine down to the rectum and anus. The myenteric plexus of nerves regulates intestinal peristalsis, the contraction and relaxation of the muscular wall of the intestines during digestion. The relaxation phase of peristalsis has long been a mystery. Researchers had strived unsuccessfully for many years to identify the neurotransmitter that causes relaxation. That the myenteric plexus neurons stained intensely for NO synthase suggested that NO could be involved.

Researchers can easily monitor the neurotransmission process in the intestine by placing strips of fresh intestine in an organ bath and then electrically stimulating the nerves while measuring contraction and relaxation. Stimulating the nerves of the myenteric plexus typically results in relaxation. When researchers in various laboratories applied NO synthase inhibitors to such experimental setups, they observed a blockade of the relaxation that had been initiated by nerve stimulation. Taken together with evidence pinpointing NO synthase in these nerves, this evidence establishes NO as the neurotransmitter of the nerves regulating intestinal relaxation.

The passage of food from the stomach to the small intestine is a closely regulated process. If food leaves the stomach too quickly, it is

The stomachs from a normal mouse (top) and a mouse in which the gene for neuronal NO synthase was disrupted, or "knocked out," at the embryonic stage (bottom) are compared. Lack of NO-regulated stomach function in the knockout mouse caused the muscle that comprises the pyloric sphincter, which serves as a valve between the stomach and small intestine, to remain in a state of chronic contraction. As a result, food was prevented from moving readily out of the stomach, and the stomach became greatly distended. The pattern is virtually identical to that observed in a genetic disease of humans, hypertrophic pyloric stenosis. In victims of the disorder the pyloric region of the stomach also appears to lack neurons that contain NO synthase.

not adequately exposed to acid in the stomach and thus is not properly digested. On the other hand, if food remains too long in the stomach, keeping the organ distended, one gets a sickening sense of fullness. The pyloric region of the stomach lies at the junction to the small intestine and contains a plexus of nerves that regulates the opening and closing of this junction. This nerve plexus is part of the myenteric plexus of the overall gastrointestinal system and stains intensely for NO synthase. The muscle at this junction that acts as a valve between stomach and intestine is called the pyloric sphincter.

We gained insight into how NO regulates stomach function by a novel, indirect approach. We took advantage of modern molecular biological techniques that enable researchers literally to "knock out" a particular gene in the DNA of embryonic mice so that the animals that develop, dubbed knockout mice, lack that gene. In collaboration with Paul Huang and Mark Fishman at Boston's Massachusetts General Hospital, Bredt, Ted Dawson, and I developed mice in which the gene that allows neurons to make NO synthase was disrupted in embryos. The mice that developed appeared to behave fairly normally. We did not observe any gross disturbances in the structure of the brain or in any other major organs. We did observe one striking abnormality, however. All the knockout mice possessed greatly distended stomachs. On microscopic examination we saw that the muscle layer in the pyloric region of the stomach was markedly overdeveloped. The sphincter region of the stomach was in a state of chronic contraction, preventing food from moving readily from the stomach to the small intestine, In response, the stomach became distended.

This pattern is virtually identical to that observed in a rather common disease of human beings, hypertrophic pyloric stenosis. In this genetically determined condition the pyloric region of the stomach is contracted so that food is unable to exit. The disease is frequently encountered in newborns, who must have surgery within the first few weeks after birth to enable them to digest food. Interestingly, in human infants with hypertrophic pyloric stenosis, Jean-Marie Vanderwinden and Pierre Mailleux of the Free University of Brussels discovered that the pyloric region of the infants' stomachs fails to stain for NO synthase. Thus, knocking out the gene for neuronal NO synthase in mice creates an animal model of pyloric stenosis, which is fairly faithful to the human disease process. We do not think that a loss of the gene for NO synthase causes the disease in humans because the victims' NO synthase appears to be normal in other parts of the gastrointestinal pathway. Nonetheless, it is evident that NO somehow participates in the disease process. Consequently, drugs that regulate NO function may well be therapeutic.

NO and penile function

In collaboration with Arthur Burnett and Thomas Chang in the department of urology at Johns Hopkins, Bredt, Charles Lowenstein, a cardiology fellow in our laboratory, and I investigated the role of nitric oxide in the normal functioning of the male penis. How does the penis proceed in a matter of seconds from its usual flaccid state to one of marked rigidity with a several-fold increase in volume and length? Penile erection occurs when arteries of the penis become engorged with blood. The main erectile bodies of the penis, termed the corpora cavernosa, contain compartments that enlarge and become rigid when filled with arterial blood. The engorgement of the penis with blood occurs as a result of the firing of specific neurons to the penis. Those neurons are part of the involuntary, autonomic nervous system. Researchers have shown that the neurotransmitter known to occur in these nerves does not cause erection.

When our group used antibodies to NO synthase to stain sections of penis tissue taken from rats, we noted pronounced staining throughout the nerves that regulate erection. To explore the role of these nerves in penile erection, Burnett used mild electrical stimulation of the penis in living rats to produce a robust penile erection. When we treated rats with low intravenous doses of inhibitors of NO synthase, we were able to prevent penile erection completely. Thus, NO appears to be a neurotransmitter of the nerves to the penis and can, by means of its dilator action on blood vessels, fully account for the process of penile erection.

Carbon monoxide: another gaseous transmitter

Our awareness that a gas may be a neurotransmitter inspired the following line of thought. Most neurotransmitters occur in classes containing several members. There are about 10 different amine neurotransmitters, 5 different amino acid neurotransmitters, and dozens of peptide neurotransmitters. Is nitric oxide the only gaseous one? Students in our laboratory brainstormed about other candidate molecules that could serve as gaseous transmitters. Ajay Verma, an M.D.-Ph.D. student, suggested carbon monoxide.

The formation of CO in the body is a normal process. There is an enzyme whose function is to destroy heme, the iron-containing, oxygen-carrying subunit of hemoglobin, in aging red blood cells. The enzyme, named heme oxygenase, breaks the large ring-shaped heme molecule and converts it into biliverdin, which in turn is transformed into bilirubin. Bilirubin is well known as a pigment that accumulates in tissues of newborn babies, often causing a yellow color termed jaundice. In addition to forming bilirubin, breaking the heme ring releases CO.

Heme oxygenase had been studied in detail by Mahin Maines of the University of Rochester, New York, who discovered two distinct forms of the enzyme. One form occurs in the spleen and other organs that degrade red blood cells. The activity of this form, called heme oxygenase-I, is greatly increased by various stimuli that are associated with red cell breakdown, such as heme itself or high fever. Maines discovered a second form of the enzyme, which she called heme oxygenase-II, that is not activated by these stimuli. Heme oxygenase-II occurs in high concentrations in the brain. This fact, together with the enzyme's insensitivity to red cell breakdown, suggested to us that the ability of heme oxygenase-II to form CO may play some specific role in the brain.

Another feature of carbon monoxide hinted at a neurotransmitter function. As described above, when nitric oxide diffuses into neurons, it causes a rise in levels of the second messenger cyclic GMP. It does this by activating an enzyme in the neuron, called guanylyl cyclase, that forms cyclic GMP. Guanylyl cyclase, like hemoglobin, contains a molecule of heme, which gives the enzyme its catalytic activity. NO stimulates this enzyme by binding to the iron atom in the heme group. The binding changes the shape of the enzyme molecule and activates it. The fact that carbon monoxide also binds to heme is well known. It is, in fact, by binding to heme in red blood cells—and thus preventing the binding of oxygen—that CO produces its deadly effect. By binding to heme in guanylyl cyclase, CO, like NO, can increase cyclic GMP levels. This would provide a means whereby CO could function as signaling molecule.

To explore the possibility of CO as a neurotransmitter, Verma, David Hirsch, Charles Glatt, Gabriele Ronnett, and I worked to learn where heme oxygenase-II occurs in the brain. This time we looked not for the enzyme itself, as in the case of NO synthase, but for the messenger RNA that codes for it. Messenger RNA is genetic material that serves as an intermediary in the translation of genetic information into proteins. When a particular cell is found to contain messenger RNA carrying the genetic code for a specific protein, it indicates that the cell is actively making that protein. We discovered that messenger RNA that codes for heme oxygenase-II occurs in discrete populations of neurons throughout the brain. Moreover, we found its locations to be virtually identical to those of guanylyl cyclase. This suggested that CO could be even more prominent as a regulator of cyclic GMP levels in the brain than NO.

Just as inhibitors of NO synthase clarified functions of NO, zinc protoporphyrin-9 (ZnPP), a potent inhibitor of heme oxygenase, has provided insight into functions of CO. In one study that made use of cultures of olfactory neurons, we found that ZnPP markedly reduced levels of cyclic GMP in the cultures, whereas inhibitors of NO synthase had no effect. Thus, the enzyme that makes CO occurs in distinct groups of neurons, and CO can regulate an important second-messenger molecule like cyclic GMP. Both facts imply that CO is a neurotransmitter.

CO and memory

Our first publication on carbon monoxide as a possible neurotransmitter appeared early in 1993. Since then evidence has rapidly accumulated that the gas has important functions in the body. CO may mediate a form of learning and memory. Today most researchers agree that memory depends on the modification of synaptic activity, specifically that the synaptic connections between particular groups of brain neurons become facilitated, or strengthened, after their repeated activation. As a result, these connections are much easier to activate in the future. This type of facilitation probably occurs throughout the brain but may be particularly prominent in the hippocampus, a brain region that is crucial for memory. Stimulating particular neuronal pathways in the hippocampus can make synaptic transmission more effective through these pathways for many days. This process is called long-term potentiation (LTP).

Some research has suggested a role for NO in LTP, while even stronger evidence has implicated CO. Using immunohistochemical staining techniques, we found that certain cells of the hippocampus, called pyramidal cells, contain very high levels of heme oxygenase-II. When stimulated synaptically by other neurons, these cells could generate CO as part of a potentiation process. In this speculative model the released CO would diffuse from the pyramidal cells into the stimulating cells, somehow priming them to release more neurotransmitter when they fire again. Thus, CO would function as a retrograde messenger, traveling opposite to the direction of the neuronal signal. On the basis of our results, Charles Stevens of the Salk Institute for Biological Studies, San Diego, California, and Eric Kandel of Columbia University, New York City, applied ZnPP to prepared slices of rat hippocampus and observed a profound reduction in LTP. Moreover, application of CO facilitated LTP. Accordingly, CO may be a regulator of learning and memory.

CO as a regulator in breathing

Carbon monoxide may regulate how we breathe by influencing how the human body responds to gases carried in the blood. There exists a small organ, called the carotid body, that lies at the junction of the internal and external carotid arteries in the neck. The carotid body regulates breathing responses to changes in the blood's oxygen content. When oxygen levels in the blood fall, cells in the carotid body, designated glomus cells, fire. This action in turn elicits firing of the carotid sinus nerve. This nerve extends into the brain stem and, after a stop en route, reaches the brain's breathing center and augments its activity. When the carotid sinus nerve fires, breathing is stimulated in order to raise blood levels of oxygen.

In collaboration with Nanduri Pradnahkar of Case Western Reserve University, Cleveland, Ohio, Jay Dinerman, a cardiology fellow in our

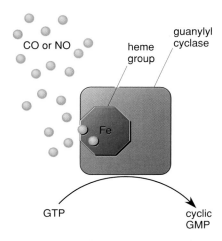

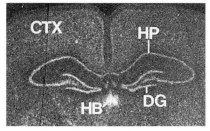

(Top) When CO diffuses into neurons, it, like NO, can stimulate a rise in levels of the second-messenger molecule cyclic GMP. An enzyme in neurons, guanylyl cyclase, forms cyclic GMP from another molecule called guanosine triphosphate (GTP). A molecule of heme present in guanylyl cyclase gives the enzyme its activity. NO stimulates the enzyme by binding to the iron atom (Fe) in heme, an action that changes the enzyme's shape and activates it. CO likewise can bind to heme in guanylyl cyclase and so increase cyclic GMP levels. Such a mechanism provides a way for CO to function as a signaling molecule. (Above) Discrete groups of neurons that contain heme oxygenase-II stand out as light areas in a section of rat brain that has been stained for messenger RNA carrying the code for the enzyme. The highlighted areas turn out to be virtually identical to areas that stain for messenger RNA coding for guanylyl cyclase. (CTX is cortex; HP, hippocampus; DG, dentate gyrus; and HB, habenula.)

From "Carbon Monoxide: A Putative Neural Messenger," A. Verma, et al., Science, vol 259. no. 5093, pp. 381-384, January 15, 1993, © 1993 AAAS

laboratory, and I found that the glomus cells in the carotid body stained intensely for heme oxygenase-II. ZnPP caused a marked increase in the firing of the carotid sinus nerve, whereas application of CO inhibited firing. Thus, in the normally functioning body, CO formed by the glomus cells inhibits the firing of the carotid sinus nerves. And, somehow, low oxygen levels must decrease the formation of CO. Interestingly, heme oxygenase-II requires oxygen for its activity. It may be that low oxygen levels directly inhibit the activity of heme oxygenase-II so that less CO is produced and, consequently, the carotid sinus nerve is stimulated to fire.

The future

Research into the biological functions of nitric oxide and carbon monoxide is in its infancy. Even so, researchers have uncovered numerous major activities regulated by these transmitters. NO and CO appear relevant to important disease processes. Since the formation of NO and CO is directly regulated by specific enzymes, one can readily inhibit production of these transmitters with drugs that are enzyme inhibitors. The inhibitors of NO synthase and heme oxygenase-II that have been used in recent research are common chemicals that had been fortuitously observed to affect these enzymes. Chemists in the pharmaceutical industry possess powerful technology that should enable them to sculpt extremely potent and selective enzyme inhibitors. Thus, in the coming years drug companies can be expected to introduce potentially important therapeutic tools that act through the manipulation of NO or CO.

Nitric oxide is generated in blood vessel cells, macrophages, and neurons, and each kind of cell uses a distinct NO synthase enzyme specified by its own gene. Scientists already know of differences in the biochemical properties of the three types of NO synthase. It is quite likely that inhibitors specific for each NO synthase will soon be available. This development will have important therapeutic applications. Currently available NO synthase inhibitors, like nitroarginine, inhibit all forms of NO synthase. By inhibiting NO synthase in blood vessels, nitroarginine causes marked blood vessel constriction. Were this compound to be used,

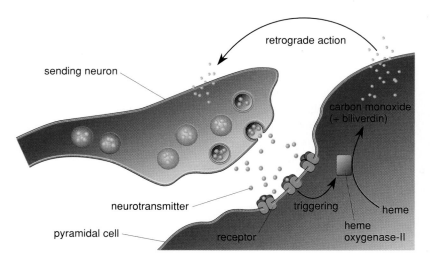

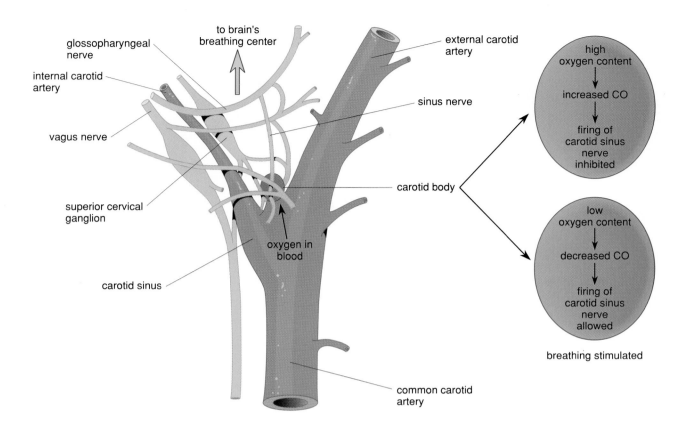

for example, to mitigate the effects of vascular stroke by reducing the production of NO in the brain, it could have the contrary side effect of decreasing blood flow to the brain. Drugs that inhibit only neuronal NO synthase would not suffer from this drawback.

In contrast to inhibitors of NO and CO production, agents that stimulate the formation of NO and CO could have unique utility. Both NO and CO have been implicated in LTP, which is likely to be relevant to learning and memory. Because inhibition of NO and CO formation disrupts LTP, one would expect agents that increase the formation of NO and CO to assist learning and memory and so perhaps be of use in treating the memory disruption of Alzheimer's disease. Similarly, agents that form NO at appropriate sites in the penis may alleviate impotence.

The concrete therapeutic potentials thus described may be only the proverbial tip of the iceberg. Researchers are at the earliest stages in learning the normal functions of NO and CO, which may turn out to be involved in many other neuronal activities. Moreover, NO and CO may not be the only gaseous neurotransmitters. Ethylene (C_2H_4), another small molecule that exists as a gas at ordinary temperatures, is of considerable importance in the plant kingdom, where it functions as a hormone in growth, leaf fall, and fruit ripening. Could ethylene play a role in the brain? Research efforts now under way are exploring this intriguing possibility.

The carotid body, which lies at the junction of the internal and external carotid arteries in the neck (left), regulates the body's breathing response to changes in the oxygen content of the blood. The regulation is carried out by the carotid body's glomus cells, whose activity appears to be controlled in turn by the formation of CO in the cells (right). When the oxygen content of the blood is low, CO formation is inhibited in the glomus cells. The decrease in CO levels allows the glomus cells to fire, an action that elicits firing of the carotid sinus nerve and thus initiates a signal that eventually reaches the brain's breathing center to stimulate breathing. When the oxygen content of the blood is high, the glomus cells form CO, which prevents them from firing. Consequently, stimulation of breathing is suppressed.

101

When the Mind Grows Older

Perspectives on Cognitive Aging

by Douglas H. Powell

*Considerable research is under way
as scientists seek to understand the effects of aging on
intellectual ability. One striking discovery is that the range of
intellectual functioning within age groups expands
as people grow older.*

The U.S. Congress has designated the 1990s as the "decade of the brain." It might be said that this applies especially to "older" brains. This is because funds are being invested at record high levels to increase the understanding and the amelioration of the effects of aging on intellectual as well as physical vigor. Indeed, understanding the differences between normal and impaired cognition among older women and men may be a more important goal today than at any other time in history. The reasons are demographic, legislative, physical-psychological, and economic.

Today there are more old people in the United States than ever before. At the beginning of the 20th century, the average American would not see a 50th birthday. When the 21st century begins, the average life expectancy will be about 80 years for women and 76 for men. People living beyond 85, numbering more than three million in 1993, constitute the fastest-growing segment of the U.S. population. By the year 2000, 13% of all Americans will be 65 or older; 25 years later the proportion will be one in four.

DOUGLAS H. POWELL is a psychologist and Director of Research in Behavioral Science at the University Health Services, Harvard University, Cambridge, Massachusetts.

Illustrations by Hugh Van Zanten

Growth in the population of older citizens is not unique to the United States. Successful efforts to reduce mortality in East Asian countries have created demographic changes paralleling those in the U.S. By the year 2025 the population of those 65 and over in Japan will double. In China and Latin America this percentage will triple. A quadrupling is projected for South Korea, Singapore, and Malaysia. Population estimates for other parts of the world follow these trends, though the rate of increase is less. In Europe and Africa the growth rates for those 65 and older are expected to be 46% and 26%, respectively.

Compelling a worker to retire because of age was prohibited by Public Law 99-592 in the United States as of Jan. 1, 1994. This law eliminated mandatory retirement for nearly everyone, exceptions being public safety officers and tenured faculty. As part of the new legislation, Congress directed that studies be carried out prior to the effective date of the law to assess the potential impact of eliminating mandatory retirement for those two groups.

For public safety officers the secretary of labor and the Equal Employment Opportunity Commission (EEOC) had the responsibility for determining whether valid physical and mental tests could be used to assess the competency of police officers and firefighters to perform their jobs beyond the normal retirement age. For tenured faculty the law required the EEOC to enter into an agreement with the National Academy of Sciences to form a committee to study the impact that the elimination of mandatory retirement would have on institutions of higher education.

After careful review of the extensive research in this area, it was recommended that the mandatory age ceiling for both public safety officers and professors be lifted. The reasoning for eliminating mandatory retirement for police officers and firefighters could be applied to faculty as well. It was based on two well-established research findings: many older public safety officers are able to match their younger colleagues in both cognitive and physical vigor, and because variability increases with age, it is necessary to distinguish between chronological and functional age.

There is no doubt that the physical vigor of many present-day 65-, 75-, and even 85-year-olds is far superior to that of their parents and grandparents at the same age. The quality of life, especially for the "youngest old," those from about 60 to 75, surpasses that of their parents. A large number remain physically and mentally robust, are comfortable financially, and, if retired, devote leisure time to personally fulfilling activities such as travel, study, gardening, sports, service to others, and politics. A significant minority of this young-old group continue to work full- or part-time.

Much of this improvement has to do with an understanding of the benefits of eating more healthfully—reducing the amount of fat, cholesterol, and calories in one's diet. Adults of all ages know about the value of stopping smoking and moderating the intake of alcohol and caffeine. Exercise is a priority for many.

104

For the economy of the United States to continue to grow in the first quarter of the 21st century, it will need the services of its senior citizens longer than in the past. This is because fewer young people are entering the workforce today. In 1990 about 1.3 million young people aged 18–24 started full-time employment, compared with approximately 3 million just over a decade earlier. This reduction in the number of young people going to work is a direct result of what has been called the "baby-bust" generation. During the years 1965–77 the birth pools were substantially smaller than those in the two previous decades. The trough of the baby-bust generation was the years 1973–77, when about 3.2 million births occurred yearly. Ten years earlier the number had been 4.2 million.

Because members of the baby-boom generation will be in their working prime until beyond the end of the first decade of the 21st century and all of the baby-bust generation will have entered employment by then, the year 2000 will find the average U.S. worker closer to 40 than 30. For these reasons the economy will need to continue to employ those who have passed their 65th birthday.

From a purely economic point of view, it seems clear that older Americans will have to work longer than their parents for two reasons. First, the growing elderly population consumes an increasing share of the federal budget. Social Security and Medicare payments to seniors presently account for about one-third of the budget. The proportion is expected to rise to 50% by 2025. Government policies are already changing to reflect these realities. Those born in 1960 and later will have to wait until they are 67 to receive Social Security benefits. Second, people are returning to the workforce for a second career after retirement in larger numbers than in previous years. The reasons for this include the elimination of the age ceiling for mandatory retirement; longer and healthier life expectancy, resulting in the need to supplement retirement income; and the need to obtain the satisfactions that accrue from working.

Age-related variability

Changing laws to eliminate mandatory retirement resolves one problem but exposes another. This is the increasing variability in most human physiological and intellectual functions with age. For the most part, studies of age-related changes have concentrated their attention on what are called "measures of central tendency"—averages or mean scores. Typically, the mean scores of 45- and 55-year-old subjects are compared with the average performance in groups aged 65 and 75. To no one's surprise, the average scores drop with age. Overlooked in many of these investigations, however, is the growing variability within the advancing age groups. Intellectual capability is one example. Overall scores on nearly all cognitive scales trend downward with each advancing decade, but it is also a fact that many older individuals retain a remarkably high degree of intellectual vitality. Their retention of their mental capacity while many in their age cohort are declining accounts for this variability. Evidence suggests that the portrait of linear decline based on group mean scores greatly oversimplifies what happens to individuals in a census decade.

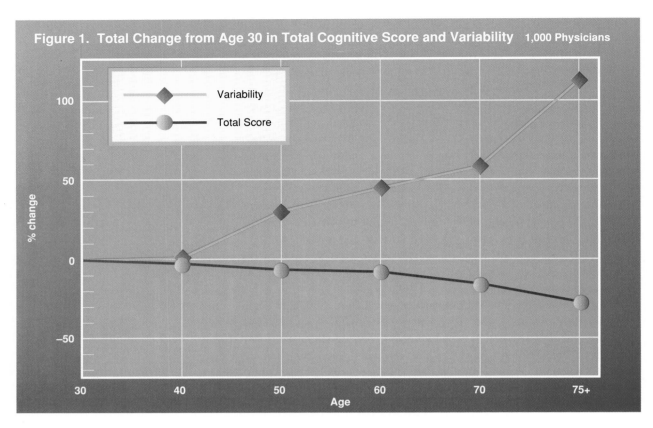

Figure 1 shows the relative changes in total average score on MicroCog: Assessment of Cognitive Functioning, a test designed to measure the intellectual capability among adults with high levels of education— in this case, physicians. A computerized test, MicroCog measures the intellectual functions of reaction time, attention (the subject is asked to indicate whether two names displayed on a computer screen are the same), memory for story content and strings of numbers, reasoning (solving analogies), math calculation, and visuospatial abilities (counting the number of cubes in a design). Figure 1 reveals that the total MicroCog score for 70-year-old physicians is about 14% lower than that for those 34 years of age and below. But as a group those 65–74 are 59% more variable (as measured by the standard deviation) than are the younger subjects. In other words, the increase in variability is more than four times the average cognitive decline at 70. A careful inspection of Figure 1 shows that at every decade, beginning with those aged 45–54, the dispersion is at least four times the mean decrease in total score.

Growing age-related variability is not specific to this test. Studies in the biological, cognitive, psychological, and social domains found that age-group variance increased with age in 80% of the cases.

Alzheimer's disease

If the 1990s are the "Decade of the Brain," it also could be said that the 1980s were the decade in which Alzheimer's disease (AD) emerged

106

as a recognizable threat to all those entering late middle age. In 1980 the Alzheimer's Disease and Related Disorders Association (ADRD) was founded. During that year the *New York Times* mentioned AD or dementia in only 13 articles. At the end of that decade, in 1989, AD was the topic of 212 separate reports in that same newspaper. Today it is difficult to pick up a Sunday newspaper or periodical without coming upon some reference to AD.

AD was first described by German psychiatrist Alois Alzheimer in 1907. His first case was a 50-year-old German woman who exhibited memory, language, and behavioral changes over a five-year period and then died. An autopsy revealed abnormal brain structures, which are now referred to as neurofibrillary tangles (NFT) and neuritic plaques (NP). As this case demonstrated, the relatively young age of onset differentiates AD from senile dementia. Health care workers distinguish between presenile (prior to age 65)- and senile (after age 65)-onset AD.

The criteria for AD include a gradual decline in at least two intellectual functions, such as memory, language, reasoning, or spatial ability, sufficient to impair social relationships and/or performance at work. The deteriorating cognitive skills may be connected with depression, emotional outbursts, apathy, or insomnia. However, these intellectual declines often occur in individuals who otherwise are in good physical health and have no emotional problems that could explain the cognitive decline.

By the year 2000 an estimated five million people in the United States will be afflicted with AD and other dementing illnesses. Prevalence estimates, however, depend upon the standards used in making the diagnosis. For instance, a research team rated 100 elderly citizens in Cambridge, England, on seven different sets of standards for AD. They found that the prevalence ranged from 3% to 63%, depending on which criteria were used. A survey of the incidence of AD in seven countries varied from 1.9% to 52.7%. If one were to trim off the high and low extreme estimates for older populations, mild to severe forms of AD would appear to afflict about 3% of those 65–69, 6% among individuals 70–74, and 11% in the 75–79 category. Beyond 80 the proportion of those with AD rises sharply.

As with any physical or psychological disorder, the most severe forms are easiest to diagnose reliably. A particular problem in diagnosing AD is that individuals afflicted with this illness are often free of other serious physical complaints. This seems particularly true of people in the early stages of AD. As a result, such persons may not attract the medical attention they need because they are otherwise healthy. Milder forms of AD are difficult to distinguish from normal cognitive aging. It used to be thought that AD and normal cognitive aging were distinct conditions, as in either having cancer or not having cancer. The present thinking is that AD and normal cognitive aging lie on a continuum in much the same way that blood pressure among a group of 75-year-olds might range from normal to hypertensive. Because there are no well-established marker variables distinguishing AD from normal aging, differentiating individuals with AD from those with a decline in cognitive functioning associated

107

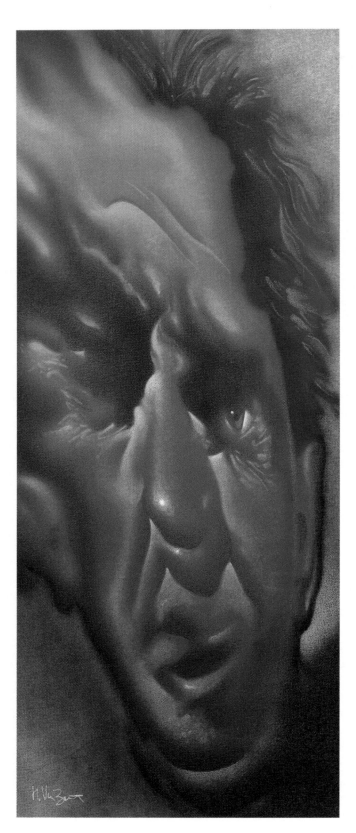

with normal aging is one of the most challenging tasks confronting clinicians and gerontological researchers today. Autopsies on the brains of those diagnosed when they were alive as having or not having AD have revealed quantitative and qualitative differences. Quantitatively, scientists found a far greater percentage of NFTs and NPs and a larger amount of neuronal loss in the brains of those diagnosed with AD. Qualitatively, others discovered that the location in the brain where NFTs and NPs appear and where neuronal loss occurs is significant in the development of AD.

Cognitive changes across the life span

What happens to intellectual functions over a person's life span? What areas are most dramatically affected, and how soon can these losses be detected?

Figure 2 shows the percentage of total correct answers on MicroCog among 1,002 physicians and 581 people in a control group, ranging in age from 25 to 75 and over. The picture of overall cognitive functioning for both groups reveals relatively little change up to age 64. The average 60-year-old physician scored only 8% lower than a young doctor. A control group subject in the same decade was only 12 percentile points lower than someone aged 25–34. After age 65, however, the mean scores tumble downward far more rapidly. Among the physicians the total MicroCog score at 70 was 7% lower than at age 60. At 75 and older overall cognition dropped another 14% from age 70. Similar percentage declines occurred in the normal group.

At all measurement points the control group subjects scored lower than the physicians. This is most likely due to the lower educational level of the members of that group. They averaged 14.13 years, compared with the more than 20 years of the medical group.

Figure 3 shows age-related patterns of three early casualties of the aging process: reasoning, visuospatial ability, and verbal memory. One can see that the steepest decline occurs in reasoning, with visuospatial ability and verbal memory following. Research findings on cognition and aging are, however, not all bad news for seniors. Some cognitive functions are spared until quite late in

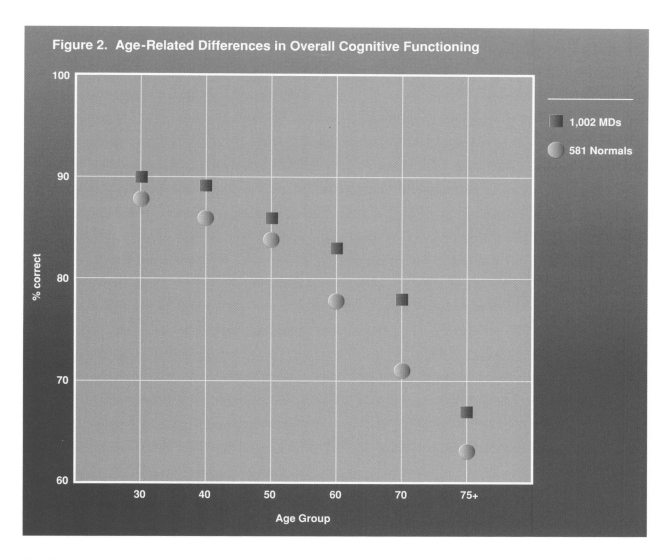

Figure 2. Age-Related Differences in Overall Cognitive Functioning

■ 1,002 MDs

● 581 Normals

life. For most, the ability to pay attention to conversation and to written material, the capacity for immediate recall, and calculation skills hold up well until the eighth decade of life.

It is possible to detect differences in the overall intellectual functioning quite early, often as young as 40. It should be remembered, however, that because of sophisticated statistical procedures, reliable differences among scores can be detected when the actual disparity in performance is tiny.

What influences the rate at which intellectual aptitudes decline over a life span? Recent research suggests that number of years of education plays an important role. It appears that remaining in school longer is highly associated with retaining higher levels of cognitive performance into the third and fourth quarters of life. Socioeconomic status is another correlate of relatively higher levels of intellectual capability beyond age 65. This, of course, could be due to higher overall ability to begin with, or it could be related to better nutrition or health care. Gender seems to play a comparatively small role in cognitive ability over the decades.

Adapted from T.A. Salthouse, *Theoretical Perspectives on Cognitive Aging* (1991), Lawrence Erlbaum Associates, Inc., Publishers, Hillsdale, N.J.

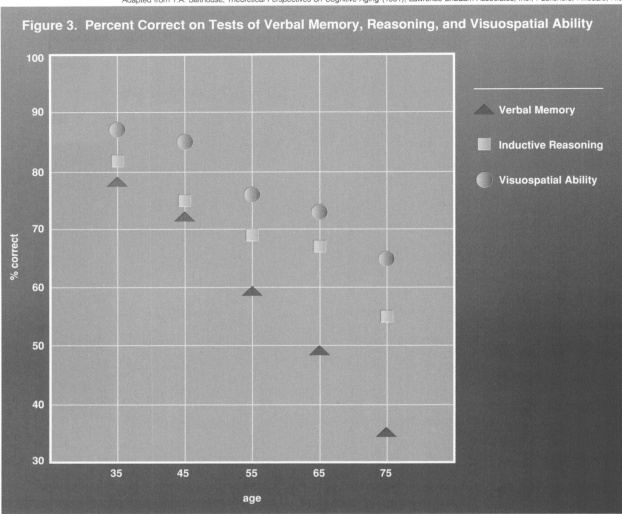

Figure 3. Percent Correct on Tests of Verbal Memory, Reasoning, and Visuospatial Ability

It is relatively well established that, on the whole, women tend to score slightly higher on verbal tasks than do men in the young and middle adult years, while men outperform females in mathematical and visuospatial ability by a small amount. What is interesting, however, is that the differences in abilities between the sexes have narrowed during the past two decades. For instance, studies prior to 1974 found on average that females outperformed males by about 9% on verbal tests, while men scored about 12% higher in math. Since 1974 the gap has closed to 4% in the verbal domain and 6% in math. The shrinking distance between females and males in math is easier to understand than the change in the verbal scores. Three reasons have been suggested. First, greater efforts have been made to encourage women to take courses in mathematics, and opportunities in vocations where quantitative courses are a prerequisite, such as medicine and the piloting of airplanes, have been opened to women. Second, the pools of subjects tested, who were mostly in high school or college, have been more representative of the general

110

population since 1974 than they were previously. The tests revealed that the less elite the group, the narrower the gender differences on cognitive tests. Third, psychological and educational journals may have been more willing to report nonsignificant differences between the two sexes in the past two decades than they had been earlier. This is because the finding that the sexes do not differ on particular aptitudes was recognized to be important information. It will be interesting to see whether the gap in ability scores between females and males continues to close.

Maintaining or regaining cognitive ability in later years

Rapidly growing numbers of older people have increased interest in what can be done to enable the elderly to optimize their intellectual capability or regain aptitudes that may have diminished during the aging process. There has been, for example, an increasing interest in the "use it or lose it" theory. This phrase has a number of meanings. One understanding of the statement is that individuals who continue to use their intellectual skills may be able to retain their keenness well beyond the time when normal decline occurs. Another version of this theory is that greater physical fitness may be correlated with enhanced cognitive vigor.

This author's research, however, tempers both versions of this theory. While it is tempting to believe that individuals who continue to stretch their intellect will remain cognitively robust, it is also true that to continue to "use it" intellectually, one cannot have "lost it." That is, it is not clear whether exercising the mind is possible only because someone has not yet been afflicted with AD or if exercising the mind postpones the onset of AD.

It also seems true that there is a low relationship between physical fitness and mental fitness. Research with more than 2,000 men and women has found a very low correlation between physical and intellectual vigor. Many of the people who were tested had multiple physical problems—cancer, heart disease, stroke, diabetes, high blood pressure, and glaucoma—yet they performed well on cognitive tasks.

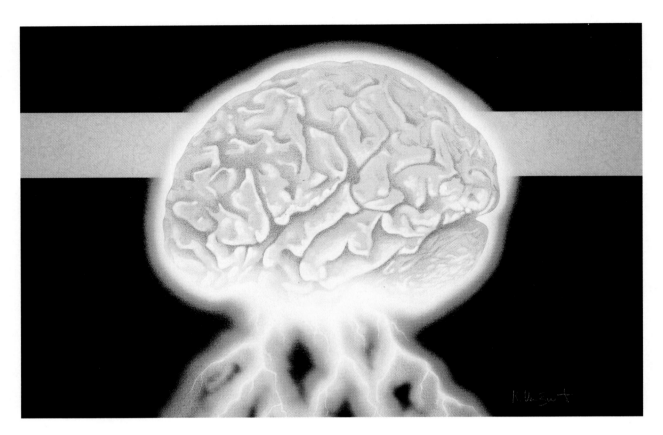

That having been said, however, it is also true that some types of activities seem to be highly correlated with high levels of intellectual capability. These include regular moderate physical activity, reading for both challenge and amusement, having reasonably close relationships with at least one family member, and experiencing a regular sense of competence. Attractive as the "use it or lose it" theory is and as much as researchers would like to believe it, this idea appears to require further empirical verification.

The question of whether age-related cognitive decline can be reversed by training has been exciting the interests of gerontological specialists for the past decade. Do aging individuals have the reserve capacity to improve their intellectual functioning with training? Is it possible, with practice, to reverse the decline in specific aptitudes, such as memory, reasoning, or visuospatial ability?

A great deal of research has been carried out in this area during the past 10 years. What investigators generally have done is give subjects tests before and after they have been given a short course of cognitive training. Many different approaches have been used successfully. Most programs have emphasized memory-enhancing techniques, such as associating words that are on a list to be memorized with rooms in a house. But other programs without specific memory training have produced positive findings. They range from group discussions about aging to relaxation training. Also remarkable is that aptitudes *not* targeted for

112

intervention failed to improve with training. Generally, training programs have been most successful with those under 75 who are free from AD, though some improvement has been reported with the "old-olds" and those with mild impairment. What is striking is how little intervention is required for substantial improvement to take place. These findings argue for a much higher degree of plasticity or reserve capacity in the cognition of seniors than was previously imagined.

Impressive as these results have been, two questions remain unanswered. First, there is a question of generalizability. Do improvements demonstrated in a laboratory setting extend to the real world? Can a 76-year-old whose spatial-relations skills were shown to be enhanced by training on the basis of psychometric test scores find her car in a mall's parking lot more easily than before? Can an older man remember the names of his children's friends on first meeting more accurately than in the past? Second, the durability of the cognitive-remediation programs remains a question. How long might someone's improved memory be expected to endure after the memory-training program ends? Those studies that have assessed the maintenance of progress at 6- or 12-month intervals have found that the initial gains have been maintained.

Future prospects

At this moment researchers are in the beginning stages of understanding those variables that contribute to maintaining and regaining cognitive skills in the later years. With increasing numbers of older people interested in optimizing their cognitive vigor and with research rapidly expanding in this area, there is a growing likelihood that biological, nutritional, and psychological interventions will be discovered that will enhance the quality of life for older people.

FOR ADDITIONAL READING

A.F. Jorm, A.E. Korten, and A.S. Henderson, "The Prevalence of Dementia: A Quantitative Integration of the Literature," *Acta Psychiatrica Scandinaviaca* (1987, vol. 76, pp. 465–79).

L.W. Poon, D.C. Rubin, and B.A. Wilson (eds.), *Everyday Cognition in Adulthood and Late Life* (Cambridge, 1989).

D.H. Powell, *Profiles in Cognitive Aging* (Harvard University Press, 1994).

D.H. Powell, E.F. Kaplan, D.K. Whitla, S. Weintraub, R. Catlin, and H.H. Funkenstein, *MicroCog: Assessment of Cognitive Functioning* (The Psychological Corp., 1993).

T.A. Salthouse, *Theoretical Perspectives on Cognitive Aging* (Erlbaum, 1991).

S.L. Willis, "Improvement with Cognitive Training: Which Old Dogs Learn What Tricks?" In L.W. Poon, D.C. Rubin, and B.A. Wilson (eds.), *Everyday Cognition in Adulthood and Late Life* (Cambridge, 1991).

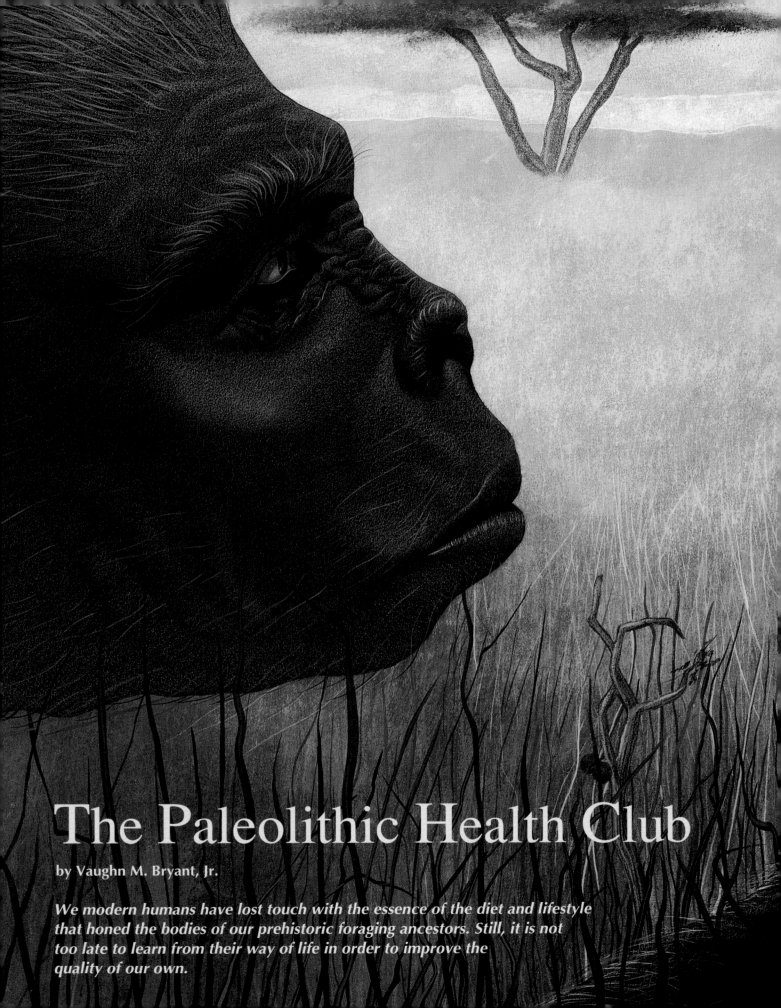

The Paleolithic Health Club

by Vaughn M. Bryant, Jr.

We modern humans have lost touch with the essence of the diet and lifestyle that honed the bodies of our prehistoric foraging ancestors. Still, it is not too late to learn from their way of life in order to improve the quality of our own.

It is the dawn of the Paleolithic Period. On the East African plains a small group of humans form tiny silhouettes against the distant horizon. Five naked adults lead the band. The tallest is only a meter and a half high—barely five feet—yet all are trim and muscular. None has much body hair. Some carry wooden clubs or the leg bones of antelope for protection. Others cradle young babies in their arms or clutch the hands of small children. They all have been on the move about two hours now, since first light. The leaders trot ahead, slow down to wait for the rest, then continue east toward a spot over which buzzards are circling on the early-morning thermals.

The band stops at the remains of a dead zebra. While some members chase away the vultures, others devour scraps of flesh cut from the bones with sharpened flint or crack open the largest bones to suck out the rich marrow. Several women dig up a large underground tuber, then share its juicy pulp with the others. A quick child catches a field mouse and a small lizard. Another nibbles grass seeds stripped from ripened stalks. While picking berries from a bush, one small boy plucks and eats several caterpillars as well.

The scene whirls and blurs as the perspective suddenly leaps into the distant future. Almost two million years have passed. At a strip mall on the outskirts of town, a party of urbanites pulls up in front of the local all-you-can-eat cafeteria. Grunting, they haul their flaccid bodies out of padded car seats and waddle into the restaurant to "forage" for food. They push trays along the buffet line, pondering the pale iceberg-lettuce salads with their rich dressings, mayonnaise potato salad, hot dogs, smoked sausage, hamburgers and fries, pepperoni pizza, cheese-stuffed pasta, barbecued ribs, fried chicken, and baked potatoes oozing butter and sour cream. They encounter bowls of beans and corn in buttery sauce, overcooked broccoli topped with cheddar, and white rice smothered in gravy. Biscuits and rolls come next, followed by a selection of cakes, custards, pies, and ice-cream confections. The diners find it hard work just to carry all their selections to their table.

Nutritionists and doctors lately have been telling us that our Paleolithic ancestors "ate the perfect human diet" and "lived the perfect lifestyle" and that modern humans have lost touch with the essential principles that these activities embodied. The result, the experts say, is a health disaster. For Americans the U.S. Senate's Select Committee on Nutrition and Human Needs has warned that 6 of the 10 most common diseases—heart disease, cancer, dental disease, diabetes, hypertension (high blood pressure), and obesity—are linked to poor eating habits or dietary deficiencies. More than 30% of American men and 20% of American women are considered obese, defined as weighing 20% or more above what insurance actuary tables call an "ideal" weight.

The problem is that for people who live in the world's affluent and technologically advanced nations, lifestyles and diets have changed radically, while human physiology has remained literally locked in the Stone Age. The human body and digestive system operate essentially the same way that they did when bands of the earliest humans—the most ancient

VAUGHN M. BRYANT, JR., is Department Head and Professor of Anthropology, Texas A&M University, College Station.

(Overleaf) Illustration by Ruben Ramos

116

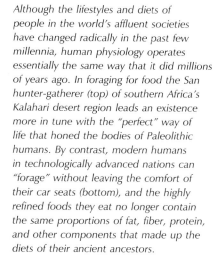

Although the lifestyles and diets of people in the world's affluent societies have changed radically in the past few millennia, human physiology operates essentially the same way that it did millions of years ago. In foraging for food the San hunter-gatherer (top) of southern Africa's Kalahari desert region leads an existence more in tune with the "perfect" way of life that honed the bodies of Paleolithic humans. By contrast, modern humans in technologically advanced nations can "forage" without leaving the comfort of their car seats (bottom), and the highly refined foods they eat no longer contain the same proportions of fat, fiber, protein, and other components that made up the diets of their ancient ancestors.

members of the genus *Homo*—walked the African plains. Their functions were honed to perfection during that 99% of human existence when everyone was a nomadic hunter and gatherer. Only 10,000 years ago in the Middle East did humans first domesticate plants and animals and settle down. Later this new way of life took hold elsewhere, including western Africa, southeastern Asia, and Central and South America. The subsequent changes that these events created in human lifestyles were phenomenal, rapidly outstripping any evolutionary changes in human genetics and biology.

Some people believe that farming was the most important invention in all of human existence. Others, like physiologist Jared Diamond of the University of California at Los Angeles, think that "the adoption of agriculture, supposedly our most decisive step towards a better life, was in many ways a catastrophe from which we have never recovered."

117

Harvesting in ancient Egypt is depicted in a wall painting from the tomb of a high ranking agricultural official of the 18th dynasty. The domestication of plants and animals created changes in human lifestyles that far outstripped evolutionary changes in human genetics and biology, becoming, as physiologist Jared Diamond contends, "in many ways a catastrophe from which we have never recovered."

How can Diamond's statement be true? Are not students of history taught that the growing of crops and raising of animals freed humans from the perils of an uncertain food supply and gave them the leisure time to develop art, music, and science? For most of the affluent societies of the world, have not the fruits of the Industrial Revolution been a longer life span, electricity, central heating and cooling, automobiles, airplanes, television, and countless other contributions to a life of pampered comfort? For people of those societies, does not the only strenuous exertion come from short periods of self-imposed exercise?

Even if our preagricultural ancestors lived the "perfect lifestyle" and ate the "perfect diet," are we really willing to trade our 20th-century way of life for theirs? For the great majority of us, the answer would be "no." But what if we changed aspects of our life and diet to reflect the lessons we can learn from our Paleolithic ancestors? Could that improve our health and daily lives without sacrificing the technological achievements we cherish?

Ancient hunters and gatherers

Paleolithic humans inherited a body that evolved during the era of their primate progenitors. Fortunately, several physical traits acquired from this primate past proved advantageous. Instead of being physically specialized and restricted to life in a single habitat, the generalized physiology of humans enabled our ancestors to adapt to many different environments. It is true that minor physiological changes have occurred. For example,

118

some groups of humans living at high altitudes have developed larger lung capacities, while those living in hot deserts tend to be tall and thin because such a form maximizes the body's ability to dissipate heat. Nevertheless, a highly developed, technologically inventive brain rather than specialized physiology was the key factor that enabled humans to spread to and survive in virtually every environment on Earth. To live in cold climates we use warm clothes and heated enclosures in place of fur, to travel in water we use boats in place of gills and flippers, and to travel overland we use wheeled vehicles and, more recently, planes instead of long legs or wings.

Our hairless bodies and an ability to sweat probably developed early, yet they are uniquely human characteristics and are not shared with other primates. They enable us to work in hot environments yet cool ourselves quickly when needed. Our ability to consume and digest both plant and animal foods is another advantage, enabling us to use many different resources and eat almost anything.

Archaeological work has revealed quite a bit about our Paleolithic hunting and gathering ancestors. Our most recent ancestors, the first modern *Homo sapiens* (designated *Homo sapiens sapiens*), emerged as a distinct group around 35,000–40,000 years ago. They became the world's first artists; they also invented a spear-throwing device called the atlatl, the bow and arrow, and harpoon points, and they learned how to make and use razor-thin stones, called blades. In northern climates they fashioned tailored clothes to protect themselves against the cold and roamed over

The couch potato is a modern icon for the "catastrophe" brought about by the adoption of agriculture. The growing of crops and the raising of animals gave humans the leisure time to develop technology, but the fruits of technology in turn have transformed daily life into one of pampered comfort in which a healthful diet and exercise no longer play a natural part.

119

A campsite occupied by Homo habilis, *who are generally accepted as the earliest species of the genus* Homo, *is shown in an artist's conception. Paleolithic humans inherited a body that evolved during the era of their primate progenitors. The evidence indicates that these early men and women, as well as the later* H. erectus *and the first modern* H. sapiens, *were physically fit and that they consumed a diet in harmony with their biological design. As a result it appears that they enjoyed healthier lives than their descendants who first turned to farming.*

vast areas of the Arctic following their quarry, mostly large game animals such as the mammoth and wooly rhinoceros. Accumulating evidence indicates that these Paleolithic men and women were physically fit and that they consumed a diet that was in harmony with their biological design. As a result, it appears that they enjoyed longer, healthier lives than their descendants who first turned to farming.

Studies of the skeletons and other remains of Paleolithic hunters and gatherers and of later farming cultures have given important clues about the ways of life, diets, and nutritional states of these two broad groups and have allowed comparisons to be made. Such comparisons offer chilling evidence of what has happened to the lives and health of most of the world's postagricultural and urban peoples. According to anthropologist George Armelagos of Emory University, Atlanta, Georgia, high levels of bone porosity in the vault of the skull and around the eye orbits, called porotic hyperostosis, are obvious indicators of long-term anemia, commonly attributed to iron deficiency. Although anemia can be caused by other conditions, like severe hookworm infection, it is frequently linked to long-term reliance on diets that are low in meat and high in carbohydrates and are focused on a single dietary staple.

For example, anemia seems to have been a common problem in early farming cultures found in the Americas where diets relied heavily on one cereal grain, maize (corn). When Armelagos compared human skeletons from preagricultural foraging peoples with those of later farming cultures, both of which had lived in the Illinois and Ohio river valleys, the evidence of anemia in the farming group was overwhelming—a 400% increase in porotic hyperostosis among skeletons from the farming period, when diets consisted mostly of maize.

Anthropologist Jane Buikstra of the University of Chicago notes that humans who experience episodes of severe physical stress often carry a record of those events in the long bones of their arms and legs and in the enamel layers of their teeth. She identifies typical types of stress as periods of prolonged or serious famine, periods of severe infection, or acute malnutrition. One kind of stress indicator seen in bone are Harris lines, which form when a person's bone growth is temporarily halted because of stress, especially stress caused by famine or malnutrition. Harris lines are internal and can be seen only in X-ray or cross-sectional examinations of human long bones. Although they occasionally appear in the skeletons of foragers, they are more commonly found in skeletons from farming cultures. It is thought that some types of Harris lines reflect relatively short periods of stress, while others indicate prolonged periods.

Buikstra also notes other differences that have emerged from comparative studies of skeletons of North American foraging groups and early farming cultures. The long bones from the farming groups have a thinner cortex (the dense outer layer) and are shorter, indicating a reduction in body height after the switch to farming. She believes that these changes represent the physical effects of chronic malnutrition.

Another reliable indicator of poor diet and of nutritionally related stress is abnormal development in the enamel layer of teeth. One type of tooth abnormality, called linear enamel hypoplasia, seems to be caused by severe stress. The condition, which appears as depressed and pitted areas in the enamel layers, is more commonly seen in the teeth of early farming cultures than in those of foragers. Wilson bands, a second type of tooth-enamel abnormality, are also linked to stress-induced growth disruptions. They, too, are much more prevalent in skeletons from farming cultures than foraging ones.

Susceptibility to tooth decay varies with individuals, but the potential for decay is known to be greatest in humans who rely on diets containing large amounts of refined carbohydrates, especially sugars. About 2% of fossil teeth from Paleolithic foraging cultures contain small and shallow caries of the pit and fissure type, which are found mostly on the top, chewing surfaces of teeth. Nevertheless, as notes anthropologist John Lukacs of the University of Oregon, after cultures turned to farming, incidence of tooth decay increased dramatically. Lukacs' study of skeletons from an early farming period in the Indus Valley region of Pakistan revealed that 43.6% of that population had at least one dental cary and that 6.8% of all the skeletal teeth examined contained caries. Because many of those early farmers had lost quite a few teeth before they died, Lukacs believes that the actual incidence of dental caries was much higher than the reported 7%.

Even so, it was not until the use of refined carbohydrates became widespread during the last few hundred years that tooth decay reached epidemic proportions. One study in 1900 of workers in England showed that 70% of their teeth contained caries. More important, most of the caries developed on side surfaces where teeth abut each other, locations associated almost entirely with postagricultural diets containing high levels of sugar.

Examinations of preserved human feces, or coprolites, are yet another valuable source of information about our prehistoric ancestors. Coprolites are ideal because they contain the nondigestible remains, like fiber,

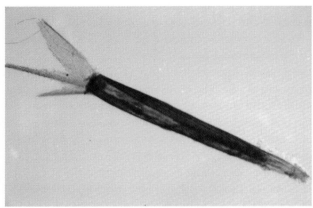

Preserved human feces, or coprolites— like the 6,000-year-old specimen shown (top left), from southwest Texas—provide valuable information about the diets and nutrition of prehistoric humans because they contain the nondigestible remains of foods that were actually eaten. The contents of just half of one coprolite (top right) from a southwest Texas site offer some idea of the amount of fiber consumed on a regular basis by the ancient foragers who lived there; the fiber in the sample is mostly from cactus pads. Teeth and bones from mice (bottom left), birds, and other small animals are commonly found in coprolites, as are seeds from grasses (bottom right), flowers, fruits, nut trees, and various other plants.

bones, seeds, and leaves, of foods that were actually eaten. In recent years the study of coprolites has provided valuable clues about the diets, health, and nutrition of Paleolithic foraging peoples and those living in early farming communities.

Anthropologist Kristin Sobolik of the University of Maine has spent most of her career examining human coprolites from prehistoric sites of the arid U.S. Southwest. She has found that ancient foragers ate mostly nutritious plant foods that are high in fiber—for example, sunflower seeds; ground seeds of mesquite and cactus; acorns, walnuts, and pecans; persimmons, grapes, and berries; the soft basal leaf portion of sotol and agave; and cactus flowers, fruits, and pads. These ancient foragers balanced their mostly plant-food diets with about 10–20% meat obtained from small animals like mice and rat-sized rodents, fish, freshwater clams, small lizards, caterpillars, grasshoppers, small birds and eggs, and, when they were lucky, rabbits and deer.

Anthropologist Karl Reinhard of the University of Nebraska is a leading authority on ancient human parasitic infections. He notes that intestinal parasites can be debilitating and potentially fatal, especially when they infect a person who has already been weakened by episodes of famine or prolonged malnutrition. His examinations of human coprolites recovered from southwestern American Indian sites indicate that hunting and gath-

122

ering populations were almost totally free of internal parasitic infections. Once groups turned to farming, however, they became heavily infected. High population densities, poor sanitation, and the compactness of living spaces in pueblos helped increase infections by nearly a dozen types of parasites including pinworms, tapeworms, and thorny-headed worms.

Inherited dietary needs

Although scientists are finding that preagricultural peoples in general were healthier than their farming descendants, what can be learned from looking at the specific dietary requirements and preferences that we inherited from our ancestors? The human body, like those of our primate forebears and of animals in general, has evolved to function as a kind of engine, releasing the energy present in food, the body's fuel, to do muscular work. Unlike mechanical engines, however, the body is also continually breaking down and building up its component parts. Food thus has another purpose; it serves as a supply of materials essential for the body's growth and maintenance and as an energy source for the chemical reactions involved in those processes.

Three primary components of food serve the body as energy sources and building materials—carbohydrate, protein, and fat—and it is upon the continual replenishment of these components that our need and desire to eat is based. In addition, the body requires certain amounts of other substances like sodium, potassium, various other minerals, and vitamins, which are also obtained from the diet.

Carbohydrate

Primates, including humans, use plant products as their main source of energy. Each gram (about $\frac{1}{28}$ of an ounce) of carbohydrate provides four dietary calories of energy when completely digested. (The term *calorie* used in the dietary sense is the "large" calorie, equivalent to one kilocalorie, or 1,000 "small" calories.) There are two main types of carbohydrates, simple and complex. The simple carbohydrates are sugars, the complex ones mostly starch and cellulose.

Simple carbohydrates exist naturally as different types of single-molecule sugars (glucose or dextrose, fructose, galactose) called monoshaccharides or as double-molecule sugars (sucrose, maltose, lactose) called disaccharides. The human body digests both types, and both are found naturally in fruits, flower nectars, and the sap of some plants.

Our taste buds love sweet things. The reason may be that our primate progenitors learned that sweet fruits were good, safe sources of food. Ounce for ounce, fruits offer more usable calories than do leaves, bark, or stems. In addition, the sweeter the fruit, the riper and more digestible it is, since in the ripening process starchy carbohydrates are converted into sugars and any bitter alkaloids present are broken down. The association of sweetness with "good tasting," ready-to-eat, high-calorie-value fruits served the early primates and our Paleolithic ancestors well. It encouraged them to seek out these tasty food sources and to avoid most sour- and bitter-tasting fruits, which often were poisonous or not yet ripe.

123

(Top left) Mary Evans Picture Library; (top right) by permission of the British Library; (bottom) collection of the The New–York Historical Society

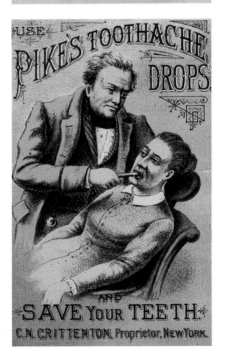

Paleolithic humans never ate too much sugar. Our foraging ancestors, and even early farming peoples, encountered sugar in small amounts—in fruits, in some other natural foods, and in an occasional lucky find of honey—but never in concentrated, potentially unhealthful quantities. This may explain why, of the four essential taste sensations (sour, salty, bitter, and sweet), humans usually avoid all but low levels of the first three but rarely turn away from foods that are too sweet.

Two events increased the consumption of sugar by later cultures. First, Columbus carried sugarcane to the New World and found that it grew well in the soils of the Caribbean. Second, the Spanish and Portuguese pioneered the importing of slaves as an inexpensive labor source for their plantations, which soon produced tons of sugar at a competitive market price. The effects were profound. In England the availability of inexpensive sugar reduced the per-pound cost from the equivalent of a laborer's yearly salary in 1600 to that of a dozen eggs a century later. Increased sugar consumption paralleled the drop in sugar cost, and the U.S. and most European countries soon followed the English in their new predilection for sugar. By 1913 the annual consumption of sugar in the U.S. reached 34 kilograms (75 pounds) per person. By 1976 it had climbed to 57 kilograms (126 pounds)—a level of consumption equivalent to 20% of the daily caloric intake of every American.

Anthropologist Sidney Mintz of Johns Hopkins University, Baltimore, Maryland, believes that U.S. sugar consumption, and world consumption, continues to climb not because we are sprinkling more into our food or drink at home but because food makers are putting more "hidden" sugar in their products. Bakers add sugar even to non-yeast-based products because it makes cakes, cookies, and breads smoother, softer, and whiter and improves their texture. Soft-drink manufacturers know from taste tests that heavily sugared, syrupy drinks "feel" better in the mouth than flavored water. Sugar retards staleness in breads, serves in place of fats

124

as a stabilizer in cakes, cloaks the acidity of tomatoes in catsup, and "improves" the flavor of bland-tasting meats like fish and poultry.

The complex carbohydrates, mainly starches, pectin, and cellulose, are long chains of linked sugar molecules called polysaccharides. Humans cannot digest some types of polysaccharides, like cellulose, which thus become the so-called fiber content of our diets. Other polysaccharides, like starch, are digestible into simpler sugars and so can be converted to energy.

Paradoxically, until very recently too much fiber was often a problem in human diets. Paleolithic peoples used pounding and grinding to process plant foods, but these techniques did not reduce their intake of high amounts of fiber. The result for some groups was a diet so high in fiber that food often passed through the digestive tract too quickly for all nutrients to be absorbed. Physician S. Boyd Eaton and his colleagues at the Emory University School of Medicine, Atlanta, Georgia, calculate that our foraging ancestors probably consumed about 150 grams (a third of a pound) of fiber each day, compared with the daily average of 20 grams for modern Americans.

Coprolite evidence supports Eaton's finding. My coprolite studies of preagricultural groups living in North and South America reveal diets that were very high in fiber. In many instances a half to three-fourths of the total weight of a coprolite consists of indigestible fiber.

The digestive system of modern humans still needs lots of fiber but no longer gets it from many of today's foods. During the processing of cereal grains into flour, the natural fiber, called bran, is removed to give flour a powdery texture and prevent coarseness in the final products. Fiber speeds the passage of food through the small intestine, adds needed bulk to the large intestine, stimulates peristalsis (waves of muscular contraction in the intestine) necessary for the excretion process, and minimizes

Ancient humans encountered sugar in very small amounts—in natural plant foods and honey. Only after sugarcane was imported to the New World and cultivated on plantations by cheap slave labor (opposite page, right) did sugar become affordable in quantity by the general population in the West. By the late 19th century sugar-based sweets were ubiquitous "food" items, as is in evidence in a British advertisement from the 1890s (opposite page, top left). With the widespread use of sugar came dental caries in epidemic numbers (opposite page, bottom left), one study in 1900 of English workers revealing that 70% of their teeth showed decay. By contrast, anthropologists have found that only about 2% of the fossil teeth of Paleolithic foraging cultures contain dental caries. (This page) The diets of modern foraging peoples are high in fiber, and coprolite studies confirm that the same was true for the diets of ancient foragers. The fruits, roots, and other plant material on display (below left) are the rewards of a San woman of the Kalahari after a day of gathering. Anthropologist Vaughn Bryant (below) assembles an assortment of plant foods—among them pecans, persimmons, scallions, sotol, agave, and seeds of mesquite and hackberry—that reflect the coprolite contents of preagricultural gatherers who lived in Texas 6,000 years ago.

(Left) Irven DeVore—Anthro–Photo; (right) © Martha Cooper—Peter Arnold, Inc.

the effects of ingested cancer-causing substances, which might otherwise cause cells of digestive-tract tissues to mutate into cancer cells. Low-fiber diets are also a factor in the occurrence of such disorders as spastic colon, diverticulosis, hiatal hernia, and hemorrhoids—conditions that scientists believe were unknown to our high-fiber-eating ancestors.

Protein

The human body requires a constant supply of protein because it does not store protein in the form of reserves, as it does carbohydrate and fat. Raw meat from mammals, fish, and fowl contains 15–40% protein by weight and is called a "complete" protein source. By contrast, most plant foods often contain no more than 2–10% protein and are called "incomplete" because most are deficient in at least one of the amino acids, the molecular building blocks of proteins, that are essential nutrients for humans. Of the approximately 20 amino acids that constitute proteins, 8 are essential; that is, they are required, but not made, by the human body and so must be obtained from the diet.

Dietary protein supplies the amino acids used by the body to build new tissues like muscles, tendons, ligaments, and the walls of blood vessels. All growth and repair from birth to death depend on the amino acids in protein. In addition, skin, hair, and nails need the correct amounts and mixture of amino acids to form properly. Some protein is also involved in the body's energy production.

How much protein do we require? Nutritionists say that about 10–20% of the total calories in our diets should come from protein, a percentage within the current range eaten by most non-poverty-level Americans. Anthropologist Richard Lee of the University of Toronto has spent his career studying the diets of contemporary foraging societies that live in the rural and desert regions of southwestern Africa. He estimates that most of today's foraging groups obtain only a third of their calories from animal protein and fat combined, with the remainder coming from plant foods. This estimate is considered reliable for most temperate and tropical regions, although some groups living in the Arctic eat diets composed almost exclusively of animal products. Lee also notes that among contemporary foragers a significant percentage of their meat often comes from small reptiles, birds, and mammals. My coprolite evidence confirms that such a pattern of small-animal protein sources seems to be ancient and that for some geographic regions it may extend back to the beginning of the Paleolithic Period. Nevertheless, some of the Paleolithic "big-game hunters," especially those who hunted mammoths, wooly rhinoceroses, wild horses, and aurochs, may have relied on meat for as much as 50–60% of their total calories.

Can we eat too much protein? A prolonged diet consisting almost entirely of meat is known to cause permanent kidney damage or total kidney failure and death. Medical authorities are not certain at what level dietary protein becomes excessive. Eskimos derive 30–35% of their total calories from meat protein without harming their kidneys, and some Paleolithic people may have consumed considerably higher levels. Most

A San hunter removes a guinea fowl from a trap. Among contemporary foraging peoples like the San, only a third of the calories in their diet is estimated to come from animal protein and fat combined. Furthermore, that contribution often takes form of small birds, reptiles, and mammals rather than large game.

modern humans eat less meat than either of these groups and are thus in little danger of protein "poisoning." The greater danger for us is that eating more meat than we need increases our intake of fat and leaves less room in the diet for nutritious plant foods.

Fat

Most natural fats or oils are composed of triglycerides, chemical compounds containing three long chainlike fatty-acid molecules linked to a backbone molecule of glycerol. Many types of fatty acids are found in nature. Some are saturated—they contain carbon atoms linked only by single chemical bonds—and so the fats that they make up are called saturated fats. Other fatty acids are unsaturated—they contain at least one double bond linking a pair of carbon atoms—and their corresponding fats are called unsaturated fats. Further, unsaturated fats can be either monounsaturated or polyunsaturated depending on whether their fatty acids contain one or more than one double bond.

Some polyunsaturated fats are termed structural fats; the body uses them to build and repair nearly all the membranes that surround or exist inside cells. The body also needs these fats to make various types of hormones that regulate body functions. By contrast, most saturated fats are termed storage or adipose fat, because excess amounts can be stored for later use. In animals some of this fat is deposited in tissue layers under the skin, where it provides thermal insulation. Most saturated fat, however, is stored in other body locations, such as the abdominal cavity and within muscle tissue. When digested by the human body, each gram of fat provides nine calories of energy, more than twice that of the same amount of carbohydrate.

Throughout most of human prehistory, fat was a hard-to-find food source. Fats are found in some plant foods, like seeds and nuts, and in the meat of animals. The meat of land-dwelling wild animals provides more protein than fat, and what fat it does have, less than 4%, is usually distributed uniformly throughout the body. Also, except for a few species of marine mammals, most fat on wild animals is of the unsaturated, structural type. The domestic animals that we raise for slaughter, and many of the animals that we overfeed as pets or keep in zoos, all have one thing in common: their meat contains more fat than protein, and most of that fat is saturated, storage fat. For example, 30% or more of the total carcass weight of most American cattle and pigs is fat.

Of the foods that people of affluent nations like most, the majority contain fats. It is unfortunate that we enjoy eating fats and that fats satisfy our hunger pangs more quickly than either protein or carbohydrate. Perhaps it is nature's way of encouraging us to eat this essential food item, and if so, it must have served our foraging ancestors well. Today, however, it is a liability for many of those who are struggling with weight problems. What is worse, our intestine is highly efficient at digesting fats, generally allowing no more than 5% to escape unabsorbed. This digestive advantage secured a hard-won, essential source of calories and materials for our prehistoric ancestors, but it is another factor that contributes to making more than 50% of the people in the U.S. overweight.

A direct comparison between the types and amounts of fats eaten by us today and by our hunting and gathering ancestors is revealing. During Paleolithic times a given quantity of meat from wild game contained one-sixth the amount of total fat and one-tenth the amount of saturated fat found in the same quantity of supermarket beef. Worse still, the U.S. Department of Agriculture (USDA) continues to grade beef according to the amount of fat it contains. The most expensive grade, prime beef, must contain at least 46% fat by weight.

The amount of saturated fat in today's diet is a particular cause for concern. According to a recent USDA study, American children eating in the typical school lunch program get 38% of their calories from fat, with 15% from saturated fat. By comparison, the USDA recommends a diet of no more than 30% fat, with a maximum of 10% from saturated fat—and some nutritionists consider even these levels too high. The U.S. Senate's Select Committee on Nutrition and Human Needs reports that the typical American diet derives 42% of its total calories from fat and that the ratio of polyunsaturated to saturated fat is an alarming 7 to 16. By comparison, Paleolithic humans ate meat with a fat ratio of 7 to 5, and they obtained no more than 20–25% of their total calories from fat.

It is both the high fat content and the high percentage of saturated fat that make many modern diets unhealthy. For example, Edward Giovannucci and his research team at the Harvard University School of Medicine reported in a 1993 study that high-fat diets, specifically when the fat is derived primarily from animal rather than plant sources, appear to contribute to the development of advanced forms of prostate cancer. This finding supports earlier research by others who found a correlation between some forms of breast and colon cancer and diets rich in fats, especially saturated fat.

Of the foods that the people of affluent nations like most, the majority unfortunately contain fats. The human intestine is 95% efficient at absorbing fats, an evolutionary adaptation that helped prehistoric humans secure a scarce, essential dietary need but that is a liability today when fatty foods are all too available.

128

Eaton writes in *The Paleolithic Prescription* (1988) that he doubts our Paleolithic ancestors ever had to worry about coronary heart disease, one of today's major killers in the world's developed countries. High levels of cholesterol in the blood, diet, age, sex, and genetics are all potential contributors to coronary atherosclerosis, yet of these we can potentially control only one, our diet.

Cholesterol, which is often discussed with dietary fat, is a building-block molecule needed to produce cell membranes, numerous hormones, and bile acids, but it is not really a fat. It is made of atoms bonded into rings, rather than long chains like fatty acids, and is more waxy than fatty in nature. Present in meats and animal products like eggs, butter, and cheese, cholesterol is known to be a major player in the causation of coronary atherosclerosis. In this disorder cholesterol and certain fatty substances circulating in the blood accumulate in the interior walls of the arteries that supply blood to the heart. This buildup can constrict the blood flow, leading to heart attacks. Consequently, one of the major strategies in heart attack prevention has been to reduce the amount of cholesterol in the blood (serum cholesterol).

It is a mistaken belief that the level of serum cholesterol is directly linked to the amount of cholesterol a person eats. Ironically, a high-cholesterol diet usually raises a person's cholesterol level only slightly. For example, members of the Masai tribe of East Africa drink large amounts of milk, and their daily intake of cholesterol often exceeds 1,000–2,000 milligrams, which is two to four times the daily intake of the average American. However, Masai warriors have serum cholesterol levels of 115–145 milligrams per deciliter (100 cubic centimeters) of blood, levels considered exceptionally good in view of today's medical recommendation of 200 milligrams per deciliter or below.

Like the Masai, our Paleolithic ancestors probably had low serum cholesterol levels even though anthropologists estimate that they consumed 300–1,000 milligrams or more of cholesterol daily, depending on their meat supply. Recent research supports the idea that high-fat diets, especially those high in saturated fat, have a greater influence on raising serum cholesterol levels than does the amount of cholesterol a person eats.

Salt

Sodium and potassium, present as ions (electrically charged atoms) in body fluids and within cells, are essential minerals. An excess or deficiency of either leads to imbalances in the body's cellular chemistry and disturbances in body functions. The natural foods of mammals contain a low ratio of sodium to potassium, and for millions of years our progenitors normally consumed much less sodium than potassium. As physiologist Henry Blackburn of the University of Minnesota's Medical School points out, the mammalian kidney is a marvelous organ for maintaining the delicate balance between sodium and potassium in the body. He also notes, however, that the kidney has been fashioned by evolution to retain, not excrete, sodium.

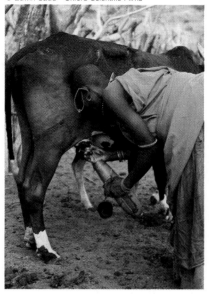

Milk constitutes a significant part of the diet of the Masai people of East Africa, and their daily intake of cholesterol can be two to four times that of the average American. Nevertheless, their serum cholesterol levels are well below the maximum level recommended by doctors, in part because their diets are low in saturated fat.

The link between hypertension and heavy salt use is supported by observations that hypertension seems nonexistent among cultures with traditional diets low in sodium and high in potassium, such as the Eskimo of the Arctic (top) or the Yanomami of Venezuela and Brazil (above).

One of the greatest changes in human diets from prehistoric times to the present has been the switch from diets rich in potassium and low in sodium to diets containing nearly twice as much sodium as potassium. The source of the extra sodium is the salt that we add to our foods at home or that food manufacturers process into their products. Table salt, or sodium chloride, is 40% sodium by weight. A typical prehistoric diet of 3,000 calories, 60% coming from fresh plant foods (leaves, nuts, tubers, berries, fruits) and 40% from meat (mammals, birds, eggs, reptiles, fish), is estimated to have contained about 7,000 milligrams of potassium and 900 milligrams of sodium. By comparison, although the U.S. National Academy of Sciences Food and Nutrition Board reports that the average human requirement for sodium is no more than 250 milligrams per day, most people in the U.S. now consume 6–18 grams of salt per day (about 2,400–7,200 milligrams of sodium) and eat foods that are low in potassium.

Medical researchers believe that high sodium use, especially among people who have a genetic predisposition to retaining much of the sodium they ingest, is a primary cause of hypertension. Years ago some believed that the high levels of salt use in modern diets resulted from a physiological craving for sodium. Today the medical opinion is that our high salt diets are based strictly on an acquired taste, not on a physiological need.

Additional evidence linking hypertension with high levels of salt use come from worldwide statistics that reveal the incidence of the disease to be greatest in countries with the highest per capita consumption of salt. Likewise, hypertension does not seem to exist among cultures with traditional low-sodium–high-potassium diets, such as the Yanomami of Venezuela, the Eskimo of the Arctic, the San of the African Kalahari, and some Polynesian groups in the South Pacific. To anthropologists it seems reasonable that Paleolithic humans also were free from hypertension because their estimated daily intake of sodium was no more than 600–1,000 milligrams.

Physical activity

In addition to certain dietary requirements, human beings have inherited from their ancestors a body fashioned for a fairly high level of physical activity. Hunting and gathering, as they are observed today, are activities that require strength and stamina. Hunters on the trail of game generally must walk long distances before they overtake and kill it. Men, women, and children then help carry the meat back to camp. Gatherers dig up large tubers and collect other food as well as water and firewood—often while toting children—before they carry everything back to camp. Studies of modern foraging groups reveal that this kind of vigorous daily activity helps ensure that individuals will remain strong and retain great stamina even into old age. Moreover, such activity burns calories and so is a natural way of preventing obesity.

Like modern foragers, our preagricultural ancestors also had strength and stamina; the evidence is seen in their skeletons. When humans spend a lifetime engaged in heavy physical labor, the bone thickness

in their legs increases to provide added support and strength. Likewise, these same leg bones often have pronounced bony areas near their ends where the enlarged muscles and tendons are anchored. Human skeletons dating from the early farming era begin to lose these robust features, and by modern times these features are almost gone in the skeletons of people from the industrialized countries. Such changes suggest that even though early farmers worked long hours, their efforts no longer required the levels of physical stamina and endurance common in the lives of foraging cultures. Finally, after the Industrial Revolution human strength was replaced by machines. Since then many people, especially those of the affluent class, have enjoyed a life requiring little physical effort.

In the 1960s muscular strength and endurance testing of Americans of high school and college age revealed that they were considerably weaker than earlier generations in the same age groups. I saw similar evidence in 1976 when I directed the excavation of a large archaeological site in southwestern Texas that was located halfway up the side of a canyon. Of the 21 college-age students who participated, 13 could not make the climb to the site without the aid of ropes and ladders. As we later discovered, the site had been occupied for nearly 9,000 years by many generations of foragers. Men, women, and children in these groups probably climbed unaided from the canyon bottom to the site dozens of times each day, relying only on their strength and endurance.

Reconnecting with our past

Our Paleolithic ancestors were remarkable humans. They beat the odds and survived as foragers for two million years before being replaced by farmers and herders. Most lived the "perfect" lifestyle and ate the

San gatherers (left) use dead branches as ladders to climb to a honeybee nest in a giant baobab tree, while a young San boy (right) harvests mongongo nuts. Hunting and gathering activities, as they are observed today, involve much walking, climbing, and carrying and require strength and stamina. Preagricultural humans engaged in the same kind of vigorous daily activity, the evidence for which is apparent in their skeletons.

131

In modern times successive generations of young people in affluent nations have enjoyed lives demanding less and less physical effort while providing increasingly more opportunity for sedentary pursuits (left). In the 1960s strength and endurance testing of Americans of high school and college age revealed that they were considerably weaker than earlier generations of youths. Similar evidence was observed in the 1970s during the excavation of an archaeological site in Texas that was located up the side of a canyon. Of the college-age students who participated, most could not make the climb to the site without using ropes or ladders (right), even though the site's prehistoric occupants probably had done so dozens of times daily.

"perfect" diet for which their bodies were designed. When we compare ourselves with them, we notice some stark differences.

As a group, our ancestors were slim and trim because they relied on physical strength and stamina for survival. They ate less than half the amount of fat eaten by today's affluent people, and the fat they did consume was mostly polyunsaturated. They ate large amounts of complex carbohydrates and very little sugar. On average they ate 5, 10, or even 15 times more fiber than most of us eat, and their foods were bulky and filling, not the calorie-rich, highly refined fare available today. Our ancestors ate foods high in potassium and low in sodium, and their foods probably contained more than twice the amount of calcium we consume today.

Rather than be depressed by these comparisons, we ought to use them to our advantage. The change from nomadic hunters and gatherers to urbanites has brought mixed blessings. Our own problems are many—overcrowded cities, pollution, new diseases, wars, famine, and poverty, to name a few. Nevertheless, they are offset by our many achievements in art, literature, science, and medicine; in many Western nations life expectancy is now more than double what it was just 200 years ago.

It is this very aspect, increased longevity, that should be of special concern to each of us. In many Western societies the healthiness of individuals is fairly constant until their mid-20s. Afterward, with each increasing decade the gap widens between those who are still in excellent health and those who are not. Until recently, medical professionals believed that the degenerative process seen in many of the elderly was a normal part of aging. Growing evidence suggests, however, that much of the degeneration is due to our diet and way of life.

The challenge we face is to make informed choices about our personal lives. We do not need to give up the blessings of civilization, but we do need to live in harmony with our body's physiology. By choosing foods that approximate the proportions of fats, fiber, protein, and complex carbohydrates eaten by our Paleolithic ancestors and by reducing our intake of sugar and sodium, we can approach that "perfect" diet. Then, by adding regular exercise to the mix and by avoiding tobacco and other harmful substances, we can approach the "perfect" lifestyle and maintain reasonable levels of strength and stamina as we age.

Today our greatest advantage is an ability to direct our destiny, something our Paleolithic ancestors could not do. If as individuals we are willing to make the needed changes, we can better our chances for enjoying lives of health, fitness, and quality in our last decades.

FOR ADDITIONAL READING

S. Boyd Eaton, Marjorie Shostak, and Melvin Konner, *The Paleolithic Prescription* (Harper & Row, 1988).

Robert I. Gilbert, Jr., and James H. Mielke (eds.), *The Analysis of Prehistoric Diets* (Academic Press, 1985).

Marvin Harris and Eric B. Ross (eds.), *Food and Evolution: Toward a Theory of Human Food Habits* (Temple University Press, 1987).

Elizabeth S. Wing and Antoinette B. Brown, *Paleonutrition: Method and Theory in Prehistoric Foodways* (Academic Press, 1979).

Until recently the degenerative process that relegates many of the elderly to nursing homes (below) and hospital beds in their last years was believed to be a normal and inevitable part of aging. Growing evidence suggests, however, that much of the degeneration is due to diet and lifestyle. By making proper food choices, exercising regularly, and avoiding tobacco and other harmful substances, people can approximate the Paleolithic diet and lifestyle for which the human body was designed and so improve their chances for maintaining high levels of health and fitness into old age (below left).

Computing With Light

by David A. B. Miller

Beams of light transmitted through glass fiber or a simple lens offer significant advantages over electrons through wires and may soon be the medium through which information is processed in computers.

Optics and optoelectronics are major technologies in computing today. No computer is complete, for example, without a crucial piece of optoelectronics—its display. The screen reveals the results of the computer's arcane musings in words and pictures that the viewer can understand. Optics is central also to some of the current changes in computing. Lasers are essential in the compact disc read-only memories (CD-ROMs) that power the emerging multimedia applications for consumers and business. Advances in flat-panel liquid-crystal displays are enabling the revolution in portable computing.

Optics continues to have a major impact on the information age through the revolution of fiber-optic telecommunications. Fiber optics in long-distance telephone networks have resulted in much lower costs and higher quality. Transoceanic fiber-optic cables capable of carrying hundreds of thousands of telephone calls simultaneously make intercontinental phone calls clearer and cheaper than simple long-distance calls were only a few years ago. In Germany, Japan, and the United States, fiber-optic networks that may reach as far as individual homes and businesses are beginning to be installed. Such networks will be the highways that will transport vastly greater amounts of information than ever before. The difference between the information capacity of a normal telephone line and a single optical fiber is like the difference in speed between walking and flying in the space shuttle.

It is easy to see how optics has changed the ways in which information is displayed, stored, and communicated. But can it change the way that information is processed, the actual "computer" part? This is a question that may become increasingly important—ironically, perhaps—because of the changes that optics is helping to make in the other aspects of

information technology. For example, so much information is sent over fibers that a way must be found to route that information to where it is supposed to go, the equivalent of the telephone exchange for today's phone calls. To do so will require some 1,000 times more information-handling capacity than is available at present. Perhaps, for example, one might want grandparents to see their grandchild's birthday party as it happens, by means of a live video "phone" call. The fiber networks of the future will have the capacity to send all of this information in and out of each house, but they do not themselves solve the problem of routing it to where it needs to go.

The improved displays and greater communication capacity (band-width) will also encourage more and more use of images. Images are perhaps the best-liked form of information, but in many ways they strain the ability of current computers. Although electronics can perform some operations on images, such as bandwidth compression to allow more or higher-quality television channels over the same bandwidth, others are currently extremely difficult to achieve. Techniques do exist to "create" artificial images that look real, and moviemakers take advantage of these as soon as they are available. But such "image rendering" taxes even the most powerful computers. It has not been possible to make a truly re-alistic video game that generates a "virtual reality" world through which players can move, interacting and changing it as they go (although video sequences from CD-ROMs can give an illusion of this).

Essentially all of the "thinking," or logic, in information processing is done by silicon electronics. The increasing capabilities of this medium have been nothing short of phenomenal. The number of transistors on a silicon integrated circuit, or chip, has been rising by more than a factor of two every 18 months for the last 30 years. By the year 2000 there will likely be about one billion transistors on a chip. The investment behind this growth is formidable, and no other technology is likely to come close to electronics as the best way to perform the logic functions (those needed for computation) for the vast majority of information-processing tasks in the foreseeable future. This raises the question as to whether there is a role in information processing for other technologies, such as optics. To answer this question, it is necessary to look more closely at some of the problems of information-processing systems. Increasing the number of transistors on a chip solves some, but not all, of them.

Communicating information within computers

Within electronic processors all of the communications are done by wires. On the chip itself, the advances in transistor technology have actually made the problems for wires worse. Larger chips require longer wires. Increased transistor densities tend to need narrower wires so that the whole chip surface is not filled with wires. Narrower wires, however, have higher electrical resistance and therefore must carry more current per unit cross section of the conductor. Despite these problems, however, wiring on chips, at least over short distances, is likely to remain a cost-effective solution.

DAVID A.B. MILLER is Head of the Advanced Photonics Research Department, AT&T Bell Laboratories, Holmdel, New Jersey.

136

The real wiring problems occur when one tries to take information on and off the chips and the boards that carry the chips and also tries to send it over the back planes, wiring boards that interconnect the circuit boards. None of these problems has been helped by the advances in chip technology. If such interconnection difficulties are not solved, the architecture of the machines will be severely constrained. In particular, an effort must be made to design, or "partition," the machines so that they send as little information as possible between parts of the system.

Putting the whole computer on one chip so that few wires between chips or boards are needed may be a solution for some problems. A personal computer, for example, might be fitted essentially onto one chip with a keyboard connection going in and a video connection coming out. Relatively little information flows in and out, although quite a lot of processing of that information might be done internally. For problems such as telecommunication switching, however, a considerable amount of information in and out must be handled.

Image processing may also require large amounts of information to flow. Often it might be necessary to know the relationship between widely separated pieces of information in a picture, which in turn requires communication between those different parts of the image. Such problems may best suit a layered architecture with highly parallel connections between the planes, rather like the "architecture" of the human visual cortex that is so successful in enabling us to understand the images from the world around us. Such an architecture does not suit the way information is communicated by wires inside electronic machines.

Physical differences between optical and electrical communication

To understand the problems of wires and how optics may be able to help resolve them, one must look at some of the physics of communication on wires and of light beams. At a fundamental level, the two are similar. The information in both cases is carried on electromagnetic waves. Of course, electrical currents themselves are carried by electrons moving in wires,

For both a beam of light and a properly designed low-loss electrical transmission line, such as a coaxial cable, signals propagate as waves at about the same speed, the velocity of light. For some other kinds of electrical connections, such as those on silicon chips, signals move more slowly, at speeds set by the resistance and capacitance of the lines. In all electrical lines, the signals usually move much faster than the electrons themselves because they are carried on electromagnetic waves rather than directly on the electrons.

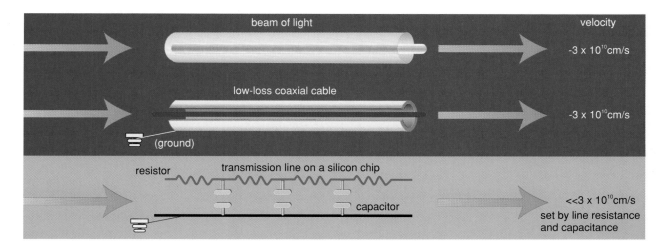

beam of light — velocity — -3×10^{10} cm/s

low-loss coaxial cable — (ground) — -3×10^{10} cm/s

resistor — transmission line on a silicon chip — capacitor — $\ll 3 \times 10^{10}$ cm/s set by line resistance and capacitance and so one might conclude that information in electrical wires is carried by electrons moving from one end of the wire to another. Though it is true sometimes within electronic devices that the information is carried directly by electrons and, therefore, moves at the electron velocity, this is seldom true between devices. In wires the speed of the movement of information is limited either by the velocity of light (as in, for example, the coaxial cables that carry television signals) or at a slower speed established by the resistance and capacitance of the wires (as it is for signals on typical electronic chips). This is generally good news because the velocity of light (300 million meters [984.3 million feet] per second) is about 100 times faster than the electrons move in solids. The actual function of the conducting metals, other than supplying electrical power, is to guide the electromagnetic waves to where the information should go.

At low frequencies, such as those in a simple audio amplifier, the fact that one is dealing with electrical waves is not apparent. But at the frequencies of about 100 million cycles per second (100 megahertz) that are common in computers, the wavelength (about 3 meters [9.84 feet] at 100 megahertz) is such that the problem arises of waves reflecting up and down the electrical lines, causing the information to become garbled. Anyone who has sent waves down a piece of string knows that they generally reflect back from the end of the string. The solution to this problem is to "terminate," or "impedance match," the line with just the right value of resistor. Termination makes the end of the electrical line appear to the wave as if it goes on forever, resulting in no reflections. Unfortunately, the value of resistor needed is always small (typically 50 ohms), which means that a lot of power must be dissipated in it to send the voltages needed in computers. It is also difficult to make several connections to a line and avoid wave reflections—a particular problem for the design of back planes that must connect several boards.

Wires also become increasingly good antennae for broadcasting and receiving waves as the frequency is increased. This results in the phenomenon of cross talk, in which the information on one wire is transmitted to another, further confusing the information.

Another difficulty with wires that becomes worse at high frequencies is the so-called skin effect. When a high-frequency signal is sent down a wire, the current is flowing only in a thin "skin" near the outer surface of the wire. As a result, the wire has much higher effective resistance than one might think. This high resistance causes signal loss and also distortion of the shape of the signal as it propagates down the wire.

These drawbacks of impedance matching, cross talk, signal loss, and distortion are all relatively fundamental problems of electrical interconnection and greatly complicate and limit the design of electronic systems. Even in a common desktop computer, although the microprocessor may run at speeds of 50 megahertz or more internally, many of the packets of wires that send the signals between chips and boards typically run much more slowly, precisely to avoid these problems.

Light beams differ in three fundamental ways from the electrical waves normally found inside computers. First, the frequency of light waves is

138

much higher—about 5 times 10^{14} cycles per second (5 followed by 14 zeros, or 500 terahertz). This is about five million times larger than the typical 100-megahertz frequency in an electronic machine. Second, the wavelength of visible light is much shorter than the wavelengths on electrical wires—about half a millionth of a meter. Third, the photon energy of light is much larger—about 2 electron volts for visible light, compared with about 400 billionths of an electron volt for electrical waves at 100 megahertz.

Understanding the third difference requires an explanation of photons. Electromagnetic radiation, which includes visible light, can be described as waves. But when light is considered from the standpoint of quantum mechanics, it can also simultaneously be described as being made up of particles, known as photons. (It is one of the more bizarre consequences of quantum mechanics that there is no contradiction between these two descriptions—a strange end to a dispute that had raged for more than 200 years as to which picture was correct!) These particles have specific energies that are proportional to the frequency, and the energy is conveniently measured in units of electron volts, an electron volt being the energy required for moving an electron through a voltage of one volt. The very small photon energies at frequencies of 100 megahertz result in practically negligible photon effects at that frequency, and so voltages are measured. By contrast, the photon energies of visible light are very large and, therefore, one usually measures light by counting photons—essentially a "quantum" measurement.

The high frequency of light has several consequences. To send signals on light, a light beam can be turned on and off. The "modulation" frequency at which it is turned on and off (such as 100 megahertz) is, however, so low compared with the light beam's own carrier frequency (about 500 terahertz) that this modulation has essentially no effect on any other properties of the light beam (such as its color, for example, or the way that it propagates). Therefore, although there may be cross talk and loss with optics, it does not get any worse as modulation frequencies become higher. The relatively low modulation frequency also permits the use of antireflection coating to eliminate wave reflections. This works for only a narrow range of frequencies around a carrier frequency, and

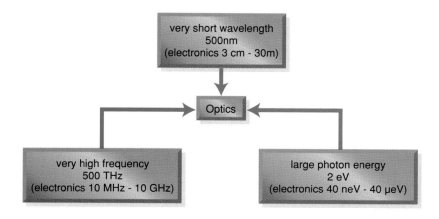

In comparing electronic and optical signals, optics has a shorter wavelength, a higher frequency, and a larger photon energy. These three attributes are at the root of all the differences between electrical and optical communication. (Nanometer, nm, is a billionth of a meter; terahertz, THz, is a trillion cycles per second; megahertz, MHz, is a million cycles per second; gigahertz, GHz, is a billion cycles per second; nanoelectron volt, neV, is a billionth of an electron volt; and microelectron volt, µeV, is a millionth of an electron volt.)

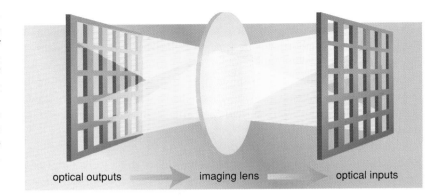

optical outputs → imaging lens → optical inputs

it cannot in practice be used in digital electronics. (An antireflection coating is a thin transparent layer that can eliminate reflections from a surface by a carefully controlled wave "interference.")

The short wavelength of light allows the viewer to see a whole picture at once without everything becoming confused. The reason for this is that the smallest objects that one can "see" are about one wavelength in size. If one tries to distinguish objects separated by less than the wavelength, one simply sees a blur. Because the wavelength of light is so small, one can look at scenes with lots of detail and still make sense of them. The practical consequence of this is that optics can be used to make many information connections simultaneously, using just a simple lens. For example, there could be many light sources on one chip and many light detectors on another. Putting a lens in between them allows the light from one source to go to one detector, thus making a free-space connection between them. A very important point is that the light from the different sources going to the different detectors does not get confused. With the use of a simple lens, it is possible to make thousands of connections from one chip to another, something that is difficult with wires. Furthermore, the information is clearly flowing out of the surface of the chip rather than from the edges, and so the number of connections can increase proportionately as the chip is made larger. Such a connection would not be possible with waves at 100 megahertz; the information from different points on the chip would be blurred because the chip is much smaller than the wavelength. Such free-space connections are among the more exciting possibilities with optics because they may allow completely new classes of architectures of information-processing machines to be made.

The fact that light uses waves also allows information scientists to do something that they would never contemplate with wires—allow different channels of information to cross right through one another. Two flash-light beams can be shone through one another without affecting each other, but if two electrical wires are passed even close to one another, the result might be cross talk or even a disastrous short circuit. This ability of light could make a significant difference, especially in computer designs where many paths must cross. Imagine the difference to the traffic flow on Manhattan Island if all of the cars could simply pass through one another.

140

Another feature of using lenses to make interconnections is that all of the "paths" from the sources on one chip to their detectors on the other chip are, to a good approximation, the same length, which means that all of the signals take the same time to get from one chip to the other. This avoids a problem common in electronics, called signal skew, which results from the difficulty of making all of the wires the same length. If the signals do not arrive at the right time relative to the "clock," they can be misinterpreted. It is equally important that all parts of a digital system use the same clock, which can be more difficult than one might imagine because the clock is also subject to the same kinds of "skew" problems itself. (Digital systems essentially make decisions at each "tick" of a very fast clock based on the information they see just at that time. Therefore, all the right information must be present just at the time of the "tick.")

Another subtle consequence of the small wavelength of light is that it allows the use of the very-low-loss optical fibers that are so successful in carrying high-bandwidth information over long distances. It is difficult to squeeze and guide waves if they are pushed into spaces much smaller than the wavelength. Doing so requires metallic conductors, and this is the real function of the wires inside computers as far as the information is concerned. But metallic conductors always tend to dissipate electrical energy, especially at high frequencies, as discussed above. In the case of optical fibers, even though they are only about the thickness of a human hair, they are still much larger than the wavelength of light. As a result, there is no need for metallic conductors, with all of their loss problems, to guide the wave; instead, essentially lossless materials, such as glass, can be used.

Because light has a large photon energy, one measures it by counting photons rather than undertaking a direct measurement of voltage. Most photodetectors will produce one electron of current for every incident photon. Because voltage is no longer being directly measured, some of the problems of voltages can be avoided. One common problem is that it is difficult to keep the "ground" voltage constant throughout a large electrical system. Thus, a signal that may be meant to be 0 volts and therefore represent a logic "0" might appear to be one volt at another part of the system and might therefore be interpreted as a logic "1." This problem has been solved by the use of optical isolators. An optical isolator consists of a light source and a detector. A voltage at the light source turns it on and, consequently, current flows in the detector, but there need be no connection between the voltage levels in the light source and the detector, thereby eliminating the ground-voltage problems. All optical connections, because they count photons rather than measuring voltage, have this useful feature. A second advantage of counting photons rather than measuring voltage is that the large power dissipation associated with terminating resistors or charging up the capacitance of the lines between chips or boards can be avoided, an effect called quantum impedance conversion.

In summary, optics appears to be attractive for connections as they become faster, denser, and longer. It can handle high-speed signals with-

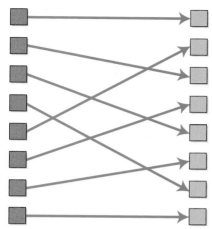

An interconnection pattern useful for telecommunications switching and in mathematical operations is the "perfect shuffle" (so named because it is like taking a pack of cards and perfectly "interleaving" them with a shuffle). In such a pattern, shown here for eight connections, there are many paths that cross one another, especially for large numbers of inputs and outputs. Beams of light can be shone through one another with no harmful effects, but two electrical wires passed even close to one another might result in cross talk or even a short circuit.

out loss and cross talk. It can make very large numbers of connections, without problems of signals crossing over one another. It can also solve timing problems and reduce the power required for interconnections.

Using optics inside digital machines

Fiber optics is already used in computer systems to make some important connections between parts of the machine, especially between some of the larger cabinets. Researchers are using sets of many fibers simultaneously to make connections from board to board within a cabinet. The practical challenge in using fiber to replace wire in such systems is one of reducing cost. Although such optical connections may offer much better performance in the end, the electrical wire connections have many decades of engineering behind them that result in low cost for the performance they do achieve. Just when and to what extent optical fiber will substitute for wire inside machines is a matter of debate. It seems likely, however, that there will be a significant move toward increased use of optical fiber in the 1990s, especially in large, high-performance machines.

Given all of the many advantages of optics for interconnecting information inside computers, the question arises as to why it has not already been used more extensively. To some extent this is because these benefits were not fully understood until comparatively recently. More important, however, the technology that would allow a computer owner to take advantage of optics did not exist and is only starting to exist now in many cases. For all of its shortcomings, metal wire is cheap, simple, and generally reliable and is a mature technology. Optoelectronics, on the other hand, is much less mature. In integrated electronic circuits computer scientists can make patterns of transistors and wire connections of unmatched complexity and sophistication. By contrast, optoelectronic circuits, although serving many purposes well, were in 1993 still at the complexity level of the vacuum-tube electronics of the 1950s. Typical optoelectronic modules, such as the readout head for a compact disc player or a fiber-optic receiver, contain only one or a few optoelectronic components. Although it is possible to make integrated optoelectronics, these have never approached the complexity levels of even the simple electronic integrated circuits.

Integrating optoelectronics and electronics

One of the recent areas of development is the integration with electronic devices of large numbers of optoelectronic devices, such as photodetectors, optical modulators, and, to a lesser extent, lasers. One experimental technology, field-effect transistor self-electro-optic-effect devices (FET-SEEDs), for example, offers integrated transistors, optical detectors, and optical modulators in circuits having 400 transistors and 96 optical input or output beams. Other simple optoelectronic logic gates (computer circuits that facilitate the nonarithmetic operations in a computer) have been made in arrays of 2,000 or more elements, each operating with its own light beams.

142

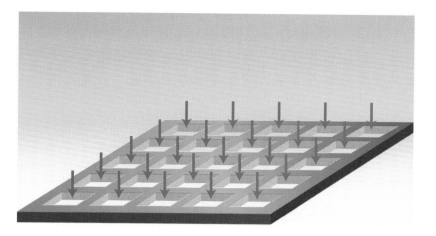

(Left) A two-dimensional array of light beams lands on the optical inputs on the surface of a chip. Using arrays in this way allows information to flow directly into (or out of) the surface of the chip. (Below) Optoelectronic chip contains 400 transistors and 96 optical inputs or outputs. It is made up of 16 "smart pixel" circuits that perform a switching function, routing each input to the output. All of the information, including the setting of the routing switches, is carried optically into and out of the chip by light beams landing on the chip surface.

While such complexities are small compared with electronic circuits, they are large compared with previous optoelectronic circuits. In terms of the numbers of high-speed interconnections on or off a chip, they already rival or exceed the capabilities of most electronic chips. The experimental FET-SEED circuits require less power for sending signals from chip to chip than do normal electrical connections at the same speeds.

These SEED circuits also illustrate the small size needed for optical inputs and outputs compared with electrical ones. Typical electrical outputs from chips use bonding pads that are about 100 microns (one-tenth of a millimeter) square. (Bonding pads are metallized areas on the surface of a semiconductor device, to which connections can be made.) The SEED circuits use modulator and detector pads that are only about 10 microns square.

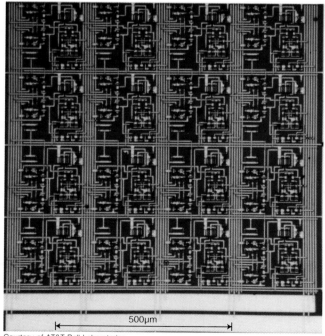

500μm

Courtesy of AT&T Bell Laboratories

Courtesy of Abbas Ourmazd, AT&T Bell Laboratories

Cross section of quantum well structure (top), seen through an electron microscope, reveals a thin layer of one semiconductor material, gallium arsenide (GaAs), sandwiched between two layers of another semiconductor, aluminum gallium arsenide (AlGaAs). The micrograph shows the individual columns of atoms. Below, a processed version of the upper picture shows the fraction of aluminum (Al conc.) in each column of atoms. As the concentration of aluminum increases, there is more energy for electrons.

Devices such as the FET-SEED rely on fundamental advances in the growth and physics of layered semiconductor structures. Semiconductors in layers as thin as about 40 atoms (about 0.0001 the thickness of a human hair), known as quantum wells, have many special properties. Among these is an effect discovered in the mid-1980s known as the quantum-confined Stark effect, which allows electrical voltages to change quantum wells from being transparent to being opaque. This effect is used in the modulators in the FET-SEED. The same technology is used to make other promising devices, such as tiny lasers that may also one day be integrated with electronics. Many other ways of joining these and other kinds of optical and electronic devices are being researched, and there are exciting future possibilities for integration with large silicon integrated circuits. Such technologies would enable computer designers to take advantage of the best of both optics and electronics, and significant practical progress in this area can be expected in the next few years.

New architectures for optical machines

The reasons why optics is not used more often inside digital machines are not only technological. A more subtle issue is that designers have learned, over many decades, to build machines around the weaknesses of wire. As a result, attempts to replace wire with optical fiber or free-space light beams often do not seem to be feasible at first. The real benefits

144

of optics may be fully apparent only when the system architectures are redesigned to exploit the abilities of this technology.

Perhaps the most revolutionary approach is to redesign entire machines around the radical possibilities of free-space optics. Such work is still experimental, but substantial progress has been made in the past few years, with significant experiments in various laboratories in Germany, Japan, the United Kingdom, the United States, and other countries.

Work at the AT&T Bell Laboratories in the U.S. in 1990 demonstrated a simple computer using an early version of the SEED technology. Although that computer was too small to be of any practical use, it did communicate all of its information internally by using only light beams. Subsequent work focused on demonstrating experimental processors for switching telecommunications data.

The largest free-space optical system built as of early 1994 was a switching system with more than 60,000 light beams designed to switch more than 1,000 channels of information. That system was too slow for current telecommunications systems, but it did demonstrate the feasibility of systems that have very large numbers of light beams. More recent experiments used FET-SEEDs for high-speed, low-energy switching, with speeds of 155 million bits of information per second in each channel in system experiments and more than 650 million bits per second in laboratory tests. It was hoped that larger versions of such switches would attain total throughputs of from 100 billion bits per second to perhaps more than one trillion bits per second through the use of many (such as 1,000) high-speed channels communicated by a single lens between chips.

One might ask why any switching systems would need to handle that many bits per second. A typical large telephone exchange today might handle about five billion bits per second, corresponding to about 100,000 phone calls. The need for greater capacity in the exchange is not so much to provide for many more phone calls but to allow larger amounts

In this experimental optical digital computer, all of the information flows with two-dimensional arrays of light beams, using lenses and mirrors. At each corner of the computer is an array of optoelectronic logic gates (circuits that facilitate the nonarithmetic operations in a computer).

Experimental telecommunications switching system (top) handles 2,048 parallel channels of information. All of the information in the channels is communicated optically inside the system by means of arrays of light beams and lenses. There are more than 60,000 light beams in the system. Smart pixels (below) typically have optical inputs, optical outputs, and electronics; the electronics provides "smartness" (such as logical functions and nonlinear operations) between the inputs and outputs. The pixels are arranged in two-dimensional arrays to form the chip (below right), thereby allowing the electronics to take advantage of parallel free-space interconnections out of the surface of the chip.

of information to be routed to customers—so-called broadband services. A simple example of a broadband service would be the transmission of television pictures instead of just voices. Standard television signals need roughly 100 to 1,000 times as much information as telephone calls. Optical fibers can easily send this amount of information, but telephone exchanges with 100 times their present capacity will be needed to route this information as easily as phone calls are routed today.

In these and other systems experiments, the optoelectronics are often arranged in two-dimensional arrays of smart pixels. A smart pixel usually consists of optical inputs and outputs together with some electronic smartness that might be in the form either of logic gates, as in the FET-SEED switching chips, or of an artificial "neuron" for neural network processing. The idea of arranging such smart pixels in regular two-dimensional arrays, like a sort of smart checkerboard, particularly suits the use of lenses to make the connections to other similar smart pixel

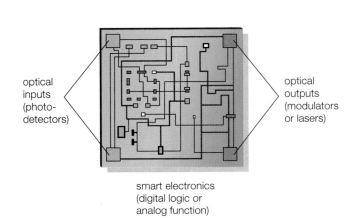

optical inputs (photo-detectors)

optical outputs (modulators or lasers)

smart electronics (digital logic or analog function)

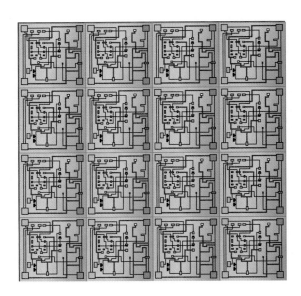

arrays. Researchers are looking at other possible applications of smart pixels in areas as diverse as high-speed parallel memory access from CD-ROM discs and parallel image processing to perform cancer screening.

Future prospects

Optics has some other tricks up its sleeve. So-called nonlinear optics can make ultrafast logic gates, some with speeds of one-trillionth of a second or even faster. These kinds of gates are not yet very practical, and at present no one can contemplate any complex systems with them, but perhaps technology may eventually advance enough to make them useful. Optics may be useful too for holographic memories that potentially could store very large amounts of information. Such memories do not store information just on the surface (like compact discs) but can instead use the entire volume of a crystal. The free-space-array technologies, like smart pixels, may help to get the information into and out of such memories, overcoming one of the problems of such memories in the past.

Though optics has already helped greatly in communicating and displaying information, it still has some way to go in helping to process information inside computers. Optoelectronic technology is relatively young, and much of the investment to reduce cost and improve ease of manufacture has yet to be made. New classes of integrated optoelectronic technology, such as smart pixels, are, however, emerging from the research laboratory. Furthermore, the arguments from physics for optics in digital computers are so strong, the difficulties in design of current electronic computers so daunting, and the reality of computational problems that cannot be solved so striking that one would be a pessimist indeed not to believe in a future for optics in digital computing. Enabled by fiber optics, we will be transmitting more information in the future. Silicon electronics will continue to put ever more staggering numbers of transistors on a chip. These revolutionary advances will create demands for communications inside processors, much greater than anything that can be handled today. It may be that these advances in telecommunications and, ironically, electronics will make the use of optics in digital computing not only desirable but inevitable.

FOR ADDITIONAL READING

H.S. Hinton and D.A.B. Miller, "Free-Space Photonics in Switching," *AT&T Technical Journal* (January–February 1992, pp. 84–92).

IEEE Journal of Quantum Electronics, Special Issue on Smart Pixels (February 1993).

D.A.B. Miller, "Optics for Low-Energy Communication Inside Digital Processors: Quantum Detectors, Sources, and Modulators as Efficient Impedance Converters," *Optics Letters* (Jan. 15, 1989, pp. 146–148).

D.A.B. Miller, "Optoelectronic Applications of Quantum Wells," *Optics and Photonics News* (February 1990, pp. 7–14).

N. Streibl, K.-H. Brenner, A. Huang, J. Jahns, J. Jewell, A.W. Lohmann, D.A.B. Miller, M. Murdocca, M.E. Prise, and T. Sizer, "Digital Optics," *Proceedings of the IEEE* (December 1989, pp. 1954–69).

The Rebirth of Electric Vehicles

by Gill A. Pratt

*New developments in charger, motor
control, motor, and—especially—battery technologies
are setting the stage for electric vehicles to challenge
the longtime supremacy of the internal
combustion engine.*

Like many other "green" technologies, electric vehicles have for many years had a following of starry-eyed enthusiasts. Recently, however, reality has begun to catch up with the dream. Two major forces—energy conservation and air-pollution control—are motivating electric vehicle development, and efforts are being made to remove the worst remaining handicaps—range and recharge convenience.

History

Electric vehicles (EVs) have been made since the beginning of the automobile industry. The first EV (La Jamais Contente) was built in 1888. In the early 1900s automobile buyers had a choice of electric, internal combustion, or steam power. Electric power held several advantages; electric vehicles were cleaner, quieter, less shaky, and more reliable than the internal combustion models, and they were far more easy to operate than steam. EVs were especially popular with women drivers because they did not require manual crank starting—a dangerous task that could cause severe injury in case of engine backfire.

But in the electric vehicle's battery and motor lurked the means of its demise. The same technology that propelled electric vehicles could also be used to start internal combustion engines. Charles F. Kettering patented the electric starter for internal combustion engines in 1912, and thereafter the electric vehicle was doomed. As internal combustion engines continued to be refined, they gave their vehicles superior power, range, and fueling convenience compared with electric models. By the late 1920s internal combustion cars (as typified by Henry Ford's Model T) almost totally dominated the automobile landscape. Internal combustion would remain the overwhelmingly popular means of propulsion for the next half century.

The first electric vehicle, La Jamais Contente (right), was built in 1888. Below is an electric car of about 1912. Because they did not require manual crank starting, electric cars were especially popular with women.

GILL A. PRATT *is an Assistant Professor of Electrical Engineering and Computer Science at the Massachusetts Institute of Technology, Cambridge.*

(Overleaf) Illustration by John Zielinski

The first sign of trouble for the internal combustion engine occurred in 1966. In that year worsening smog in cities prompted legislation requiring exhaust emission-control devices in new automobiles. In 1970 the Clean Air Act further required that harmful emissions from automobiles be reduced by 90%. While manufacturers were eventually—a decade later—able to meet this goal, the inherent difficulty of accurately controlling combustion in hundreds of millions of vehicles, each operating at highly variable temperatures and power levels and with uncertain maintenance, made the electric vehicle once again seem attractive. Electric vehicles could be recharged by a small number of carefully maintained power plants operating continuously at slowly varying power levels. As a result, total air pollution could be reduced and local air pollution could be redistributed to the power plant sites—typically outside the city.

150

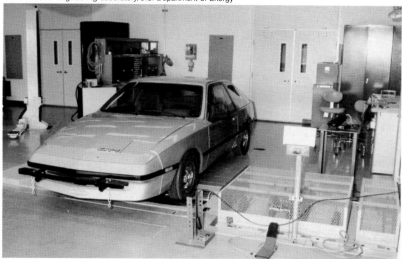

Car produced by the U.S. Department of Energy's Near-Term Electric Vehicle program undergoes testing at the Idaho National Engineering Laboratory in 1979. Because of the immature state of several important technologies in the 1970s, resulting in such problems as high cost, poor battery lifetime, and poor motor efficiency, the program did not live up to expectations.

The oil crisis of the 1970s added further impetus to the move away from internal combustion. Pollution considerations aside, electric vehicles promised to lessen the dependence of the United States and many other nations on imported oil. Unlike gasoline, the electric power used to charge an EV's battery could be generated from a wide variety of fuels, including coal and natural gas; renewable sources, such as wind and solar power; and nuclear power. Gasoline, by contrast, could be made economically only from oil.

In 1976 the U.S. Department of Energy (DOE) undertook an ambitious program to push electric vehicles to the brink of practicality. With funding from the Electric and Hybrid Vehicle Research, Development, and Demonstration Act, the DOE launched the Near-Term Electric Vehicle (NTEV) program. "Development and Demonstration" was the program's foremost goal, culminating in the construction of two prototype electric vehicles. All necessary technology would be developed during the program. As its name implied, results were expected in the "near term."

Unfortunately, economic practicality proved a difficult goal to reach. Although both prototypes were completed, the NTEV program failed to develop an economically practical electric vehicle. The immature state of several key technologies in the 1970s prevented success. Among the worst problems were high cost, poor battery energy density, poor battery power density, poor battery lifetime, poor motor efficiency, high vehicle weight, and unreliable power electronics.

By 1993, however, a new era was at hand. Government agencies, automakers, and parts manufacturers were once again funding large research programs in electric vehicle technology. The most striking example was the $100 million-per-year U.S. Advanced Battery Consortium, an industrywide research effort to address the electric vehicle's worst handicap—limited range—by developing better batteries. Several automakers announced plans to produce electric vehicles, and the U.S. automobile manufacturers were cooperating in a joint program to develop advanced

151

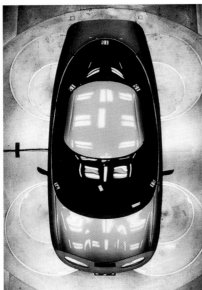

The Impact (top right), developed by General Motors Corp., is the most advanced high-performance electric vehicle. Under the hood of the Impact is the motor controller (top), which transfers the proper amount of electrical current to the car's motor. Overhead view of the Impact (above) reveals its teardrop shape, which makes it the most aerodynamic car yet produced.

electric vehicles. The state of California, in an effort to further combat smog, mandated that by 1998, 2% (and by 2003, 10%) of all cars sold there be zero-emission vehicles.

Most tangibly, the nation's largest automaker, General Motors Corp., and its subsidiary, Hughes Electronics, successfully developed the most advanced electric vehicle to date (the GM Impact). While plans for the Impact's production have been somewhat delayed, it is the automobile industry's first economically practical high-performance electric vehicle; 50 Impacts were scheduled to be produced in 1993.

How an electric vehicle works

The power train of an electric vehicle consists of four components: a charger, a battery, a motor controller, and an electric motor. The charger, which may be carried on board the car or may be stationary, is used to replenish the car's energy supply from the electrical power grid. The battery stores electrical energy for use during the journey.

The motor controller modulates the amount of power transferred between the battery and motor, as commanded by the driver's accelerator and brake pedals. The car's one or more motors translate electric power into mechanical power (and from mechanical to electrical during braking). The motor may be followed by a mechanical transmission and differential (transaxle), as in conventional cars.

Chargers

Most electric vehicles carry an onboard charger, a lightweight device that allows recharging anywhere one finds a conventional electrical socket. The function of the charger is to convert the AC voltage from the electrical outlet into the DC used by the battery and to regulate the amount of power fed to the battery.

Chargers can be designed to operate from either low-power 110-volt lines (commonly found in homes) or higher-power, higher-voltage lines. To extend the life of an electric vehicle's battery, the charger must follow

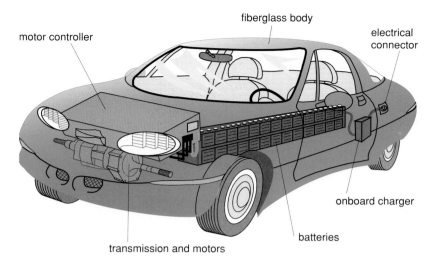

motor controller

fiberglass body

electrical connector

transmission and motors

batteries

onboard charger

Diagram reveals the four components of the power train of an electric vehicle. The onboard charger replenishes the car's energy supply through an electrical connector to the local power grid. The batteries store electrical energy for use during a journey. The motor controller (inverter) modulates the amount of power transferred between the batteries and the motor, and the one or more motors translate electric power into mechanical power (and mechanical into electrical during braking).

a precise schedule in regard to the rate at which it charges the battery, dependent on both the battery's temperature and its depth of discharge. This is a perfect application for microprocessor control, which today adds very little to the charger's cost. In the future, microprocessor control will also allow the power utility to vary the customer's charging rate at different times throughout the night. By adjusting load in this fashion, the utility will be able to maximize plant utilization. Utilities are keenly interested in electric vehicles because nighttime charging would utilize (and gain revenue from) otherwise surplus generation capacity.

The more powerful the charger, the faster an electric vehicle can be recharged. But even if batteries are eventually developed that can be fully charged in a few minutes, the required power input would stress present electrical distribution systems. For example, recharging the GM Impact (whose batteries store 13.6 kilowatt-hours) in three minutes requires an instantaneous power of 272 kilowatts. Four cars charging simultaneously at that rate would require more than one megawatt of electrical power. While this power level is not uncommon in industrial settings, substantial investment would be required for every corner service station to be equipped with such high power. The inconvenience of a long recharge time is a serious handicap of electric vehicles.

Advances in power and control electronics during the past two decades have significantly improved the quality and economics of battery chargers. A recent innovation by Hughes is inductive coupling, in which the usual metallic power connector is replaced by a two-part high-frequency transformer. A stationary base station contains most of the charger and one-half of the transformer. The second half of the transformer is contained in the car. The chief advantage of this system is that each half can be hermetically sealed to ensure complete safety against electrocution, even in wet environments. Another recent advance, by Electronic Power Technology, Inc., is pulse charging, where power is fed to the battery in a series of six-millisecond bursts. This seems to allow more efficient charging at higher power levels and may also extend the life of the battery.

153

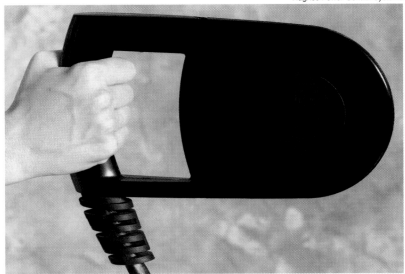

Plastic-covered paddle (right) is part of a 220-volt charging system called inductive coupling. The paddle, which can be used safely in any weather, contains a metal coil that is inserted into a charging port in an electric vehicle. The port contains another coil that receives the charge and transmits it, through an AC-DC converter, to the batteries. Another curbside charger (below) contains a cord that can be plugged into a vehicle's onboard charger and a means for metering the charge.

WRI, Topeka/EHV Corp./Kansas State University, Manhattan

Batteries

Batteries have been, and remain, the weakest component of electric vehicles. Compared with conventional internal combustion engines, electric batteries suffer from serious handicaps on a multitude of fronts: lower specific power, much lower specific energy, shorter lifetime, and longer recharge time.

Specific power is a measure of how much power can be drawn from each kilogram of battery weight. Specific energy is a measure of how much electrical energy can be stored in each kilogram of battery weight. Insufficient specific power reduces a vehicle's acceleration and hill-climbing capacity and also adversely affects its regenerative braking capability and recharge time. (Regenerative braking is braking in which electrical energy that is produced by the motor is returned to the battery.) Low specific energy results in reduced driving range between recharges.

The GM Impact, with an exhilarating 0–96-kilometer-per-hour (0–60-mile-per-hour) time of eight seconds, demonstrated that even lead-acid batteries have sufficient power density if they are used in a lightweight, aerodynamic vehicle with high-efficiency tires. Unfortunately, battery lifetime (particularly for lead-acids) and efficiency tend to suffer at high power levels.

The specific power and specific energy of various power sources can be visualized on a two-dimensional graph known as a Ragone plot. Because batteries can be built in many different configurations (for example, in lead-acid batteries the thickness and number of plates can be varied), each battery type traces a curve, rather than a point, on the graph.

Low-performance power sources are found in the lower left-hand corner of this plot, while higher performance power sources are in the upper right-hand corner. In terms of specific energy of currently popular electric vehicle batteries, lead-acid performs worst of all, followed by nickel-iron, nickel-cadmium, nickel-metal-hydride, and sodium-sulfur.

Ragone Plot of Batteries and Engines

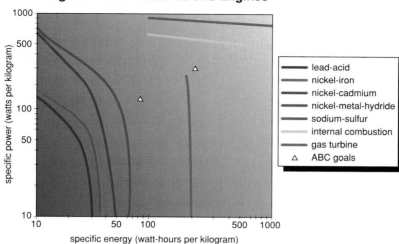

Legend:
- lead-acid
- nickel-iron
- nickel-cadmium
- nickel-metal-hydride
- sodium-sulfur
- internal combustion
- gas turbine
- △ ABC goals

x-axis: specific energy (watt-hours per kilogram)
y-axis: specific power (watts per kilogram)

Ragone plot reveals the specific power and specific energy of various power sources. Specific power is a measure of the amount of power that can be drawn from each kilogram of battery weight, and specific energy is a measure of how much electrical energy can be stored in each kilogram of battery weight. Low-performance power sources are found in the lower left-hand corner of the plot, and high-performance sources are in the upper right-hand corner.

Nickel metal hydride is a promising new battery technology developed by Energy Conversion Devices, Inc. It has roughly twice the energy density of nickel-cadmium and, because of its lack of cadmium, is more environmentally sound. The medium- and long-term goals of the Advanced Battery consortium are also plotted on the graph.

The Ragone plot reveals the huge advantage of internal combustion engines over electric batteries. Without considering fuel, modern internal combustion engines have a specific power—the power produced per unit mass of fuel—of about 500 watts per kilogram. Because of their lightweight and energy-dense fuel tanks, internal combustion systems also have a very high specific energy—the internal energy of a substance per unit mass. Gasoline, for example, has a thermal specific energy of 13,400 watt-hours per kilogram. If one-quarter of this energy is converted into useful work, gasoline yields about 3,350 watts of mechanical energy per

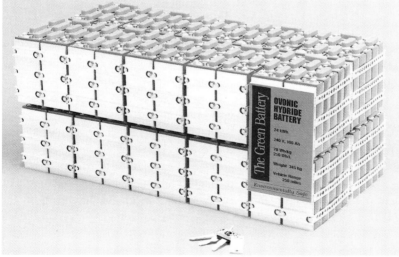

Energy Conversion Devices, Inc.; Troy, Michigan

Ovonic modular battery pack provides enough energy to drive an electric vehicle more than 320 kilometers (200 miles) with a single charge. The nickel-metal-hydride batteries, developed by Energy Conversion Devices, Inc., have approximately twice the energy density of nickel-cadmium batteries.

A fleet of electric vehicles awaits field testing and evaluation at Sandia National Laboratories in Albuquerque, New Mexico. Because of the low energy capacity and long recharge time of conventional batteries, electric vehicles are more suitable for fleet, rather than individual consumer, use. Most fleet vehicles travel short distances every day and are not used at night, at which time they can be recharged.

kilogram of fuel. To arrive at a simultaneous power and energy density figure for the internal combustion system, one must know the ratio of engine weight to fuel tank weight. As this ratio varies, an internal combustion system follows the curve shown in the upper right-hand corner of the Ragone plot. By comparison, sodium-sulfur batteries, which are among the highest-energy density batteries available for electric vehicle use, provide only about 200 watt-hours of energy per kilogram.

The result of this dreadful inequality is a range for most electric vehicles of only about 200 kilometers (about 120 miles) before the battery must be recharged. Although a typical U.S. commute is only about 30 kilometers (20 miles) each day, this recharge limitation is a great nuisance, as it seriously limits unplanned use of the vehicle.

To achieve maximum life, most batteries must be recharged more slowly than they are discharged. This both limits the amount of regenerative braking that may be utilized and slows the maximum rate of recharging. In an emergency stop a car's braking system may be called upon to absorb four times more power than is used for acceleration. If the battery must supply all of this power, its life is seriously shortened. However, for such emergency braking, one can use mechanical brakes, which do not require the battery for their operation. Unfortunately, no similar solution exists for recharging. To maximize battery life and not overload their electrical utility supply, electric vehicles typically take several hours to recharge, in sharp contrast to the few minutes required by internal combustion vehicles at a gasoline service station.

Several new energy-storage technologies promise some hope of improvement in recharge time. These include "supercapacitors," high-rate battery designs, pulse charging, and flywheels. However, by 1994 none of these had yet been demonstrated to be economically feasible, and all suffered from the limitations of the electrical power distribution system.

The low energy capacity and long recharge time of conventional batteries make electric vehicles more suitable for fleet, rather than individual consumer, use. Most fleet vehicles travel short total distances along identical routes every day and are not used at night (which allows time for recharge).

156

Motor control

The job of the motor controller is to efficiently generate a controlled amount of electrical current in the car's motors. To regulate current efficiently, motor controllers utilize a technique called "switched power conversion." In this method the fixed battery voltage is modulated by electronic switches (which are either on or off) into a high-frequency series of pulses with a duty cycle (the time the voltage is high versus the time it is low) that has been altered to create a variable average motor voltage. The magnetic inductance of the motor's coils then smoothes this pulsed voltage to achieve a steady motor current, which is regulated by feedback circuitry to generate the desired mechanical power.

Present-day motor controls can transfer power in both directions, for acceleration or for regenerative braking. In the acceleration mode power is drawn from the battery and delivered to the wheels. During regenerative braking, power is fed from the wheels to the battery, recovering a significant part of the kinetic energy of the decelerating automobile mass.

To create the proper pulsed voltage, an electric vehicle's motor controller requires two types of electronic circuits: a high-power switching circuit and a low-power switching controller. Until recently, high-power switching devices were limited to low-efficiency SCRs (silicon-controlled rectifiers), and the low-power control circuitry was primitive, unreliable, and expensive.

By 1994, however, both high-power switches and low-power control circuitry had dramatically improved. Several high-power semiconductors were competing for use in electric vehicle motor controls. In the realm of low-power control, the extraordinary advances of digital electronics in the past two decades, particularly with regard to high-performance microprocessors, have allowed sophisticated, reliable control circuits to be manufactured at very little expense.

As with chargers, further advances in electronics will no doubt be made. However, the present availability of reliable and inexpensive high-performance motor controllers makes it unlikely that future improvements will significantly affect the economic practicality of future vehicles.

Motors

Many types of motors are used in electric vehicles. Among the most common are the permanent magnet DC brushless (also known as AC synchronous) motors and the AC induction (also known as AC asynchronous) motors. Each has its own advantages and disadvantages. Briefly, the AC induction motor tends to be more efficient at high speeds and with light loads, while the DC brushless motor leads the way at low speeds and with heavy loads. A third type, the AC variable reluctance motor, has the potential for slightly reduced cost below that of the DC brushless and AC induction and may also reduce the need for gear reduction—lowering of the output speed by means of a gear train.

Though the electric motor is at the heart of an electric vehicle's drivetrain, future motor refinements are likely to have little impact on the economic viability of the electric vehicle. The brushed motors used by the NTEV prototypes and many past EV programs were heavy, were difficult to cool, had poor efficiency, and required periodic maintenance. Today's motors are, however, a significant improvement over those of the past, with very high efficiencies and light weight, and so no future improvement in motor design is likely to have a significant impact on the environmental or economic practicality of the electric car.

Thus, as explained above, by far the most limiting technology in an electric vehicle is the battery. To make EVs more viable, either batteries must be improved or alternative energy-storage systems must be found. Charger, motor control, and motor technologies will continue to improve in the future, but their present state of the art is "good enough," and further improvements will have relatively little impact on the economic practicality of electric vehicles.

Energy conservation and source flexibility

Do electric vehicles save energy? The answer is "yes," but how much depends very much on driving conditions. A present-day electric vehicle motor converts about 90% of its electrical input energy into mechanical work. At moderate power levels, an advanced EV battery is about 80% efficient at storing electrical energy during charge and releasing it during discharge. Thus, from electrical input to mechanical output, state-of-the-art electric vehicles are about 72% efficient. Regenerative braking, which returns a significant fraction of a decelerating car's kinetic energy back into the onboard battery, allows this efficiency to be somewhat maintained despite stop-and-go driving, but regenerative braking does not improve upon the efficiency stated above.

The power to recharge an electric vehicle is produced by an electrical power plant. In 1988 U.S. power plants converted fossil fuel into electricity at an average efficiency of 33%. During that same year electrical transmission was accomplished at an average efficiency of 92%, for a total fuel-to-user efficiency of about 30%. In 1989 the urban fuel-to-user efficiency of electrical generation was 31.5%; because electric vehicles will initially be used in urban areas, it makes sense to use this latter number for comparisons.

Multiplying the vehicle and power-plant efficiencies gives an urban EV fuel-to-wheel efficiency of about 23%. In 1988 all transportation (both gasoline- and diesel-fueled) in the U.S. was estimated to have a thermal-to-mechanical efficiency of 25%, and a large fraction of this was for long-haul and/or diesel consumption, both of which are more efficient than commuter use of gasoline. Thus, at first glance the efficiency of electric and internal combustion cars seems close.

To obtain more accurate numbers, one must turn to direct comparisons of gasoline and electric vehicles of approximately the same weight and size. Both gasoline and electric vehicles can achieve much higher energy efficiency and lower pollution emissions by adopting more streamlined, lighter-weight structures and by using more efficient tires. However, because of the typically low specific energy of electric vehicle batteries, the impetus to lighten and streamline EVs is much greater than

158

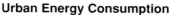
Urban Energy Consumption

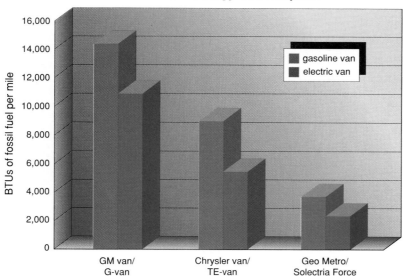

A study by the Electric Power Research Institute compares the energy consumption of two pairs of vans having the same body shape and approximately the same weight. In each pair, one van is powered by a gasoline internal combustion engine and the other by electricity. A similar comparison performed by the California Air Resources Board on a small car is also shown. The electric vehicles required only 60% to 75% of the energy consumed by their internal combustion counterparts.

it is for gasoline cars. Any comparison of state-of-the-art electric with average gasoline cars must, therefore, be viewed with suspicion, as the electric will have had the benefit of a more enthusiastic weight and drag reduction. For example, the advanced body and tires of the GM Impact are claimed to result in a vehicle of four times higher efficiency than a conventional gasoline-powered sports car.

Fortunately, for purposes of comparison, many electric vehicles are conversions of gasoline models, having the same body shape and approximately the same weight. The chart above summarizes comparisons made by the Electric Power Research Institute on two converted vans used in urban fleets. An additional column has been added to the table for the Force, a converted Geo Metro made by Solectria Corp. with more efficient components than are used in the vans. Gasoline energy was assumed to be 144,000 British thermal units per gallon by adding its energy of combustion, 127,650 British thermal units per gallon, to an approximate energy for mining, transport, and refining of 16,000 British thermal units per gallon. An overall efficiency of 31.5% (or 10,800 British thermal units per kilowatt-hour) was assumed for the generation of electrical power.

As can be seen from the chart, the electric vans require only between 60% and 75% of the energy consumed by their internal combustion counterparts. The Solectria Force's urban energy consumption, as measured by the California Air Resources Board and Southern California Edison, was approximately 63% that of a gasoline Metro. Because of its radical body and tires, the GM Impact cannot be compared to any conventional vehicle.

Thus, electric vehicles, recharged by fossil-fuel power plants, have significantly better energy efficiency than their gasoline-powered equivalents in urban use but are slightly worse for long distances on the

159

"Mom's Taxi" (above) is a Voltsrabbit, a Volkswagen Rabbit that has been converted to electricity. The car's fuel gauge (above right) looks normal but is measuring the charge of the Voltsrabbit's batteries.

highway. Because power plant efficiency dominates this calculation of EV efficiency, other technological EV improvements (such as more efficient motors or batteries) cannot significantly change this result. On the other hand, if power plant efficiency were to improve, much larger energy savings could be realized, even for long-haul transportation.

Energy flexibility

Along with energy efficiency, the electric vehicle offers another important benefit to national energy management. At present, internal combustion fuels with high energy densities are made more economically from crude oil than from other sources (such as grain). As a result, the United States depends almost exclusively on crude oil for its transportation energy supply. In 1989 crude oil constituted approximately 45% of the U.S. energy supply and accounted for 97% of the nation's transportation energy consumption.

As was made evident in the late 1970s, this almost total dependence on oil for transportation translates into a very real vulnerability. It has brought about continuing research into internal combustion engines that can run on such fuels as methanol, ethanol, and natural gas and has also been a strong impetus for electric vehicle development. If transportation could be decoupled from its total dependence on oil, even without improvements in overall efficiency, the U.S. would gain tremendously in terms of energy flexibility—the ability to switch to other energy sources should crude oil fall into short supply.

Of course, once transportation relies on electricity as an energy source, the switch to alternative fuels becomes a far more simple (and more economically attractive) matter. For example, the lower energy density of alcohols, compared with gasoline, is a major impediment to their use in mobile vehicles (where each extra liter of fuel requires more space and adds weight). But because its fuel tank is immobile, an electric power plant is not as seriously penalized for consuming a less energy-dense fuel. Electric power plants can also be modified more economically (per unit of energy generated) to switch fuels than can automobiles.

160

Air pollution

As in the case of energy efficiency, the degree to which electric vehicles reduce pollution depends on what takes place at the power plant. If only the vehicle itself is considered and one neglects pollution generated by manufacturing, electric vehicles generate virtually no air pollution. While this may satisfy California's "zero emissions" criteria, less emission at the tailpipe usually means more emission at the smokestack. On the other hand, even if no net pollution reduction is achieved, the moving of air pollution from the automobiles inside a city to a power plant on the out-skirts can be beneficial, particularly in regard to smog trapped in natural basins such as in Los Angeles. But on a national or global scale, the important concern is the total pollution generated, regardless of location.

What types and how much pollution a power plant generates depends on the fuel it consumes and the sophistication of its pollution controls. In most areas power is generated from a variety of plants, some "dirty" (such as coal-burning) and some very "clean" (such as hydroelectric). Thus, to estimate the amount of pollution in a given area, one must take the type of plants into account.

As was the case with energy consumption, in comparisons of the pollution generated by EVs with that emitted by internal combustion vehicles, the most accurate are obtained from vehicles that have been converted from internal combustion to electric power. When this is done, one can calculate, for each type of pollutant, the number of grams of pollutant generated per distance driven, taking into account all pollution from the oil well to the road. Exactly this type of study was performed by the Electric Power Research Institute in 1989. As with the energy-use comparisons, the pollution comparison was made for electric conversions of two different gasoline-powered vans, one from General Motors and the other from Chrysler. Separate studies were done for the Los Angeles basin and the entire U.S.

Because only a small fraction of the power used in the Los Angeles basin is generated by burning coal, the use of electric vehicles there will significantly reduce levels of hydrocarbons, nitrous oxides, and carbon monoxide; this, in turn, reduces the region's infamous smog. Because total power plant-to-road pollution is being measured, these results do not just reflect a transplantation of pollution to outside Los Angeles.

In the rest of the U.S., where burning coal to generate power is more common, the result is less clear. Improvements were realized for some pollutants (hydrocarbons, carbon monoxide, and carbon dioxide), but higher levels of pollutant were produced for sulfur dioxide and nitric oxide. There was a positive impact on global warming but a negative one on acid rain. At first glance, therefore, the impact of the electric vehicle on national air pollution is mixed. However, as was true for energy consumption, electric vehicles, by decoupling the consumption of fossil fuel from the production of mechanical work, provide the flexibility to improve air quality by changing the future means of power generation.

The emissions characteristics of gasoline engines have steadily im-proved but, with computerized carburetion and ignition controls already

161

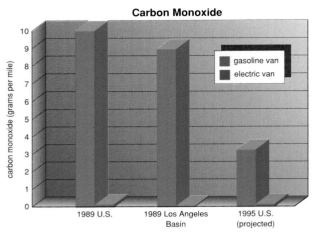

Carbon Monoxide

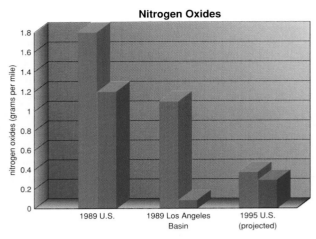

Nitrogen Oxides

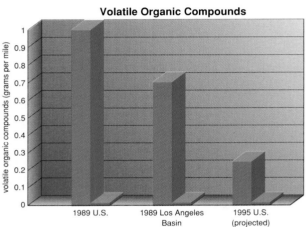

Volatile Organic Compounds

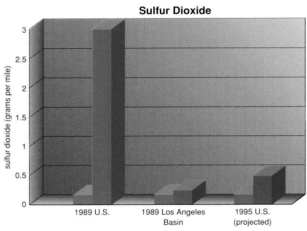

Sulfur Dioxide

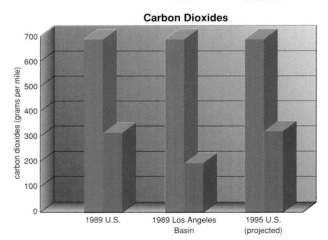

Carbon Dioxides

A study of air pollution in the United States in 1989 compared the pollutants emitted by two different gasoline-powered vans with those generated by electric conversions of those vans. The number of grams of each pollutant generated per distance driven were calculated, taking into account total power-plant-to-road pollution. In the Los Angeles basin, where only a small fraction of the electric power is generated by burning coal, the advantages of the electric vans were most pronounced.

in place, additional improvements are becoming more difficult to realize. On the other hand, many electrical power sources—nuclear, hydroelectric, and solar—can be used in a stationary installation to produce the electricity that recharges electric vehicles without generating any air pollution.

As was demonstrated by the favorable power-generation scenario in the Los Angeles basin, a significant improvement in air quality can be achieved by adoption of electric vehicles while electric power plants are also improved. It is the latter part of this approach that must not be forgotten. High-technology coal plants, which produce less sulfur dioxide and nitric oxide, can provide an interim answer, with some help from hydroelectric, solar, and wind sources. If nuclear power can regain public trust, the renewed construction of nuclear plants, perhaps with intrinsically safe reactor designs, will greatly improve the environmental advantages of electric vehicles.

Other EV advantages

In addition to the above-mentioned energy and environmental issues, EVs offer other advantages. Among them is their simplicity. For example, almost no conventional automobile drivetrain components are easily tested once removed from the vehicle, and few, if any, mechanics utilize wheel dynamometers for accurately testing automobile performance in the shop. A poorly controlled (and usually perfunctory) road test usually follows most present-day car repairs, and the rate of return of vehicles to the shop for persistent problems is high. An electric vehicle's components, by contrast, can be easily tested outside the vehicle with little investment in diagnostic hardware. As a result, the level of consumer satisfaction with EV repairs will likely be much higher than with internal combustion cars. Furthermore, because of the modular structure of their drivetrains, EVs may eventually have more standardized drivetrain components that can be used for many model types than do present automobiles. This will be a boon to parts recyclers.

Internal combustion engines, even with the best of mufflers, generate a substantial amount of noise and cause a significant degree of chassis vibration. Many electric vehicles of the 1970s and 80s utilized high-speed motors with noisy gear trains, generating what has come to be known as the "electric whine." In some cases this noise was even more irritating than the rumble of a tailpipe. But the newer EVs are becoming as quiet as their tires will allow. This reduction seems certain to have a substantial impact on noise within cities.

In regard to maintenance, present-day EV motors have one moving part, the rotor, and no slow-moving or delicate mechanical controls. Unlike an internal combustion automobile, most electric vehicles have no pressurized fluid systems, nor do they have hot exhaust systems susceptible to corrosion. As a result, a number of required maintenance operations are eliminated. With sufficient design development and manufacturing quality, the electronic components of an EV can be expected to have near-perfect reliability with zero maintenance. Regenerative braking reduces brake wear in electric vehicles to a minimum, and so it will be unusual for an electric vehicle ever to require replacement of brake pads or resurfacing of brake discs or drums.

To be sure, present EV batteries require several replacements over the lifetime of the vehicle. Automobile manufacturers' estimates of the cost of battery replacement are preliminary, but in 1993 most were a few cents per kilometer. Thus, it is clear that battery lifetime and replacement costs are significant considerations for electric vehicles and, along with other current battery handicaps discussed below, justify serious research efforts.

On the bright side, with proper manufacturing quality, the lifetime of an electric vehicle's battery is highly predictable on the basis of recorded use patterns and continuous measurement by onboard instrumentation. Unlike many systems in conventional automobiles, an electric vehicle's battery pack can give warning months before sufficient degradation causes failure.

Because of its mechanically controlled engine and friction brakes, a conventional automobile presents its driver with a highly variable level of sensitivity from the accelerator and brake pedals. By contrast, electric motors deliver precise amounts of torque, making possible the enactment of industrywide standards specifying the amount of vehicle acceleration or deceleration resulting from a given applied force on the accelerator or brake pedal. This will enhance driver confidence and vehicle safety, particularly in the rental-car market. Cruise controls, which have sometimes behaved poorly in internal combustion cars, can be made highly precise in electric vehicles.

Conventional automobiles utilize friction clutches to provide limited-slip acceleration on slippery surfaces. Recently, hydraulic pressure-reduction systems have been incorporated into conventional braking systems to prevent the wheels from locking when the car is decelerating. In an electric vehicle, with separate motors for each wheel, the implementation of precise limited-slip traction and antilock braking is a straightforward matter. Electric vehicle motors have built-in rotation sensors, and with the ability to precisely modulate the force applied to the driveshaft, an EV's motor controller can easily guard against acceleration slip or brake lockup.

Similarly, although detailed studies have yet to be made, high-speed handling can be improved with the intelligent application of unequal torque to the wheels during turns. On a more mundane front, the difficult art of clutching a manual transmission to start on a steep grade will finally be relegated to history, as electric motors produce maximum torque at zero speed and thus cannot be stalled.

One of the less apparent, but most important, recent developments has been safety improvements in lightweight vehicles. Because low vehicle weight is necessary for extended range (and better performance), this change is a major factor in the new viability of electric vehicles. Air bags and high-strength, lightweight composite materials are responsible for this improvement. Air bags lessen the chance of injury in case of a crash, while composites promise great energy absorption without the weight of steel. In the 1970s vehicles weighing less than 1,375 kilograms (3,000 pounds) were considered unsafe. By 1994, however, 900-kilogram (2,000-pound) vehicles were common. Future electric vehicles may approach 450 kilograms (1,000 pounds).

The Solectria Flash is a two-passenger electric racing car made of lightweight composite materials. Reducing the weight of electric vehicles allows them to travel farther before needing to be recharged.

Hybrids and fuel cell cars

The poor energy density of EV batteries has long inspired a simple solution: the incorporation of an onboard miniaturized power plant that consumes energy-dense fuel and acts as a charger (or direct mechanical power source) for long journeys. In the most simple hybrid systems, an ordinary mechanical drivetrain is connected in parallel with the electric drivetrain, with clutches selecting the power source that is to be used at any given moment. More sophisticated systems utilize highly tuned internal combustion engines connected to generators that charge on-board batteries.

Many features have been cited in support of internal combustion hybrid vehicles. For example, hybrids can choose to run their internal combustion engines only outside the city (thus reducing city noise and air pollution) and can also ensure nearly ideal, fixed-load, operating conditions for their internal combustion engines. This improves efficiency and lowers generated pollution.

But modern electronics have drastically improved the fuel and ignition-control systems of conventional automobiles, and so the advantage of running the internal combustion engine of a hybrid at a fixed load is not nearly so great as it once was. Furthermore, as in ordinary cars, internal combustion hybrids suffer the complexity, poor reliability, and cost of the engine (as well as the cost of the generator added onto the cost of the electric drivetrain). These factors combine to make the competitive outlook of internal combustion hybrids marginal, if not poor. Nevertheless, several automakers, including General Motors, Volkswagen, Audi, and Mercedes-Benz, were pursuing research programs on internal combustion hybrids in 1993. A more-promising technology is the gas turbine, which can achieve high efficiency and reduce air pollution. Much of this technology, however, remains experimental, and it is yet to be seen if small, high-efficiency turbines can be made economically.

Fuel-cell hybrids offer another great hope. Fuel cells, which convert chemical fuel into electricity at high (up to 50%) efficiency with no moving parts, have been used for many years in the space program. The

165

The Audi duo (right) contains both a four-cylinder internal combustion engine that drives all four wheels and an auxiliary electric motor that drives the rear wheels when required; the battery pack for the electric motor is mounted in the rear of the car (above). Several automakers are undertaking research programs to determine the feasibility of such hybrid cars. One important advantage of these vehicles is that the internal combustion engine can be used only outside of urban areas, thereby reducing city noise and air pollution. Disadvantages of hybrids are their complexity and high cost.

three auxiliary power units of the space shuttle are fuel cells, and they provide the electrical power used to run its onboard systems.

Unfortunately, fuel cells have in the past been expensive to manufacture (owing to the use of platinum catalysts), and reliability has been poor (the smallest impurity in the fuel can ruin the cell). Recently, however, promising new techniques to construct fuel cells more economically have been developed. The most economical fuel cells consume hydrogen and air to produce electricity. Air is easy to come by, but the storage of hydrogen is more troublesome. Because of weight, handling, and safety considerations, compressed hydrogen storage, while often used in prototype vehicles, is not likely to be feasible in production cars. The two most likely alternatives are onboard reformation of liquid methanol into hydrogen and storage of hydrogen in metal hydride form. Unfortunately, hydrogen makes up only a small percentage of the weight of the hydrides, and the metals themselves are heavy. Nevertheless, despite the weight handicap, the use of metal hydrides in fuel cells results in higher energy densities than can be achieved with most batteries.

Producing and distributing the hydrogen for fuel-cell hybrids may not be as difficult. This is because of the already-in-place natural-gas-distribution system, which would allow filling stations to operate methane-to-hydrogen reformers on site, on an on-demand basis. Storage of hydrogen in hydride form is safe, and while this system still needs much development, it holds great promise for achieving extended-range electric vehicles in the years to come.

Conclusion

In conclusion, it is appropriate to recall the technological premise of the NTEV program, drawn up in 1976:

(1) That, in fact, the complete spectrum of requirements placed on the automobile (including safety, producibility, and utility) can be satisfied if electric power train concepts are incorporated in place of contemporary power train concepts, and (2) That the resultant sets of vehicle characteristics are mutually compatible, technologically achievable, and economically achievable.

The specific objectives, as stated at the program's outset, were: (1) The electric car resulting from this program is to be suitable for future production at a cost comparable to conventional (internal combustion engine) autos. (2) When produced in quantities of 100,000 or more per year, the electric car should be available at a consumer price equivalent to $5,000 in 1975 dollars. (3) Life-cycle costs of EVs are not to exceed 9 cents per kilometer (15 cents per mile), on the basis of a 10-year life span and 16,100 kilometers (10,000 miles) of operation per year.

At the program's end in 1981, the final report stated: "The DOE objectives have generally been achieved. With some further advances in battery technology expected by 1982, all performance and cost objectives can be satisfied."

This was, at the time, wishful thinking, but since then several important factors have changed:

1. Environmental pollution, particularly with regard to global warming, is considered a much more threatening problem than it was in the 1970s.

2. Charger, motor control, and motor technologies have matured.

3. The public, partly because of air bags, has come to accept lighter-weight vehicles as safe. Composite materials promise even further reductions in acceptable vehicle weight.

4. Higher-efficiency tires have been developed.

5. Battery technology has improved significantly, and several alternatives, including flywheel batteries, hybrid gas turbines, and fuel cells, are being developed at a rapid rate.

Are these new developments enough to make electric vehicles practical? As of 1994, despite their own internal development efforts, the big three U.S. automobile manufacturers (GM, Ford, and Chrysler) said no; they were lobbying against the California zero-emission mandate, arguing that battery technology is not yet up to the task. It is unclear whether these objections have merit. U.S. automobile manufacturers have historically opposed technically feasible innovations in vehicle safety, fuel efficiency, and air-pollution control. When standards were imposed by the government over such opposition, as was the case for pollution control, the automakers found a way to meet the standards—by developing the catalytic converter, for example. Perhaps a similar impetus (like the California mandate) is what is needed to make the electric vehicle a reality.

It is the opinion of many small electric vehicle manufacturers, some foreign automakers, and most technical researchers that electric cars, if produced in high volume, would make practical commuter vehicles even with today's technology. Presently, the inconveniences of range, recharge time, and battery replacement make electric vehicles less attractive than conventional gasoline-powered models. But other features, including less noise, less pollution, lower energy consumption, and simpler maintenance make electric vehicles more attractive. As evidenced by the overwhelming response to GM's offer to allow a handful of the public to borrow an "Impact" for a short time, many drivers seem willing to give electric vehicles the benefit of the doubt. The coming decade will be exciting as the rebirth of the electric vehicle unfolds.

167

Borrowing the Best from Nature

by Julian F.V. Vincent

In the struggle to survive, plants and animals have evolved solutions to the same kinds of problems that scientists and engineers confront today. The effort to exploit those solutions, called biomimetics, is promising new materials and processes and may even lead to buildings that reshape their own structures.

Biomimetics is the abstraction of good design from nature. It is the process by which ideas from biology can be applied within such disciplines as chemistry, engineering, and materials science. Although not a new approach—nature has always inspired invention—biomimetics is becoming important enough to attract increasing interest. To understand why this is so, it is necessary to understand the nature of biology and its relationship with other sciences.

Looking for the questions

Biology is the study of living organisms and their interrelationships. Every organism can be viewed as a bag of solutions to problems posed by the needs of survival. An organism is successful when it can survive and reproduce with the least possible energy since it is always in competition with other individuals and species for the food, sunlight, and other energy sources available. It allocates this energy among its various functions—respiration, digestion, reproduction, sensing, movement, mechanical support, chemical defenses, and the like—in order to maximize its efficiency. Each of these functions overlaps one or more of the others, so the energy allocation has to be optimized between them. In addition, organisms cannot be considered in isolation. Each is a member of the population of organisms with which it coexists; it is also a product of populations past, and its own products will supply populations to come. The name of this game is resource allocation and recycling.

It is one of the aspirations of the biologist to find and define the problems that organisms are solving. In short, a large part of biology can be summarized as looking at a particular microbe, plant, or animal and saying, "Here are the answers. What were the questions?" Ideally the answers represent especially efficient ways of performing particular functions in order to solve particular problems. In fact, the efficiency

of organisms in optimizing and adapting is such that if a particular function seems to be inefficient, the chances are that the observer has not properly identified the problem or understood the nature of the optimizations. This is an important point, because a poor grasp of the optimizations makes it more difficult for any basic concepts to be extracted from the function.

An example of optimization in biology is the balance between stiffness, the ability to carry a load without excessive bending, and toughness, the ability to resist breaking, that must be achieved in a material that can perform different functions. This is illustrated by the work of John D. Currey of the University of York, England, on bone. Bone is a composite material consisting primarily of mineral crystals (crystals of hydroxyapatite, a form of calcium phosphate) that are bound to a fiber-forming protein called collagen. The hard mineral particles, the inorganic component, give bone stiffness and strength, while the protein fibers, the organic component, add the needed toughness. Cow leg bone, which contains 50% mineral, is fairly stiff but not very tough. Antler bone, which is only one-third mineral, has mechanical properties that are very similar to those of cow leg bone when dry. When wet, however, which is its normal state in use, antler bone is half as stiff but nearly 10 times tougher. In contrast to both cow leg bone and antler bone, the ear bone (tympanic bulla) of a whale must be very massive and so contains a large proportion of mineral; consequently, it is very stiff but also rather brittle.

It could be argued that because antler bone is lost every year when the antlers are shed, it is less wasteful of metabolic energy to put less mineral into antlers. However, antlers still must be massive enough to win battles for their owner. A further optimization that comes into play was discovered by Andrew Kitchener when he was a Ph.D. student at the University of Reading, England. Each year the antlers that grow are closely matched to the body size and strength of their owner. This size matching and annual renewal allow safety margins to be cut to a minimum, with the result that about a third of antlers are broken, totally or partially, during fighting. That figure probably represents the largest fraction of antlers that can be broken without putting all stags at risk of having one antler broken (implying a breakage rate of 50%) and therefore being incapable of fighting. The design of antlers has evolved such that they can be as small, and therefore as cheap, as is safe for use in winning fights.

There is, nevertheless, an alternative strategy for the same problem. Antlers could be made so much more bulky that they would not be damaged and then would not need to be renewed each season, although they might still need to be repaired. This is approximately what horned animals such as antelope, sheep, and goats do. Horns are not shed every year, so the bony cores grow larger at the base as their owners increase in size. However, they then need a tough outer covering—keratinous "horn"—so that surface damage from previous fights does not weaken the bone.

JULIAN F.V. VINCENT is Codirector of the Centre for Biomimetics at the University of Reading, England.

(Overleaf) Illustration by Tim Jonke

(Left, top and bottom) The antlers of deer and the leg bones of cows are an example of optimization in biology. Each kind of bone achieves a balance between stiffness and toughness that is matched to its functions. Cow leg bone, which is half mineral, is fairly stiff but not very tough. Antler bone, only one-third mineral, is less than half as stiff but 10 times as tough when wet, its normal state in use. Antlers and the horns of such animals as goats (above) also show optimization at work. Antlers are renewed annually and closely matched to the size and strength of their owner; they have evolved to be as small and as cheap as is safe for use in winning fights. Horns represent an alternative solution to the same problem. Horns are so bulky that fighting rarely causes major damage; they thus do not need to be renewed each season.

Finding good answers

In contrast to biology, engineering and, to a lesser extent, chemistry and physics are concerned with finding answers to specific questions and turning them into technological solutions. If one wants to build a bridge, make a bulletproof vest, or fly through the air, the problem has been stated; the task is to find out how to do it. This is opposite to the logic of the biologist, but the nature of the question and answer can be very similar. The engineer must take into account a number of factors such as stiffness, toughness, stability, weight, and cost and find the best compromise. For example, a bulletproof vest has to stop a bullet, most effectively by being massive, but must still be light enough to wear. In this instance, since life is at stake, cost is not the limiting criterion that it might be with the construction of a building. Nor may weight be a limitation, since fear enhances strength. Such factors have to be balanced against each other to produce an optimized solution, the object being made.

Engineering and biology are related in that they each represent a half turn around a circle of the delineation of a practical problem and its op-

171

Early inventors' attempts to mimic nature retarded the development of flight. Flapping wings work with small objects like birds and model ornithopters but not with larger machines. The power requirement for flapping flight scales in a nonlinear way with size, setting an upper limit on both birds and aircraft.

timized solution. Whereas the limitations and optimizations are different in the two disciplines, there is nonetheless a strong symbiosis that, once experienced, seems totally logical and indissoluble. In using biology as a source of optimized solutions to problems, it is absolutely necessary to understand the biological system and what one wants to abstract from it; *i.e.*, a proper definition of the problem. It is deceptively easy to approach the biological system as if it were the ultimate solution and total arbiter of what can work. The biological system has limitations on factors—such as types of materials, ways of making materials, operating temperatures, and energy—that do not constrain technology and so is optimized in ways that may not be immediately apparent. It is therefore important to appreciate what the biological solution represents before attempting to exploit it.

An example is the development of flying machines. The attempt to mimic nature retarded the development of flight since flapping wings were widely seen as the most obvious source of propulsion. Although flapping wings work with small objects such as birds and model ornithopters, they fail with larger machines; the power requirement for flapping flight scales nonlinearly with size, putting an upper limit on the size of birds (the albatross does not flap its wings much) as much as on aircraft (the largest successful ornithopter is about the size of a goose). Manned flight therefore requires fixed wings and a separate source of power. It may well be, however, that some of the subtle aerodynamic tricks that birds and, more especially, insects use for increasing lift or reducing drag can be adapted for aircraft.

The world of biological materials

One of the first and most obvious characteristics of biological materials is the limited number of components from which they are made. For their

172

ceramics, most organisms use calcium salts, either as carbonate (chemically, chalk) or as a phosphate (hydroxyapatite). Silica (silicon dioxide) is sometimes used where high performance is needed; since the atoms in silica are much more tightly bonded, silica is stiffer and stronger. Biological fibers in animals are mostly collagen, a protein; in plants they are mostly cellulose, a sugar polymer (polysaccharide). Chitin, a polysaccharide fiber closely related to cellulose, also occurs in arthropods—insects, crabs, prawns, and spiders, for example—and in some plants and fungi. Other proteins commonly found as structural materials are the keratins. These are protein fibers formed within cells that become glued together and die, and they contribute to certain skin layers, nail, horn, hair, and feather. In total, nature probably has no more than two main types of ceramic, a single type of fibrous polysaccharide (cellulose and chitin count as one), four types of fibrous protein, a number of less well-defined, nonfibrous structural proteins, and several space-filling sugar polymers whose main function is to stabilize water and act as a

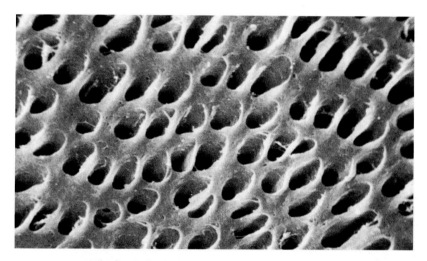

Biological materials are made of a strikingly limited number of components. Their variety and versatility in use lies largely in their form and structure at the molecular level. Dentine (top), the tissue that makes up the bulk of the tooth, is shown in a scanning electron micrograph (SEM). Like bone, dentine is made up mostly of calcium phosphate and collagen; it is more mineralized than bone, however, and thus is harder. In the living tooth the channels passing through the dentine carry projections from odontoblasts, the dentine-producing cells. Lamellae from compact bone of the thigh bone (bottom) appear in a false-color SEM. Bone lamellae are made of bundles of collagen fibers held together with polysaccharides. During bone formation cells called osteoblasts lay down a collagenous matrix in a layered form, which is then mineralized with calcium phosphate.

lubricant. Fatty molecules called lipids are also used, but as membranes for containing and organizing biochemically reactive components rather than in a structural role.

All of these components are manufactured, albeit slowly, at temperatures between −5° and 40° C (23° and 104° F) and at normal atmospheric pressure in a watery environment. With them are made the entire range of biological materials and structures seen in nature. Their variety and versatility in use lies largely in their form and structure at the molecular level. Given that animals and plants tend to minimize energy expenditure, whether that be in the form of synthesizing materials or controlling their shape, and to maximize performance, the conservative number of components found in biological materials implies that it is energetically expensive to acquire raw materials. This limitation may be determined by the direct energy needed for sequestering the materials or by the fact that it is cheapest to maintain the means of extracting only a few materials. Most structural raw materials used by living organisms

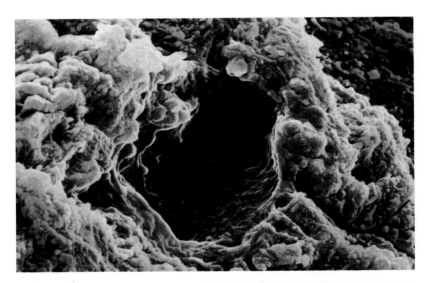

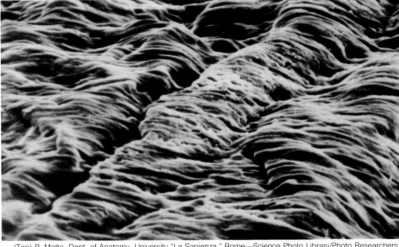

Nature probably uses no more than a single type of polysaccharide and four types of protein for its fibers. The intercellular matrix of cartilage tissue (top, shown in a false-color SEM) is composed mainly of fibers of collagen and elastin, both of which are proteins. The large cavity originally contained a cartilage cell, called a chondrocyte. (Bottom) Tightly grouped bundles of collagen fibers are visible in a false-color SEM of connective tissue. Where properties of strength and elasticity are required, as in the case of ligaments and tendons, the fibers are densely and regularly packed.

(Top) P. Motta, Dept. of Anatomy, University "La Sapienza," Rome—Science Photo Library/Photo Researchers; (bottom) CNRI/Science Photo Library/Photo Researchers, Inc.

(Top left and bottom) From J.F.V. Vincent and P. Owers (1986),
Journal of Zoology, London, reproduced by permission; (top right) L.L. Rue III—Bruce Coleman

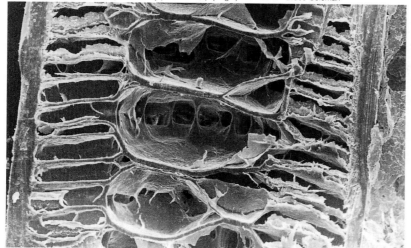

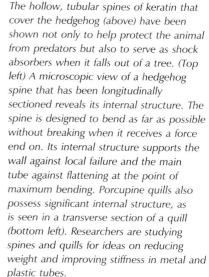

The hollow, tubular spines of keratin that cover the hedgehog (above) have been shown not only to help protect the animal from predators but also to serve as shock absorbers when it falls out of a tree. (Top left) A microscopic view of a hedgehog spine that has been longitudinally sectioned reveals its internal structure. The spine is designed to bend as far as possible without breaking when it receives a force end on. Its internal structure supports the wall against local failure and the main tube against flattening at the point of maximum bending. Porcupine quills also possess significant internal structure, as is seen in a transverse section of a quill (bottom left). Researchers are studying spines and quills for ideas on reducing weight and improving stiffness in metal and plastic tubes.

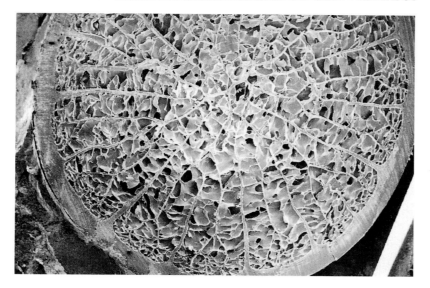

either are abundant in the surrounding environment (the geographic distribution of a plant or animal can be limited by the availability of raw material for making its skeleton; hence, snails are more common on chalk land) or are used very sparingly.

One way of putting a finger on the optimization of materials is to observe how well a material is put to use in a structure. For instance, work at the University of Reading by a student, Paul Owers, and me showed that the sharp hollow spines of keratin that cover the European hedgehog not only protect against attack from other animals but also serve as shock absorbers when the animal falls out of a tree. In either case the spines receive the force end on, resulting in elastic bending (Euler buckling). The spines are designed to bend as far as possible without breaking, having internal structures that support the wall of the tubular spine against local failure and support the main tube against flattening into an oval cross section at the point of maximum bending. Indeed, the

175

spine is so well made that it breaks only when the compressive strength of the keratin of the tube is exceeded.

In the design of their materials and structures, animals and plants demonstrate just the sort of optimization that modern engineers want to incorporate into their own new, efficient, lightweight designs. A large part of optimization involves not just choosing the right material for the job but also tailoring the material for a particular application and making the resulting structure as light as practicable. The impetus for the production of materials and structures using a biomimetic approach comes from the realization that increased efficiency, specialization, and optimization are common driving forces in both engineering and biology.

Compare the paucity of components for natural materials with the synthetic riches that human beings have available to them. At the latest count there were about 10 main types of ceramic, 15 types of plastic, and 10 types of fiber. For the most part these products of technology perform much better than the natural equivalents and function reliably at much higher temperatures. On the other hand, they are frequently toxic or involve toxic intermediate steps or solvents, and it takes high temperatures, pressures, or both and rather large amounts of energy to make them. The methods of synthesis currently used are often relatively uncontrolled, resulting in a more random molecular structure than may be desired. As scientists and engineers are now recognizing, nature can help solve problems in materials processing as well as design.

The artificial-silk road: a historical example

Materials and structures have frequently been derived by means of what is now called a biomimetic process. The best-known example is the long search for an artificial silk. The molecular structure of natural silk gives it an unusual combination of high strength and extensibility, which implies that it can absorb large amounts of mechanical energy before it breaks. Nearly 75% of this energy can be given off as heat when the silk thread stretches, making the thread very tough and durable. Modern uses for such a fiber include high-performance composites and lightweight body armor. Artificial silk is thus a useful material to aim for. The idea seems to have occurred first to the Chinese, the originators of the natural-silk industry, more than 2,000 years ago. It was revived by the English scientist Robert Hooke, who wrote in his *Micrographia* (1665) of the possibility of making "an artificial glutinous composition much resembling the substance out of which the silkworm wire-draws his clew."

The first attempts to make artificial silks involved natural polymers. Between 1855 and 1885 a number of English and French workers dissolved nitrocellulose (guncotton), a chemically modified form of cellulose, in mixtures of ether, acetic acid, and alcohol, sometimes adding caoutchouc, gelatin, or fish glue. At first they drew threads from the gummy mass; these were dried and wound on a spool. In 1862 the Frenchman Ozanam showed how a solution of real silk could be spun from orifices in the way that a spider spins from spinnerets and so invented spinning jets,

176

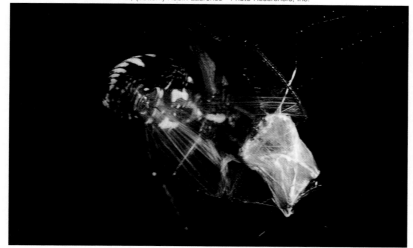

The best-known instance of the biomimetic process at work is the long search for an artificial silk. Natural silk (top), spun by spiders, caterpillars, and other animals, possesses an unusual combination of strength, toughness, and durability. These outstanding qualities were appreciated by people thousands of years ago, and their desirability in an artificial fiber (bottom) spurred the development of rayon and nylon in modern times. The very concept of, and inspiration for, artificial fibers was biomimetic since all fibers were products of nature.

although he never used them to spin artificial silks. Another Frenchman, Count Hilaire de Chardonnet, in 1885 manufactured the first practical artificial silk, rayon, by using a more complex mix of chemicals for spinning and then chemically removing the nitrate groups that made the material highly flammable. This left a rather degraded type of cellulose that was nevertheless strong and durable enough to be a commercial success. Cellulose-based fibers, however, are chemically different from silk, being polysaccharides rather than proteins, and do not possess even the potential for the extreme stiffness and strength of silk. Although fibers can be made from protein—one of the most successful was Aralac, made from casein, the protein in milk—none that have been made to date has the outstanding properties of natural silk.

The material that is most silklike in its properties, nylon, was the product of fundamental research by Wallace H. Carothers, a brilliant American organic chemist working at the Du Pont Co. In 1928, when polymers were not a favorite subject for study owing to their intractability,

177

Carothers realized that fiber-forming molecules need to be very long. He therefore took molecules that could react at both ends and made a polymer from which fibers could be pulled, eventually producing proteinlike molecules, polyamides, that were very silklike in their properties. The reasoning behind the production of this first truly synthetic fiber did not, as far as is known, rely on nature for details of the chemistry. Nevertheless, since all fibers were products of nature, the concept of, and inspiration for, an artificial fiber was biomimetic.

Far from its application as a fiber, nylon came to be used much more widely in the form of complex solid shapes. It is durable and, like silk, can be used in aqueous environments. Thus, the first synthetic biomimetic material found its most important use in machine bearings in environments that are too destructive for metals. By slight changes to its chemistry, different kinds of nylon can be made with different properties in the same way that animals can make different silks and collagens. Kevlar, a strong, tough aramid fiber, is a direct descendant of nylon with a structure at the molecular level that is even more silklike.

Biotechnology has opened up a new route to silk, that of using the spider's own genetic instructions. Of the several project teams around the world, the most advanced seems to be that headed by biochemist David L. Kaplan of the U.S. Army Research, Development and Engineering Center, Natick, Massachusetts. Although researchers still appear to be some way from producing a practical bioengineered silk, the journey toward the goal is proving interesting and educative and may well be more important than the goal itself. One particularly significant discovery is that the protein solution that forms natural silk is processed into an insoluble fiber only partly by the spinneret of a spider or silkworm. By the time the silk proteins are ready to be spun, they have already achieved a high degree of alignment by progressive loss of water and adoption of a liquid-crystalline phase, a state partway between the molecular chaos of liquids and the high ordering of crystals. This partial ordering reduces the energy required for spinning the fibers and may be important

A bullet that flattened while failing to penetrate a piece of fabric made with Kevlar demonstrates why the strong, tough synthetic fiber has found wide use in bullet-proof vests. A direct descendent of nylon, Kevlar has a structure at the molecular level that is even more silklike.

Du Pont Fibers

Heather Angel

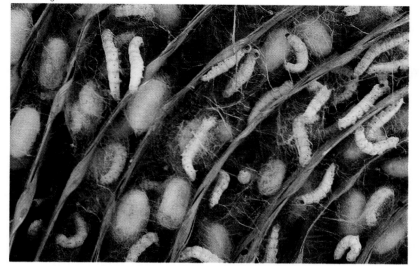

The path toward an artificial silk has taken researchers on a varied journey in the nearly three and a half centuries since Robert Hooke wondered about making "an artificial glutinous composition much resembling the substance out of which the silkworm wire-draws his clew" (left). In recent years biotechnology has opened up a new lane on the path to silk, and scientists are exploring the possibility of producing bioengineered silk using the genetic instructions of animals such as orb-weaving spiders (below). The journey may prove at least as useful as the goal, for the knowledge gained in unlocking the silk-making secrets of spiders and silkworms will likely be important in inspiring novel molecular design and processing methods for existing fibers.

in producing a fiber with fewer defects due to inclusions of "foreign" molecules or due to bad molecular alignment. By chance, or perhaps because it is silklike and stiff, Kevlar also passes through a liquid-crystalline phase before spinning. An advantage of silk is the benignity of the processing reagents—Kevlar is spun from concentrated sulfuric acid—but a disadvantage of silk will be the expense of producing it in commercial quantities. It seems likely that biomimicry of silk will be more important in inspiring novel molecular design and processing methods for existing fibers than in generating entirely new types of fiber.

Once it has been accepted that nature provides paradigms for technology, it makes sense to categorize the different routes by which those paradigms can be used in order to understand their strengths and weaknesses. These routes vary from the complete mimicry of a natural material or structure to simple inspiration.

Total and partial mimicry

Total mimicry involves the production of a chemical, material, or structure that is indistinguishable from the natural product. The greatest successes in total mimicry to date have been achieved through the use of biotechnology; for instance, the manufacture of real human insulin in genetically engineered bacteria. Although this approach uses state-of-the-art technology, it can be very expensive and time-consuming and necessarily incorporates the weaknesses as well as the strengths of the natural material. There are still uses for it, however. For example, bacterial cellulose, which is much finer and purer than that obtained from plants, has found application in high-quality cones for miniature loudspeakers.

Partial mimicry leads to the production of a modified version of a biological material; for instance, the early attempts to make silklike fibers from cellulose. The final product, however, does not even need to be made of materials of biological origin. Probably the best example to date

Laura Riley—Bruce Coleman Inc.

179

is provided by Dan W. Urry, a biophysicist at the University of Alabama at Birmingham, who has produced a molecular model of the rubbery protein elastin, a component of skin, blood vessel walls, ligaments, and many other tissues. The most spectacular example of elastin is the nuchal ligament of grazing animals, which runs from the spines between the shoulders to the back of the head. This strong elastic band counterbalances the weight of the head and neck, rather in the manner of a spring-balanced overhead garage door. The animal can raise and lower its head, alternately looking for predators and grazing, with the minimum of muscular energy.

Many molecular mechanisms had been proposed for elastin. The main problem had been to reconcile the fact that elastin appears fibrous in the electron microscope and has defined molecular structures, both of which features suggest a semicrystalline and ordered structure, with other data suggesting rubbery elastic mechanisms that can be achieved only by materials having molecular disorder. Urry overcame this problem by proposing an open-coiled coil structure, which will form fibers yet will exhibit rubbery characteristics because the structure is so open. The reality of his hypothesis has been supported by exhaustive chemical and physical analysis and modeling. The elastic properties reside primarily in the rotational freedom of the bonds in a structural feature of proteins called the beta-turn, the so-called librational entropy mechanism. This freedom of rotation is assured by the hydrophobic nature of the protein and the large amount of water entrained, which together keep the structure open.

Urry has made a family of protein models of elastin based on a repeating series of five amino acids (the molecular building blocks of proteins): valine-proline-glycine-valine-glycine, or VPGVG. He makes this pentapeptide using conventional synthetic chemistry, which is cheaper and more reliable than a biotechnological approach using microorganisms. The pen-

University of Alabama biophysicist Dan W. Urry produced the sheet of transparent rubbery material shown (right) from poly(VPGVG) by irradiation with gamma rays, which cross-linked the polymer's structure. Urry has made a family of protein models of the natural protein elastin by synthesizing the pentapeptide valine-proline-glycine-valine-glycine (VPGVG) and then polymerizing it. (Opposite page) Four tubular constructs made by Urry comprise different gamma-ray–cross-linked and plastic protein-based polymers.

Dan W. Urry, School of Medicine, University of Alabama at Birmingham

Dan W. Urry, School of Medicine, University of Alabama at Birmingham

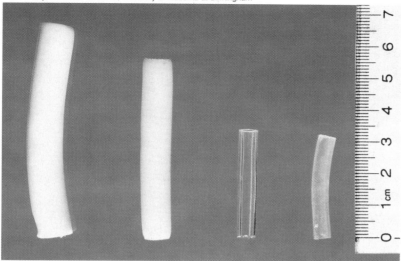

tapeptides are then polymerized into long molecular chains, producing poly(VPGVG) dispersed in solution with the chains extended. When the temperature of this essentially hydrophobic material is raised, it undergoes a reversible transition into the more ordered open-coiled structure typical of elastin. Also like elastin, if this coiled structure is cross-linked (by being bombarded with gamma rays), the result is a material having nearly perfect rubberlike properties.

During the transition from extended to ordered state, the poly(VPGVG) contracts, doing mechanical work. The temperature range over which this transition occurs can be varied from 0° to 60° C (32° to 140° F) by slight variations in the chemistry: the more hydrophobic the polymer, the lower the transition temperature. Poly(VPGVG) can also convert changes in pH (acidity or alkalinity), pressure, salt concentration, or electrical energy into mechanical work, yielding what might be considered a whole family of molecular engines. Potential applications range from medical uses—Urry suggests fashioning tiny capsules of the material that slowly squeeze out drugs at specific sites in the body—to entirely artificial machines. Like elastin, which can last for many decades in the human body, poly(VPGVG) is remarkably stable and durable.

Nonbiological analogues

Nonbiological analogues are functional mimics of biological materials. For instance, the natural and artificial minerals known as zeolites have a crystalline framework riddled with microscopic pores or channels. These pores can immobilize complex molecules and promote specific chemical changes to them. They are therefore rather like enzymes, which are proteins that serve to catalyze specific biochemical reactions. In the context of biological analogues, robots are also biomimetic since they imitate certain functions of a living organism.

Yet other examples are artificial joints and organs made from metals and plastics. Part of the problem with artificial replacements of

181

An SEM image of spruce wood shows wood to made up of tiny hollow tubes (large vertical structures in the image) whose walls comprise spirally wound microfibers. The microfibers, composed of cellulose, are held together by a glue of lignin, a phenolic polymer. When wood is pulled along the grain, the tubes are stretched and collapse inward; the constituent microfibers separate laterally, forming spiral splits in the tube (arrows), but remain unbroken along their lengths.

Thus, as wood is loaded toward its breaking point, it clicks and cracks as the tubes collapse, but it continues to support a load because the microfibers are intact. Because this toughening mechanism relies on the way the components are put together rather than on their chemistry, it can be reproduced with other materials.

natural body parts is their mechanical mismatch with the tissues into which they are introduced. For instance, no bone is as stiff as the metal rod that is the basis of the hip prosthesis, and the bone can be wrongly loaded and respond unpredictably, in extreme cases dissolving away and leaving a bigger problem than before. One goal in developing modern prostheses is to match them better mechanically with their biological environment.

Abstraction and inspiration

Abstraction, borrowing a structure or mechanism from a biological material for use in a totally different material, will probably turn out to be the most successful pathway to biomimicry. An excellent example is the identification by James E. Gordon and George Jeronimidis of the University of Reading of the main mechanism that gives wood its toughness. Wood is made of large numbers of tiny hollow tubes whose walls are composed of spirally wound microfibers of cellulose. The microfibers are held together by a glue of lignin, a brittle phenolic polymer. When wood is pulled along the grain, these tubes are stretched and collapse inward, absorbing energy; the constituent microfibers separate laterally as the lignin breaks but remain unbroken along their length. Thus, when wood is loaded toward its breaking point, it clicks and crackles as the tubes collapse but continues to support the load because the microfibers are intact. As long as the wood is making noise—sometimes referred to as talking—it is safe; *i.e.*, it is still absorbing energy. Wood is dangerous only when silent, which happens when there are no more tubes to collapse and total failure is imminent. The force-deflection curve of wood under load looks very much like that of a ductile metal with yield and post-yield plasticity. Hence, nature can mimic the properties of metal in a much lighter material.

Because this toughening mechanism for wood relies on the way the components are put together rather than on their chemistry, it can be reproduced with other materials. A simple way to mimic the mechanism is by means of tubes made of glass fibers wound around a nylon monofilament one millimeter (0.04 inch) in diameter, which is then removed. The tubes are then glued together in quantity to make the mimetic material. Although the tubes are about 10 times larger than those in wood, the fracture mechanism is the same. And as with real wood, one can drive a nail or screw through the mimetic wood, an impossible task with a solid fiber-composite material.

Using glass-fiber-reinforced resin as the material, Gordon and Jeronimidis devised another wood analogue that looks somewhat like corrugated cardboard and can be made with the same machinery. When two corrugated layers of the material are glued together such that the troughs of one layer are stuck to the peaks of the next, the result looks like a row of tubes. The spiral winding of the tube walls in wood is modeled by fibers arranged in the layers so that they run at an angle to the corrugations. This structure effectively reproduces the fracture mechanism of wood. Under impact it is, weight for weight, the toughest artificial material known.

Inspiration is rather like abstraction, but the route to expression may be more convoluted. A famous example is the design of the roof of the glass-and-iron Crystal Palace at the Great Exhibition in London in 1851, which the English gardener-turned-architect Joseph Paxton based on the large floating leaves of the *Victoria* water lily of South America.

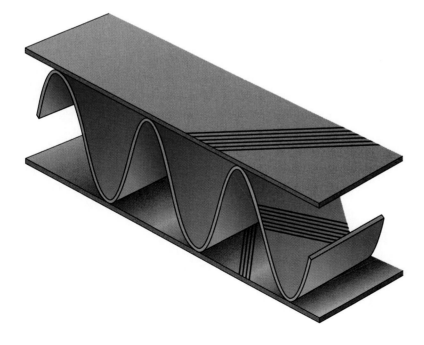

Resembling corrugated cardboard, a wood analogue devised by James E. Gordon and George Jeronimidis of the University of Reading effectively reproduces the toughening mechanism of real wood. Each layer of the structure, made of glass-fiber-reinforced resin, is positioned such that its fibers are oriented as shown. The overall structure reproduces the tubes found in wood, while the fibers, in running at an angle to the corrugations, model the spiral winding of the tube walls.

Georges de Mestral, a Frenchman, contributed the hook-and-loop fastening system known as Velcro, inspired by the hooked seeds that adhered to the coat of his dog. Another French contribution was the Eiffel Tower designed by civil engineer Gustave Eiffel for France's Centennial Exposition of 1889. Eiffel was inspired by the work of the Swiss engineer and mathematician Carl Culmann on the bony internal architecture of the head of the human femur, or thigh bone.

Nanotechnology

Nanotechnology is the manipulation and arrangement of materials at a nanometer, and therefore a molecular, scale of size. (A nanometer is a billionth of a meter.) This comparatively recent endeavor, which aims to construct materials from the bottom up, molecule by molecule or even atom by atom, is also profiting from mechanisms of nature—in two dimensions, for example, in the production of oriented molecular layers on substrates of liquids or solids, and in three dimensions, for example, in the production of molecules, mainly proteins, having specific shapes. This approach to biomimicry will lead to advantages in the control of structural hierarchy and the production of much more versatile materials in the same way that, from relatively limited or simple chemistry, nature can make a wide variety of materials. The mechanical properties of many materials, especially their fracture properties, are strongly dependent on the size of their component particles. One of the basic reasons that biological ceramic composites such as bone, shell, and mother-of-pearl are so durable is that the ceramic particles are very small and isolated from each other in a protein matrix and therefore less likely to break. They are nanocomposites; that is, composites made of nanometer-sized components.

Pursuing this idea, Stephen Mann of the University of Bath, England, has been studying ways of controlling the size of crystals formed from

False-color SEMs compare a barb on the surface of a hooked seed of goosegrass snagged on a strand of wool (left) and the hook-and-loop components of Velcro (right), the fastening system inspired by the hooked seed.

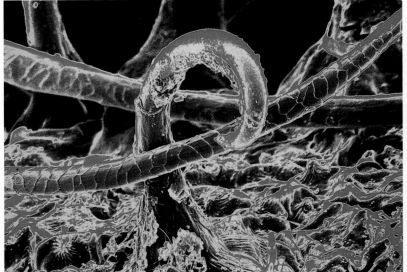
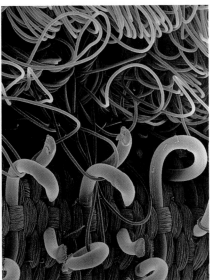

Photos, Science Photo Library/Photo Researchers, Inc.; (left) Jeremy Burgess

solution, a necessary step in the production of the tough ceramics at which nature excels. He and Paul Calvert of the University of Arizona are developing routes to making nanocomposites that might resemble mother-of-pearl. The nanotechnological approach may also give technology and industry more freedom to choose nonpolluting routes for making materials without limiting the types of material produced. Furthermore, by affording better control of synthesis (delivering the molecular components to the right place at the right time and in the right amount), it may reduce the energy required for making the materials.

Toward "smart" materials and structures

Biomimicry is leading not only toward materials that perform better mechanically but also toward those that can react in some way to their environment. This concept has been called "intelligence" in a material, and such materials and associated structures are also called "smart." A simple example is given by the skin's connective tissue layer, the dermis, which is made of collagen fibers arranged more-or-less randomly in a sheet of so-called ground substance, a complex mixture of proteins and polysaccharides.

In 1981 Peter Purslow, working at the University of Reading, showed that when a crack or notch spreads in a sheet of soft fibrous material, the constituent fibers can become reoriented across the tip of the notch simply because the material stretches more in this area. One can get an idea of this by cutting a slit in a sheet of rubber; for instance, a piece of uninflated party balloon. If one stretches the sheet, it deforms more where the slit has weakened it. Using large-angle X-ray diffraction, Purslow measured the degree of orientation of collagen fibers around a slit made in a sheet of the middle layer, or media, of a pig's aorta that was being stretched in two directions at once. The collagen reoriented across the path of the crack at its tip, effectively stopping it. The reorientation is very local; if the media is stretched by 30%, the reorientation extends a distance of only 0.5 millimeter (0.02 inch) from the tip of a five-millimeter (0.2-inch) crack. Since the reorientation is a direct result of the damage, it follows that it constitutes an automatic response of the material to wounding.

Exactly the same response has been observed, qualitatively, in thin sheets of cartilage, which like dermis is made of collagen fibers in a ground substance. When polarized light is shone through the cartilage, the reorientation of collagen at the tip of the notch is easily seen, as are the strands of collagen pulled from the torn surface. The response of skin and cartilage to damage could be called intelligent in that further damage is thereby inhibited. It appears that the reorientation effect occurs in any soft collagenous composite.

A biological material in a living organism can also be remodeled or modify itself structurally in response to environmental stresses. The transduction between deformation of the material and cellular response is usually thought to occur as a result of piezoelectric properties of a component of the material. So, if the material is being deformed, the

185

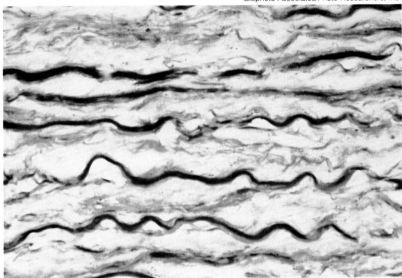

A micrograph of a section of aorta reveals its fibrous structure. Research by Peter Purslow at the University of Reading showed that when a slit was made in a sheet of the middle layer (media) of a pig's aorta and the sheet was stretched, the collagen fibers in the tissue oriented across the path of the slit, effectively stopping it from spreading. Such an automatic response of a material to damage could be called intelligent in that the response serves to inhibit further damage.

piezoelectric effect will cause the generation of a small electric potential, which can be detected by the cells responsible for synthesizing the material. For example, collagen is piezoelectric (although only weakly so when wet), so the osteocytes—the cells that make bone and are embedded within it—may be able to detect whether the bone is being bent or being loaded off-center, as might happen if a broken bone does not join properly in line. The bone can then be remodeled to give the proper shape.

Claus Mattheck, a materials scientist at the Institute for Nuclear Research, Karlsruhe, Germany, has applied computer analysis to a number of biological shapes, mainly trees, and has shown that they conform to two general design principles—they have sufficient strength for all relevant instances of loading, and they are of minimum weight for the job they do. This is elegant structural optimization, in many instances achieved by means of subtle changes to the shape and radiusing of joints. The net effect of a such mechanism is to cause more material to be deposited in areas of greater load.

This process is the very opposite of what occurs in a conventional structure built from passive inorganic components—a loaded spring corrodes much more quickly than a nonloaded one. Such stress corrosion always guarantees that the most highly stressed places are the first ones to break. By contrast, a smart technological material would act like living bone or wood by reinforcing itself with additional material in highly stressed areas. This kind of ability would allow the development of self-designing and self-repairing structures. For example, an engineer might make a wire-frame representation of the desired structure, load it in the way that it is expected to be loaded in use, and allow it to accrete material where stresses are greatest until all stresses in the structure are evenly distributed. Something along these lines is being tried in an effort to produce self-building structures in the sea; calcium salts are made to precipitate on various materials that are connected to the negative terminal of a small battery. If the distribution of electric charge could be controlled by strain detectors sensing local loads, then a self-designing structure would be possible.

Some modern architects envision smart buildings that will be able to change the shape and loading of their structures on a short time scale. Rather than supporting loads from various directions by virtue of additional mass and stability—the solution chosen by the builders of cathedrals—a smart building will reshape itself to accommodate the forces acting on it. This, of course, is what animals and plants do all the time, supporting loads much more cheaply than can current technology. Imagine, instead of a passive monolithic structure, a house supported in a web of tensile elements that can adjust their forces individually in response to changing external stresses—the way the muscles in a person's arm tense or relax according to the weight being held in an outstretched hand.

The ultimate in biomimicry will involve not just materials and structures but also control mechanisms. A young animal must learn how to integrate with its environment, partly because it cannot guarantee the environment into which it is born and partly because no two animals are the same shape and size. Turning this observation around, one may state that if a control system is provided with the ability to adapt, say, through a computer-based learning system, then it can not only learn particular tasks but also learn how to do those tasks with the particular set of hardware that it is controlling. This then releases the hardware, *i.e.*, the machinery, from constraints such as precise angles of movement, precise sizes and lengths, and even the precise stiffness or load-bearing capacity of components. The only critical parts are bearings and joints and sensor-actuator systems. With hardware constraints removed, many of the requirements for precise dimensions and quality control are relaxed, reducing costs. The machine will learn how to be accurate rather than needing accuracy built in.

Although newly named, biomimicry is an old concept made practicable by modern methods of science and technology. With the coming 21st century being widely hailed as the century of materials, the study of biological materials and structures is set to increase in importance and influence. To paraphrase Penrose, "Biology is the basic science. Materials science is just a special case."

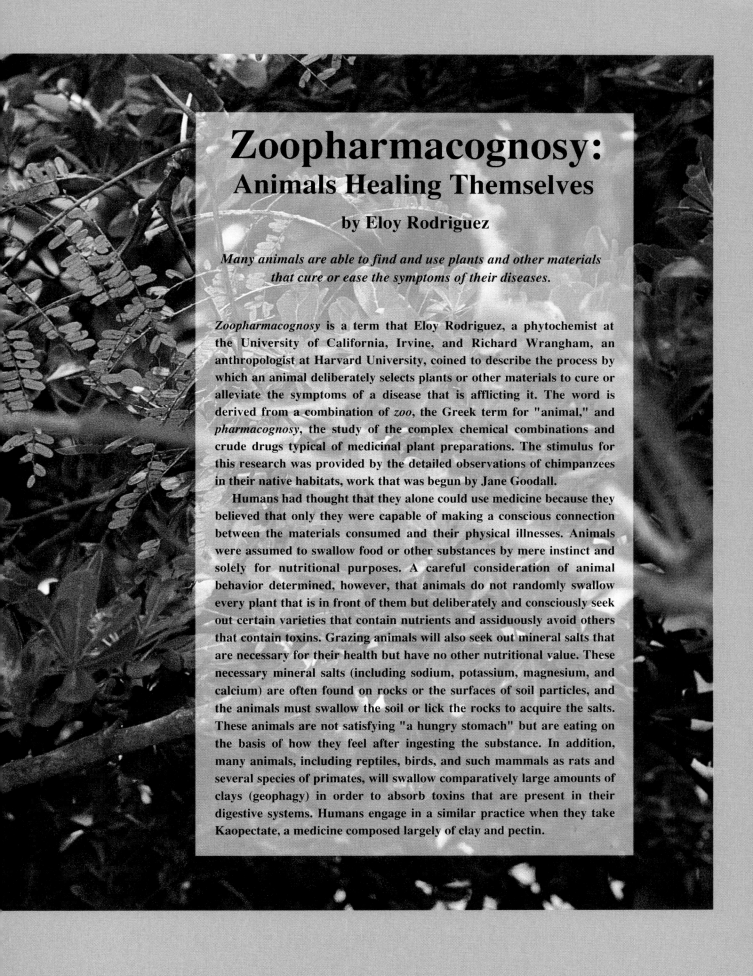

Zoopharmacognosy:
Animals Healing Themselves

by Eloy Rodriguez

Many animals are able to find and use plants and other materials that cure or ease the symptoms of their diseases.

Zoopharmacognosy is a term that Eloy Rodriguez, a phytochemist at the University of California, Irvine, and Richard Wrangham, an anthropologist at Harvard University, coined to describe the process by which an animal deliberately selects plants or other materials to cure or alleviate the symptoms of a disease that is afflicting it. The word is derived from a combination of *zoo*, the Greek term for "animal," and *pharmacognosy*, the study of the complex chemical combinations and crude drugs typical of medicinal plant preparations. The stimulus for this research was provided by the detailed observations of chimpanzees in their native habitats, work that was begun by Jane Goodall.

Humans had thought that they alone could use medicine because they believed that only they were capable of making a conscious connection between the materials consumed and their physical illnesses. Animals were assumed to swallow food or other substances by mere instinct and solely for nutritional purposes. A careful consideration of animal behavior determined, however, that animals do not randomly swallow every plant that is in front of them but deliberately and consciously seek out certain varieties that contain nutrients and assiduously avoid others that contain toxins. Grazing animals will also seek out mineral salts that are necessary for their health but have no other nutritional value. These necessary mineral salts (including sodium, potassium, magnesium, and calcium) are often found on rocks or the surfaces of soil particles, and the animals must swallow the soil or lick the rocks to acquire the salts. These animals are not satisfying "a hungry stomach" but are eating on the basis of how they feel after ingesting the substance. In addition, many animals, including reptiles, birds, and such mammals as rats and several species of primates, will swallow comparatively large amounts of clays (geophagy) in order to absorb toxins that are present in their digestive systems. Humans engage in a similar practice when they take Kaopectate, a medicine composed largely of clay and pectin.

ELOY RODRIGUEZ is a Professor and Research Scientist at the University of California, Irvine.

Cats will seek out catnip for effects that have nothing to do with nutrition. Dogs and cats are commonly observed to eat grass to induce vomiting to rid themselves of something irritating their stomachs. European starlings engaged in the process of building nests do not collect plants at random but select plant materials for their nests that will suppress the external parasites such as body lice that infest starling nests.

The largest number of reports of animal consumption of plants for medicinal purposes have postulated that the animals are attempting to rid themselves of intestinal parasites. Virtually all animals in warm, humid climates are infested by one or more species of parasitic roundworms, flatworms, or protozoans that can on occasion cause considerable distress to the animal. Daniel H. Janzen, a biologist at the University of Pennsylvania, wrote a paper in 1978 in which he discussed a series of accounts by naturalists describing how animals such as elephants, bison, monkeys, tigers, and bears apparently ingest plants that will rid them of intestinal parasites.

Medicines used by chimpanzees

The recent work on zoopharmacognosy of mammals has centered on two areas, medicinal plant consumption by chimpanzees and fur rubbing of plant gums (exudates) by primates and carnivores. In regard to the first, the investigations of the primatology groups at Harvard and Kyoto (Japan) universities identified a number of plants consumed by chimpanzees for medicinal properties. Several laboratories, most notably the Laboratory of Phytochemistry and Toxicology at the University of California, Irvine, extracted and identified compounds with potent antibiotic activity, some of the compounds being new to science. A partial listing of these plants is given in Table I; subsequent research has indicated that many other plants are probably consumed for medicinal purposes.

Table I. Chimpanzee Plant Medicine		
Plant	Plant part	Presumed medicinal compound
Ficus exasperata	young leaves	furanocoumarins
Rubia cordifolia	young leaves	cyclic peptides
Aspilia mossambicensis	young leaves	thiarubrines
Vernonia amygdalina	pith	steroidal glycosides, sesquiterpene lactones

The attention of the anthropologists Richard Wrangham of Harvard University and Toshisada Nishida of Kyoto University was drawn in 1983 to the highly unusual way that chimpanzees of Mahale Mountains National Park, Tanzania, consume the leaves of a particular shrub, *Aspilia mossambicensis*. First, individual leaves are selected more slowly and

190

Zebras savor a salt lick in Africa. Grazing animals seek out mineral salts that have no nutritional value but are necessary for their health.

A rhesus monkey (below) digs and eats soil at a cave in Puerto Rico. (Right) At a clay lick in Peru, macaws eat clay as a mineral supplement to detoxify seeds. Edible clay is gathered from a site in Sardinia (bottom right). Many animals eat soil and clays in order to absorb toxins present in their digestive systems.

European starlings (above) select materials for their nests that suppress parasites such as body lice that can infest starling nests. Cats eat grass (above right) to induce vomiting that will rid them of stomach irritants. The hoatzin (below) harbors few parasites or disease-causing bacteria. Its diet is 95% leaves.

carefully than normal, and only young leaves are eaten. Each leaf that is selected is held in the mouth for several seconds while it is rolled around by the tongue; leaves are difficult to swallow because they are covered with bristly hair and have rough surfaces. The median rate of leaf consumption was 5 per minute, compared with 37 when chimpanzees ate the leaves of *Mellera lobulata,* a shrub with leaves of similar size that are collected and chewed for nutritional purposes. Second, the leaves are not chewed and can be recovered intact in the feces. Third, chimpanzees tend to select *Aspilia* leaves within an hour of leaving their sleeping nests, before their first big meal, and presumably when their stomachs are empty and the postulated medicinal compounds would not be diluted by large volumes of food. Fourth, although all individuals at least two years old occasionally eat these leaves, the sexes do differ in frequency. Females selected *Aspilia* leaves significantly more often than did males.

Several other observations support the fact that *Aspilia* leaves are not eaten for nutritional purposes. First, on some days chimpanzees make special journeys, which may be short or long, to obtain only those specific leaves. Yet on other days they do not forage for *Aspilia* even when fresh leaf is abundant close to the nest site.

The supposition that chimpanzees might be consuming *Aspilia* leaves for medicinal purposes leads to the question: what disease or illness are the chimpanzees treating? Fecal examinations have shown that the digestive tracts of wild chimpanzees are affected by a variety of parasites, mainly several species of roundworms.

Medicinal properties of thiarubrine A

These observations of chimpanzee feeding behavior prompted Wrangham and Nishida to collect leaves of *Aspilia* plants and send them to the research facilities of the University of California at Irvine for chemical

192

Aspilia *plants, members of the sunflower family, have long been used as folk medicines in Tanzania. Chimpanzees eat one* Aspilia *leaf at a time, swallowing it whole rather than chewing it. The leaf then ruptures during digestion, presumably enabling the animal to extract the right amount of thiarubrine A. This sulfur-containing oil kills disease-causing bacteria, fungi, and parasitic worms.*

analysis. A chemical extraction of the plant material (leaves) yielded several chemical compounds, one of them being thiarubrine A, an antibiotic that is intensely red and unstable in the presence of light. In vitro experiments established that a solution of 10 micrograms per milliliter of thiarubrine A is extremely toxic to a roundworm closely related to those that infest humans and chimpanzees. Similar toxicity was observed in laboratory studies with two other species of roundworms, *Caenorhabitis elegans* and *Trichostrongyloides columbiformis.*

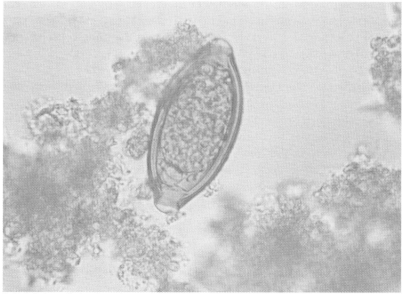

The whipworm (left) and hookworm (below) are among the most common parasites of chimpanzees.

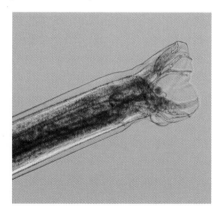

Red extract of Aspilia mossambicensis *leaves, in beaker, contains the anitbiotic thiarubrine A, which is extremely toxic to a roundworm that is closely related to those that infest humans and chimpanzees. Experiments have revealed that doses of thiarubrine, such as those obtained from eating 30–100 leaves at one sitting, are not harmful to chimpanzees.*

Follow-up experiments were conducted to establish the toxicity of these compounds to mammals. To be effective as a medicine, a chemical compound must be more toxic to the parasite than it is to the animal or person swallowing it. Injections of thiarubrine A into the peritoneal cavity of mice established that doses below 15 milligrams per kilogram were tolerated and caused no significant damage to the major organs of mice. These figures suggest that a chimpanzee that weighs 40 kilograms (88 pounds) could presumably consume 3,000 leaves without any significant toxicity problems from the thiarubrine (one leaf contains approximately 100 micrograms of thiarubrine). Wrangham and Nishida reported that 30–100 leaves are consumed in one sitting; no toxicity from thiarubrine should be expected at that dosage. In contrast, the same concentration of thiarubrine should be toxic to all the roundworms that would infest the intestine of the chimpanzee.

The fact that chimpanzees carefully swallow the leaves of *Aspilia* without chewing is significant. Any chewing would destroy the leaf structures that contain the thiarubrine and release it into the highly acidic digestive fluids of the stomach, where it would be destroyed. It appears that the intact leaf protects the thiarubrine and acts as a delivery vehicle that enables sufficient antibiotic to survive passage through the stomach. The greatest number of parasitic worms are found in the small intestine, so it is critical that the antibiotic be released there and not in the stomach. Chewing would also release any bitter compounds present in the leaf, and this would probably be unpleasant to the chimpanzee. When humans swallow medicine, they generally attempt to swallow it quickly without chewing because most pharmaceutically active chemicals have a bitter, unpleasant taste.

194

Adult male chimpanzee (left) prepares to swallow a Commelina leaf in the same way that it would ingest an Aspilia leaf. As with Aspilia leaves, the Commelina leaves are not chewed and pass intact through the chimpanzee's digestive tract (below). For Aspilia leaves, chewing would destroy the leaf structures that contain the thiarubrine, releasing it into the acidic digestive fluids of the stomach, where it would be destroyed.

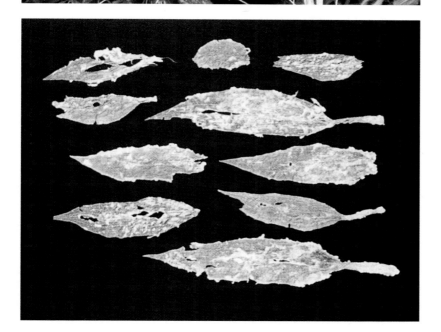

Other medicinal plants

The possibility that another shrub, *Veronia amygdalina* (bitter leaf), could have possible medicinal value to chimpanzees was suggested in 1989 after the observations of an ailing chimpanzee at Mahale by the anthropologists Michael A. Huffman and Mohamedi Seifu. A female chimpanzee meticulously removed the leaves and outer bark from several young shoots and chewed on the exposed pith, sucking out only the

Adult female howling monkey feeds on fig leaves, swallowing them unchewed. Analyses of these leaves reveal that they contain 5 methoxypsoralen, a compound used to treat several human illnesses.

extremely bitter juice. Within 24 hours the anthropologists observed that the chimpanzee had fully recovered from its lack of appetite, malaise, and constipation. A similar incident was observed two years later; in this case the anthropologists collected the feces and observed a decline in the number of parasites in the chimpanzee. Among many African peoples, *Veronia* is used to treat stomachaches and intestinal parasites. Huffman and Nishida reasoned that the presence of medicinal compounds in the pith, the low frequency of ingestion, the association of use with illness, and the uncommmonly bitter taste of *Veronia* leaves suggest that the nutritional value for chimpanzees is not likely to be significant when compared with its medicinal effect.

The fact that the chimpanzees carefully select the pith of the stem and deliberately reject other parts of the plant is significant. The leaf and the bark contain most of nutrients and larger amounts of several toxic compounds (sesquiterpene lactones) that could have harmful effects on the health of the chimpanzees. In contrast, the pith has little nutritional value, but it has only a small quantity of the toxic compounds and a relatively larger amount of a different class of compounds (the steroidal glycosides) that are much less toxic to the chimpanzees. These relatively nontoxic compounds have been shown in laboratory tests to suppress parasites such as *Schistosoma* that infect chimpanzees.

Four species of *Ficus* (figs) were investigated for biological activities. Chimpanzees were observed to consume leaves of *Ficus exasperata* in a medicinal manner; the young leaves were carefully selected and then swallowed early in the morning without being chewed. Separation of the constituents in the Laboratory of Phytochemistry and Toxicology at the University of California, Irvine, led to the purification and isolation of a 5 methoxypsoralen, a compound with previously described medicinal properties used to treat several illnesses.

Leaves of Rubia cordifolia *are swallowed whole by chimpanzees in Uganda. Plant material of this species was found to contain several medicinal compounds, some of which may have therapeutic value for human cancer patients.*

Female Kodiak bear (above left) smells and tastes the root of Ligusticum porteri *(above). After chewing the root, the bear puts the paste back on its paws and rubs the paste on its fur (left). One explanation of this behavior is that the paste repels or kills such pests as lice, ticks, and mosquitoes; it also might help prevent fungal and bacterial infections of the skin.*

Another plant swallowed whole by chimpanzees in Uganda that was suspected to be of medicinal value is *Rubia cordifolia;* the genus *Rubia* contains several species that are used extensively in the folk medicine of Africa and Asia. Plant material of this species was collected and was found to contain several medicinal compounds, including anthraquinones and a cyclic hexapeptide that were being investigated by the U.S. National Institutes of Health as therapeutic agents for cancer patients.

Wrangham observed chimpanzees consuming several other plants that are suspected of having medicinal properties. Preliminary studies with

197

Muriqui monkeys in Brazil eat 17 different plants that humans in the area use to control parasites. Female muriquis consume several species of legumes that contain chemicals which increase fertility.

Aneilema aequinoctiale indicate the presence of an antibiotic agent that is being studied; other species that are reported to be used as "medicines" by chimpanzees in Mahale and in Kibale, Uganda, include *Lippia plicata* and *Hibiscus aponeurus*. Medicinal plants are also being recorded at new chimpanzee study sites such as Lope, Gabon, and also through long-term observation. Studies of these species have just begun but are expected to lead to the discovery of new antibiotic compounds.

Fur-rubbing behavior

Research has recently begun to investigate the chemistry of plant products that animals rub into their fur. This fur-rubbing phenomenon occurs in several mammals and is yet unexplained. The fact that nothing is eaten obviously excludes the possibility that the animals are consuming these plant products for nutritional purposes.

One likely explanation of the fur-rubbing behavior is that it repels or kills external parasites such as lice, ticks, or mosquitoes; a similar procedure is practiced by birds and is termed "anting." The chemicals rubbed

Table II. Fur-Rubbing Animals		
Animal	Plant	Plant part
Coati	*Trattinnickia aspera*	resin
Bear	*Ligusticum wallichii*	root
Capuchin monkey	*Hymenaea courbaril*	trunk exudate
	Piper	
	Dieffenbachia longispatha	leaves
	Eugenia nesiotica	fruit
	Tetrathylacium johansenii	fruit
	Protium	fruit
	Virola surinamensis	fruit

into the fur could also stop or prevent fungal or bacterial infections of the skin. However, at this time researchers cannot exclude the possibility that the peculiar odor of the plant product might serve as a repellent or attractant to communicate with members of the same species.

Table II lists some of the species of plants that have been reported to be used in this peculiar behavior. The plants used by the capuchin monkey include groups that contain many volatile terpenes (*Eugenia, Protium, Virola*) and bioactive alkaloids (*Piper and Virola*). *Ligusticum* has been used by several human groups in North America, and *Trattinnickia* is in a family (Burseraceae) that has been used medicinally by many indigenous cultures.

Future prospects

Public interest in the discovery of new medicinal products from plants has increased noticeably, mainly as a result of the AIDS epidemic and the

Tropical rain forests, the source of many medicines used today and perhaps containing undiscovered medicinal compounds, are being destroyed at a rapid rate (left). Also disappearing are the human cultures that have existed in these forests. Among them are the Machiguenga of the Amazon basin in Peru; a chief of the tribe offers traditional herbal remedies (below).

increase in diseases resistant to conventional antibiotics. Accompanying this interest has been the outcry of scientists who are observing the rapid destruction of the tropical rain forests. Plants and fungi in these and other regions have supplied human societies with the great majority of medicinal agents used today. However, sorting and testing the thousands of plants and fungi present in the tropics are overwhelming tasks. To simplify them, scientists have found it useful to examine the plants used by traditional cultures. Unfortunately, the cultures indigenous to the tropical rain forests are disappearing rapidly as their environment is destroyed and their members are incorporated into the prevailing culture. Zoopharmacognosy and the observation of animals that have coexisted and coevolved with the plants of the tropical rain forest open a new approach to help scientists select plants with medicinal properties. Zoopharmacognosy has also brought an increased understanding of the complexities of primate behavior and its similarities to human behavior.

199

Species That Need No Introduction

by Stuart L. Pimm

When species are brought into biological communities in which they have never been before, they can create enormous ecological and economic damage. Preventing unwanted introductions requires finding good answers to some basic questions, and even then the challenges are formidable.

Look outside. What birds do you see? Pigeons (descendants of the wild rock dove, *Columba livia*), house sparrows (*Passer domesticus*), and starlings (*Sturnus vulgaris*) will be common answers. In New Delhi, Honolulu, or Sydney, Australia, you could see common mynahs (*Acridotheres tristis*), and in Beijing (Peking), London, or Miami, Florida, you might find collared doves (*Streptopelia decaocto*). In general, if you live in or near a city almost anywhere in the world, the replies are likely to be similar. As ubiquitous as these species of birds will be the house mice (*Mus musculus*), brown rats (*Rattus norvegicus*), and German cockroaches (*Blattella germanica*) that are nearby, though more secretive and surely less welcome.

The explanation behind the consistency in answers is not that these species have spread widely on their own. We humans have been moving these and other species around the world for millennia. The New Yorkers of the 1890s who wanted the birds of Shakespeare in Central Park were merely following a long-established tradition when they introduced the starling to North America. The Romans may have taken the common pheasant (*Phasianus colchicus*) to Britain. In turn, Roman historians thought that the pheasant was taken to Europe from Asia by the Argonauts of 1300 BC returning from Colchis. Even today hunters demand exotic birds and mammals to shoot, anglers want challenging fish, and gardeners seek out novel and beautiful ornamental plants.

Not all introductions of species are deliberate. Rats of several species were stowaways on oceanic voyages, probably those of Columbus and certainly those of the Polynesians as they colonized Pacific islands. Infected humans took the human immunodeficiency virus, the virus that causes AIDS, from Africa to the rest of the world. In much the same way, early European colonists of the New World and the Pacific carried other sexually transmitted microbes, common cold viruses, smallpox virus, and a variety of other organisms to populations with no resistance to them.

Kudzu as a farm crop

The familiar sight of domestic pigeons in New York's Central Park (right) is duplicated in cities throughout the world— evidence that humans have been moving species of plants and animals around with them for millennia. (Below) During the post-Columbian era of European exploration and colonization the modern horse was introduced to the Americas and other new lands.

From an 18th-century manual, courtesy of the Bancroft Library, University of California, Berkeley

The Asian tiger mosquito (*Aedes albopictus*), a native of Japan and a potential carrier of serious diseases such as dengue, has been spreading through the U.S. Southeast and Midwest since its accidental importation, probably in old tires, in the mid-1980s.

While English garden birds in New York or New Zealand may be quaint curiosities, many introductions have been devastating. Human diseases are all-too-obvious examples, but the health of natural ecosystems has suffered as well. Zebra mussels (*Dreissena polymorpha*), likely taken to North America from Europe in ship ballast water, clog the inlets of power plants over an increasing portion of the drainage of the North American Great Lakes and Mississippi River. The Pacific island of Guam has lost almost all of its forest birds to an introduced tree snake, *Boiga irregularis*. (The snake is also aggressive and poisonous enough to hospitalize about 50 people a year on Guam.) Rats taken to oceanic islands eliminate the ground-nesting birds. Kudzu (*Pueraria lobata*), a vine introduced from Japan to the southeastern U.S. to stabilize steep banks of soil exposed by road construction, spreads up and over the native forest, choking it. In Australia introduced rabbits, currently estimated at 300 million, devour vast quantities of farm crops and indigenous vegetation, while alien plants such as India-rubber vine (*Cryptostegia grandiflora*), mimosa (*Mimosa pigra*), and water hyacinth (*Eichhornia crassipes*), many of them deliberately imported, threaten that country's native forest, rangeland, and wetland species. Introduced cacti in many parts of the world reduce productive rangeland to impenetrable, thorny bushland.

Ecological communities take millions of years to develop, often in isolation. The result is a rich and fragile patchwork of organisms. Guam once had, and Hawaii still has, distinct assemblages of plants and animals. Mix all the species, and many will not survive. Biological diversity drops. In the restaurant world a small handful of international fast-food chains have driven countless numbers of independent eateries out of

202

It is likely that zebra mussels (top) were introduced to eastern North America in the mid-1980s in discharged ballast water from ships arriving from Europe. In the absence of natural predators, the species has been expanding into the Great Lakes and Mississippi River basin. Their habit of clustering causes the animals to clog water-intake systems, necessitating costly cleaning operations. (Bottom) A worker uses a high-pressure water spray to scour zebra mussels from a screen house, part of the water-intake system of a Detroit Edison power plant in Monroe, Michigan.

STUART L. PIMM is Professor of Ecology in the Department of Zoology and the Graduate Program in Ecology, University of Tennessee, Knoxville.

(Page 201) Kudzu, a fast-growing vine native to Japan and China, blankets poles and trees south of Roanoke, Virginia (top). Introduced to the U.S. as a soil stabilizer and fodder crop (bottom), kudzu has become a pest in the Southeast wherever it has escaped from cultivation.
(Bottom) From Roland McKee and J.L. Stephens, Kudzu as a Farm Crop, USDA Farmer's Bulletin no. 23, October 1943; courtesy of the Botany Libraries, Harvard University; (top and background) photograph © Stephen J. Shaluta, Jr.— Dembinsky Photo Associates

business. Similarly, each country's special animals and plants may be replaced by the competitively superior sparrow, starling, rat, cockroach, and their plant equivalents. Hawaii, perhaps largely because of all the introduced species there, has lost a third of its bird species in the last century and suffers from the highest rates of species extinction across all its animal and plant groups.

Introduced species are a major cause of the accelerating loss of the Earth's biological diversity. We are becoming increasingly concerned with that loss. It is this diversity, for example, that provides us with the source of many of the effective drugs used in modern and traditional medicine. There is a real danger that the next apparently undistinguished plant to

More than a dozen species of prickly pear cactus (species of Opuntia*), which are native to the Americas, have become established in Australia. In the early 20th century O.* stricta, *known locally as the common pest pear, rendered vast tracts of Australian grazing land almost totally unproductive until its rampant growth was brought under biological control with the aid of a species of moth.*

be grazed to oblivion by feral pigs might have been the source of the next anticancer drug. Or it might have been the source of a gene that, bred into crop plants, would have conferred resistance to a mold or an insect pest. Biological diversity matters for these and myriad other reasons, as Harvard University ecologist Edward O. Wilson catalogs in his book *The Diversity of Life* (1992).

The problems associated with introduced species may well be multiplying. Faster and more frequent international travel makes accidental introductions more likely, and deliberate introductions continue to proliferate. They include potential introductions that are radically new, such as genetically engineered organisms, be they microbes, plants, or domestic animals.

Simply put, introduced species create enormous economic and ecological damage worldwide. Awareness is the first step toward preventing future catastrophes, and people today are more aware of the problems than in the past. Prior to landing at Honolulu International Airport, for example, aircraft passengers are now shown a short film warning them of the dangers of importing insect pests in fruit or flowers. Yet many species arrive in the cargo bays. The snake that destroyed Guam's birds has already turned up on the runways at Honolulu's airport. So far, those found have been dead; the live ones, of course, may have already slithered away. Many species continue to slip through the quarantine net. (Paradoxically, tourists' luggage is inspected when it leaves Hawaii, rather than on the way in, because Hawaii is now host to so many potential pests. The Mediterranean fruit fly [*Ceratitis capitata*] is one that California citrus growers, in particular, do not wish to see again in their state.)

Introduced wild pigs forage through the forests of Hawaii for food, contributing to the reduction of the Earth's biological diversity in the process. The ecological disruptions that such introductions can create increase the possibility that the next species devoured to extinction might well have been the source of a lifesaving drug or a beneficial gene.

Quarantine signs (top) became common highway sights in California in the 1980s when the Mediterranean fruit fly (bottom) reappeared in that state. The fly's potential for wreaking economic devastation on the citrus industry made it necessary to implement worldwide quarantine laws for regulating the transport of fruits between countries.

In preventing unwanted importations it would help to know exactly where to stretch the quarantine net. Knowing where, however, means finding answers to a number of questions. Which species travel? Where do they come from and where do they go? Can one predict which species will invade which communities? How fast will they spread? Some deliberately or accidentally introduced species that had been initially thought to be benign in fact turned out to be major destroyers of natural communities, whereas other introductions apparently had little effect. Can the progress of the introduction and its results be predicted, or can they only be described after the fact?

205

A researcher uses a plankton net to sample ballast water in the cargo hold of a bulk carrier. The particular hold being tested is about 20 meters (70 feet) deep and can hold more than 3,800 cubic meters (more than a million gallons) of water. A recent survey of the contents of ballast water transported from port to port in oceangoing ships identified the presence of hundreds of species of animals and plants across a broad range of taxonomic groups.

Which species travel?

From what has been observed to date, the answer to this question is "almost anything." We have deliberately introduced plants, insects and other invertebrates, fish, mammals, amphibians, lizards and snakes, and birds. We have even taken the organisms' diseases along with them. The virus rinderpest was introduced to Africa in 1889 in cattle taken there by the invading Italians. It devastated not only the introduced cattle and the indigenous cattle on which native peoples such as the Masai depended but also wild populations of wildebeest, zebra, buffalo, and giraffe. Those changes, in turn, effected major changes in vegetation across wide areas. Now, a century later, rinderpest continues to pose a threat to these and other species.

A recent study by James T. Carlton of Williams College, Williamstown, Massachusetts, and Jonathan B. Geller of the University of North Carolina at Wilmington shows just how broad a selection of plants and animals can be transported by just one mechanism, the ballast tanks of oceangoing ships. Oceangoing ships take on seawater as ballast in port and release it at subsequent ports of call. The water taken on in Japan and released in Oregon contained more than 360 species, among them crustaceans (including shrimp, crabs, ostracods, and clado-

206

species often have rather specialized adaptations. This simplicity and specialization make island communities so vulnerable that the loss of key plant species can cause widespread extinctions. Many of the now extinct Hawaiian birds, for example, had long curved beaks adapted to extracting nectar from an impressive set of plants with long curved flowers. In the process of feeding, the birds served to pollinate the plants. It may be that the introduced goats and pigs exterminated many of these spectacular plants, and their pollinators vanished as a result. Alternatively, the birds may have disappeared first, then the plants for lack of pollinators.

What happens when an introduced species feeds high in the food web? If the invader is a predator with a fairly specialized diet, it can affect only a few species and may not affect any of them much before their new rarity slows the predator's population growth. A generalized predator, in contrast, can eliminate many prey species before being limited by the few resistant species that remain. *Boiga* on Guam probably relied on small mammals and lizards once the birds became rare. The chestnut blight fungus survived in other species of trees without killing them.

Again, islands often suffer for the reasons outlined above. Generalized plant eaters may devastate island plant communities; consequently, the simple food chains based on those plant species will also disappear. A generalized predator may eliminate not only many animal species on the island but also, indirectly, the plants that depend on those animals for a vital service such as pollination or seed dispersal.

Genetically engineered organisms

Will organisms that have been given new genes via the tools of modern biotechnology—and thus endowed with traits not found in wild species—spread through a community with unexpected effects? Current legislation in many countries views the introduction of genetically engineered

A ranger takes measurements of a standing dead American chestnut tree in Great Smoky Mountains National Park. Even though an accidentally introduced fungus destroyed virtually all of the American chestnut trees in eastern North America, no vertebrates and probably few insects became extinct as a result. Because of the complexity of the food web, those animals for which the chestnut provided food had other food sources as well.

The specialized beak of the akiapolaau, a Hawaiian honeycreeper, is adapted to chiseling and prying insect larvae from the bark of large trees. Other members of the family possess beaks adapted to drawing nectar from plants having long curved flowers; in the process these birds serve to pollinate the plants. The introduction of foreign birds and mammals may have contributed to the extinction of many of the Hawaiian honeycreepers; most of the survivors, including the akiapolaau, are endangered. The now extinct nectar-feeding species may have died out when introduced mammals such as goats and pigs exterminated the plants on which the birds fed. Alternatively, the birds may have disappeared first, then the plants for lack of pollinators.

As they feed, goats can strip leaves, bark, and twigs from small trees, eventually killing them. On islands, where the food web is often simple, the destruction by introduced animals of one or more plant species at the base of the web can have a catastrophic effect on native animal species by removing a critical source of food.

organisms as being no different from that of organisms whose genetics have been changed by conventional breeding techniques. Thus, goes the argument, it does not matter how a gene is inserted into a crop plant such as sorghum, which has a good chance of jumping the fence and invading native communities. Many environmental scientists have no reason to think that this view is incorrect. It is, however, rather like saying that Genghis Khan was just another Asian on a horse. Genetically engineered organisms are being rapidly developed for commercial purposes. Whereas it is likely that the first developments, like most introductions, will fail to penetrate native habitats, one cannot be certain that every one will fail.

Consider the argument that genetic changes typically handicap a species in the wild and so prevent it from being a threat. The presence of thriving introduced populations of once-domesticated goats, cattle, pigs, rabbits, and cats rejects this argument. Work by the Swedish ecologist Torbjörn Ebenhard has enumerated the number of cases worldwide in which introduced mammals have caused ecological damage. On his list organisms that have been genetically modified by conventional means dominate the top ten globally most destructive species—the "ecological Genghis Khans." For example, pigs of a wide variety of shapes and colors have managed to trash the rain forests on many of the Hawaiian islands. In short, the handicap argument is often wrong, and it is clear why. It is not just the natural history of the potential invader that matters. The features of the potential host community play a crucial role as well.

What can be done?

When one thinks of introduced species as being harmful to the health of natural ecosystems, some useful analogies to human health emerge. Conventional wisdom teaches that prevention is better than cure, some

216

diseases are more dangerous than others, some people are immune while others are not, and treating the disease in its early stages may be the only way to save the patient. This wisdom applies equally to ecosystem health.

As with any disease, the best strategy is prevention. Most countries make an effort to prevent the spread of species, although people are not always sympathetic—for example, when the family cat or dog has to endure six months in quarantine on entering Britain. (Britain does not have rabies, while the European continent does.) Education is crucial in order that the traveler with fruit in her bag or mud on his boots knows why such a situation is cause for concern.

There are so many ways in which human beings around the world move so many species that it is not always clear on which species to concentrate. As discussed above, examples are beginning to teach us which species are likely to be the most damaging. A species implicated in one crime has a reasonable chance of being a repeat offender. Whereas special efforts are being made to exclude the snake *Boiga* from Hawaii, clearly the destructive potential of species like this one needs to be anticipated before damage is done to even one area. This is a considerable scientific challenge and one that ecologists are beginning to address.

Of the many deliberate introductions, there are enough prior examples having unexpected effects to require the most careful scrutiny of any planned release of an alien species. Many countries have gone from encouraging the importation of alien fish, birds, mammals, and plants to prohibiting them. Some deliberate introductions that were intended to control earlier introductions have now become pests themselves. A snail planted on Hawaii to control another introduced snail has eaten many of the beautiful and unique Hawaiian land snails to extinction. Despite that outcome, the mistake has been repeated on Moorea in the Society

An example of a deliberate introduction that backfired is that of the carnivorous land snail Euglandina rosea (long shell in lower left), which was planted on Hawaii to control another introduced snail. Instead, Euglandina ate many of Hawaii's unique native land snails (six smaller shells; species of Achatinella) to extinction.

Efforts to control introduced species have their success stories. In Hawaii wild goats that had been devouring the unique native plants at Haleakala crater on the island of Maui were removed. As a result, the plants are now recovering.

Islands of the South Pacific, resulting in extinction of an entire genus of indigenous snails and destruction of an important field study concerning evolution on islands. How we learn to avoid these real-life versions of the story of the old woman who swallowed a fly, and then a spider, and eventually a horse presents yet another scientific challenge.

Just as the potential host communities on natural islands are especially vulnerable to destructive invasions, so also are the "habitat islands" of human making—those fragments of once-continuous forest, prairie, and other habitats being formed as we claim more and more land for development. The communities in those habitat islands are ripe for invasions by the species in the surrounding disturbed areas. Such invasions add another insult to damaged ecosystems, and our knowledge of their effects provides another justification for minimizing that damage. Following Hurricane Andrew in 1992, ecologists were most concerned about whether and to what extent the effects of the storm might favor introduced trees over native trees in and around south Florida's national parks. Native trees must experience hurricanes many times in their long lives and are probably adapted to them. What is new and potentially threatening, however, is the small size of the remaining areas of native vegetation and the vastness of the surrounding areas filled with introduced trees and weeds.

Control is the last resort and one that gets progressively more expensive every year as the species spreads, particularly if the spread is Malthusian. Control may mean spraying herbicides on plants, introducing yet more

218

The South Island saddleback numbers among a group of birds, lizards, and invertebrates that are recovering on Breaksea Island south of New Zealand after a carefully planned eradication campaign succeeded in exterminating the island's population of introduced brown rats with poisoned bait. Control measures, even when they work, are expensive and usually difficult to implement and offer a poor alternative to the prevention of species introductions.

species, or physically removing the plant or animal. None of these solutions is easy, and they all can harm native plants and animals if applied carelessly. There are success stories, nevertheless. Goats were removed from Haleakala crater on the Hawaiian island of Maui, and its unique plant life is recovering. On some small New Zealand islands, introduced rats that had been depleting the indigenous animals and plants for at least a century and a half were eliminated with poisoned bait, allowing natural and assisted recovery of a number of birds, lizards, and insects. All too often the control will be local and, therefore, ongoing as animals and plants continue to move in from outside. In such cases we will indefinitely, and quite literally, pay the price for our lack of vigilance in preventing species introductions.

See also *1990 Yearbook of Science and the Future* Feature Article: Islands—Natural Laboratories for Biologists; *1992 Yearbook of Science and the Future* Feature Article: Invader from the South: The Africanized "Killer" Bee; *1993 Yearbook of Science and the Future* Feature Article: The Salvation Islands.

FOR ADDITIONAL READING

Rob Hengeveld, *Dynamics of Biological Invasions* (Chapman and Hall, 1989).

R.L. Kitching (ed.), *The Ecology of Exotic Animals and Plants: Some Australian Case Histories* (J. Wiley, 1986).

H.L. Mooney and J.A. Drake (eds.), *Ecology of Biological Invasions of North America and Hawaii* (Springer-Verlag, 1986).

Stuart L. Pimm, *The Balance of Nature?: Ecological Issues in the Conservation of Species and Communities* (University of Chicago Press, 1991).

Lecture Demonstrations: Science's Live Theater

by George B. Kauffman

The heyday of the great scientific lecture demonstrations was the 19th century, which produced virtuosos of the caliber of Humphry Davy and Michael Faraday. Today's masters of the art carry on the same tradition of making science fun and understandable to students and the public.

When former students visit me, a professor of chemistry, the parts of my lectures that they invariably recall most vividly are the demonstrations, usually the more spectacular ones, even though in some cases almost four decades have elapsed. Indeed, the "live" scientific lecture demonstration remains an effective means of communication, even in the modern era of film, television, and other "canned" media. According to veteran demonstrator Charles Taylor, professor of experimental physics at London's Royal Institution and professor emeritus at University College, Cardiff, Wales, "It seems to work with all age groups and is a great way of inculcating a sense of excitement about science, especially in children."

In Taylor's 1988 book *The Art and Science of Lecture Demonstration*, a demonstration is any "illustration of a point in a lecture or lesson by means of something other than conventional visual-aid apparatus" such as blackboards, overhead projectors, slides, or films. Whereas the spoken lecture reaches the brain mainly through the ears, the demonstration adds a second channel, that of vision, to the input, and occasionally one of smell or taste as well. Unlike a blackboard or slide, however, the live demonstration is more than simple visual support. It is kin to the traditional performing arts, with which it has maintained affinities for centuries and with which it shares a critical dependency on personal skills of communication and a sense of the dramatic. When it is done well, the lecture demonstration reaches both the logical and emotional brain to drive home a message of knowledge, awe, and enthusiasm that can remain with the spectator for life.

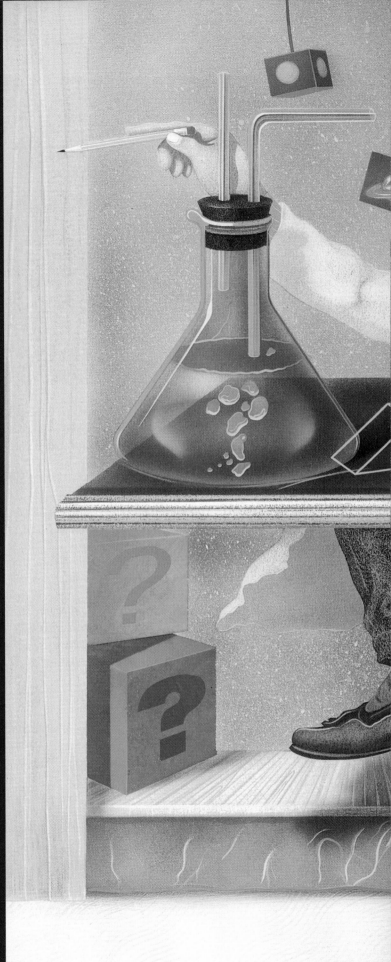

The ancient Greek Pythagoras, famous as a mathematician, may also have investigated and demonstrated acoustic phenomena, as depicted (above) in a 12th-century copy of a manuscript by the Roman scholar Boethius. A fresco (below) by Giuseppe Bezzuoli shows Galileo demonstrating an apparatus comprising an inclined trough and a bronze ball, which he used to study bodies in motion.

Lecture demonstrations have been integral to science education since the 17th century and have roots that extend back even earlier. The golden age of the great demonstrators was the 19th century, which enjoyed the likes of Michael Faraday and Humphry Davy. Today modern masters of the art continue the tradition to achieve the same ends—to make science fun and understandable, to encourage students to pursue science as a career, and to enhance the scientific literacy of the general public.

Ancient roots

Depending upon how broadly one defines the term, the beginnings of the lecture demonstration can be traced back several thousand years. In ancient times eclipses, particularly of the Sun, were regarded as portents of disaster, and not only astronomical writings but also history and literature are replete with descriptions of these striking occurrences. The Babylonians, Assyrians, Chinese, Greeks, Romans, and Aztecs were able to predict eclipses, and their priests and rulers undoubtedly conducted "demonstrations" of them to awe their superstitious subjects.

Archimedes, the most famous inventor and mathematician of ancient Greece, may have performed at least two demonstrations before King Hieron II of Syracuse. His observation of the overflowing of water caused by his stepping into his bath purportedly enabled him to answer Hieron's question of whether a crown made for the king was pure gold or adulterated with silver. According to a second anecdote, when Hieron asked Archimedes to prove his contention that an extremely great weight could be moved by a very small force ("Give me a place to stand and I will move the Earth"), Archimedes provided him with a mechanical device (sources vary as to its exact nature) that enabled him to move a fully

laden ship. Another famous Greek mathematician, Pythagoras, may have demonstrated principles of vibration, if one interpretation of a drawing in a medieval manuscript is to be believed.

The earliest well-documented scientific demonstrations date to the period just after the Renaissance, when the seeds of modern science began to sprout. Although the story that the Italian astronomer and physicist Galileo Galilei dropped weights from the Leaning Tower of Pisa to show that bodies fall with uniform acceleration is apocryphal, he did demonstrate an apparatus for studying bodies in motion to an audience that included Giovanni de' Medici, half brother of Grand Duke Ferdinand I of Tuscany, as a fresco by Giuseppe Bezzuoli depicts.

One of the most renowned scientific demonstrations of this period was that of Otto von Guericke, the German physicist and engineer who in 1650 invented the first air pump. In a famous series of experiments carried out in 1654 before Holy Roman Emperor Ferdinand III, Guericke formed a hollow sphere about the size of a beach ball from two copper bowls placed mouth to mouth. In this first demonstration of the tremendous force that air pressure exerts, he exhausted the air from the sphere with his air pump. Even though the bowls were held together only by the air around them, horses were unable to pull them apart.

It is in the field of medicine that demonstrations most closely approaching Taylor's definition have been used since ancient times. Galen,

Otto von Guericke carried out his renowned demonstration of the powerful force of atmospheric pressure in 1654 before the Holy Roman Emperor Ferdinand III. After fitting two large copper hemispheres together and evacuating the enclosed air with a pump, Guericke harnessed the apparatus between two eight-horse teams, which were unable to pull it apart.

GEORGE B. KAUFFMAN *is Professor of Chemistry at California State University, Fresno. He has written extensively on chemical education and the history of science and was the 1993 recipient of the American Chemical Society's George C. Pimentel Award in Chemical Education.*

Illustration on pages 220–221 by Ruben Ramos

223

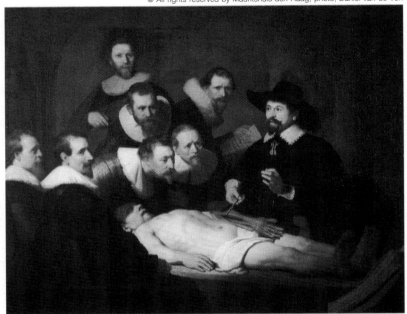

In the mid-1500s the Renaissance physician Andreas Vesalius performed his own lecture dissections of cadavers at the University of Padua, Italy, eschewing the customary practice of delegating the task to assistants. By the following century, as Rembrandt's 1632 painting "Anatomy Lesson of Dr. Nicolaes Tulp" (right) testifies, anatomy lessons conducted personally by the foremost European professors of anatomy were regarded as educational and social highlights.

the most important physician in the ancient world after Hippocrates, achieved renown in the Roman Empire in the 2nd century AD. Admitted to the court of Marcus Aurelius, Galen performed public lectures and dissections that were well attended by the most famous persons of the day. One of his most significant demonstrations proved that the arteries carry blood rather than air, as had been erroneously taught for four centuries.

In 1537 the Renaissance Flemish physician Andreas Vesalius was appointed *explicator chirurgiae* at the medical school of the University of Padua, Italy, with the responsibility of lecturing on surgery and anatomy. His lectures and demonstrations were unusual in that he dissected cadavers himself rather than consigning the task to an assistant, the customary practice. By the following century the annual anatomy lesson by the presiding professor of anatomy in the Amsterdam Surgeon's Guild was considered the high point of the social season and the subject for oil paintings. "Anatomy Lesson of Dr. Nicolaes Tulp" (1632) was one of Rembrandt's most important and successful commissions.

Demonstrations and the beginnings of academic science

The lecture demonstration, in the modern sense of the term, became popular during the 17th century. Inasmuch as chemistry is an experimental science, it is not surprising that demonstrations were an integral part of its teaching from the beginnings of academic chemistry itself, which entered the traditional university curriculum as an introductory "service course" for students of medicine and pharmacy. In Paris the first real chemistry courses were private ones given in the chemists' own homes or laboratories. About 1604 Jean Beguin and Jean Ribit opened a school of chemistry and pharmacy, and Beguin's lectures were the first public expositions of chemistry in the French capital. Also in Paris,

224

Detail from "Experiment on a Bird with an Air Pump" (1768), by the English painter Joseph Wright, illustrates a popular demonstration of the itinerant lecturer-demonstrators who flourished in Great Britain and the United States in the late 18th and early 19th centuries.

outside of the universities, public lectures with demonstrations by such chemists as the Dane Ole Borch and the Frenchman Nicolas Lemery attracted not only medical and pharmacy students but ordinary citizens, including women, as well as foreigners.

In Great Britain and the United States, the tradition of itinerant lecturer-demonstrators became popular only later, in the late 18th and early 19th centuries. These private lecturers, some of whom were university professors, traveled from town to town, where university education was often unavailable. At each stop they presented short courses on chemistry, pneumatics, and other topics to groups of laypeople, usually sponsored by local ministers, educators, or natural-history societies.

Development of the art of the chemical demonstration is inseparably linked with the history of a famous institution whose name and purpose would seem to have nothing to do with chemistry. In 1572 the poet, botanist, and alchemist Jacques Gohory founded a garden in Paris for the preservation of herbs for medicinal uses. Because medicines were prepared from the plants, pharmaceutical laboratories were built in the garden, which in 1626 was reestablished by Jean Héroard and Guy de la Brosse, Louis XIII's physicians, as the Jardin Royal des Plantes Médicinales, known until 1793 as the Jardin du Roi (thereafter as the Jardin des Plantes). The Royal Garden soon developed into a center for scientific studies and assumed the organizational form of a university.

The first professor of chemistry at the Jardin du Roi, appointed in 1648, was a Scottish physician, William Davison. Subsequent appointments to the post included some of the most famous French chemists of the 17th and 18th centuries. At first the general practice at the Jardin du Roi was for the *professeur* to present his lecture, followed by illustrative experiments carried out by the *demonstrateur*, who held a lower rank.

225

Guillaume-François Rouelle conducts one of his more impressive demonstrations at the Jardin du Roi in the 1750s, as conceived by a 19th-century artist. Said to be the best lecturer in France of his day, Rouelle achieved a worldwide reputation during his tenure at the Jardin du Roi.

By the late 18th century in France, however, the professor performed his own demonstrations or was aided by a lecture assistant.

Guillaume-François Rouelle, who was the teacher of Antoine-Laurent Lavoisier, the father of modern chemistry, was reputed to have been the best lecturer in France in the mid-1700s, and during his tenure at the Jardin du Roi he attained a worldwide reputation. Although well liked by his contemporaries, Rouelle was eccentric in habits and blunt in speech. According to one eyewitness report,

He would come to the lecture room elegantly attired with a velvet coat, powdered wig and a little hat under his arm. Collected enough at the beginning of his demonstrations, he gradually became more animated. If his train of thought became obscure, he would lose patience and would gradually divest himself of his clothing, first putting his hat on a retort, then taking off his wig, then untying his cravat. Then, talking all the while, he would unbutton his coat and waistcoat and take them off one after the other. He was helped in his experiments by one of his nephews, but as help was not always to be found close at hand, he would shout at the top of his lungs, "Nephew! O' the eternal nephew" and the eternal nephew not appearing, he would himself depart into the back regions of his laboratory to find the object he needed. Meanwhile he would continue his lecture as though he were still in the presence of his audience. When he returned, he had generally finished the demonstration he had begun and would come in saying, "There, gentlemen, this is what I had to tell you." Then he was begged to begin again, which he always did with the best grace in the world, in the conviction he had merely been badly understood.

In England in 1662 the newly founded Royal Society of London appointed the English physicist Robert Hooke as curator and demonstrator "to provide new experiments for almost every occasion when the Royal Society met." However, a later curator of experiments at the Royal Society, John Keill, is generally regarded as the real popularizer of demonstration lectures. According to fellow scientist John Theophilus Desaguliers, Keill, who began a series of experimental lectures on Newtonian philosophy in 1694,

was the first who publicly taught Natural Philosophy [as science was then called] by Experiments in a mathematical Manner; for he laid down very simple Propositions, which he prov'd by Experiments. . . . He began these courses in Oxford about the year 1704 or 1705.

In Scotland the first chemistry courses were given at the University of Glasgow by the physician William Cullen, who taught there from 1746 to 1755. When Cullen moved to the University of Edinburgh in 1755, where he made both chemistry and medicine popular studies, he was succeeded at Glasgow by his former student Joseph Black, the British physicist and chemist who discovered latent heat and rediscovered "fixed air" (carbon dioxide). Both men were brilliant lecturer-demonstrators. Cullen's innovative teaching methods and forceful lectures attracted students to Edinburgh from all over the English-speaking world. As for Black, in *History of Chemistry* (1830), the first book in English on the subject, Thomas Thomson wrote:

Dr. Black [endeavored] every year to make his courses more plain and familiar, and illustrat[ed] them by a greater variety of examples in the way of experiment. No man could perform these [lecture demonstrations] more neatly or successfully; they were always ingeniously and judiciously contrived, clearly establishing the point in view, and were never more complicated than was sufficient for the purpose. . . . No quackery, no trickery, no love of mere dazzle and glitter, ever had the least influence upon his conduct. He constituted the most complete model of a perfect chemical lecturer that I have ever had an opportunity of witnessing.

One of Black's pupils was Philadelphia-born Benjamin Rush, who became the first professor of chemistry in America (1769), a popular lecturer-demonstrator in his own right, and a signer of the Declaration of Independence.

During the second half of the 18th century, grand lectures primarily for show were accompanied by bombastic experiments, and natural scientists served as magicians and entertainers at court functions. By the century's end scientific demonstrations had developed into theatrical events, and many private scholars organized them for their own amusement. An invitation to a grand dinner at Lavoisier's house, for example, often included an experimental lecture lasting an hour or longer.

In Germany, at Munich's Bavarian Academy of Sciences, Maximus von Imhof demonstrated the classical experiments of the new "pneumatic chemistry," determining the composition of air and exploding various gas mixtures. In the Weimar of Goethe's time, Alexander Nicolaus von Scherer offered experimental lectures, sponsored by Grand Duke Karl

August, to the public with great success. In 1799 the author Joseph Rückert wrote:

In Weimar nothing is spoken of now except gas, oxygen, combustible materials, easily—and difficultly fusible things. All the citizens of Weimar, male and female, seem to want to become chemists and want Weimar to become a big smelting furnace.

At Göttingen in 1781 Georg Christoph Lichtenberg began to lecture in the first university chair of experimental physics in Germany, which was established specifically for him. His best known demonstration was that of the images ("Lichtenberg figures") formed when an electrical discharge is created near or in contact with a plate of insulating material dusted with powdered insulator. The demonstration illustrates the principle on which the modern photocopier is based and is still performed today.

Masters of the "golden age"

The 19th century was the heyday of popular scientific lecture demonstrations carried out in large lecture halls for the benefit of a diverse public, many of whom were of the working class. First among the organizations fostering such lectures was London's Royal Institution (RI) of Great Britain. Founded as a center for the popularization of the "mechanical arts" in 1799 by the American-born British physicist and administrator Benjamin Thompson (also known as Count Rumford), the RI is described by Sir John Meurig Thomas, a former director, as England's "oldest repertory theatre of science" and "the foremost repertory theatre for the popularization of science in the world." When the balcony is full, its lecture hall of unsurpassed design—half a hemisphere only about six meters (20 feet) in radius—accommodates more than 400 persons, who can hear the lecturer even at a whisper.

The RI's first professor of chemistry, Thomas Garnett, who was appointed in 1799, had been a successful lecturer at Anderson's College in Glasgow. He was broken in spirit by his wife's death in childbirth, however, and he soon died of typhus. His assistant lecturer, the largely self-taught Cornish youth Humphry Davy, succeeded him in 1802 as professor and lecturer. A true Romantic—he was a poet and a friend of William Wordsworth, Lord Byron, and Samuel Taylor Coleridge, the last of whom even attended Davy's lectures "to increase his stock of metaphors"—Davy quickly rose from being merely the son of an often-unemployed wood-carver to become "the most brilliant chemist of his age" and "one of the most respected and most disliked men of science ever" (many perceived his social unease as haughtiness or snobbery). Considered the Newton of his day, he was the first scientist to be knighted (at age 33) since Newton, and when he received a baronetcy, the highest honor ever conferred on a British scientist, he surpassed even Newton.

Davy's showmanship and zeal in popularizing his discoveries made him "the first preacher of applied science." He invented the carbon arc light, the miner's safety lamp, and "cathodic protection" for preventing saltwater corrosion of copper sheathing on British naval vessels. Davy's

first RI lecture brought him tremendous social success and constant dinner invitations. His lectures were attended by large and fashionable audiences, whose support made the RI Britain's premier research institute. They became so popular that on the nights he discoursed at the RI, traffic on Albemarle Street was made one-way; when he lectured in Ireland, a black market in tickets developed.

The presentation of Davy's latest research results in his lectures, together with his strong sense of theater, made them particularly exciting. Yet, unlike the audiences of chemistry lecturers at medical schools, Davy's audiences were not students, and any hopes he might have cherished that some of his spectators would take up scientific research were not fulfilled. In Regency England chemistry was largely confined to the training of physicians and was not considered a suitable subject for a liberal education. Davy's lectures remained primarily entertainment.

At the pinnacle of his meteoric career, Davy resigned his professorship in 1813 and devoted the remainder of his life to travel and research. The previous year he had hired Michael Faraday as his assistant on the basis of the notes and drawings that Faraday had made of some of his lectures. Faraday, regarded as Davy's "greatest discovery," like his mentor was poor and self-taught. While apprenticed to a bookbinder, the youthful Faraday worked his way through the electrical articles in the

The efforts of London's newly founded Royal Institution (RI) to demonstrate the latest discoveries of science to the public were not always taken seriously. In a 1802 caricature captioned in part, "New Discoveries in Pneumaticks," Thomas Young, the RI's first professor of natural philosophy, administers laughing gas (nitrous oxide) to a volunteer while Humphry Davy stands ready with a bellows. That Young's audiences often found his lectures too technical and obscure may have helped make him a target for farce.

229

Encyclopædia Britannica; he later enunciated Faraday's laws of electrolysis, which established the intimate connection between electricity and chemistry and placed electrochemistry on a modern basis.

After returning to London from an 18-month tour of the Continent with Davy and his wife, Faraday, with Davy's backing, was reappointed laboratory assistant at the RI, where he carried out a number of revolutionary chemical and physical researches. In 1825 he was promoted, again with Davy's backing, to laboratory director, and in 1833 he became Fullerian professor of chemistry, an endowed chair created for him.

Davy had made showmanship the essence of the RI, and his protégé Faraday continued the tradition, becoming the darling of society like his mentor and even more popular as a lecturer and demonstrator par excellence. In 1826 Faraday established the series of weekly lectures called Friday Evening Discourses—which are still held today—being timed to begin exactly at 9 PM and end exactly at 9:59:50 PM. These "penny lectures" for everybody, named after their entrance price, brought in considerable sums to the RI, for they were well attended. After 1835 Faraday's health began to deteriorate, and he successively abandoned his various activities; the last to go were his Friday Evening Discourses. He said that his need to perfect experiments for these lectures, such as the production of artificial rubies, the reproduction of worms, and the silvering of mirrors, stimulated his research.

In 1826 Faraday also initiated the famous series of annual Christmas Lectures for young people, long before such efforts became fashionable. Except for a short hiatus during World War I, scientists have continued these lectures to the present day. The first series (1826) was given by an astronomer, John Wallis, but the next year Faraday presented a "Course of Six Elementary Lectures on Chemistry," the first of 19 series that he was to give. The most famous of Faraday's Christmas Lectures is "The Chemical History of a Candle," six lectures presented in 1848–49 and repeated in 1860–61. The latter version, edited by Sir William Crookes, another ardent popularizer of science, is a true classic of science and has been reprinted in many anthologies, including *The Harvard Classics* and *Gateway to the Great Books.*

On the Continent a number of 19th-century chemists found fame for their lectures and demonstrations in addition to their research. In Sweden during the 1820s, Jöns Jacob Berzelius, the great systematizer of chemistry, in his Academy of Sciences uniform bedecked with medals, lectured before the Swedish royal family—women in elaborate, decolleté gowns and men in full dress uniforms adorned with swords. Justus von Liebig, one of the founders of organic chemistry, absorbed the lecture tradition of the Jardin des Plantes while studying in Paris and took it to Germany upon his return. Later in life, as professor of chemistry at the University of Munich, Liebig simultaneously served at Bavaria's Academy of Sciences, where, despite the fact that he was said to be a sloppy demonstrator, he continued the tradition of presenting Evening Lectures for Hearers of All Social Classes, which became a great social event that attracted many of the women of Munich.

230

In his long, distinguished association with the RI, Michael Faraday brought the popularity of scientific lectures and demonstrations to new heights. Two lecture series that he established—the Friday Evening Discourses and the annual Christmas Lectures for young people— endure to the present day and are often emulated. Faraday's 1855 Christmas Lecture (top) was attended by the Prince Consort Albert, shown seated directly facing the lecturer's table, and, on his left, the young Prince of Wales (the future King Edward VII). A cartoon from a 1857 issue of Punch (center) pictures Faraday demonstrating electrical effects to a group of young women. Faraday and his work to popularize science recently were honored on a £20 note issued by the Bank of England (bottom).

An ever gleeful Hubert Alyea, the undisputed 20th-century master of the chemistry lecture demonstration, touches off an attention-getting reaction during one of the thousands of lectures he delivered during his long teaching career. Alyea's distinctive lecturing style led him to serve as a model for the title character in Walt Disney's 1961 film The Absent-Minded Professor.

In the New World the aforementioned appointment in 1769 of Benjamin Rush as professor of chemistry at the College of Philadelphia (now the University of Pennsylvania Medical College) marked the formal beginning of chemistry in America. Noted 19th-century American chemical demonstrators included Amos Eaton, an itinerant lecturer who wrote a handbook for such lectures; Robert Hare of the University of Pennsylvania, inventor of the oxyhydrogen blowpipe; Thomas Duché Mitchell, one of the Midwest's earliest chemistry teachers; John Webster of Harvard University, famous—or infamous—for being hanged for his murder of a fellow faculty member; and Samuel P. Sadtler of the University of Pennsylvania, author of the first American book on chemical demonstrations.

Today's demonstrator virtuosos

In Britain the Davy-Faraday tradition has remained alive and well at the Royal Institution over the past century and a half. Two former directors, the 1967 Nobel chemistry laureate Lord Porter (formerly Sir George Porter) and Sir John Meurig Thomas, author of *Michael Faraday and the Royal Institution: The Genius of Man and Place* (1991), are well known for their lecture demonstrations, as are the RI's Taylor, David Phillips, professor of chemistry at Imperial College, London, and Brian Iddon, reader in chemistry at the University of Salford. Brian Bowers of London's Science Museum has also established a similar reputation.

In the United States the grand old master of chemistry lecture demonstrations has for many years been Hubert Newcombe Alyea (born in 1903), professor emeritus at Princeton University. In 1928 Alyea proposed the domino theory to explain how chemical inhibitors break chains in chemical reactions, and it became the first of the hundreds of demonstrations that he devised. More than two decades later U.S.

Pres. Dwight D. Eisenhower applied Alyea's domino analogy to political conditions in the Far East (the "domino effect"). Alyea's "Old Nassau reaction," a clock (or delayed-time) chemical reaction so called because the solution of reactants turns first orange and then black (the colors of the Nassau line of German nobility and of Princeton, whose Old Nassau Hall was the world's first undergraduate chemistry laboratory) is probably the most imitated chemical demonstration.

A living legend, Alyea delighted and enlightened countless audiences with his thousands of lectures through the years. He presented his popular demonstration lecture "Lucky Accidents, Great Discoveries, and the Prepared Mind" alone on more than 3,000 occasions. Between 1945 and 1960, mostly under U.S. government auspices, he delivered "Atomic Energy, Weapon for Peace," in which he described the benefits and perils of nuclear knowledge, more than 2,600 times. In 1958 Walt Disney, after seeing Alyea lecture in Brussels, invited him to Hollywood to tape his atomic energy talk. Alyea's lecturing technique and gestures subsequently became a model for actor Fred MacMurray's character in the Disney film *The Absent-Minded Professor* (1961).

In the 1960s, with National Science Foundation (NSF) support, Alyea developed the Tested Overhead Projection Series, or TOPS, a series of small-scale, real-time chemical experiments designed to be viewed in enlarged form on an overhead projector. He conducted workshops on the technique for the NSF, the Atomic Energy Commission, the Asia Foundation, the Fulbright Foundation, the U.S. Department of State Agency for International Development, Unesco, and the U.S. Department of Commerce in more than 75 countries. Alyea also wrote several books of demonstrations and contributed hundreds of articles to the *Journal of Chemical Education* and other periodicals devoted to science teaching.

The currently reigning dean of American chemistry lecture demonstrators is Bassam Zekin Shakhashiri, professor of chemistry at the University

By courtesy of Bassam Shakhashiri

Bassam Shakhashiri, the currently reigning dean of American chemistry lecture demonstrators, is probably best known to the public for his annual entertainment "Once Upon a Christmas Cheery in the Lab of Shakhashiri," which he has performed for more than 20 years. The show, comprising explosions, dramatic color changes, and other chemical "magic," commemorates Faraday's Christmas Lectures while promulgating Shakhashiri's ubiquitous motto that "science is fun."

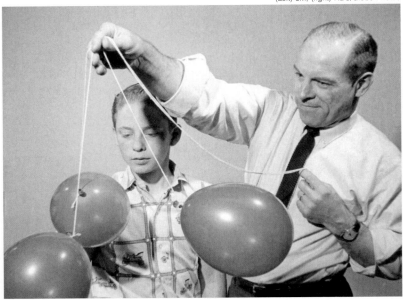

The mass media, especially television, has allowed demonstrators and popularizers of science in the past few decades to reach a wide audience outside the academic setting. In the long-running network TV series "Mr. Wizard," which premiered in 1951, Don Herbert (right) used simple experiments involving common household objects to communicate science to young people. Keeping pace with the high-tech advances of the '90s, David Heil (above), host of the PBS series "Newton's Apple," dons a virtual reality helmet and straps himself into a Cybertron cage to demonstrate how one takes a simulated jet plane flight.

of Wisconsin. Born in Lebanon in 1939, he is probably best known to the public for his Faraday-inspired annual entertainment "Once Upon a Christmas Cheery in the Lab of Shakhashiri," which he has performed since 1970. His 1991 performance at the University of Wisconsin was taped by the Public Broadcasting Service (PBS) for nationwide airing just before Christmas.

As an articulate advocate for science, Shakhashiri, like many of his distinguished predecessors and contemporaries, seeks to impart the joy of discovery that has aroused young minds throughout history. He believes that this excitement will lure future generations to careers as researchers, entrepreneurs, and teachers. He is famed for his creation and use of demonstrations in teaching chemistry not only in lecture halls and laboratories but also in less formal settings like convention centers, shopping malls, and retirement homes. His interactive chemistry exhibit has been on display at Chicago's Museum of Science and Industry since 1983, the year in which he founded and became first director of the Institute for Chemical Education. Between 1984 and 1990 he served as the NSF's assistant director for science and engineering education.

In the late 20th century demonstrators and popularizers of science outside the academic setting have influenced a wide audience of young and old alike, most profoundly through the mass media. No less an authority than Shakhashiri dedicated a recent volume of his chemical demonstrations series "to Don Herbert, television's Mr. Wizard, who has perfected the art of communicating science to kids of all ages." In his long-running network series, "Mr. Wizard," which first aired in 1951, Herbert explained basic scientific principles and demonstrated them by way of experiments to a young boy or girl onlooker. He later returned to act as host of the cable TV show "Mr. Wizard's World," which began in 1983. Another popular TV science program making extensive use of demonstrations has been the PBS series "Newton's Apple," begun in 1983 and with David Heil, associate director of Portland's Oregon Museum of Science and Industry, as host since 1987.

Science popularization and the medium of the performing arts were perhaps never linked more closely than in 1967 with the founding in England of the Molecule Club by actor-director Bernard Miles and his wife, actress Josephine Wilson. Their intent in this endeavor was "to enthuse young children with the wonders of science and the natural world through the impact and drama of live theatre." For more than a quarter century the theatrical company has entertained and enlightened several million British children with dramatic spectacles that explore heat, light, sound, electromagnetism, air pollution, and other scientific and technological topics. In addition to their shows, presented in London, formerly at the Mermaid Theatre and currently at the Bloomsbury Theatre, Molecule Club actors conduct weeklong "residences" in secondary schools and daylong workshops in museums. Both Davy and Faraday undoubtedly would have approved of their efforts.

When demonstrations go wrong

Jearl Walker, professor of physics at Cleveland (Ohio) State University and a flamboyant master demonstrator, has been quoted as saying, perhaps with only some exaggeration: "The way to capture a student's attention is with a demonstration where there is a possibility the teacher may die." In the "old days," when safety precautions that are now taken for granted were routinely neglected, demonstration accidents were not uncommon. For example, as R. Winderlich recounted in a 1950 issue of the *Journal of Chemical Education*,

During a lecture by Justus Liebig before a selected audience in Munich he exhibited the strikingly beautiful combustion of carbon bisulfide in nitric oxide. The delight of the onlookers led him to repeat the demonstration. This time, to the great horror of all present, there was a terrific explosion, the flask was shattered to bits. Queen Therese, Prince-regent Luitpold, and Liebig himself were seriously wounded by the flying glass. The accident would have been fatal for Liebig if his snuff box had not prevented a large splinter of glass from penetrating his femoral artery.

Another demonstration accident, from the late 1700s, is described by the American chemist Benjamin Silliman in his 1830 textbook, *Elements of Chemistry:*

[Jean-François] Pilatre de Rozier was accustomed, not only to fill his lungs with hydrogen gas, but to set fire to it as it issued from his mouth, where it formed a very curious jet of flame. He also mixed pure hydrogen gas with one ninth of common air, and respired the mixture as usual; "but when he attempted to set it on fire, the consequence was an explosion so dreadful, that he imagined his teeth were all blown out."

To help prevent such occurrences, modern professional science societies publish safety guidelines for lecture demonstrations. The guidelines adopted in 1988 by the American Chemical Society, for example, cover such issues as fire safety, eye protection, spectator safety shields, loud

235

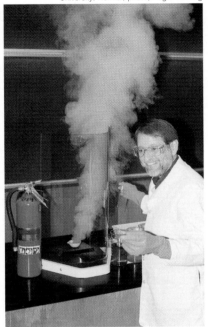

Proper safety measures including a fire extinguisher, a spectator shield, eye wear, and protective clothing are present as chemist Otis Rothenberger of Illinois State University carries out a potentially hazardous demonstration. In bygone days, when safety precautions were routinely neglected, demonstration accidents happened all too frequently.

noises and noxious gases produced in the demonstrations, proper ventilation, and waste disposal, and they ask that demonstrators know the properties of the chemicals and reactions involved. Demonstrators are also cautioned not to taste, or invite spectators to taste, any nonfood substance and not to conduct demonstrations in which parts of the human body are endangered (as by placing dry ice in the mouth or dipping hands into liquid nitrogen). For demonstrations that the spectators are encouraged to repeat later, the demonstrator is asked to provide written information on procedures, hazards, and disposal.

It has been aptly said that students and the demonstrator can learn more from a demonstration that does not proceed as expected than from one that does. In the words of master chemistry demonstrator Henry A. Bent,

Nature's an ideal lecture assistant. *She* never fails. . . . What may fail, however, is the lecturer's imagination. There are no failed experiments, only unimaginative responses to unexpected occurrences.

The classic example of an incredibly productive demonstration that "failed" is the one performed in 1882 by the German chemist Victor Meyer, whose histrionic ability and theatrical perfection of his lecture demonstrations had attracted many students from Europe and the U.S. In his course of lectures on derivatives of benzene at the famed Polytechnic Institute (now the Swiss Federal Institute of Technology) in Zürich, Meyer applied what was thought at the time to be a test for benzene to a sample prepared by decarboxylation (removal of carbon dioxide) from benzoic acid, a benzene derivative. To his amazement the test, which produces the blue compound indophenine and which was expected to result in a deep blue color, proved negative. Meyer's lecture assistant reminded him that the benzene sample used earlier that morning in

The German chemist Victor Meyer lectures at the chalkboard as associates assist with demonstration equipment in this late 19th-century photograph. While investigating the reason why one of his demonstrations did not go as expected, Meyer discovered the organic compound thiophene and consequently opened up an entirely new area of chemical research.

the successful rehearsal of the test had been commercial benzene prepared from coal tar.

That same day Meyer began to investigate the failed indophenine reaction. Soon he found that even the purest benzene samples from coal tar always gave a positive reaction, while the same samples, after extraction with sulfuric acid, did not, nor did benzene prepared from benzene derivatives. He concluded that coal-tar benzene was a mixture of two substances with similar chemical and physical properties, only one of which gave a positive indophenine test. The next year he reported isolating the unknown compound (C_4H_4S), which he called thiophene because it contains sulfur (from the Greek *theion,* "sulfur") and because of its similarity to benzene (C_6H_6) and the similarity of its derivatives to benzene derivatives. It was the thiophene present in coal-tar benzene, rather than benzene itself, that had undergone the indophenine reaction. This, Meyer's most brilliant discovery, opened an entirely new area of research, and within five years he and his students had published more than 100 articles on the topic.

Behind the scenes: goals, principles, and techniques

As did Faraday and other great demonstrators of the past, today's practitioners frequently offer their own thoughts about the purposes and goals of lecture demonstrations and their advice on the best techniques for achieving those goals. Almost every book of demonstrations, including those of Taylor and Shakhashiri, features an introduction discussing the writer's general philosophy. According to Shakhashiri,

Lecture demonstrations help to focus students' attention on chemical behavior and chemical properties, and to increase students' knowledge and awareness of chemistry. . . . The lecture demonstration should be a process, not a single event. . . . [He feels that] the single most important purpose that lectures serve is to give teachers the opportunity to convey an attitude toward chemistry—to communicate to students an appreciation of chemistry's diversity and usefulness, its cohesiveness and value as a central science, its intellectual excitement and challenge.

Demonstrations thus can enhance scientific literacy and help combat modern society's prevalent antiscientific attitude, an attitude fostered by one-sided stories from the news media that paint a misleading picture of science and scientists. Chemistry, in particular, has been singled out for abuse; the phenomenon of "chemophobia," an irrational fear of chemicals, is widespread. Scientists are blamed for such technological disasters as Three Mile Island, Bhopal, and Chernobyl and such current environmental problems as pollution, the greenhouse effect, acid rain, the erosion of the ozone layer, oil spills, and the proliferation of pesticides and of nuclear weapons and wastes. Education of the public, in which demonstrations can play a vital part, is critical to overcoming the problem of misinformation and distortion.

Biochemist Paul Saltman of the University of California, San Diego, believes that, for students and their teachers, demonstrations can play a strong role in cultivating the hierarchy of intellectual skills that are

237

needed for pursuing science. By observing demonstrations students can develop their abilities, first, to observe phenomena and learn facts; second, to understand scientific models and theories; third, to develop reasoning skills; and, finally, to examine the limits and validity of fundamental scientific knowledge. To encourage the first skill—making

238

observations—demonstrators may refrain from announcing beforehand what should happen. The technique of "show and tell" rather than "tell and show" also increases suspense and interest, treats the demonstration as an experiment, and avoids embarrassment to the lecturer if the demonstration does not proceed as expected.

Wesley Smith of Ricks College, Rexburg, Idaho, maintains that a truly effective demonstration has six essential ingredients: it is related to what is being taught, it is well prepared and rehearsed, it is easily visible and large in scale, it is simple and uncluttered, it is quick and lively, and it is dramatic and striking. Because a demonstration has much in common with a stage play, theatrical considerations—for example, mental and physical preparation, presentation, audibility, audience participation, audience psychology, appropriateness for the audience's age group, contrasts, and climaxes—are important.

Because Faraday insightfully analyzed the art of lecture demonstrating in a series of letters to Benjamin Abbott, a friend of his youth, excellent advice for lecturers is available in the words of a true master of the art. Among other observations, he wrote:

The best experiments are simple and on a large scale, and their workings are obvious to the audience. . . . The most prominent requisite to a lecturer . . . is a good delivery; for though to all true philosophers science and nature will have charms innumerable in every dress, yet I am sorry to say that the generality of mankind cannot accompany us one short hour unless the path is strewn with flowers. . . . A lecturer should exert his utmost to gain completely the mind and attention of his audience, and irresistibly make them join in his ideas to the end of the subject. . . . A flame should be lighted at the commencement and kept alive with unremitting splendour to the end.

In the introduction to the first lecture of his classic "Chemical History of a Candle," Faraday had words for his young audience that elegantly express much of what is worthy about the scientific demonstration and much of what the best demonstrators share in their aims as teachers and in their passion for science:

I have taken this subject on a former occasion; and were it left to my own will, I should prefer to repeat it almost every year—so abundant is the interest that attaches itself to the subject, so wonderful are the varieties of outlet which it offers into the various departments of philosophy. There is not a law under which any part of this universe is governed which does not come into play, and is touched upon in these phenomena. There is no better, there is no more open door by which you can enter into the study of natural philosophy than by considering the physical phenomena of a candle. I trust, therefore, I shall not disappoint you in choosing this for my subject rather than any newer topic, which could not be better, were it even so good.

And before proceeding, let me say this also—that though our subject be so great, and our intention that of treating it honestly, seriously, and philosophically, yet I mean to pass away from all those who are seniors amongst us. I claim the privilege of speaking to juveniles as a juvenile myself. I have done so on former occasions—and, if you please, I shall do so again. And though I stand here with the knowledge of having the words I utter given to the world, yet that shall not deter me from speaking in the same familiar way to those whom I esteem nearest to me on this occasion.

Today's master demonstrators continue the Davy-Faraday tradition of combining zeal and a sense of the dramatic to make science entertaining and comprehensible and to awaken a sense of wonder about the world. Brian Iddon (facing page, top left) of the University of Salford, England, lights a tube containing a mixture of nitric oxide gas and carbon disulfide vapor before an audience at the RI. The RI's Charles Taylor (top right) repeats part of a Christmas Lecture entitled "Exploring Music" at a gathering in Tokyo. Clad in 19th-century garb, Ronald Ragsdale and Jerry Driscoll (bottom right, Ragsdale in light hat) of the University of Utah concoct a fuming brew during one of their own annual Faraday Christmas Lectures. Physicist Jearl Walker (bottom left) of Cleveland (Ohio) State University plunges his hand briefly into molten lead after first dipping it in water. The demonstration, which is quite dangerous and not for amateurs, relies on the instant conversion of some of the water to steam, which forms a momentary insulating coat for the hand.

Faraday's passion for science arose from his sense of awe over the seemingly ordinary in nature, and he sought to kindle that same sense in his audiences, especially young children. Today's best lecture demonstrators share Faraday's desire to show that underlying even the simplest of things is something often miraculous, if only one has the childlike curiosity to look.

In concluding the sixth and last "Candle" lecture Faraday, an extremely pious and high-principled man, urged his listeners:

All I can say to you at the end of these lectures . . . is to express a wish that you may, in your generation, be fit to compare to a candle; that you may, like it, shine as light to those about you; that, in all your actions, you may justify the beauty of the taper by making your deeds honourable and effectual in the discharge of your duty to your fellow-men.

FOR ADDITIONAL READING

Henry A. Bent, "What Do I Remember?: The Role of Lecture Demonstrations in Teaching Chemistry," in Shakhashiri, cited below, vol. 2, pp. xiii–xxviii.

George M. Bodner, "Lecture Demonstration Accidents from Which We Can Learn," *Journal of Chemical Education* (December 1985, pp. 1105–1107).

Michael Faraday, *The Chemical History of a Candle* (Harper, 1861).

William B. Jensen, "To Demonstrate the Truths of 'Chymistry': An Historical and Pictorial Celebration of the Art of the Lecture Demonstration in Honor of Dr. Hubert Alyea," *Bulletin for the History of Chemistry* (Fall 1991, pp. 3–15).

Thomas O'Brien, "The Science and Art of Science Demonstrations," *Journal of Chemical Education* (November 1991, pp. 933–936).

Bassam Z. Shakhashiri, *Chemical Demonstrations: A Handbook for Teachers of Chemistry* (University of Wisconsin Press; vol. 1, 1983; vol. 2, 1985; vol. 3, 1989; vol. 4, 1992).

Charles Taylor, *The Art and Science of Lecture Demonstration* (Adam Hilger, 1988).

Hans Toftlund, "History of the Lecture Demonstration," *Education in Chemistry* (July 1988, pp. 109–111).

Encyclopædia
Britannica
Science Update

Major Revisions from the 1994 *Macropædia*

The purpose of this section is to introduce to continuing *Yearbook of Science and the Future* subscribers selected *Macropædia* articles or portions of them that have been revised or written anew. It is intended to update the *Macropædia* in ways that cannot be accomplished fully by reviewing the year's events or by revising statistics annually, because the *Macropædia* texts themselves—written from a longer perspective than any yearly revision—supply authoritative interpretation and analysis as well as narrative and description.

Several sections of the major article MATTER: Its Properties, States, Varieties, and Behaviour have been chosen from the 1994 printing. Each is the work of distinguished scholars, and each represents the continuing dedication of the *Encyclopædia Britannica* to bringing such works to the general reader.

Matter: Its Properties, States, Varieties, and Behaviour

SOLID STATE

Quasicrystals

Quasicrystals are metal alloys whose novel symmetries challenge the traditional dogma of crystallography. Although they appear at casual inspection to be ordinary crystals, they are not. Their symmetries elude the classification scheme of crystal structures, which enumerates the combinations of translational and rotational symmetries that are allowed according to the laws of crystallography. While ordinary crystals place atoms in periodic lattices, quasicrystals arrange atoms in a quasiperiodic fashion. Although these structures surprised the scientific community, it now appears that quasicrystals rank among the most common structures in alloys of aluminum with such metals as iron, cobalt, or nickel. While no major commercial applications yet exploit properties of the quasicrystalline state directly, quasicrystals form in compounds noted for their high strength and light weight, suggesting potential applications in aerospace and other industries.

STRUCTURE AND SYMMETRY

Dan Shechtman, a researcher from Technion, a part of the Israel Institute of Technology, and his colleagues at the National Bureau of Standards (now the National Institute of Standards and Technology) in Gaithersburg, Md., discovered quasicrystals in 1984. A research program of the U.S. Air Force sponsored their investigation of the metallurgical properties of aluminum-iron and aluminum-manganese alloys. Shechtman and his coworkers mixed aluminum and manganese in a roughly six-to-one proportion and heated the mixture until it melted. The mixture was then rapidly cooled back into the solid state by dropping the liquid onto a cold spinning wheel, a process known as melt spinning. When the solidified alloy was examined using an electron microscope, a novel structure was revealed. It exhibited fivefold symmetry, which is forbidden in crystals, and long-range order, which is lacking in amorphous solids. Its order, therefore, was neither amorphous nor crystalline. Many other alloys with these same features have subsequently been produced.

Discovery of quasicrystals

The electron microscope has played a significant role in the investigation of quasicrystals. It is a versatile tool that can probe many important aspects of the structure of matter. Low-resolution scanning electron microscopy magnifies the shapes of individual grains. Grains of a quasicrystalline aluminum-copper-iron alloy imaged with this technique are shown in Figure 18. Symmetries of solid grains often reflect the internal symmetries of the underlying atomic positions. Grains of salt, for example, take cubical shapes consistent with the cubic symmetries of their crystal lattices. The shape observed in Figure 18 is called a pentagonal dodecahedron. Its 12 faces are regular pentagons, with axes of fivefold rotational symmetry passing through them. That is to say, rotations about this axis by 72° leave the appearance of the grain unchanged. In a full 360° rotation the grain will repeat itself in appearance five times, once every 72°. There are also axes of twofold rotational symmetry passing through the edges and axes of threefold rotational symmetry passing through the vertices. This is also known as icosahedral symmetry because the icosahedron is the geometric dual of the pentagonal dodecahedron. At the centre of each face on an icosahedron, the dodecahedron places a vertex, and vice versa. The symmetry of a pentagonal dodecahedron or icosahedron is not among the symmetries of any crystal structure, yet this is the symmetry that was revealed in the electron microscope image of the aluminum-manganese alloy produced by Shechtman and his colleagues.

High-resolution electron microscopy magnifies to such a great degree that patterns of atomic positions may be determined. In ordinary crystals such a lattice image reveals regularly spaced rows of atoms. Regular spacing implies spatial periodicity in the placement of atoms. The angles between rows indicate rotational symmetries of the atomic positions. A high-resolution electron microscope image of quasicrystalline aluminum-manganese-silicon is shown in Figure 19. Rows of atoms may be visualized by glancing along the page. Parallel rows occur in five sets, rotated from one another by 72°, confirming that the fivefold symmetry suggested by the shape of the pentagonal dodecahedron grain reflects a fivefold symmetry in the actual placement of atoms.

F.W. Gayle, *Journal of Metals*, vol. 40, no. 5, May 1988

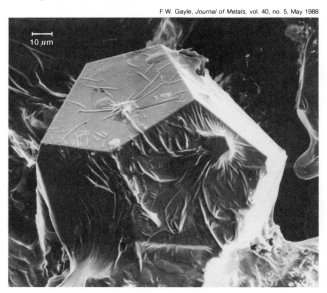

10 μm

Figure 18: A scanning electron microscope image of quasicrystalline aluminum-copper-iron, revealing the pentagonal dodecahedral shape of the grain.

Trans-
lational
periodicity

Fivefold symmetry axes are forbidden in ordinary crystals, while other axes, such as sixfold axes, are allowed. The reason is that translational periodicity, which is characteristic of crystal lattices, cannot be present in structures with fivefold symmetry. Figures 20 and 21 can be used to illustrate this concept. The triangular array of atoms in Figure 20 has axes of sixfold rotational symmetry passing through each atomic position. The arrows represent translational symmetries of this crystalline structure. That is, if the entire array of atoms is displaced along one of these arrows, say the one labeled *a*, all new atomic positions coincide with the locations of other atoms prior to the displacement. Such a displacement of atoms that leaves atomic positions invariant is called a symmetry of the crystal. In Figure 20, if two different symmetries are combined such that the structure is first displaced along arrow *a* and then along arrow *b*, the net result is equivalent to a displacement along arrow *c*, which itself must be a symmetry of the structure. Again, atomic sites coincide before

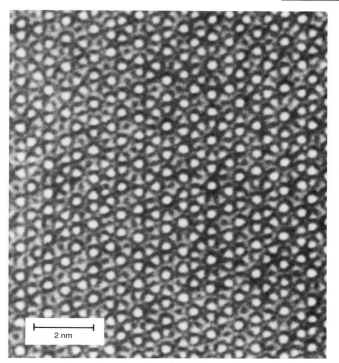

2 nm

Figure 19: A high-resolution electron microscope image of quasicrystalline aluminum-manganese-silicon, revealing a fivefold symmetry of atomic positions. A glancing view along this figure reveals a Fibonacci sequence of dark and light rows.
Courtesy, Kenji Hiraga

and after the displacement. Repeated displacements along the same arrow demonstrate the translational periodicity of the crystal.

The atomic arrangement shown in Figure 21 exhibits fivefold rotational symmetry but lacks the translational symmetries that must be present in a crystalline structure. The arrows (other than arrow *c*) represent displacements that leave the arrangement invariant. Assume they are the shortest such displacements. Now, as before, consider the combinations of two symmetries *a* and *b* with the net result *c*. The length of *c* is smaller than either *a* or *b* by a factor $\tau = (\sqrt{5} + 1)/2$, which is known as the golden mean. The new atomic position, outlined with a dotted line, does not coincide with a previous atomic position, indicating that the structure does not exhibit translational periodicity. Therefore, an array of atoms may not simultaneously display fivefold rotational symmetry and translational periodicity, for, if it did, there would be no lower limit to the spacing between atoms.

In fact, the compatibility of translational periodicity with sixfold rotational symmetry (as shown in Figure 20) is a remarkable accident, for translational periodicity is not possible with most rotational symmetries. The only

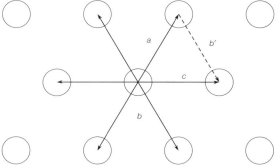

Figure 20: *Hexagonal lattice of atomic sites.*
Arrows indicate translational symmetries of the lattice.
Combining two symmetries (*a* and *b*) produces a third (*c*).

Figure 21: *Pentagonal arrangement of atoms.*
Arrows indicate hypothetical shortest translational symmetries. Combining two displacements produces a new displacement that is shorter than the hypothetical symmetries.

allowed symmetry axes in periodic crystals are twofold, threefold, fourfold, and sixfold. All others are forbidden owing to the lack of minimum interatomic separation. In particular, fivefold, eightfold, tenfold, and twelvefold axes cannot exist in crystals. These symmetries are mentioned in particular because they have been reported in quasicrystalline alloys.

Since the aluminum-manganese-silicon quasicrystal shown in Figure 19 clearly reveals an axis of fivefold symmetry, it may be concluded that the arrangement of atoms lacks translational periodicity. That, in itself, is no great surprise, for many materials lack translational periodicity. Amorphous metals, for example, are frequently produced by the same melt-spinning process that was employed in the discovery of quasicrystals. Amorphous metals have no discrete rotational symmetries, however, and high-resolution electron microscope images reveal no rows of atoms. The arrangement of atoms in a quasicrystal displays a property called long-range order, which is lacking in amorphous metals. Long-range order permits rows of atoms to span Figure 19 and maintains agreement of row orientations across the figure. Ordinary crystal structures, such as that of Figure 20, display long-range order. Strict rules govern the relative placement of atoms at remote locations in solids with long-range order.

Electron diffraction confirms the presence of long-range order in both crystals and quasicrystals. Quantum mechanics predicts that particles such as electrons move through space as if they were waves, in the same manner that light travels. When light waves strike a diffraction grating, they are diffracted. White light breaks up into a rainbow, while monochromatic light breaks up into discrete sharp spots. Similarly, when electrons strike evenly spaced rows of atoms within a crystalline solid, they break up into a set of bright spots known as Bragg diffraction peaks. Symmetrical arrangements of spots reveal axes of rotational symmetry in the crystal, and spacings between the discrete spots relate inversely to translational periodicities. Amorphous metals contain only diffuse rings in their diffraction patterns since long-range coherence in atomic positions is required to achieve sharp diffraction spots.

The original electron diffraction pattern of quasicrystalline aluminum-manganese published by Shechtman and his coworkers is shown in Figure 22. Rings of 10 bright spots indicate axes of fivefold symmetry, and rings of six bright spots indicate axes of threefold symmetry. The twofold symmetry axes are self-evident. The angles between these axes, indicated on the figure, agree with the geometry of the icosahedron. The very existence of spots at all indicates long-range order in atomic positions. Recalling the earlier result that fivefold symmetry axes are forbidden in crystalline materials, a paradox is presented by quasicrystals. They have long-range order in their atomic positions, but they must lack spatial periodicity.

Dov Levine and Paul Steinhardt, physicists at the University of Pennsylvania, proposed a resolution of this apparent conflict. They suggested that the translational order

of atoms in quasicrystalline alloys might be quasiperiodic rather than periodic. Quasiperiodic patterns share certain characteristics with periodic patterns. In particular, both are deterministic—that is, rules exist that specify the entire pattern. These rules create long-range order. Both periodic and quasiperiodic patterns have diffraction patterns consisting entirely of Bragg peaks. The difference between quasiperiodicity and periodicity is that a quasiperiodic pattern never repeats itself. There are no translational symmetries, and, consequently, there is no minimum spacing between Bragg peaks. Although the peaks are discrete, they fill the diffraction pattern densely.

The most well-known quasiperiodic pattern may be the Fibonacci sequence, discovered during the Middle Ages in the course of studies conducted on rabbit reproduction. Consider the following rules for birth and maturation of rabbits. Start with a single mature rabbit (denoted by the symbol L for large) and a baby rabbit (denoted by S for small). In each generation every L rabbit gives birth to a new S rabbit, while each preexisting S rabbit matures into an L rabbit. A table of rabbit sequences may be established as follows. Start with an L and an S side by side along a line. Replace the L with LS and the S with L to obtain LSL and repeat the procedure as shown in Table 1. The numbers of rabbits present after each generation are the Fibonacci numbers. The population grows exponentially over time, with the population of each generation approaching τ (the golden mean) multiplied by the population of the previous generation. The sequence of L and S symbols forms a quasiperiodic pattern. It has no subunit that repeats itself periodically. In contrast, a periodic sequence such as LSLLSLLSLLSLLSL . . . has a fundamental unit (LSL) that is precisely repeated at equal intervals. In crystallography such a repeated unit is called a unit cell. Quasiperiodic sequences have no unit cell of finite size. Any portion of the Fibonacci sequence is repeated in-

(Left) D. Shechtman, *Physical Review Letters*, vol. 53, no. 20, Nov. 1984

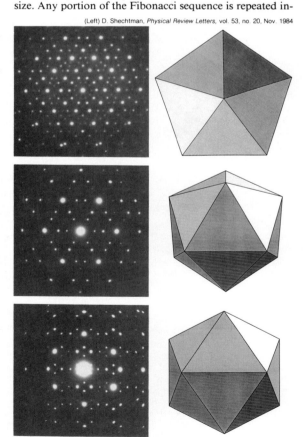

Figure 22: (Left) Electron diffraction patterns of quasicrystalline aluminum-manganese. (Top left) View is along the fivefold symmetry axis; (centre left) rotating by 37.38° reveals the threefold axis, and (bottom left) rotating by 58.29° reveals the twofold axis. (Right) Corresponding views of icosahedrons show that quasicrystalline symmetries match those of the icosahedrons.

generation	sequence	mature rabbits	babies
1	LS	1	1
2	LSL	2	1
3	LSLLS	3	2
4	LSLLSLSL	5	3
5	LSLLSLSLLSLLS	8	5
6	LSLLSLSLLSLLSLSLLSLSL	13	8

Table 1: Fibonacci Sequences of Rabbits

finitely often, but at intervals that are not periodic. These intervals themselves form a Fibonacci sequence.

An example of a two-dimensional pattern that combines fivefold rotational symmetry with quasiperiodic translational order is the Penrose pattern, discovered by the English mathematical physicist Roger Penrose and shown in Figure 23. The diffraction pattern of such a sequence closely resembles the fivefold symmetric patterns of Figure 22. The rhombic tiles are arranged in sets of parallel rows; the shaded tiles represent one such set, or family. Five families of parallel rows are present in the figure, with 72° angles between the families, although only one of the five has been shaded. Within a family the spacings between rows are either large (L) or small (S), as labeled in the margin. The ratio of widths of the large rows to the small rows is equal to the golden mean τ, and the quasiperiodic sequence of large and small follows the Fibonacci sequence. An example of the use of Penrose tilings in an architectural application is shown in Figure 24.

Levine's and Steinhardt's proposal that quasicrystals possess quasiperiodic translational order can be examined in terms of the high-resolution electron micrograph in Figure 19. The rows of bright spots are separated by small and large intervals. As in the Penrose pattern, the length of the large interval divided by the length of the small one equals the golden mean, and the sequence of large and small reproduces the Fibonacci sequence. Levine's and Steinhardt's proposal appears consistent with the electron diffraction results. The origin of the name quasicrystals arises from the fact that these materials have quasiperiodic translational order, as opposed to the periodic order of ordinary crystals.

Figures 18, 19, and 22 represent quasicrystals with the symmetry of an icosahedron. Icosahedral quasicrystals occur in many intermetallic compounds, including aluminum-copper-iron, aluminum-manganese-palladium, aluminum-magnesium-zinc, and aluminum-copper-lithium. Other crystallographically forbidden symmetries have been observed as well. These include decagonal symmetry, which exhibits tenfold rotational symmetry within two-dimensional atomic layers but ordinary translational periodicity perpendicular to these layers. Decagonal symmetry has been found in the compounds aluminum-copper-cobalt and aluminum-nickel-cobalt. Structures that are periodic in two dimensions but follow a Fibonacci sequence in the remaining third dimension occur in aluminum-copper-nickel.

All the compounds named thus far contain aluminum. Indeed, it appears that aluminum is unusually prone to quasicrystal formation, but there do exist icosahedral quasicrystals without it. Some, like gallium-magnesium-zinc, simply substitute the chemically similar element gallium for aluminum. Others, like titanium-manganese, appear chemically unrelated to aluminum-based compounds. Furthermore, some quasicrystals such as chromium-nickel-silicon and vanadium-nickel-silicon display octagonal and dodecagonal structures with eightfold or twelvefold symmetry, respectively, within layers and translational periodicity perpendicular to the layers.

The origin of quasicrystalline order remains in question. No proven explanation clarifies why a material favours crystallographically forbidden rotational symmetry and translational quasiperiodicity when at nearby compositions it forms more conventional crystal structures. The American chemist Linus Pauling noted that these related crystalline structures frequently contain icosahedral motifs within their unit cells, which are then repeated periodically. Pauling proposed that quasicrystals are really ordinary crystalline materials caught out of equilibrium by a

type of crystal defect called twinning, in which unit cells are attached at angles defined by these icosahedral motifs. While this may be a reasonable model for rapidly cooled alloys such as Shechtman's original aluminum-manganese, other compounds, such as aluminum-copper-iron, possess quasicrystalline structures in thermodynamic equilibrium. These quasicrystals can be grown slowly and carefully using techniques for growth of high-quality conventional crystals. The more slowly the quasicrystal grows, the more perfect will be its rotational symmetry and quasiperiodicity. Measuring the sharpness of diffraction pattern spots shows perfect ordering on length scales of at least 30,000 angstroms in these carefully prepared quasicrystals. Twinning cannot account for such long-range order.

Levine and Steinhardt proposed that matching rules, such as those Penrose discovered to determine proper placement of his tiles to fill the plane quasiperiodically, may force the atoms into predefined, low-energy locations. Such a mechanism cannot be the complete explanation, though, since the compound forms ordinary crystalline structures at nearby compositions and temperatures. Indeed, it appears that, when quasicrystals are thermodynamically stable phases, it is only over a limited range of temperatures close to the melting point. At lower temperatures they transform into ordinary crystal structures. Thermodynamics predicts that the stable structure is the one that minimizes the free energy, defined as the ordinary energy minus the product of the temperature and the entropy. It is likely that entropy (a measure of fluctuations around an ideal structure) must be considered in addition to energy to explain stability of quasicrystals.

PROPERTIES

Along with their novel structures and symmetries, quasicrystals are expected to exhibit unusual properties. Both their elastic and their electronic behaviour distinguish quasicrystals from ordinary crystalline metals. Elastic response may be studied by measuring the speed of sound waves propagating through the metal. Sound speeds usually vary depending on the direction of propagation relative to axes of high rotational symmetry. Because the icosahedron has such high symmetry—it is closer to a sphere than is, for instance, a cube—the sound speeds turn out to be independent of the direction of propagation. Longitudinal sound waves (with displacements parallel to the direction of propagation) have speeds different from transverse waves (with displacements perpendicular to the direction of propagation), as is the case for all matter. Because the sound speeds do not depend on direction of propagation, only two elastic constants are required to specify acoustic properties of icosahedral quasicrystals. In contrast, cubic crystals require three elastic constants, and lower-symmetry crystals require up to 21 constants.

As a consequence of the translational quasiperiodicity, there exists a second type of elastic deformation beyond the ordinary sound wave, or phonon. Known as phasons,

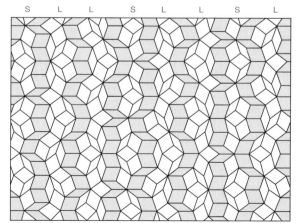

Figure 23: A Penrose tiling.
The plane is covered by rhombuses (deformed squares). Tiles with parallel edges lie in rows (shaded) separated by large (L) and small (S) intervals.

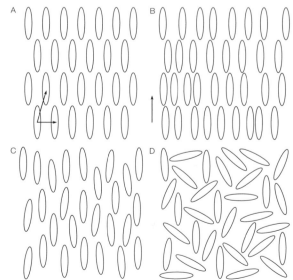

Figure 24: *Penrose tiles*.
Penrose tilings are used in architectural applications, as in these ceramic tiles coloured to
emphasize the five-pointed stars and bands.
By courtesy of Saxe-Patterson Ceramics for Architecture

these elastic deformations correspond to rearrangements
of the relative atomic positions. Removal of a phason
requires adjusting positions of all atoms within a row of
atoms in a quasicrystalline structure. At low temperatures
motion of atoms within the solid is difficult, and phason
strain may be easily frozen into the quasicrystal, limiting
its perfection. At high temperatures, close to the melting point, phasons continually fluctuate, and atoms jump
from place to place.

The electric properties of quasicrystals have proved to be
rather unusual. Unlike their constituent elements, which
tend to be good electrical conductors, quasicrystals conduct electricity poorly. For alloys of aluminum-copper-
ruthenium these conductivities differ by as much as a
factor of 100. As the perfection of the quasicrystalline
order grows, the conductivity drops. Such behaviour is
consistent with the appearance of a gap in the electronic
density of states at the Fermi surface, which is the energy
level separating filled electronic states from empty ones.
Since it is only Fermi-surface electrons that carry current,
a vanishingly small density of such electronic states leads
to low electrical conductivities in semiconductors and insulators. Such a gap in the density of states may also
play a role in explaining the formation of quasicrystalline
structures. This is known as the Hume-Rothery rule for
alloy formation. Since the Fermi-surface electrons are the
highest-energy electrons, diminishing the number of such
electrons may lower the overall energy.

The mechanical properties of quasicrystals are especially
significant because the desire to develop a material that
exhibited these properties motivated the investigators who
discovered quasicrystals. Mechanical properties also relate
to their first potential practical applications. Quasicrystals
are exceptionally brittle. They have few dislocations, and
those present have low mobility. Since metals bend by
creating and moving dislocations, the near absence of dis-
location motion causes brittleness. On the positive side,
the difficulty of moving dislocations makes quasicrystals
extremely hard. They strongly resist deformation. This
makes them excellent candidates for high-strength surface
coatings. Indeed, the first successful application of quasicrystals was as a surface treatment for aluminum frying
pans.

Liquid crystals

Liquid crystals, their very name an oxymoron, blend
structures and properties of the normally disparate liquid
and crystalline solid states. Liquids can flow, for example,
while solids cannot, and crystalline solids possess special
symmetry properties that liquids lack. Ordinary solids melt
into ordinary liquids as the temperature increases—*e.g.*,
ice melts into liquid water. Some solids actually melt twice

or more as temperature rises. Between the crystalline solid
at low temperatures and the ordinary liquid state at high
temperatures lies an intermediate state, the liquid crystal.
Liquid crystals share with liquids the ability to flow but
also display symmetries inherited from crystalline solids.
The resulting combination of liquid and solid properties
allows important applications of liquid crystals in the displays of such devices as wristwatches, calculators, portable
computers, and flat-screen televisions.

STRUCTURE AND SYMMETRY

Crystals exhibit special symmetries when they slide in
certain directions or rotate through certain angles. These
symmetries can be compared to those encountered when
walking in a straight line through empty space. Regardless
of the direction or distance of each step, the view remains
the same, as there are no landmarks by which to measure one's progress. This is called continuous translational
symmetry because all positions look identical. Figure 25A
illustrates a crystal in two dimensions. Such a crystal lat-

Figure 25: *Arrangements of molecules*.
(A) Ordinary crystals break the continuous rotational and
translational symmetry of free space; discrete symmetries
remain. (B) Smectic liquid crystals show broken translational
symmetry in only one direction. (C) Nematic liquid crystals
break only rotational symmetry. (D) Isotropic liquids share
the continuous translational and rotational symmetry of
free space. This symmetry may not be apparent in a single
snapshot of molecular positions and orientations.

Electric
properties

Trans-
lational
symmetry

tice breaks the continuous translational symmetry of free space; starting at one molecule there is a finite distance to travel before reaching the next. Some translational symmetry is present, however, because, by moving the proper distance in the proper direction, one is guaranteed to locate additional molecules on repeated excursions. This property is called discrete translational periodicity. The two-dimensional picture of a crystal displays translational periodicity in two independent directions. Real, three-dimensional crystals display translational periodicity in three independent directions.

Rotational symmetries can be considered in a similar fashion. From one point in empty space, the view is the same regardless of which direction one looks. There is continuous rotational symmetry—namely, the symmetry of a perfect sphere. In the crystal shown in Figure 25A, however, the distance to the nearest molecule from any given molecule depends on the direction taken. Furthermore, the molecules themselves may have shapes that are less symmetric than a sphere. A crystal possesses a certain discrete set of angles of rotation that leave the appearance unchanged. The continuous rotational symmetry of empty space is broken, and only a discrete symmetry exists. Broken rotational symmetry influences many important properties of crystals. Their resistance to compression, for example, may vary according to the direction along which one squeezes the crystal. Transparent crystals, such as quartz, may exhibit an optical property known as birefringence. When a light ray passes through a birefringent crystal, it is bent, or refracted, at an angle depending on the direction of the light and also its polarization, so that the single ray is broken up into two polarized rays. This is why one sees a double image when looking through such crystals.

In a liquid such as the one shown in Figure 25D, all the molecules sit in random positions with random orientations. This does not mean that there is less symmetry than in the crystal, however. All positions are actually equivalent to one another, and likewise all orientations are equivalent, because in a liquid the molecules are in constant motion. At one instant the molecules in the liquid may occupy the positions and orientations shown in Figure 25D, but a moment later the molecules will move to previously empty points in space. Likewise, at one instant a molecule points in one direction, and the next instant it points in another. Liquids share the homogeneity and

Symmetry of liquids

isotropy of empty space; they have continuous translational and rotational symmetries. No form of matter has greater symmetry.

As a general rule, molecules solidify into crystal lattices with low symmetry at low temperatures. Both translational and rotational symmetries are discrete. At high temperatures, after melting, liquids have high symmetry. Translational and rotational symmetries are continuous. High temperatures provide molecules with the energy needed for motion. The mobility disorders the crystal and raises its symmetry. Low temperatures limit motion and the possible molecular arrangements. As a result, molecules remain relatively immobile in low-energy, low-symmetry configurations.

Liquid crystals, sometimes called mesophases, occupy the middle ground between crystalline solids and ordinary liquids with regard to symmetry, energy, and properties. Not all molecules have liquid crystal phases. Water molecules, for example, melt directly from solid crystalline ice into liquid water. The most widely studied liquid-crystal-forming molecules are elongated, rodlike molecules, rather like grains of rice in shape (but far smaller in size). A popular example is the molecule p-azoxyanisole (PAA):

$$CH_3-O-\!\!\!\bigcirc\!\!\!-N=N-\!\!\!\bigcirc\!\!\!-O-CH_3$$
$$\downarrow$$
$$O$$

Liquid crystal structures

Typical liquid crystal structures include the smectic shown in Figure 25B and the nematic in Figure 25C (this nomenclature, invented in the 1920s by the French scientist Georges Friedel, will be explained below). The smectic phase differs from the solid phase in that translational symmetry is discrete in one direction—the vertical in Figure 25B—and continuous in the remaining two. The continuous translational symmetry is horizontal in the figure, because molecule positions are disordered and mobile in this direction. The remaining direction with continuous translational symmetry is not visible, because this figure is only two-dimensional. To envision its three-dimensional structure, imagine the figure extending out of the page.

In the nematic phase all translational symmetries are continuous. The molecule positions are disordered in all directions. Their orientations are all alike, however, so that the rotational symmetry remains discrete. The orientation of the long axis of a nematic molecule is called its director. In Figure 25C the nematic director is vertical.

It was noted above that, as temperature decreases, matter tends to evolve from highly disordered states with continuous symmetries toward ordered states with discrete symmetries. This can occur through a sequence of symmetry-breaking phase transitions. As a substance in the liquid state is reduced in temperature, rotational symmetry breaking creates the nematic liquid crystal state in which molecules are aligned along a common axis. Their directors are all nearly parallel. At lower temperatures continuous translational symmetries break into discrete symmetries. There are three independent directions for translational symmetry. When continuous translational symmetry is broken along only one direction, the smectic liquid crystal is obtained. At temperatures sufficiently low to break continuous translational symmetry in all directions, the ordinary crystal is formed.

The mechanism by which liquid crystalline order is favoured can be illustrated through an analogy between molecules and grains of rice. Collisions of molecules require energy, so the greater the energy, the greater the tolerance for collisions. If rice grains are poured into a pan, they fall at random positions and orientations and tend to jam up against their neighbours. This is similar to the liquid state illustrated in Figure 25D. After the pan is shaken to allow the rice grains to readjust their positions, the neighbouring grains tend to line up. The alignment is not perfect across the sample owing to defects, which also can occur in nematic liquid crystals. When all grains align, they have greater freedom to move before hitting a neighbour than they have when they are disordered. This produces the nematic phase, illustrated in Figure 25C. The freedom to move is primarily in the direction of molecular alignment, as sideways motion quickly results in collision with a neighbour. Layering the grains, as illustrated in Figure 25B, enhances sideways motion. This produces the smectic phase. In the smectic phase some molecules have ample free volume to move in, while others are tightly packed. The lowest-energy arrangement shares the free volume equitably among molecules. Each molecular environment matches all others, and the structure is a crystal like that illustrated in Figure 25A.

Rice-grain analogy

There is a great variety of liquid crystalline structures known in addition to those described so far. Table 2 relates some of the chief structures according to their degree and type of order. The smectic-C phase and those listed below it have molecules tilted with respect to the layers. Continuous in-plane rotational symmetry, present within smectic-A layers, is broken in the hexatic-B phase, but a proliferation of dislocations maintains continuous translational symmetry within its layers. A similar relationship holds between smectic-C and smectic-F. Crystal-B and crystal-G have molecular positions on regular crystal lattice sites, with long axes of molecules (directors) aligned, but allow rotation of molecules about their directors. These are the so-called plastic crystals. Many interesting liquid crystal phases are not listed in this table, including the discotic phase, consisting of disk-shaped molecules, and the columnar phases, in which translational symmetry is broken in not one but two spatial directions, leaving liquidlike order only along columns. The degree of order increases from the top to the bottom of the table. In general, phases from the top of the table are expected at high temperatures, and phases from the bottom at low temperatures.

Table 2: Selected Phases Characteristic of Liquid-Crystal-Forming Molecules

phase		order
Isotropic liquid Nematic		full continuous translational and rotational symmetry molecular orientation breaks rotational symmetry
untilted	tilted	
Smectic-A Hexatic-B Crystal-B	Smectic-C Smectic-F Crystal-G	layering breaks translational symmetry; smectic-C molecules are tilted bond orientational order breaks rotational symmetry within layers crystallization breaks translational symmetry within layers; molecules may rotate about their long axis
Crystal-E	Crystal-H	molecular rotation freezes out

Structure of soap molecules

Liquid-crystal-forming compounds are widespread and quite diverse. Soap (see Figure 26) can form a type of smectic known as a lamellar phase, also called neat soap. In this case it is important to recognize that soap molecules have a dual chemical nature. One end of the molecule (the hydrocarbon tail) is attracted to oil, while the other end (the polar head) attaches itself to water. When soap is placed in water, the hydrocarbon tails cluster together, while the polar heads adjoin the water. Small numbers of soap molecules form spherical or rodlike micelles (Figure 26B), which float freely in the water, while concentrated solutions create bilayers (Figure 26C), which stack along some direction just like smectic layers. Indeed, the name smectic is derived from the Greek word for soap. The slippery feeling caused by soap reflects the ease with which the layers slide across one another.

Biologically important liquid crystals

Many biological materials form liquid crystals. Myelin, a fatty material extracted from nerve cells, was the first intensively studied liquid crystal. The tobacco mosaic virus, with its rodlike shape, forms a nematic phase. In cholesterol the nematic phase is modified to a cholesteric phase characterized by continuous rotation of the direction of molecular alignment. An intrinsic twist of the cholesterol molecule, rather like the twist of the threads of a screw, causes this rotation. Since the molecular orientation rotates steadily, there is a characteristic distance after which the orientation repeats itself. This distance is frequently comparable to the wavelength of visible light, so brilliant colour effects result from the diffraction of light by these materials.

Perhaps the first description of a liquid crystal occurred in the story *The Narrative of Arthur Gordon Pym,* by Edgar Allan Poe:

> I am at a loss to give a distinct idea of the nature of this liquid, and cannot do so without many words. Although it flowed with rapidity in all declivities where common water would do so, yet never, except when falling in a cascade, had it the customary appearance of *limpidity.* ... At first sight, and especially in cases where little declivity was found, it bore resemblance, as regards consistency, to a thick infusion of gum Arabic in common water. But this was only the least remarkable of its extraordinary qualities. It was *not* colourless, nor was it of any one uniform colour—presenting to the eye, as it flowed, every possible shade of purple, like the hues of a changeable silk. ... Upon collecting a basinful, and allowing

it to settle thoroughly, we perceived that the whole mass of liquid was made up of a number of distinct veins, each of a distinct hue; that these veins did not commingle; and that their cohesion was perfect in regard to their own particles among themselves, and imperfect in regard to neighbouring veins. Upon passing the blade of a knife athwart the veins, the water closed over it immediately, as with us, and also, in withdrawing it, all traces of the passage of the knife were instantly obliterated. If, however, the blade was passed accurately between two veins, a perfect separation was effected, which the power of cohesion did not immediately rectify.

The liquid described in this passage is human blood. In its usual state within the human body, blood is an ordinary disordered isotropic fluid. The disklike shape of red blood cells, however, favours liquid crystallinity at certain concentrations and temperatures.

OPTICAL PROPERTIES

An understanding of the principal technological applications of liquid crystals requires a knowledge of their optical properties. Liquid crystals alter the polarization of light passing through them. Light waves are actually waves in electric and magnetic fields. The direction of the electric field is the polarization of the light wave. A polarizing filter selects a single component of polarized light to pass through while absorbing all other components of incoming waves. If a second polarizing filter is placed above the first but with its polarization axis rotated by 90°, no light can pass through because the polarization passed by the first filter is precisely the polarization blocked by the second filter. When optically active materials, such as liquid crystals, are placed between polarizing filters crossed in this manner, some light may get through, because the intervening material changes the polarization of the light. If the nematic director is not aligned with either of the polarizing filters, polarized light passing through the first filter becomes partially polarized along the nematic director. This component of light in turn possesses a component aligned with the top polarizing filter, so a fraction of the incoming light passes through the entire assembly. The amount of light passing through is largest when the nematic director is positioned at a 45° angle from both filters. The light is fully blocked when the director lies parallel to one filter or the other.

During the last decades of the 19th century, pioneering

From G.H. Brown, J.D. Doane, and V.D. Neff, *A Review of the Structure and Physical Properties of Liquid Crystals,* CRC Press, Inc., 1971; reproduced by permission of the *Journal of the Society of Cosmetic Chemists*

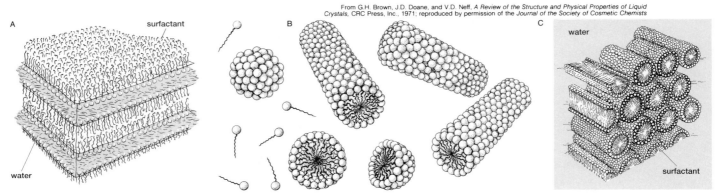

Figure 26: *Structures of soap in water.*
(A) The smectic phase, also called the neat phase. (B) Spherical and rodlike micelles formed by soap molecules; they float freely in dilute solutions. (C) Bilayer packing of rodlike micelles in a concentrated solution.

investigators of liquid crystals, such as the German physicist Otto Lehmann and the Austrian botanist Friedrich Reinitzer, equipped ordinary microscopes with pairs of polarizing filters. Typical microscope images of nematic and smectic phases taken through crossed polarizers are shown in Figure 27. Spatial variation in the alignment of the nematic director causes spatial variation in light intensity. Since the nematic is defined by having all di-

rectors nearly parallel to one another, the images arise from defects in the nematic structure. Figure 27 (bottom) illustrates a manner in which the directors may rotate or bend around defect lines. The resulting threadlike images inspired the name nematic, which is based on the Greek word for thread. The layered smectic structure causes layering of defects in Figure 27 (centre).

Nonuniformity in director alignment may be induced

(Top and bottom) From Jurgen Nehring and Alfred Saupe, *Journal of The Chemical Society, Faraday Transactions II*, 1972, vol. 68, 1–15; © copyright 1972 by The Chemical Society, London; (centre) Dietrich Demus

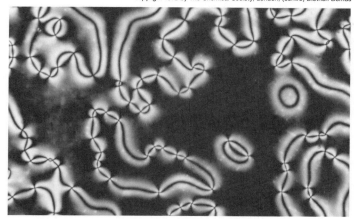

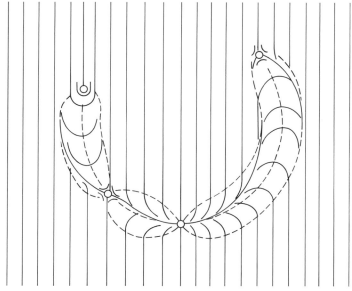

Figure 27: (Top) Nematic and (centre) smectic liquid crystals viewed through microscopes equipped with crossed polarizers. (Bottom) Spatial variation of the director, causing the threadlike image seen in the photograph at top.

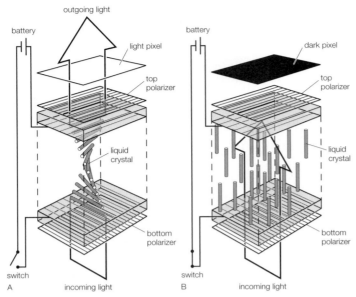

Figure 28: *A twisted-nematic cell.*
(A) The assembly is transparent to light in the absence of
an electric field. (B) An applied field destroys the twist of the
nematic, rendering the assembly opaque.

From J. Funfschilling, "Liquid Crystals and Liquid Crystal Displays," *Condensed Matter News*, vol. 1, no. 1, 1991;
Gordon and Breach Science Publishers

The twisted-nematic cell

artificially. The surfaces of a glass container can be coated
with a material that, when rubbed in the proper direction,
forces the director to lie perpendicular or parallel to the
wall adjacent to a nematic liquid crystal. The orientation
forced by one wall need not be consistent with that forced
by another wall; this situation causes the director orientation to vary in between the walls. The nematic must
compromise its preference for all directors to be parallel
to one another with the inconsistent orienting forces of
the container walls. In doing so, the liquid crystal may
take on a twisted alignment across the container (see Figure 28A.) Electric or magnetic fields provide an alternate
means of influencing the orientation of the nematic directors. Molecules may prefer to align so that their director
is, say, parallel to an applied electric field.

Optical behaviour and orienting fields underlie the important contemporary use of liquid crystals as optoelectronic displays. Consider, for example, the twisted-
nematic cell shown in Figure 28A. The polarizer surfaces
are coated and rubbed so that the nematic will align with
the polarizing axis. The two polarizers are crossed, forcing
the nematic to rotate between them. The rotation is slow
and smooth, assuming a 90° twist across the cell. Light
passing through the first polarizer is aligned with the bottom of the nematic layer. As the nematic twists, it rotates
the polarization of the light so that, as the light leaves
the top of the nematic layer, its polarization is rotated by
90° from that at the bottom. The new polarization is just
right for passing through the top filter, and so light travels
unhindered through the assembly.

If an electric field is applied in the direction of light
propagation, the liquid crystal directors align with the
orienting field, so they are no longer parallel to the light
passing though the bottom polarizer (Figure 28B). They
are no longer capable of rotating this polarization through
the 90° needed to allow the light to emerge from the
top polarizer. Although this assembly is transparent when
no field is applied, it becomes opaque when the field is
present. A grid of such assemblies placed side by side may
be used to display images. If one turns on the electric field
attached to the parts of the grid that lie where the image
is to appear, these points will turn black while the remaining points of the grid stay white. The resulting patchwork
of dark and light creates the image on the display. In a
wristwatch, calculator, or computer these may be simply
numbers or letters, and in a television the images may
be detailed pictures. Switching the electric fields on or off
will cause the picture to move, just as ordinary television
pictures display an ever-changing stream of electrically
encoded images.   (Michael Widom)

PLASMA STATE

The plasma state of matter is unique like the solid, liquid, and gaseous states and is often considered the fourth state of matter. A plasma is an electrically conducting medium in which there are nearly equal numbers of positive and negative charges. The negative charge is usually carried by electrons, each of which has one unit of negative charge. The positive charge is typically carried by atoms or molecules that are missing those same electrons. In some rare but interesting cases, electrons missing from one type of atom or molecule become attached to another component, resulting in a plasma containing both positive and negative ions. The most extreme case of this type occurs when small but macroscopic dust particles become charged in a state referred to as a dusty plasma. The uniqueness of the plasma state is due to the importance of electric and magnetic forces that act on a plasma in addition to such forces as gravity that affect all forms of matter. Since these electromagnetic forces can act at large distances, a plasma will act collectively much like a fluid even when the particles seldom collide with one another.

Nearly all the visible matter in the universe exists in the plasma state, occurring predominantly in this form in the Sun and stars and in interplanetary and interstellar space. Auroras, lightning, and welding arcs are also plasmas; plasmas exist in neon and fluorescent tubes, in the crystal structure of metallic solids, and in many other phenomena and objects. The Earth itself is immersed in a tenuous plasma called the solar wind and is surrounded by a dense plasma called the ionosphere.

A plasma may be produced in the laboratory by heating a gas to an extremely high temperature, which causes such vigorous collisions between its atoms and molecules that electrons are ripped free, yielding the requisite electrons and ions. A similar process occurs inside stars. In space the dominant plasma formation process is photoionization, wherein photons from sunlight or starlight are absorbed by an existing gas, causing electrons to be emitted. Since the Sun and stars shine continuously, virtually all the matter becomes ionized in such cases, and the plasma is said to be fully ionized. This need not be the case, however, for a plasma may be only partially ionized. A completely ionized hydrogen plasma, consisting solely of electrons and protons (hydrogen nuclei), is the most elementary plasma.

The modern concept of the plasma state is of recent origin, dating back only to the early 1950s. Its history is interwoven with many disciplines. Three basic fields of study made unique early contributions to the development of plasma physics as a discipline: electric discharges, magnetohydrodynamics (in which a conducting fluid such as mercury is studied), and kinetic theory.

Interest in electric-discharge phenomena may be traced back to the beginning of the 18th century, with three English physicists—Michael Faraday in the 1830s and Joseph John Thomson and John Sealy Edward Townsend at the turn of the 19th century—laying the foundations of the present understanding of the phenomena. Irving Langmuir introduced the term plasma in 1923 while investigating electric discharges. In 1929 he and Lewi Tonks, another physicist working in the United States, used the term to designate those regions of a discharge in which certain periodic variations of the negatively charged electrons could occur. They called these oscillations plasma oscillations, their behaviour suggesting that of a jellylike substance. Not until 1952, however, when two other American physicists, David Bohm and David Pines, first considered the collective behaviour of electrons in metals as distinct from that in ionized gases, was the general applicability of the concept of a plasma fully appreciated.

The collective behaviour of charged particles in magnetic fields and the concept of a conducting fluid are implicit in magnetohydrodynamic studies, the foundations of which were laid in the early and middle 1800s by Faraday and André-Marie Ampère of France. Not until the 1930s, however, when new solar and geophysical phenomena were being discovered, were many of the basic problems of the mutual interaction between ionized gases and magnetic fields considered. In 1942 Hannes Alfvén, a Swedish physicist, introduced the concept of magnetohydrodynamic waves. This contribution, along with his further studies of space plasmas, led to Alfvén's receipt of the Nobel Prize for Physics in 1970.

These two separate approaches—the study of electric discharges and the study of the behaviour of conducting fluids in magnetic fields—were unified by the introduction of the kinetic theory of the plasma state. This theory states that plasma, like gas, consists of particles in random motion, whose interactions can be through long-range electromagnetic forces as well as via collisions. In 1905 the Dutch physicist Hendrik Antoon Lorentz applied the kinetic equation for atoms (the formulation by the Austrian physicist Ludwig Eduard Boltzmann) to the behaviour of electrons in metals. Various physicists and mathematicians in the 1930s and '40s further developed the plasma kinetic theory to a high degree of sophistication. Since the early 1950s interest has increasingly focused on the plasma state itself. Space exploration, the development of electronic devices, a growing awareness of the importance of magnetic fields in astrophysical phenomena, and the quest for controlled thermonuclear (nuclear fusion) power reactors all have stimulated such interest. Many problems remain unsolved in space plasma physics research, owing to the complexity of the phenomena. For example, descriptions of the solar wind must include not only equations dealing with the effects of gravity, temperature, and pressure as needed in atmospheric science but also the equations of the Scottish physicist James Clerk Maxwell, which are needed to describe the electromagnetic field.

Just as a lightweight cork in water will bob up and down about its rest position, any general displacement of light electrons as a group with respect to the positive ions in a plasma leads to the oscillation of the electrons as a whole about an equilibrium state. In the case of the cork, the restoring force is provided by gravity; in plasma oscillations, it is provided by the electric force. These movements are the plasma oscillations that were studied by Langmuir and Tonks. Analogously, just as buoyancy effects guide water waves, plasma oscillations are related to waves in the electron component of the plasma called

Kinetic theory

Langmuir waves. Wavelike phenomena play a critical role in the behaviour of plasmas.

The time τ required for an oscillation of this type is the most important temporal parameter in a plasma. The main spatial parameter is the Debye length, h, which is the distance traveled by the average thermal electron in time $\tau/2\pi$. A plasma can be defined in terms of these parameters as a partially or fully ionized gas that satisfies the following criteria: (1) a constituent electron may complete many plasma oscillations before it collides with either an ion or one of the other heavy constituents, (2) inside each sphere with a radius equal to the Debye length, there are many particles, and (3) the plasma itself is much larger than the Debye length in every dimension.

Another important temporal parameter is the time between collisions of particles. In any gas, separate collision frequencies are defined for collisions between all different particle types. The total collision frequency for a particular species is the weighted sum of all the separate frequencies.

Elastic and inelastic collisions

Two basic types of collision may occur: elastic and inelastic. In an elastic collision, the total kinetic energy of all the particles participating in the collision is the same before and after the event. In an inelastic collision, a fraction of the kinetic energy is transferred to the internal energy of the colliding particles. In an atom, for example, the electrons have certain allowed (discrete) energies and are said to be bound. During a collision, a bound electron may be excited—that is, raised from a low to a high energy state. This can occur, however, only by the expenditure of kinetic energy and only if the kinetic energy exceeds the difference between the two energy states. If the energy is sufficient, a bound electron may be excited to such a high level that it becomes a free electron, and the atom is said to be ionized; the minimum, or threshold, energy required to free an electron is called the ionization energy. Inelastic collisions may also occur with positive ions unless all the electrons have been stripped away. In general, only collisions of electrons and photons (quanta of electromagnetic radiation) with atoms and ions are significant in these inelastic collisions; ionization by a photon is called photoionization.

A molecule has additional discrete energy states, which may be excited by particle or photon collisions. At sufficiently high energies of interaction, the molecule can dissociate into atoms or into atoms and atomic ions. As in the case of atoms, collision of electrons and photons with molecules may cause ionization, producing molecular ions. In general, the reaction rate for inelastic collisions is similar to that of chemical reactions. At sufficiently high temperatures, the atoms are stripped of all electrons and become bare atomic nuclei. Finally, at temperatures of about 1,000,000 K or greater, nuclear reactions can occur—another form of inelastic collisions. When such reactions lead to the formation of heavier elements, the process is called thermonuclear fusion; mass is transmuted, and kinetic energy is gained instead of lost.

All sources of energy now existing on the Earth can be traced in one way or another to the nuclear fusion reactions inside the Sun or some long-extinct star. In such energy sources, gravity controls and confines the fusion process. The high temperatures required for the nuclear fusion reactions that take place in a hydrogen, or thermonuclear, bomb are attained by first igniting an atomic bomb, which produces a fission chain reaction. One of the great challenges of humankind is to create these high temperatures in a controlled manner and to harness the energy of nuclear fusion. This is the great practical goal of plasma physics—to produce nuclear fusion on the Earth. Confinement schemes devised by scientists use magnetic fields or the inertia of an implosion to guide and control the hot plasma.

Basic plasma physics

PLASMA FORMATION

Apart from solid-state plasmas, such as those in metallic crystals, plasmas do not usually occur naturally at the surface of the Earth. For laboratory experiments and technological applications, plasmas therefore must be produced artificially. Because the atoms of such alkalies as potassium, sodium, and cesium possess low ionization energies, plasmas may be produced from these by the direct application of heat at temperatures of about 3,000 K. In most gases, however, before any significant degree of ionization is achieved, temperatures in the neighbourhood of 10,000 K are required. A convenient unit for measuring temperature in the study of plasmas is the electron volt (eV), which is the energy gained by an electron in vacuum when it is accelerated across one volt of electric potential. The temperature, W, measured in electron volts is given by $W = T/12,000$ when T is expressed in kelvins. The temperatures required for self-ionization thus range from 2.5 to 8 electron volts, since such values are typical of the energy needed to remove one electron from an atom or molecule.

Artificial production of plasmas

Because all substances melt at temperatures far below that level, no container yet built can withstand an external application of the heat necessary to form a plasma; therefore, any heating must be supplied internally. One technique is to apply an electric field to the gas to accelerate and scatter any free electrons, thereby heating the plasma. This type of ohmic heating is similar to the method in which free electrons in the heating element of an electric oven heat the coil. Because of their small energy loss in elastic collisions, electrons can be raised to much higher temperatures than other particles. For plasma formation a sufficiently high electric field must be applied, its exact value depending on geometry and the gas pressure. The electric field may be set up via electrodes or by transformer action, in which the electric field is induced by a changing magnetic field. Laboratory temperatures of about 10,000,000 K, or 8 kiloelectron volts (keV), with electron densities of about 10^{19} per cubic metre have been achieved by the transformer method. The temperature is eventually limited by energy losses to the outside environment. Extremely high temperatures, but relatively low-density plasmas, have been produced by the separate injection of ions and electrons into a mirror system (a plasma device using a particular arrangement of magnetic fields for containment). Other methods have used the high temperatures that develop behind a wave that is moving much faster than sound to produce what is called a shock front; lasers have also been employed.

Natural plasma heating and ionization occur in analogous ways. In a lightning-induced plasma, the electric current carried by the stroke heats the atmosphere in the same manner as in the ohmic heating technique described above. In solar and stellar plasmas the heating is internal and caused by nuclear fusion reactions. In the solar corona, the heating occurs because of waves that propagate from the surface into the Sun's atmosphere, heating the plasma much like shock-wave heating in laboratory plasmas. In the ionosphere, ionization is accomplished not through heating of the plasma but rather by the flux of energetic photons from the Sun. Far-ultraviolet rays and X rays from the Sun have enough energy to ionize atoms in the Earth's atmosphere. Some of the energy also goes into heating the gas, with the result that the upper atmosphere, called the thermosphere, is quite hot. These processes protect the Earth from energetic photons much as the ozone layer protects terrestrial life-forms from lower-energy ultraviolet light. The typical temperature 300 kilometres above the Earth's surface is 1,200 K, or about 0.1 eV. Although it is quite warm compared with the surface of the Earth, this temperature is too low to create self-ionization. When the Sun sets with respect to the ionosphere, the source of ionization ceases, and the lower portion of the ionosphere reverts to its nonplasma state. Some ions, in particular singly charged oxygen (O^+), live long enough that some plasma remains until the next sunrise. In the case of an aurora, a plasma is created in the nighttime or daytime atmosphere when beams of electrons are accelerated to hundreds or thousands of electron volts and smash into the atmosphere.

METHODS OF DESCRIBING PLASMA PHENOMENA

The behaviour of a plasma may be described at different levels. If collisions are relatively infrequent, it is useful to consider the motions of individual particles. In most plasmas of interest, a magnetic field exerts a force on a charged particle only if the particle is moving, the force being at right angles to both the direction of the field and the direction of particle motion. In a uniform magnetic field (B), a charged particle gyrates about a line of force. The centre of the orbit is called the guiding centre. The particle may also have a component of velocity parallel to the magnetic field and so traces out a helix in a uniform magnetic field. If a uniform electric field (E) is applied at right angles to the direction of the magnetic field, the guiding centre drifts with a uniform velocity of magnitude equal to the ratio of the electric to the magnetic field (E/B), at right angles to both the electric and magnetic fields. A particle starting from rest in such fields follows the same cycloidal path a dot on the rim of a rolling wheel follows. Although the "wheel" radius and its sense of rotation vary for different particles, the guiding centre moves at the same E/B velocity, independent of the particle's charge and mass. Should the electric field change with time, the problem would become even more complex. If, however, such an alternating electric field varies at the same frequency as the cyclotron frequency (*i.e.*, the rate of gyration), the guiding centre will remain stationary, and the particle will be forced to travel in an ever-expanding orbit. This phenomenon is called cyclotron resonance and is the basis of the cyclotron particle accelerator.

Cyclotron resonance

The motion of a particle about its guiding centre constitutes a circular current. As such, the motion produces a dipole magnetic field not unlike that produced by a simple bar magnet. Thus, a moving charge not only interacts with magnetic fields but also produces them. The direction of the magnetic field produced by a moving particle, however, depends both on whether the particle is positively or negatively charged and on the direction of its motion. If the motion of the charged particles is completely random, the net associated magnetic field is zero. On the other hand, if charges of different sign have an average relative velocity (*i.e.*, if an electric current flows), then a net magnetic field over and above any externally applied field exists. The magnetic interaction between charged particles is therefore of a collective, rather than of an individual, particle nature.

At a higher level of description than that of the single particle, kinetic equations of the Boltzmann type are used. Such equations essentially describe the behaviour of those particles about a point in a small-volume element, the particle velocities lying within a small range about a given value. The interactions with all other velocity groups, volume elements, and any externally applied electric and magnetic fields are taken into account. In many cases, equations of a fluid type may be derived from the kinetic equations; they express the conservation of mass, momentum, and energy per unit volume, with one such set of equations for each particle type.

<u>DETERMINATION OF PLASMA VARIABLES</u>

The basic variables useful in the study of plasma are number densities, temperatures, electric and magnetic field strengths, and particle velocities. In the laboratory and in space, both electrostatic (charged) and magnetic types of sensory devices called probes help determine the magnitudes of such variables. With the electrostatic probe, ion densities, electron and ion temperatures, and electrostatic potential differences can be determined. Small search coils and other types of magnetic probes yield values for the magnetic field; and from Maxwell's electromagnetic equations the current and charge densities and the induced component of the electric field may be found. Interplanetary spacecraft have carried such probes to nearly every planet in the solar system, revealing to scientists such plasma phenomena as lightning on Jupiter and the sounds of Saturn's rings and radiation belts. In the early 1990s, signals were being relayed to the Earth from several spacecraft approaching the edge of the plasma boundary to the solar system, the heliopause.

In the laboratory the absorption, scattering, and excitation of neutral and high-energy ion beams are helpful in determining electron temperatures and densities; in general, the refraction, reflection, absorption, scattering, and interference of electromagnetic waves also provide ways to determine these same variables. This technique has also been employed to remotely measure the properties of the plasmas in the near-space regions of the Earth using the incoherent scatter radar method. The largest single antenna is at the National Astronomy and Ionosphere Center at Arecibo in Puerto Rico. It has a circumference of 305 metres and was completed in 1963. It is still used to probe space plasmas to distances of 3,000 kilometres. The method works by bouncing radio waves from small irregularities in the electron gas that occur owing to random thermal motions of the particles. The returning signal is shifted slightly from the transmitted one—because of the Doppler-shift effect—and the velocity of the plasma can be determined in a manner similar to the way in which the police detect a speeding car. Using this method, the wind speed in space can be found, along with the temperature, density, electric field, and even the types of ions present. In geospace the appropriate radar frequencies are in the range of 50 to 1,000 megahertz (MHz), while in the laboratory, where the plasma densities and plasma frequencies are higher, microwaves and lasers must be used.

Aside from the above methods, much can be learned from the radiation generated and emitted by the plasma itself; in fact, this is the only means of studying cosmic plasma beyond the solar system. The various spectroscopic techniques covering the entire continuous radiation spectrum determine temperatures and identify such nonthermal sources as those pulses producing synchrotron radiations.

<u>WAVES IN PLASMAS</u>

The waves most familiar to people are the buoyancy waves that propagate on the surfaces of lakes and oceans and break onto the world's beaches. Equally familiar, although not necessarily recognized as waves, are the disturbances in the atmosphere that create what is referred to as the weather. Wave phenomena are particularly important in the behaviour of plasmas. In fact, one of the three criteria for the existence of a plasma is that the particle-particle collision rate be less than the plasma-oscillation frequency. This in turn implies that the collective interactions that control the plasma gas depend on the electric and magnetic field effects as much as, or more so than, simple collisions. Since waves are able to propagate, the possibility exists for force fields to act at large distances from the point where they originated.

Ordinary fluids can support the propagation of sound (acoustic) waves, which involve pressure, temperature, and velocity variations. Electromagnetic waves can propagate even in a vacuum but are slowed down in most cases by the interaction of the electric fields in the waves with the charged particles bound in the atoms or molecules of the gas. Although it is important for a complete description of electromagnetic waves, such an interaction is not very strong. In a plasma, however, the particles react in concert with any electromagnetic field (*e.g.*, as in an electromagnetic wave) as well as with any pressure or velocity field (*e.g.*, as in a sound wave). In fact, in a plasma sound wave the electrons and ions become slightly separated owing to their difference in mass, and an electric field builds up to bring them back together. The result is called an ion acoustic wave. This is just one of the many types of waves that can exist in a plasma. The brief discussion that follows touches on the main types in order of increasing wave-oscillation frequency.

At the lowest frequency are Alfvén waves, which require the presence of a magnetic field to exist. In fact, except for ion acoustic waves, the existence of a background magnetic field is required for any wave with a frequency less than the plasma frequency to occur in a plasma. Most natural plasmas are threaded by a magnetic field, and laboratory plasmas often use a magnetic field for confinement, so this requirement is usually met, and all types of waves can occur.

Alfvén waves

Alfvén waves are analogous to the waves that occur on the stretched string of a guitar. In this case, the string represents a magnetic field line. When a small magnetic field disturbance takes place, the field is bent slightly, and the disturbance propagates in the direction of the magnetic field. Since any changing magnetic field creates an electric field, an electromagnetic wave results. Such waves are the slowest and have the lowest frequencies of any known electromagnetic waves. For example, the solar wind streams out from the Sun with a speed greater than either electromagnetic (Alfvén) or sound waves. This means that, when the solar wind hits the Earth's outermost magnetic field lines, a shock wave results to "inform" the incoming plasma that an obstacle exists, much like the shock wave associated with a supersonic airplane. The shock wave travels toward the Sun at the same speed but in the opposite direction as the solar wind, so it appears to stand still with respect to the Earth. Because there are almost no particle-particle collisions, this type of collisionless shock wave is of great interest to space plasma physicists who postulate that similar shocks occur around supernovas and in other astrophysical plasmas. On the Earth's side of the shock wave, the heated and slowed solar wind interacts with the Earth's atmosphere via Alfvén waves propagating along the magnetic field lines.

The turbulent surface of the Sun radiates large-amplitude Alfvén waves, which are thought to be responsible for heating the corona to 1,000,000 K. Such waves can also produce fluctuations in the solar wind, and, as they propagate through it to the Earth, they seem to control the occurrence of magnetic storms and auroras that are capable of disrupting communication systems and power grids on the planet.

Types of wave motion

Two fundamental types of wave motion can occur: longitudinal, like a sound or ion acoustic wave, in which particle oscillation is in a direction parallel to the direction of wave propagation; and transverse, like a surface water wave, in which particle oscillation is in a plane perpendicular to the direction of wave propagation. In all cases, a wave may be characterized by a speed of propagation (u), a wavelength (λ), and a frequency (ν) related by an expression in which the velocity is equal to the product of the wavelength and frequency, namely, $u = \lambda\nu$. The Alfvén wave is a transverse wave and propagates with a velocity that depends on the particle density and the magnetic field strength. The velocity is equal to the magnetic flux density (B) divided by the square root of the mass density (ρ) times the permeability of free space (μ_0)—that is to say, $B/\sqrt{\mu_0\rho}$. The ion acoustic wave is a longitudinal wave and also propagates parallel to the magnetic field at a speed roughly equal to the average thermal velocity of the ions. Perpendicular to the magnetic field a different type of longitudinal wave called a magnetosonic wave can occur.

In these waves the plasma behaves as a whole, and the velocity is independent of wave frequency. At higher frequencies, however, the separate behaviour of ions and electrons causes the wave velocities to vary with direction and frequency. The Alfvén wave splits into two components, referred to as the fast and slow Alfvén waves, which propagate at different frequency-dependent speeds. At still higher frequencies these two waves (called the electron cyclotron and ion cyclotron waves, respectively) cause electron and cyclotron resonances (synchronization) at the appropriate resonance frequencies. Beyond these resonances, transverse wave propagation does not occur at all until frequencies comparable to and above the plasma frequency are reached.

At frequencies between the ion and electron gyrofrequencies lies a wave mode called a whistler. This name comes from the study of plasma waves generated by lightning. When early researchers listened to natural radio waves by attaching an antenna to an audio amplifier, they heard a strange whistling sound. The whistle occurs when the electrical signal from lightning in one hemisphere travels along the Earth's magnetic field lines to the other hemisphere. The trip is so long that some waves (those at higher frequencies) arrive first, resulting in the generation of a whistlelike sound. These natural waves were used to probe the region of space around the Earth before spacecraft became available. Such a frequency-dependent wave velocity is called wave dispersion because the various frequencies disperse with distance.

The speed of an ion acoustic wave also becomes dispersive at high frequencies, and a resonance similar to electron plasma oscillations occurs at a frequency determined by electrostatic oscillations of the ions. Beyond this frequency no sonic wave propagates parallel to a magnetic field until the frequency reaches the plasma frequency, above which electroacoustic waves occur. The wavelength of these waves at the critical frequency (ω_p) is infinite, the electron behaviour at this frequency taking the form of the plasma oscillations of Langmuir and Tonks. Even without particle collisions, waves shorter than the Debye length are heavily damped—i.e., their amplitude decreases rapidly with time. This phenomenon, called Landau damping, arises because some electrons have the same velocity as the wave. As they move with the wave, they are accelerated much like a surfer on a water wave and thus extract energy from the wave, damping it in the process.

Containment

Magnetic fields are used to contain high-density, high-temperature plasmas because such fields exert pressures and tensile forces on the plasma. An equilibrium configuration is reached only when at all points in the plasma these pressures and tensions exactly balance the pressure from the motion of the particles. A well-known example of this is the pinch effect observed in specially designed equipment. If an external electric current is imposed on a cylindrically shaped plasma and flows parallel to the plasma axis, the magnetic forces act inward and cause the plasma to constrict, or pinch. An equilibrium condition is reached in which the temperature is proportional to the square of the electric current. This result suggests that any temperature may be achieved by making the electric current sufficiently large, the heating resulting from currents and compression. In practice, however, since no plasma can be infinitely long, serious energy losses occur at the ends of the cylinder; also, major instabilities develop in such a simple configuration. Suppression of such instabilities has been one of the major efforts in laboratory plasma physics and in the quest to control the nuclear fusion reaction.

A useful way of describing the confinement of a plasma by a magnetic field is by measuring containment time (τ_c), or the average time for a charged particle to diffuse out of the plasma; this time is different for each type of configuration. Various types of instabilities can occur in plasma. These lead to a loss of plasma and a catastrophic decrease in containment time. The most important of these is called magnetohydrodynamic instability. Although an equilibrium state may exist, it may not correspond to the lowest possible energy. The plasma, therefore, seeks a state of lower potential energy, just as a ball at rest on top of a hill (representing an equilibrium state) rolls down to the bottom if perturbed; the lower energy state of the plasma corresponds to a ball at the bottom of a valley. In seeking the lower energy state, turbulence develops, leading to enhanced diffusion, increased electrical resistivity, and large heat losses. In toroidal geometry, circular plasma currents must be kept below a critical value called the Kruskal-Shafranov limit, otherwise a particularly violent instability consisting of a series of kinks may occur. Although a completely stable system appears to be virtually impossible, considerable progress has been made in devising systems that eliminate the major instabilities. Temperatures on the order of 10,000,000 K at densities of 10^{19} particles per cubic metre and containment times as high as $^1/_{50}$ of a second have been achieved.

Kruskal-Shafranov limit

APPLICATIONS OF PLASMAS

The most important practical applications of plasmas lie in the future, largely in the field of power production. The major method of generating electric power has been to use heat sources to convert water to steam, which drives turbogenerators. Such heat sources depend on the combustion of fossil fuels, such as coal, oil, and natural gas, and fission processes in nuclear reactors. A potential source of heat might be supplied by a fusion reactor, with a basic element of deuterium-tritium plasma; nuclear fusion collisions between those isotopes of hydrogen would release large amounts of energy to the kinetic energy of the reaction products (the neutrons and the nuclei of hydrogen and helium atoms). By absorbing those products in a surrounding medium, a powerful heat source could be created. To realize a net power output from such a generating station—allowing for plasma radiation and particle losses and for the somewhat inefficient conversion of heat to electricity—plasma temperatures of about 100,000,000 K and a product of particle density times containment time of about 10^{20} seconds per cubic metre are necessary. For example, at a density of 10^{20} particles per metre cubed, the containment time must be one second. Such figures are yet to be reached, although there has been much progress.

In general, there are two basic methods of eliminating or minimizing end losses from an artificially created plasma: the production of toroidal plasmas and the use of magnetic mirrors (see ATOMS: *Nuclear fusion*). A toroidal plasma is essentially one in which a plasma of cylindrical cross section is bent in a circle so as to close on itself. For such plasmas to be in equilibrium and stable, however, special magnetic fields are required, the largest component of which is a circular field parallel to the axis of the plasma. In addition, a number of turbulent plasma processes must be controlled to keep the system stable. In 1991 a machine called the JET (Joint European Torus) achieved the state known as ignition, a first step toward a practical fusion device.

Besides generating power, a fusion reactor might desalinate seawater. Approximately two-thirds of the world's land surface is uninhabited, with one-half of this area being arid. The use of both giant fission and fusion reactors in the large-scale evaporation of seawater could make irrigation of such areas economically feasible. Another possibility in power production is the elimination of the heat–steam–mechanical energy chain. One suggestion depends on the dynamo effect. If a plasma moves perpendicular to a magnetic field, an electromotive force, according to Faraday's law, is generated in a direction perpendicular to both the direction of flow of the plasma and the magnetic field. This dynamo effect can drive a current in an external circuit connected to electrodes in the plasma, and thus electric power may be produced without the need for steam-driven rotating machinery. This process is referred to as magnetohydrodynamic (MHD) power generation and has been proposed as a method of extracting power from certain types of fission reactors. Such a generator powers the auroras as the Earth's magnetic field lines tap electrical current from the MHD generator in the solar wind.

The inverse of the dynamo effect, called the motor effect, may be used to accelerate plasma. By pulsing cusp-shaped magnetic fields in a plasma, for example, it is possible to achieve thrusts proportional to the square of the magnetic field. Motors based on such a technique have been proposed for the propulsion of craft in deep space. They have the advantage of being capable of achieving large exhaust velocities, thus minimizing the amount of fuel carried.

A practical application of plasma involves the glow discharge that occurs between two electrodes at pressures of one-thousandth of an atmosphere or thereabouts. Such glow discharges are responsible for the light given off by neon tubes and such other light sources as fluorescent lamps, which operate by virtue of the plasmas they produce in electric discharge. The degree of ionization in such plasmas is usually low, but electron densities of 10^{16} to 10^{18} electrons per cubic metre can be achieved with an electron temperature of 100,000 K. The electrons responsible for current flow are produced by ionization in a region near the cathode, with most of the potential difference between the two electrodes occurring there. This region does not contain a plasma, but the region between it and the anode (*i.e.*, the positive electrode) does.

Other applications of the glow discharge include electronic switching devices; it and similar plasmas produced by radio-frequency techniques can be used to provide ions for particle accelerators and act as generators of laser beams. As the current is increased through a glow discharge, a stage is reached when the energy generated at the cathode is sufficient to provide all the conduction electrons directly from the cathode surface, rather than from gas between the electrodes. Under this condition the large cathode potential difference disappears, and the plasma column contracts. This new state of electric discharge is called an arc. Compared with the glow discharge, it is a high-density plasma and will operate over a large range of pressures. Arcs are used as light sources for welding, in electronic switching, for rectification of alternating currents, and in high-temperature chemistry. Running an arc between concentric electrodes and injecting gas into such a region causes a hot, high-density plasma mixture called a plasma jet to be ejected. It has many chemical and metallurgical applications.

Natural plasmas

EXTRATERRESTRIAL FORMS

It has been suggested that the universe originated as a violent explosion about 10 billion years ago and initially consisted of a fireball of completely ionized hydrogen plasma. Irrespective of the truth of this, there is little matter in the universe now that does not exist in the plasma state. The observed stars are composed of plasmas, as are interstellar and interplanetary media and the outer atmospheres of planets. Scientific knowledge of the universe has come primarily from studies of electromagnetic radiation emitted by plasmas and transmitted through them and, since the 1960s, from space probes within the solar system.

In a star the plasma is bound together by gravitational forces, and the enormous energy it emits originates in thermonuclear fusion reactions within the interior. Heat is transferred from the interior to the exterior by radiation in the outer layers, where convection is of greater importance. In the vicinity of a hot star, the interstellar medium consists almost entirely of completely ionized hydrogen, ionized by the star's ultraviolet radiation. Such regions are referred to as H II regions. The greater proportion by far of interstellar medium, however, exists in the form of neutral hydrogen clouds referred to as H I regions. Because the heavy atoms in such clouds are ionized by ultraviolet radiation (or photoionized), they also are considered to be plasmas, although the degree of ionization is probably only one part in 10,000. Other components of the interstellar medium are grains of dust and cosmic rays, the latter consisting of very high-energy atomic nuclei completely stripped of electrons. The almost isotropic velocity distribution of the cosmic rays may stem from interactions with waves of the background plasma.

Throughout this universe of plasma there are magnetic fields. In interstellar space magnetic fields are about 5×10^{-6} gauss (a unit of magnetic field strength) and in interplanetary space 5×10^{-5} gauss, whereas in intergalactic space they could be as low as 10^{-9} gauss. These values are exceedingly small compared with the Earth's surface field of about 5×10^{-1} gauss. Although small in an absolute sense, these fields are nevertheless gigantic, considering the scales involved. For example, to simulate interstellar phenomena in the laboratory, fields of about 10^{15} gauss would be necessary. Thus, these fields play a major role in nearly all astrophysical phenomena. On the Sun the average surface field is in the vicinity of 1 to 2 gauss, but magnetic disturbances arise, such as sunspots, in which fields of between 10 and 1,000 gauss occur. Many other stars are also known to have magnetic fields.

Current from the dynamo effect

Use in radio switching devices

Magnetic fields in space

Table 8: Various Natural Plasmas and Their Electron Densities and Temperatures		
plasma	n_e (per cu m)	T_e (K)
Sun		
Centre	10^{31}	1.5×10^7
Photosphere	10^{20}	4,200
Chromosphere	10^{17}–10^{20}	5×10^5
Corona	10^{13}	1.5×10^6
Solar wind (near Earth)	5×10^6	4×10^5
Interstellar space		
H II regions	10^6	10^4
H I regions	10^2	100–125
Intergalactic space	1	3?
Earth		
Outer magnetosphere	10^6–10^7	10^4
Plasmasphere	10^9–10^{10}	10^4
Ionosphere	10^{11}–10^{12}	250–3,000
Metals	10^{28}	10^4

Field strengths of 10^{-3} gauss are associated with various extragalactic nebulae from which synchrotron radiation has been observed.

SOLAR-TERRESTRIAL FORMS

The visible region of the Sun is the photosphere (see Table 8), with its radiation being about the same as the continuum radiation from a 5,000 K blackbody. Lying above the photosphere is the chromosphere, which is observed by the emission of line radiation from various atoms and ions. Outside the chromosphere, the corona expands into the ever-blowing solar wind (see below), which on passing through the planetary system eventually encounters the interstellar medium. The corona can be seen in spectacular fashion when the Moon eclipses the bright photosphere (see Figure 43). During the times in which sunspots are greatest in number (called the sunspot maximum), the corona is very extended and the solar wind is fierce. Sunspot activity waxes and wanes with roughly an 11-year cycle. During the mid-1600s and early 1700s, sunspots virtually disappeared for a period known as the Maunder minimum. This time coincided with the Little Ice Age in Europe, and much conjecture has arisen about the possible effect of sunspots on climate. Periodic variations similar to that of sunspots have been observed in tree rings and lake-bed sedimentation. If real, such an effect is important because it implies that the Earth's climate is fragile.

In 1958 the American astrophysicist Eugene Parker showed that the equations describing the flow of plasma in the Sun's gravitational field had one solution that allowed the gas to become supersonic and to escape the Sun's pull. The solution was much like the description of a rocket nozzle in which the constriction in the flow is analogous to the effect of gravity. Parker predicted the Sun's atmosphere would behave just as this particular solar-wind solution predicts rather than according to the solar-breeze solutions suggested by others. The interplanetary satellite probes of the 1960s proved his solution to be correct.

Solar wind

The solar wind is a collisionless plasma made up primarily of electrons and protons and carries an outflow of matter moving at supersonic and super-Alfvénic speed. The wind takes with it an extension of the Sun's magnetic field, which is frozen into the highly conducting fluid. In the region of the Earth, the wind has an average speed of 400 kilometres per second; and, when it encounters the planet's magnetic field, a shock front develops, the pressures acting to compress the field on the side toward the Sun and elongate it on the nightside (in the Earth's lee away from the Sun). The Earth's magnetic field is therefore confined to a cavity called the magnetosphere, into which the direct entry of the solar wind is prohibited. This cavity extends for about 10 Earth radii on the Sun's side and about 1,000 Earth radii on the nightside.

Inside this vast magnetic field a region of circulating plasma is driven by the transfer of momentum from the solar wind. Plasma flows parallel to the solar wind on the edges of this region and back toward the Earth in its interior. The resulting system acts as a secondary magnetohydrodynamic generator (the primary one being the solar wind itself). Both generators produce potential on the order of 100,000 volts. The solar-wind potential appears across the polar caps of the Earth, while the magnetospheric potential appears across the auroral oval. The latter is the region of the Earth where energetic electrons and ions precipitate into the planet's atmosphere, creating a spectacular light show. This particle flux is energetic enough to act as a new source of plasmas even when the Sun is no longer shining. The auroral oval becomes a good conductor; and large electric currents flow along it, driven by the potential difference across the system. These currents commonly are on the order of 1,000,000 amperes.

The plasma inside the magnetosphere is extremely hot (1–10 million K) and very tenuous (1–10 particles per cubic centimetre). The particles are heated by a number of interesting plasma effects, the most curious of which is the auroral acceleration process itself. A particle accelerator that may be the prototype for cosmic accelerators throughout the universe is located roughly one Earth radius above the auroral oval and linked to it by all-important magnetic field lines. In this region the auroral electrons are boosted by a potential difference on the order of three to six kilovolts, most likely created by an electric field parallel to the magnetic field lines and directed away from the Earth. Such a field is difficult to explain because magnetic

Stephen J. Edberg, cover photograph, *Reviews of Geophysics,* vol. 30, no. 1, published 1992 by the American Geophysical Union

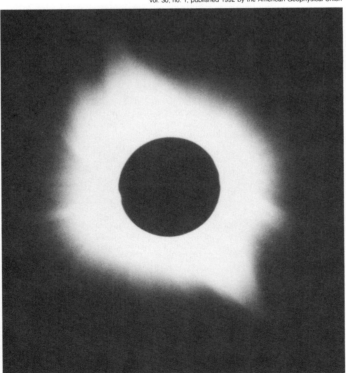

Figure 43: The solar corona as seen from La Paz, Mex., during the July 11, 1991, total eclipse. The corona is the source of the solar wind plasma that continuously bathes the Earth.

field lines usually act like nearly perfect conductors. The auroras occur on magnetic field lines that—if it were not for the distortion of the Earth's dipole field—would cross the equatorial plane at a distance of 6–10 Earth radii.

Closer to the Earth, within about 4 Earth radii, the planet wrests control of the system away from the solar wind. Inside this region the plasma rotates with the Earth, just as its atmosphere rotates with it. This system can also be thought of as a magnetohydrodynamic generator in which the rotation of the atmosphere and the ionospheric plasma in it create an electric field that puts the inner magnetosphere in rotation about the Earth's axis. Since this inner region is in contact with the dayside of the Earth where the Sun creates copious amounts of plasma in the ionosphere, the inner zone fills up with dense, cool plasma to form the plasmasphere. On a planet such as Jupiter, which has both a larger magnetic field and a higher rotation rate than the Earth, planetary control extends much farther from the surface.

The
ionosphere

At altitudes below about 2,000 kilometres, the plasma is referred to as the ionosphere. Thousands of rocket probes have helped chart the vertical structure of this region of the atmosphere, and numerous satellites have provided latitudinal and longitudinal information. The ionosphere was discovered in the early 1900s when radio waves were found to propagate "over the horizon." If radio waves have frequencies near or below the plasma frequency, they cannot propagate throughout the plasma of the ionosphere and thus do not escape into space; they are instead either reflected or absorbed. At night the absorption is low since little plasma exists at the height of roughly 100 kilometres where absorption is greatest. Thus, the ionosphere acts as an effective mirror, as does the Earth's surface, and waves can be reflected around the entire planet much as in a waveguide. A great communications revolution was initiated by the wireless, which relied on radio waves to transmit audio signals. Development continues to this day with satellite systems that must propagate through the ionospheric plasma. In this case, the wave frequency must be higher than the highest plasma frequency in the ionosphere so that the waves will not be reflected away from the Earth.

The dominant ion in the upper atmosphere is atomic oxygen, while below about 200 kilometres molecular oxygen and nitric oxide are most prevalent. Meteor showers also provide large numbers of metallic atoms of elements such as iron, silicon, and magnesium, which become ionized in sunlight and last for long periods of time. These form vast ion clouds, which are responsible for much of the fading in and out of radio stations at night.

Nocti-
lucent
clouds

A more normal type of cloud forms at the base of the Earth's plasma blanket in the summer polar mesosphere regions. Located at an altitude of 85 kilometres, such a cloud is the highest on Earth and can be seen only when darkness has just set in on the planet. Hence, clouds of this kind have been called noctilucent clouds. They are thought to be composed of charged and possibly dusty ice crystals that form in the coldest portion of the atmosphere at a temperature of 120 K. This unusual medium has much in common with dusty plasmas in planetary rings and other cosmic systems. Noctilucent clouds have been increasing in frequency throughout the 20th century and may be a forerunner of global change.

High-energy particles also exist in the magnetosphere. At about 1.5 and 3.5 Earth radii from the centre of the planet, two regions contain high-energy particles. These regions are the Van Allen radiation belts, named after the American scientist James Van Allen, who discovered them using radiation detectors aboard early spacecraft. The charged particles in the belts are trapped in the mirror system formed by the Earth's magnetic dipole field.

Plasma can exist briefly in the lowest regions of the Earth's atmosphere. In a lightning stroke an oxygen-nitrogen plasma is heated at approximately 20,000 K with an ionization of about 20 percent, similar to that of a laboratory arc. Although the stroke is only a few centimetres thick and lasts only a fraction of a second, tremendous energies are dissipated. A lightning flash between the ground and a cloud, on the average, consists of four such strokes

in rapid succession. At all times, lightning is occurring somewhere on the Earth, charging the surface negatively with respect to the ionosphere by roughly 200,000 volts, even far from the nearest thunderstorm. If lightning ceased everywhere for even one hour, the Earth would discharge. An associated phenomenon is ball lightning. There are authenticated reports of glowing, floating, stable balls of light several tens of centimetres in diameter occurring at times of intense electrical activity in the atmosphere. On contact with an object, these balls release large amounts of energy. Although lightning balls are probably plasmas, so far no adequate explanation of them has been given.

Considering the origins of plasma physics and the fact that the universe is little more than a vast sea of plasma, it is ironic that the only naturally occurring plasmas at the surface of the Earth besides lightning are those to be found in ordinary matter. The free electrons responsible for electrical conduction in a metal constitute a plasma. Ions are fixed in position at lattice points, and so plasma behaviour in metals is limited to such phenomena as plasma oscillations and electron cyclotron waves (called helicon waves) in which the electron component behaves separately from the ion component. In semiconductors, on the other hand, the current carriers are electrons and positive holes, the latter behaving in the material as free positive charges of finite mass. By proper preparation, the number of electrons and holes can be made approximately equal so that the full range of plasma behaviour can be observed.

The importance of magnetic fields in astrophysical phenomena has already been noted. It is believed that these

Frederick J. Rich, cover photograph, *Reviews of Geophysics*, vol. 28, no. 3, published 1990 by the American Geophysical Union

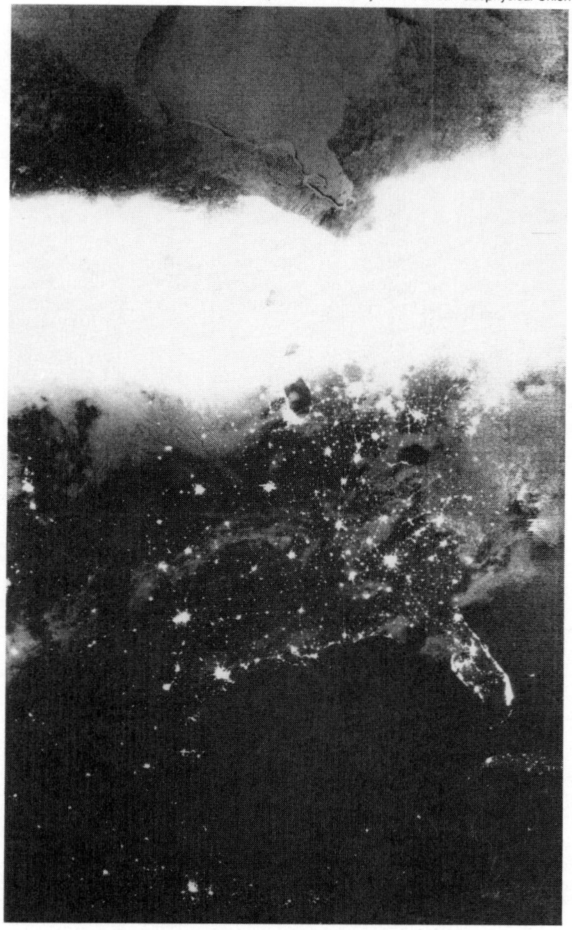

Figure 44: An image in visible light of the eastern United States and Canada, taken by the optical line scanner aboard the F9 satellite of the Defense Meteorological Satellite Program. The image was obtained on March 14, 1989, during a major magnetic storm. The white band stretching from Hudson Bay to Ohio is due to electron impact on the Earth's atmosphere that results in the creation of a dense plasma and the light emission called an aurora.

fields are produced by self-generating dynamos, although the exact details are still not fully understood. In the case of the Earth, differential rotation in its liquid conducting core causes the external magnetic dipole field (manifest as the North and South poles). Cyclonic turbulence in the liquid, generated by heat conduction and Coriolis forces (apparent forces accompanying all rotating systems, including the heavenly bodies), generates the dipole field from these loops. Over geologic time, the Earth's field occasionally becomes small and then changes direction, the North Pole becoming the South Pole and vice versa. During the times in which the magnetic field is small, cosmic rays can more easily reach the Earth's surface and may affect life forms by increasing the rate at which genetic mutations occur. Similar magnetic-field generation processes are believed to occur in both the Sun and the Milky Way Galaxy. In the Sun the circular internal mag-

netic field is made observable by lines of force apparently breaking the solar surface to form exposed loops; entry and departure points are what are observed as sunspots. Although the exterior magnetic field of the Earth is that of a dipole, this is further modified by currents in both the ionosphere and magnetosphere. Lunar and solar tides in the ionosphere lead to motions across the Earth's field that produce currents, like a dynamo, that modify the initial field. The auroral oval current systems discussed earlier create even larger magnetic-field fluctuations. The intensity of these currents is modulated by the intensity of the solar wind, which also induces or produces other currents in the magnetosphere. Such currents taken together constitute the essence of a magnetic storm. An image of the eastern United States and Canada taken during a major magnetic storm is shown in Figure 44.

(Bruce S. Liley; Michael C. Kelley)

CLUSTERS

Atoms and molecules are the smallest forms of matter typically encountered under normal conditions and are in that sense the basic building blocks of the material world. As described in the previous section, there are phenomena, such as lightning and electric discharges of other kinds, that allow free electrons to be observed, but these are exceptional occurrences. It is of course in its gaseous state that matter is encountered at its atomic or molecular level; in gases each molecule is an independent entity, only occasionally and briefly colliding with another molecule or with a confining wall.

In contrast to the free-molecule character of gases, the condensed phases of matter—as liquids, crystalline solids, and glasses are called—depend for their properties on the constant proximity of all their constituent atoms. The extent to which the identities of the molecular constituents are maintained varies widely in these condensed forms of matter. Weakly bound solids, such as solid carbon dioxide (dry ice), or their liquid counterparts, such as liquid air or liquid nitrogen, are made up of molecules whose properties differ only slightly from the properties of the same molecules in gaseous form; such solids or liquids are simply molecules packed tightly enough to be in constant contact. These are called van der Waals solids or liquids, after Johannes D. van der Waals, the Dutch physicist who described the weak forces that just manage to hold these materials together if they are cold enough. In other solids, like diamond, graphite, silicon, or quartz, the individual atoms retain their identity, but there are no identifiable molecules in their structures. The forces between the constituent atoms are roughly as strong as the forces that hold atoms together in the strongly bound covalent molecules that make up most common substances. Negatively charged electrons act as a "glue" to hold the positively charged nuclei together and are more or less confined to the vicinity of the so-called home-base nuclei with which they are associated; they are not free to roam through the entire solid or liquid. These materials are said to be covalently bound and are electrical insulators. They are best described as neutral atoms held together by covalent bonds and are essentially one giant molecule.

Another kind of bonding found in condensed matter is exhibited by sodium chloride, ordinary table salt, which is composed of positive sodium ions (Na^+) and negative chloride ions (Cl^-). Such ionic compounds are held together by the mutual attraction of the oppositely charged ions; because of their locations, these attractions are stronger than the repulsions of the ions with like charges. Each ion in an ionic crystal is surrounded by nearest neighbours of opposite charge. The consequence is that the binding energies of ionic compounds are large, comparable to those of strongly bound covalent substances.

Metallic bonding is another type of binding found in condensed matter. Electrons moving between the positive atomic cores (i.e., the nuclei plus inner-shell, tightly bound electrons) form an electron cloud; the attractions between the positive cores and the negative charges that make up

Binding in condensed phases of matter

the cloud hold metals together. Metals differ from covalently bound insulators in that those electrons responsible for the cohesion of the metals move freely throughout the metal when given the slightest extra energy. For example, under the influence of the electric field produced in a copper wire when its ends are connected to the terminals of a battery, electrons move through the wire from the end connected to the battery's negative pole toward the end connected to its positive pole. An electric field applied to a metal generates an electric current, but the same electric field applied to a covalent insulator does not (see below *Comparison with other forms of matter*). The net binding forces between electrons and atomic cores of a metal are comparable in strength to those that hold ionic compounds together.

As mentioned above, liquids constitute a condensed or dense phase of matter, but their atomic arrangement differs from that of solids. In a liquid the constituent atoms are only slightly farther apart than they are in a solid, but that small difference is significant enough to allow the atoms or molecules that constitute a liquid to move around and to assume a full range of geometric configurations. Atoms of the same kind can trade places and can wander through the liquid by the random-walk process called diffusion. In general, materials that can form solids can also form liquids, but some, such as carbon dioxide, can only enter the liquid state under excess pressure. At least one substance, helium, can form a liquid while having no known solid form.

Diffusion of liquids

Materials that form solids and liquids can exhibit another form, one that may be solidlike or liquidlike but that has properties somewhat different from those of the bulk. This is the form of matter consisting of exceedingly small particles that are called clusters. Clusters are aggregates of atoms, molecules, or ions that adhere together under forces like those that bind the atoms, ions, or molecules of bulk matter; because of the manner in which they are prepared, clusters remain as tiny particles at least during the course of an experiment. There are clusters held together by van der Waals forces, by ionic forces, by covalent bonds, and by metallic bonds. Despite the similarity of the forces that bind both clusters and bulk matter, one of the fascinating aspects of clusters is that their properties differ from those of the corresponding bulk material; that characteristic affords the opportunity to learn about the properties of bulk matter by studying how, as the number of constituent particles increases, the properties of clusters evolve into those of bulk matter. For example, a cluster of 20 or 30 atoms typically has a melting point far lower than that of the corresponding bulk. The electrical properties of clusters also differ in some instances from those of the bulk matter: clusters of only a few atoms of mercury are insulators, held together by weak van der Waals forces, but clusters of hundreds of mercury atoms are metallic. One of the puzzles posed by clusters is the question of how properties of small clusters evolve with size into properties of bulk matter.

Comparison with other forms of matter

Clusters versus bulk matter

Several characteristics differentiate clusters from molecules and bulk matter. They differ from bulk matter, first and foremost, in size; whether three particles bound together constitute a cluster is a matter of choice and convention, but an aggregate of four or more atoms or molecules certainly comprises a cluster. Such a small cluster would differ markedly from bulk matter in almost all its properties. A second difference between clusters and bulk matter is the variability of the properties of clusters with the number of their constituent particles. The properties of a lump of bulk matter remain unchanged by the addition or subtraction of a few atoms or molecules, whereas the properties of a small cluster vary significantly and, in general, neither uniformly nor even in the same direction with a change in the number of constituent particles. Medium-size clusters have properties that vary smoothly with the number of constituent particles (denoted N), but their properties, such as the melting point, differ significantly from those of the corresponding bulk. Large clusters have properties that vary smoothly with N and clearly merge into those of their bulk counterparts. This distinction, while not extremely precise, is quite useful. For example, the average binding energies—that is, the average energy per constituent atom or molecule required to separate the particles from each other—vary widely with N for small clusters. The reason for this wide range is that clusters of certain values of N, known as magic numbers, can take on unusually stable geometric structures that yield large binding energies, while others with different small values of N have no especially stable forms and therefore only relatively low binding energies. The binding energies of medium-size clusters vary rather smoothly with N, but they are in general considerably lower than the binding energies of bulk matter. The most important reason for this trend is that in a body of bulk matter almost all the particles are in the interior, while in a cluster most of the particles are on the surface. In a cluster of 13 atoms of copper or argon, for example, 12 of the atoms are on the surface. In a cluster of 55 argon atoms, 42 atoms are on the surface, and, in a cluster of 137 argon atoms, 82 are on the surface. Surface atoms are bonded only to atoms in their own layer and to those directly beneath them, so they have fewer atoms holding them to the main body of matter, whether cluster or bulk, than do atoms in the interior. Hence, the average binding energies of atoms in clusters are normally considerably less than those of bulk matter.

An important difference between clusters, in particular small and medium-size clusters, and bulk solids is the structure that is assumed by their most stable form. Most bulk solids are crystalline. This means that their atomic structures consist of periodic lattices—i.e., structures that repeat over and over so that every unit composed of a few neighbouring atoms is indistinguishable from other groups of atoms that have exactly the same arrangement. In a simple cubic crystal, for example, all the atoms lie at the corners of cubes (in fact at a point common to eight equivalent cubes), and all these lattice points are identical. Such structures are called periodic. Most clusters, by contrast, have structures that are not periodic; many have the form of icosahedrons, incomplete icosahedrons, or other polyhedral structures that cannot grow into periodic lattices. One of the challenging puzzles of cluster science is to explain how, as an aggregate grows, it transforms from a polyhedral cluster-type structure into a crystalline lattice-type structure.

Quantum mechanical considerations

Furthermore, some properties of clusters reflect their small size in more subtle ways that depend on quantum mechanical phenomena. These are generally much more pronounced in exceedingly small systems than in bulk or macroscopic samples. One such property is the nature of the energy levels occupied by the electrons. In a macroscopic sample the energies of the states available to an electron are, in principle, discrete but are merged into bands consisting of many energy levels. Within each band the intervals of energy between those discrete levels are too tiny to be discerned; only the gaps between the bands

are large enough to be important because they correspond to ranges of energy that are forbidden to the electrons. In fact, it is the contrast in the mobility of electrons that differentiates insulators from electrical conductors. In even a very cold metal, only an infinitesimal amount of excess energy is required to promote a few electrons into the previously empty energy levels in which they can move freely throughout the material. If an electric field is applied to the metal, the negatively charged electrons move toward the positive pole of the field so that a net current flows in the metal. It is the motion of these electrons, driven by an applied field, that makes metals conductors of electricity. In an insulator the electrons fill all the energy levels up to the top of the highest-energy occupied band. This means that at least the full energy of the forbidden interval, called the band gap, must be imparted to any electron to promote it to an allowed state where it may travel readily through the material. In an insulator this is far more energy than is normally available, and so no electrons are in states that allow them to move freely; such materials cannot conduct electric currents.

Clusters containing only a small number of metal atoms have so few available quantum states for their electrons that these states must be considered discrete, not as components of a dense band of available states. In this sense, small clusters of metal atoms are like conventional molecules rather than like bulk metals. Medium-size clusters of metal atoms have electronic energy states that are

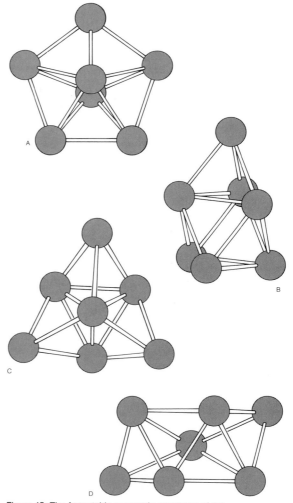

Figure 45: The four stable geometric structures of the seven-atom cluster of argon, in order of increasing energy: (A) A pentagonal bipyramid. (B) A regular octahedron with one face capped by the seventh atom. (C) A regular tetrahedron with three of its faces capped by other atoms. (D) A trigonal bipyramid with two of its faces capped by other atoms; although this has the highest energy of the four structures, it is very close in energy to the tricapped tetrahedron.

close enough together to be treated like the bands of bulk metals, but the conducting properties of these clusters are different from those of the bulk. Electrons driven by a constant electric field in a bulk metal can travel distances that are extremely long compared with atomic dimensions before they encounter any boundaries at the edges of the metal. Electrons in metal clusters encounter the boundaries of their cluster in a much shorter distance. Hence, metal clusters do not conduct electricity like bulk metals; if they are subjected to rapidly oscillating electric fields, such as those of visible, infrared, or microwave radiation, their "free" electrons are driven first one way and then back in the opposite direction over distances smaller than the dimensions of the cluster (see below *Physical properties*). If they are subjected to constant or low-frequency electric fields, such as the common 60-hertz fields that drive ordinary household currents, the electrons reach the boundaries of their clusters and can go no farther. Thus, the equivalent of conduction is not seen at low frequencies.

Clusters versus molecules

The manner in which clusters differ from molecules is more of a categorical nature than one of physical properties. Molecules have a definite composition and geometry; with few exceptions clusters can be made of any number of particles and may have any of several geometries. The four possible structures of a cluster of seven argon atoms are shown in Figure 45, and the lowest and next three higher-energy structures of a 13-atom cluster of argon are illustrated in Figure 46. The 13-atom cluster has the form

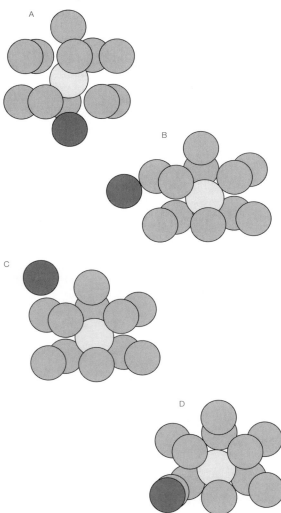

Figure 46: The four lowest-energy structures of the 13-atom cluster of argon: (A) The structure of lowest energy—the regular icosahedron of 12 atoms around a central atom. (B,C,D) The three structures, which have almost equal energy, formed by removing one of the 12 equivalent atoms from the 13-atom cluster in (A) from its shell and placing it into one of the three types of triangular faces in the resulting cluster.

of a regular icosahedron of 12 argon atoms around a central atom and is particularly stable.

Despite their multiplicity of structures, small clusters of fixed size, undergoing vibrations of small amplitude around a single geometry, are in most respects indistinguishable from molecules. If such clusters are given energy that is not great enough in magnitude to break them into separate parts, they may assume other geometries, alternating among these structural forms. This phenomenon is rarely seen with conventional molecules, but it is not unknown for energized molecules to exhibit more than one structure and to pass among them.

All in all, small clusters are much like molecules and are often considered to be molecules, while very large clusters are quite similar to bulk matter. The properties of clusters whose size is between these extremes may be like either or like neither.

Methods of study

Clusters can be studied by experiment, by theoretical analysis, and by simulation with computer-generated models. For several reasons they cannot be studied in the same manner as bulk matter. First, if individual clusters are allowed to coalesce into a mass, they will actually turn into bulk matter, so they must be kept separated. Second, it is desirable (but not always possible) to conduct experiments that distinguish the size and structure of each kind of cluster under observation. Because of these two considerations, experiments with clusters are usually more difficult than those with either specific molecules or bulk matter. Most of the difficulties arise from the same properties that make clusters interesting: the ease with which their sizes and compositions are varied and the variety of structures available for clusters of almost any given size.

Because of these difficulties, most experiments on clusters have been carried out with the clusters isolated in the gas phase; a few studies have been done with them in solution or in frozen matrices. Clusters can be prepared in the gas phase and then either studied in that form or captured into solvents or matrices or onto surfaces. They may be made by condensation of atoms or molecules or by direct blasting of matter from solids. In the most generally used method, a gas containing the gaseous cluster material is cooled by passing it under high pressure through a fine hole or slot. The expansion cools the gas rapidly from its initial temperature—usually room temperature but much higher if the cluster material is solid at room temperature—to a temperature not far above absolute zero. If, for example, argon gas is expanded in this way, it condenses into clusters if the pressure is not too high and the aperture is not too small; if the conditions are too extreme, the argon instead turns to snow and condenses.

Preparation of clusters

Inert gases are often used as the medium by which other materials, in a gaseous or vaporous state, are transported from the ovens or other sources where they have been gasified and through the jets that cool them and turn them into clusters. One especially popular and interesting method in which solids are vaporized is by the action of intense laser beams on solid surfaces. Often called ablation, this process is an effective means of vaporizing even highly refractory materials like solid carbon. The ablated material is then carried through the cooling jet by an inert gas such as helium or argon.

Once the clusters have been formed, they can be studied in a variety of ways. One of the first techniques was simply to ionize the clusters, either with ultraviolet radiation (usually from a laser) or by electron impact. The gaseous ionized clusters are accelerated by an electric field and then analyzed according to their masses (see ANALYSIS AND MEASUREMENT: *Mass spectrometry*); these results immediately reveal the number of atoms or molecules in the cluster. The analysis yields the distribution of the relative abundances of clusters of different sizes in the beam. If the experiment is done with considerable care, the abundance distribution corresponds to the true relative stabilities of the clusters of different sizes. However, like many experiments with clusters, these can either provide results consistent with the equilibrium conditions that reflect those relative stabilities, or they can give results that reflect the rates of the cluster-forming processes rather than the equilibrium characteristics, as the latter may take far longer to reach than the time required to form clusters. Some of the implications of the abundances found in such experiments are discussed below in the section *Structure and properties: Structure*.

Because of the conditions under which clusters are formed, their distributions contain many different sizes and, in some instances, different shapes. Because chemists seek to characterize clusters of a single size and geometry, the clusters must first be sorted on that basis. If the clusters carry charge, they can be separated according to size with a mass spectrometer that sorts charged particles with approximately the same energy according to their masses. This is usually done by deflecting the charged clusters or ions with an electric or magnetic field; the smaller the mass, the greater is the deflection. This is one of the most effective ways of preparing a beam of clusters of only a single selected mass. It does not eliminate the problem of multiple structures, however.

A technique that can sometimes be used to sort clusters according to their size and structure is a two-step process in which one cluster species at a time is excited with the light from a laser and is then ionized with light from a second laser. This process, called resonant two-photon ionization, is highly selective if the clusters being separated have moderately different absorption spectra. Since this is frequently the case, the method is quite powerful. As the experimenter varies the wavelength of the first exciting laser, a spectrum is produced that includes those wavelengths of light that excite the cluster. If the wavelength of the second ionizing laser is varied, the method also yields the ionization potential, which is the minimum energy that the photon in the ionizing beam must possess in order to knock an electron out of the cluster. Such data help to reveal the forces that bind the cluster together and give some indication of how the cluster will react with atoms, molecules, or other clusters.

A powerful tool for studying clusters is computer simulation of their behaviour. If the nature of the forces between the individual atoms or molecules in a cluster is known, then one can construct a computer model that represents the behaviour of those atoms or molecules by solving the equations of motion of the cluster. To describe the cluster in terms of classical mechanics, the Newtonian equations of motion are solved repeatedly—namely, force equals mass times acceleration, in which the forces depend on the instantaneous positions of all the particles. Hence, these equations are simultaneous, interlinked equations; there is one set of three (for the three instantaneous coordinates of each particle) for each atom or molecule. The results can take one of three forms: (1) the positions and coordinates of the atoms, given in tables, (2) the average properties of the entire cluster, or (3) animations. Tables are too cumbersome for most purposes, and specific average properties are frequently what the investigator seeks. Animated sequences show the same content as the tables but far more efficiently than extensive tables do. In fact, animations sometimes reveal considerably more than is expected by scientists.

It is also possible to construct computer models of clusters based on quantum mechanics instead of Newton's classical mechanics. This is especially appropriate for clusters of hydrogen and helium, because the small masses of their constituent atoms make them very quantumlike in the sense that they reveal the wavelike character that all matter exhibits according to quantum mechanics. The same kinds of data and inferences can be extracted from quantum mechanical calculations as from classical ones, but the preparation and visualization of animations for such clusters are much more demanding than their classical mechanical counterparts.

Structure and properties

STRUCTURE

The abundance distributions for several kinds of clusters show that there are certain sizes of clusters with excep-

tional stability, analogous to the exceptional stability of the atoms of the inert gases helium, neon, argon, krypton, and xenon and of the so-called magic number nuclei—*i.e.,* the sequence of unusually stable atomic nuclei beginning with the α-particle, or helium nucleus. Such unusual stability suggests that its interpretation should be associated with the closing of some kind of shell, or energy level. The overall structure that determines the cluster's stability is generally called its shell structure.

Clusters of atoms bound by van der Waals forces or by other simple forces that depend only on the distance between each pair of atoms have unusual stability when the cluster has exactly the number of atoms needed to form a regular icosahedron. The first three clusters in this series have, respectively, 13, 55, and 147 atoms. These are shown in Figure 47. In the 13-atom cluster, all but one of the atoms occupy equivalent sites. The 55-atom cluster in this series consists of a core—which is just the 13-atom icosahedron—plus 12 more atoms atop the 12 vertices of the icosahedron and 30 more atoms, one in the centre of each of the 30 edges of the icosahedron. The 147-atom cluster consists of a 55-atom icosahedral core, 12 more atoms at the vertices of the outermost shell, one atom in the centre of each of the 20 faces, and two atoms along each of the 30 edges between the vertices. The shell structure that provides special stabilities in this class of clusters is determined by the individual stabilities of the shells of the atoms themselves.

A different kind of extraordinary stability manifests itself in clusters of simple metal atoms. The shell structure for this class of clusters is determined by the electrons and the filling of those shells that have energy states available to the electrons. The numbers of electrons corresponding to closed electron shells in metal clusters are 8, 20, 40, 58, ... The electron structure can be modeled by supposing that the positively charged cores consisting of the protons and inner-shell electrons of all the cluster's atoms are smeared out into a continuous, attractive background,

Stability of icosahedral structures

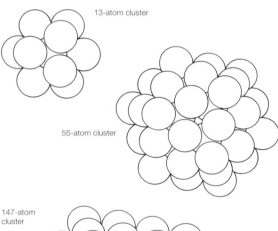

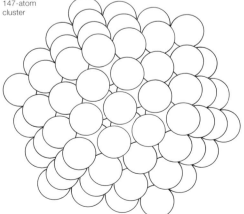

Figure 47: The first three complete icosahedral structures of 13, 55, and 147 particles. These are the structures taken on by clusters of 13, 55, and 147 atoms of neon, argon, krypton, and xenon, for example.

while the valence, or outer-shell, electrons are delocalized (*i.e.,* shared among all atoms in the cluster). The electron environment is much like a well or pit with a flat bottom and a moderately steep wall. The determination of the energy states available for electrons in such a simplified model system is relatively easy and gives a good description of clusters of more than about eight or nine alkali atoms—*i.e.,* lithium, sodium, potassium, rubidium, or cesium. The single valence, or outer-shell, electron of each alkali atom is treated explicitly, while all the others are considered part of the smeared-out core. Since each alkali atom has only one valence electron, the unusually stable clusters of alkalis consist of 8, 20, 40, . . . atoms, corresponding to major shell closings. This model is not as successful in treating metals such as aluminum, which have more than one valence electron.

Still another kind of particularly stable closed shell occurs in clusters sometimes called network structures. The best-known of these is C_{60}, the 60-atom cluster of carbon atoms. In this cluster the atoms occupy the sites of the 60 equivalent vertices of the soccer ball structure, which can be constructed by cutting off the 12 vertices of the icosahedron to make 12 regular 5-sided (regular pentagonal) faces. The icosahedron itself has 20 triangular faces; when its vertices are sliced off, the triangles become hexagons. The 12 pentagons share their edges with these 20 hexagonal faces. No two pentagons have any common edge in this molecule or cluster (C_{60} may be considered either). The resulting high-symmetry structure has been named buckminsterfullerene, after R. Buckminster Fuller, who advocated using such geometric structures in architectural design (see Figure 48).

Other network compounds of carbon are also known. To form a closed-shell structure, a network compound of carbon must have exactly 12 rings of 5 carbon atoms, but the number of rings of 6 carbon atoms is variable. Shells smaller than C_{60} have been discovered, but some of their constituent pentagons must share edges; this makes the smaller network compounds less stable than C_{60}. Shells larger than C_{60}, such as C_{70}, C_{76}, and C_{84}, are known and are relatively stable. Even tubes and "onions" of concentric layers of carbon shells have been reported in observations made with modern electron microscopes known as scanning tunneling microscopes. These devices are powerful enough to reveal images of extremely small clusters and even individual foreign atoms deposited on clean surfaces.

Fullerenes   The network compounds of carbon, which make up the class called fullerenes, form compounds with alkali and other metals. Some of these compounds of fullerenes combined with metals, such as K_3C_{60}, become superconductors at low temperatures; that is to say, they lose all resistance to electric current flow when they are cooled sufficiently. The class of network compounds as a group had been imagined from time to time, but only in the late 1980s were they realized in the laboratory and shown to have closed-shell network structures.

PHYSICAL PROPERTIES

Clusters share some of the physical properties of bulk matter, a few of which are rather surprising. Clusters of all substances except helium and possibly hydrogen are solidlike at low temperatures as expected. The atoms or molecules of a cluster remain close to their equilibrium positions, vibrating around these positions in moderately regular motions of small amplitude. This is characteristic of all solids; their atoms are constrained to stay roughly in the same position at all times. In a liquid or a gas, the atoms or molecules are free to wander through the space accessible to the substance. A gas or vapour has so much empty space relative to the volume occupied by the particles that the particles move almost unhindered, colliding only occasionally with other particles or with the walls of the container. A liquid is typically almost as dense as a solid but has some empty spaces into which the atoms or molecules can easily move. Hence, the particles of a liquid can diffuse with moderate ease. (Water is an exception; its density as a liquid is higher than its density as ice, because ice has an unusually open structure in comparison with most solids, and this open structure collapses when ice turns to water.) Clusters can be liquidlike if they are warm enough, but typically the temperatures at which clusters can become liquid are much lower than the melting points of the corresponding bulk solids. If temperatures are measured on the Kelvin scale, small clusters become liquidlike at temperatures of roughly half the bulk melting temperatures. For example, solid argon melts at approximately 80 K, while small clusters of argon become liquid at about 40 K.

Some clusters are expected to show a gradual transition from solidlike to liquidlike, appearing slushy in the temperature range between their solidlike and liquidlike zones. Other clusters are expected to show, as seen in computer simulations, distinct solidlike and liquidlike forms that qualitatively resemble bulk solids and liquids in virtually every aspect, even though they may exhibit quantitative differences from the bulk. Solid clusters, for example, show virtually no diffusion, but the particles of a liquid cluster can and do diffuse. The forces that hold a particle in place in a solid cluster are strong, comparable to those of a bulk solid; but those in a liquid cluster include, in addition to forces comparable in strength to those in solids, some forces weak enough to allow a particle to wander far from its home base and find new equilibrium positions. Those same weak forces are responsible for making a liquid cluster compliant; that is, weak forces allow the liquid to accommodate any new force, say, a finger inserted into water. Ice will not yield to such an intruding force, but when a finger is placed into liquid water, the water molecules move aside under the force of the finger. This is much like the behaviour of a bulk liquid. The greatest differences between bulk solids and liquids and solid and liquid clusters arise from the fact that a large fraction of the particles of a cluster are on its surface. As a result, the particle mobility that characterizes liquids and enables them to exhibit diffusion and physical compliance is enhanced in a cluster, for the cluster can easily expand by enlarging the spaces between particles and can also transfer particles from its interior to its surface, leaving vacancies that enhance the mobility of the interior particles. The large surface area, together with the curved shape of the cluster's surface, make it easier for particles to leave a cluster than to leave the flat surface of a bulk liquid or solid. An important consequence is that the vapour pressure of a cluster is higher than the vapour pressure of the corresponding bulk, and accordingly the boiling point of a liquid cluster—*i.e.,* the temperature at which the vapour pressure of a liquid is equal to the pressure of the surrounding atmosphere—is lower than that of the corresponding bulk liquid. The vapour pressure of

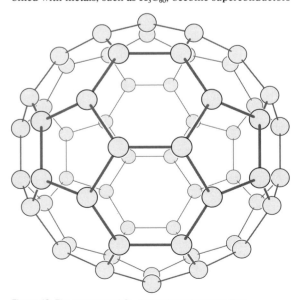

Figure 48: The structure of C_{60}, buckminsterfullerene. The geometry is that of a soccer ball with a carbon atom at each vertex (see text).

clusters decreases with increasing cluster size, while the boiling point increases.

Perhaps the greatest difference between clusters and bulk matter with regard to their transformation between solid and liquid is the nature of the equilibrium between two phases. Bulk solids can be in equilibrium with their liquid forms at only a single temperature for any given pressure or at only a single pressure for any given temperature. A graph of the temperatures and pressures along which the solid and liquid forms of any given substance are in equilibrium is called a coexistence curve. One point on the coexistence curve for ice and liquid water is 0° C and one atmosphere of pressure. A similar curve can be drawn for the coexistence of any two bulk phases, such as liquid and vapour; a point on the coexistence curve for liquid water and steam is 100° C and one atmosphere of pressure. Clusters differ sharply from bulk matter in that solid and liquid clusters of the same composition are capable of coexisting within a band of temperatures and pressures. At any chosen pressure, the proportion of liquid clusters to solid clusters increases with temperature. At low temperatures the clusters are solid, as described above. As the temperature is increased, some clusters transform from solid to liquid. If the temperature is raised further, the proportion of liquid clusters increases, passing through 50 percent, so that the mixture becomes predominantly liquid clusters. At sufficiently high temperatures all the clusters are liquid.

No cluster remains solid or liquid all the time; liquidlike clusters occasionally transform spontaneously into solid-like clusters and vice versa. The fraction of time that a particular cluster spends as a liquid is precisely the same as the fraction of clusters of that same type within a large collection that are liquid at a given instant. That is to say, the time average behaviour gives the same result as the ensemble average, which is the average over a large collection of identical objects. This equivalence is not limited to clusters; it is the well-known ergodic property that is expected of all but the simplest real systems.

Other significant physical properties of clusters are their electric, magnetic, and optical properties. The electric properties of clusters, such as their conductivity and metallic or insulating character, depend on the substance and the size of the cluster. Quantum theory attributes wave-like character to matter, a behaviour that is detectable only when matter is examined on the scale of atoms and electrons. At a scale of millimetres or even millionths of millimetres, the wavelengths of matter are too short to be observed. Clusters are often much smaller than that, with the important consequence that many are so small that when examined their electrons and electronic states can exhibit the wavelike properties of matter. In fact, quantum properties may play an important role in determining the electrical character of the cluster. In particular, as described previously, if a cluster is extremely small, the energy levels or quantum states of its electrons are not close enough together to permit the cluster to conduct electricity.

Moreover, an alternative way to view this situation is to recognize that a constant electric force (i.e., the kind that drives a direct current) and an alternating force (the kind that generates alternating current) can behave quite differently in a cluster. Direct current cannot flow in an isolated cluster and probably cannot occur in a small cluster even if it is sandwiched between slabs of metal. The current flow is prohibited both because the electrons that carry the current encounter the boundaries of the cluster and because there are no quantum states readily available at energies just above those of the occupied states, which are the states that must be achieved to allow the electrons to move. However, if a field of alternating electric force is applied with a frequency of alternation so high that the electrons are made to reverse their paths before they encounter the boundaries of the cluster, then the equivalent of conduction will take place. Ordinary 60-cycle (60-hertz) alternating voltage and even alternations at radio-wave frequencies switch direction far too slowly to produce this behaviour in clusters; microwave frequencies are required.

Magnetic properties of clusters, in contrast, appear to be rather similar to those of bulk matter. They are not identical, because clusters contain only small numbers of electrons, which are the particles whose magnetic character makes clusters and bulk matter magnetic. As a result, the differences between magnetic properties of clusters and of bulk matter are more a matter of degree than of kind. Clusters of substances magnetic in the bulk also tend to be magnetic. The larger the cluster, the more nearly will the magnetic character per atom approach that of the bulk. The degree of this magnetic character depends on how strongly the individual electron magnets couple to each other to become aligned in the same direction; the larger the cluster, the stronger is this coupling.

The optical properties of weakly bound clusters are much like those of their component atoms or molecules; the small differences are frequently useful diagnostics of how the cluster is bound and what its structure may be. Optical properties of metal clusters are more like those of the corresponding bulk metals than like those of the constituent atoms. These properties reveal which cluster sizes are unusually stable and therefore correspond to "magic-number" sizes. Optical properties of covalently bound clusters are in most cases—e.g., fullerenes—unlike those of either the component atoms or the bulk but are important clues to the structure and bonding of the cluster.

CHEMICAL PROPERTIES

The chemical properties of clusters are a combination of the properties of bulk and molecular matter. Several kinds of clusters, particularly those of the metallic variety, induce certain molecules to dissociate. For example, hydrogen molecules, H_2, spontaneously break into two hydrogen atoms when they attach themselves to a cluster of iron atoms. Ammonia likewise dissociates when attaching itself to an iron cluster. Similar reactions occur with bulk matter, but the rate at which such gases react with bulk metals depends only on how much gaseous reactant is present and how much surface area the bulk metal presents to the gas. Metal powders react much faster than dense solids with the same total mass because they have much more surface area. Small and medium-size clusters, on the other hand, show different reactivities for every size, although these reactivities do not vary smoothly with size. Furthermore, there are instances, such as reactions of hydrogen with iron, in which two different geometric forms of clusters of a single size have different reaction rates, just as two different molecules with the same elemental composition, called chemical isomers, may have different reaction rates with the same reactant partner. In the case of molecules, this is not surprising, because different isomers typically have quite different structures, physical properties, and reactivities and do not normally transform readily into one another. Isomers of clusters of a specific chemical composition, however, may well transform into one another with moderate ease and with no excessive increase in energy above the amount present when they formed. If the reaction releases energy (i.e., it is exothermic) in sufficient quantity to transform the cluster from solid to liquid, a cluster may melt as it reacts.

Some of the interesting chemistry of clusters is set in motion by light. For example, light of sufficiently short wavelength can dissociate molecules that are captured in the middle of a cluster of nonreactive atoms or molecules. A common question is whether the surrounding molecules or atoms form a cage strong enough to prevent the fragment atoms from flying apart and from leaving the cluster. The answer is that, if there are only a few surrounding atoms or molecules, the fragments escape their initial cage, and, if the energy of the light is high enough, at least one of the fragments escapes. On the other hand, if there are enough nonreacting cage atoms or molecules in the cluster to form at least one complete shell around the molecule that breaks up, the cage usually holds the fragments close together until they eventually recombine.

A related sort of reaction, another example of competition between a particle's attempt to escape from a cluster and some other process, occurs if light is used to detach an excess electron from a negative ion in the middle of an inert cluster. If, for example, light knocks the extra electron off a free, negatively charged bromine molecule, Br_2^-, the electron of course escapes. If the charged molecule is surrounded by a few inert molecules of carbon dioxide (CO_2), the electron escapes almost as readily. If 10 or 15 CO_2 molecules encase the Br_2^-, the electron does not escape; instead, it loses its energy to the surrounding molecules of CO_2, some of which boil off, and then eventually recombines with the now neutral bromine molecule to re-form the original Br_2^-.

The chemical properties of fullerenes and other network compounds have become a subject of their own, bridging molecular and cluster chemistry. These compounds typically react with a specific number of other atoms or molecules to form new species with definite compositions and structures. Compounds such as K_3C_{60} mentioned previously have the three potassium atoms outside the C_{60} cage, all as singly charged ions, K^+, and the ball of 60 carbon atoms carries three negative charges to make the entire compound electrically neutral. Other compounds of C_{60}, such as that made with the metal lanthanum, contain the metal inside the carbon cage, forming a new kind of substance. It is possible to add or take away hydrogen atoms from C_{60} and its larger relatives, much as hydrogen atoms can be added or removed from some kinds of hydrocarbons; in this way some of the chemistry of this class of clusters is similar to classical organic chemistry.

One of the goals of cluster science is the creation of new kinds of materials. The possible preparation of diamond films is one such application; another example is the proposal to make so-called superatoms that consist of an electron donor atom in the centre of a cluster of electron acceptors; the fullerene clusters containing a metal ion inside the cage seem to be just such a species but with much more open structures than had been previously envisioned. Molecular electronics is another goal; in this technology clusters would be constructed with electrical properties much like those of transistors and could be packed together to make microcircuits far smaller than any now produced. These applications are still theoretical, however, and have not yet been realized.

Clusters do indeed form a bridge between bulk and molecular matter. Their physical and chemical properties are in many instances unique to their finely divided state. Some examples of clusters, such as the network clusters of carbon, are new forms of matter. Nevertheless, such clusters, particularly the small and middle-size ones, not only exhibit behaviours of their own but also provide new insights into the molecular origins of the properties of bulk matter. They may yield other new materials—*e.g.*, possibly far more disordered, amorphous glasslike substances than the glasses now in common use—and at the same time give rise to deeper understanding of why and how glasses form at all.

(R. Stephen Berry)

LOW-TEMPERATURE PHENOMENA

The term low-temperature phenomena refers to the behaviour of matter at temperatures closer to absolute zero ($-273.15°$ C [$-459.67°$ F]) than to room temperature. At such temperatures the thermal, electric, and magnetic properties of many substances undergo great change, and, indeed, the behaviour of matter may seem strange when compared with that at room temperature. Superconductivity and superfluidity can be cited as two such phenomena that occur below certain critical temperatures; in the former, many chemical elements, compounds, and alloys show no resistance whatsoever to the flow of electricity, and, in the latter, liquid helium can flow through tiny holes impervious to any other liquid.

Superconductivity

Superconductivity was discovered in 1911 by the Dutch physicist Heike Kamerlingh Onnes; he was awarded the Nobel Prize for Physics in 1913 for his low-temperature research. Kamerlingh Onnes found that the electrical resistivity of a mercury wire disappears suddenly when it is cooled below a temperature of about $4°$ K ($-269°$ C); absolute zero is 0 K, the temperature at which all matter loses its disorder. He soon discovered that a superconducting material can be returned to the normal (*i.e.*, nonsuperconducting) state either by passing a sufficiently large current through it or by applying a sufficiently strong magnetic field to it.

For many years it was believed that, except for the fact that they had no electrical resistance (*i.e.*, that they had infinite electrical conductivity), superconductors had the same properties as normal materials. This belief was shattered in 1933 by the discovery that a superconductor is highly diamagnetic; that is, it is strongly repelled by and tends to expel a magnetic field. This phenomenon, which is very strong in superconductors, is called the Meissner effect for one of the two men who discovered it. Its discovery made it possible to formulate, in 1934, a theory of the electromagnetic properties of superconductors that predicted the existence of an electromagnetic penetration depth (see below *The Meissner effect*), which was first confirmed experimentally in 1939. In 1950 it was clearly shown for the first time that a theory of superconductivity must take into account the fact that free electrons in a crystal are influenced by the vibrations of atoms that define the crystal structure, called the lattice vibrations. In 1953, in an analysis of the thermal conductivity of superconductors, it was recognized that the distribution of

energies of the free electrons in a superconductor is not uniform but has a separation called the energy gap.

The theories referred to thus far served to show some of the interrelationships between observed phenomena but did not explain them as consequences of the fundamental laws of physics. For almost 50 years after Kamerlingh Onnes' discovery, theorists were unable to develop a fundamental theory of superconductivity. Finally, in 1957 such a theory was presented by the physicists John Bardeen, Leon N. Cooper, and John Robert Schrieffer of the United States; it won for them the Nobel Prize for Physics in 1972. It is now called the BCS theory in their honour, and most later theoretical work is based on it. The BCS theory also provided a foundation for an earlier model that had been introduced by the Russian physicists Lev Davidovich Landau and Vitaly Lazarevich Ginzburg (1950). This model has been useful in understanding electromagnetic properties, including the fact that any internal magnetic flux in superconductors exists only in discrete amounts (instead of in a continuous spectrum of values), an effect called the quantization of magnetic flux. This flux quantization, which had been predicted from quantum mechanical principles, was first observed experimentally in 1961.

The BCS theory

In 1962 the British physicist Brian D. Josephson predicted that two superconducting objects placed in electric contact would display certain remarkable electromagnetic properties. These properties have since been observed in a wide variety of experiments, demonstrating quantum mechanical effects on a macroscopic scale.

The theory of superconductivity has been tested in a wide range of experiments, involving, for example, ultrasonic absorption studies, nuclear-spin phenomena, low-frequency infrared absorption, and electron-tunneling experiments (see below *Energy gaps*). The results of these measurements have brought understanding to many of the detailed properties of various superconductors.

THERMAL PROPERTIES OF SUPERCONDUCTORS

Superconductivity is a startling departure from the properties of normal (*i.e.*, nonsuperconducting) conductors of electricity. In materials that are electric conductors, some of the electrons are not bound to individual atoms but are free to move through the material; their motion constitutes an electric current. In normal conductors these so-called conduction electrons are scattered by impurities, dislocations, grain boundaries, and lattice vibrations (phonons). In a superconductor, however, there is an ordering among the conduction electrons that prevents this scattering. Consequently, electric current can flow with no resistance at all. The ordering of the electrons, called Cooper pairing, involves the momenta of the electrons rather than their positions. The energy per electron that is associated with this ordering is extremely small, typically about one thousandth of the amount by which the energy per electron changes when a chemical reaction takes place. One reason that superconductivity remained unexplained for so long is the smallness of the energy changes that accompany the transition between normal and superconducting states. In fact, many incorrect theories of superconductivity were advanced before the BCS theory was proposed. For additional details on electric conduction in metals and the effects of temperature and other influences, see the article ELECTRICITY AND MAGNETISM.

Super-conducting materials   Hundreds of materials are known to become superconducting at low temperatures. Twenty-seven of the chemical elements, all of them metals, are superconductors in their usual crystallographic forms at low temperatures and low (atmospheric) pressure. Among these are commonly known metals such as aluminum, tin, lead, and mercury and less common ones such as rhenium, lanthanum, and protactinium. In addition, 11 chemical elements that are metals, semimetals, or semiconductors are superconductors at low temperatures and high pressures. Among these are uranium, cerium, silicon, and selenium. Bismuth and five other elements, though not superconducting in their usual crystallographic form, can be made superconducting by preparing them in a highly disordered form, which is stable at extremely low temperatures. Superconductivity is not exhibited by any of the magnetic elements chromium, manganese, iron, cobalt, or nickel.

Most of the known superconductors are alloys or compounds. It is possible for a compound to be superconducting even if the chemical elements constituting it are not; examples are disilver fluoride (Ag_2F) and a compound of carbon and potassium (C_8K). Some semiconducting compounds, such as tin telluride (SnTe), become superconducting if they are properly doped with impurities.

Since 1986 some compounds containing copper and oxygen (called cuprates) have been found to have extraordinarily high transition temperatures, denoted T_c. This is the temperature below which a substance is superconducting. The properties of these high-T_c compounds are different in some respects from those of the types of superconductors known prior to 1986, which will be referred to as classic superconductors in this discussion. For the most part, the high-T_c superconductors are treated explicitly toward the end of this section. In the discussion that immediately follows, the properties possessed by both kinds of superconductors will be described, with attention paid to specific differences for the high-T_c materials. A further classification problem is presented by the superconducting compounds of carbon (sometimes doped with other atoms) in which the carbon atoms are on the surface of a cluster with a spherical or spheroidal crystallographic structure. These compounds, discovered in the 1980s, are called fullerenes (if only carbon is present) or fullerides (if doped). They have superconducting transition temperatures higher than those of the classic superconductors. It is not yet known whether these compounds are fundamentally similar to the cuprate high-temperature superconductors.

Transition temperatures.   The vast majority of the known superconductors have transition temperatures that lie between 1 K and 10 K. Of the chemical elements,

tungsten has the lowest transition temperature, 0.015 K, and niobium the highest, 9.2 K. The transition temperatures of some of the commonly known superconducting elements are indicated in Table 9.

The transition temperature is usually very sensitive to the presence of magnetic impurities. A few parts per million of manganese in zinc, for example, lowers the transition temperature considerably.

Specific heat and thermal conductivity.   The thermal properties of a superconductor can be compared with those of the same material at the same temperature in the normal state. (The material can be forced into the normal state at low temperature by a large enough magnetic field.)

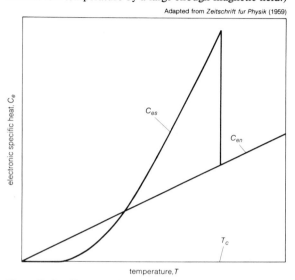

Adapted from *Zeitschrift fur Physik* (1959)

Figure 49: Specific heat in the normal (C_{en}) and superconducting (C_{es}) states of a classic superconductor as a function of absolute temperature. The two functions are identical at the transition temperature (T_c) and above T_c.

When a small amount of heat is put into a system, some of the energy is used to increase the lattice vibrations (an amount that is the same for a system in the normal and in the superconducting state), and the remainder is used to increase the energy of the conduction electrons. The electronic specific heat (C_e) of the electrons is defined as the ratio of that portion of the heat used by the electrons to the rise in temperature of the system. Figure 49 shows how the specific heat of the electrons in a superconductor varies with the absolute temperature (T) in the normal and in the superconducting state. It is evident from the figure that the electronic specific heat in the superconducting state (designated C_{es}) is smaller than in the normal state (designated C_{en}) at low enough temperatures but that C_{es} becomes larger than C_{en} as the transition temperature T_c is approached, at which point it drops abruptly to C_{en} for the classic superconductors, although the curve has a cusp shape near T_c for the high-T_c superconductors. Precise measurements have indicated that, at temperatures considerably below the transition temperature, the logarithm of the electronic specific heat is inversely proportional to the temperature. This temperature dependence, together with the principles of statistical mechanics, strongly suggests that there is a gap in the distribution of energy levels available to the electrons in a superconductor, so that a minimum energy is required for the excitation of each electron from a state below the gap to a state above the gap. Some of the high-T_c superconductors provide an additional contribution to the specific heat, which is proportional to the temperature. This behaviour indicates that there are electronic states lying at low energy; additional evidence of such states is obtained from optical properties and tunneling measurements.

The heat flow per unit area of a sample equals the product of the thermal conductivity (K) and the temperature gradient ∇T: $J_Q = -K \nabla T$, the minus sign indicating that heat always flows from a warmer to a colder region of a substance.

Temperature dependence of electronic specific heat

Table 9: Transition Temperatures and Low-Temperature Values of Critical Magnetic Fields of Some Superconducting Elements

	Tc (K)	Ho (oersted)
Zinc	0.88	53
Aluminum	1.20	99
Indium	3.41	282
Tin	3.72	306
Mercury	4.15	411
Lead	7.19	803

The thermal conductivity in the normal state (K_n) approaches the thermal conductivity in the superconducting state (K_s) as the temperature (T) approaches the transition temperature (T_c) for all materials, whether they are pure or impure. This suggests that the energy gap (Δ) for each electron approaches zero as the temperature (T) approaches the transition temperature (T_c). This would also account for the fact that the electronic specific heat in the superconducting state (C_{es}) is higher than in the normal state (C_{en}) near the transition temperature: as the temperature is raised toward the transition temperature (T_c), the energy gap in the superconducting state decreases, the number of thermally excited electrons increases, and this requires the absorption of heat.

Energy gaps. As stated above, the thermal properties of superconductors indicate that there is a gap in the distribution of energy levels available to the electrons, and so a finite amount of energy, designated as delta (Δ), must be supplied to an electron to excite it. This energy is maximum (designated Δ_0) at absolute zero and changes little with increase of temperature until the transition temperature is approached, where Δ decreases to zero, its value in the normal state. The BCS theory predicts an energy gap with just this type of temperature dependence.

According to the BCS theory, there is a type of electron pairing (electrons of opposite spin acting in unison) in the superconductor that is important in interpreting many superconducting phenomena. The electron pairs, called Cooper pairs, are broken up as the superconductor is heated. Each time a pair is broken, an amount of energy that is at least as much as the energy gap (Δ) must be supplied to each of the two electrons in the pair, so an energy at least twice as great (2Δ) must be supplied to the superconductor. The value of twice the energy gap at 0 K (which is $2\Delta_0$) might be assumed to be higher when the transition temperature of the superconductor is higher. In fact, the BCS theory predicts a relation of this type—namely, that the energy supplied to the superconductor at absolute zero would be $2\Delta_0 = 3.53\ kT_c$, where k is Boltzmann's constant (1.38×10^{-23} joule per kelvin). In the high-T_c cuprate compounds, values of $2\Delta_0$ range from approximately three to eight multiplied by kT_c.

The energy gap (Δ) can be measured most precisely in a tunneling experiment (a process in quantum mechanics that allows an electron to escape from a metal without acquiring the energy required along the way according to the laws of classical physics). In this experiment, a thin insulating junction is prepared between a superconductor and another metal, assumed here to be in the normal state. In this situation, electrons can quantum mechanically tunnel from the normal metal to the superconductor if they have sufficient energy. This energy can be supplied by applying a negative voltage (V) to the normal metal, with respect to the voltage of the superconductor.

Tunneling will occur if eV—the product of the electron charge, e (-1.60×10^{-19} coulomb), and the voltage—is at least as large as the energy gap Δ. The current flowing between the two sides of the junction is small up to a voltage equal to $V = \Delta/e$, but then it rises sharply. This provides an experimental determination of the energy gap (Δ). In describing this experiment it is assumed here that the tunneling electrons must get their energy from the applied voltage rather than from thermal excitation.

MAGNETIC AND ELECTROMAGNETIC PROPERTIES OF SUPERCONDUCTORS

Critical field. One of the ways in which a superconductor can be forced into the normal state is by applying a magnetic field. The weakest magnetic field that will cause this transition is called the critical field (H_c) if the sample is in the form of a long, thin cylinder or ellipsoid and the field is oriented parallel to the long axis of the sample. (In other configurations the sample goes from the superconducting state into an intermediate state, in which some regions are normal and others are superconducting, and finally into the normal state.) The critical field increases with decreasing temperature. For the superconducting elements, its values (H_0) at absolute zero range from 1.1 oersted for tungsten to 830 oersteds for tantalum. Values

of H_0 are listed in Table 9 for some common superconducting elements.

These remarks about the critical field apply to ordinary (so-called type I) superconductors. In the following section the behaviour of other (type II) superconductors is examined.

The Meissner effect. As was stated above, a type I superconductor in the form of a long, thin cylinder or ellipsoid remains superconducting at a fixed temperature as an axially oriented magnetic field is applied, provided the applied field does not exceed a critical value (H_c). Under these conditions, superconductors exclude the magnetic field from their interior, as could be predicted from the laws of electromagnetism and the fact that the superconductor has no electric resistance. A more astonishing effect occurs if the magnetic field is applied in the same way to the same type of sample at a temperature above the transition temperature and is then held at a fixed value while the sample is cooled. It is found that the sample expels the magnetic flux as it becomes superconducting. This is called the Meissner effect. Complete expulsion of the magnetic flux (a complete Meissner effect) occurs in this way for certain superconductors, called type I superconductors, but only for samples that have the described geometry. For samples of other shapes, including hollow structures, some of the magnetic flux can be trapped, producing an incomplete or partial Meissner effect.

Type II superconductors have a different magnetic behaviour. Examples of materials of this type are niobium and vanadium (the only type II superconductors among the chemical elements) and some alloys and compounds, including the high-T_c compounds. As a sample of this type, in the form of a long, thin cylinder or ellipsoid, is exposed to a decreasing magnetic field that is axially oriented with the sample, the increase of magnetization, instead of occurring suddenly at the critical field (H_c), sets in gradually. Beginning at the upper critical field (H_{c2}), it is completed at a lower critical field (H_{c1}; see Figure 50). If the sample is of some other shape, is hollow, or is inhomogeneous or strained, some magnetic flux remains trapped, and some magnetization of the sample remains after the applied field is completely removed. Known values of the upper critical field extend up to 6×10^5 oersteds, the value for the compound of lead, molybdenum, and sulfur with formula $PbMo_6S_8$.

Behaviour of type II superconductors

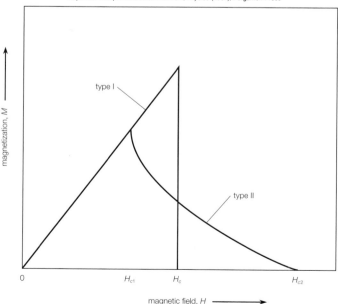

Figure 50: Magnetization as a function of magnetic field for a type I superconductor and a type II superconductor. For type I, magnetic flux is expelled, producing a magnetization (M) that increases with magnetic field (H) until a critical field (H_c) is reached, at which it falls to zero as with a normal conductor. A type II superconductor has two critical magnetic fields (H_{c1} and H_{c2}); below H_{c1} type II behaves as type I, and above H_{c2} it becomes normal.

Cooper electron pairs

The expulsion of magnetic flux by type I superconductors in fields below the critical field (H_c) or by type II superconductors in fields below H_{c1} is never quite as complete as has been stated in this simplified presentation, because the field always penetrates into a sample for a small distance, known as the electromagnetic penetration depth. Values of the penetration depth for the superconducting elements at low temperature lie in the range from about 390 to 1300 angstroms. As the temperature approaches the critical temperature, the penetration depth becomes extremely large.

Electro-magnetic penetration depth

High-frequency electromagnetic properties. The foregoing descriptions have pertained to the behaviour of superconductors in the absence of electromagnetic fields or in the presence of steady or slowly varying fields; the properties of superconductors in the presence of high-frequency electromagnetic fields, however, have also been studied.

The energy gap in a superconductor has a direct effect on the absorption of electromagnetic radiation. At low temperatures, at which a negligible fraction of the electrons are thermally excited to states above the gap, the superconductor can absorb energy only in a quantized amount that is at least twice the gap energy (at absolute zero, $2\Delta_0$). In the absorption process, a photon (a quantum of electromagnetic energy) is absorbed, and a Cooper pair is broken; both electrons in the pair become excited. The photon's energy (E) is related to its frequency (v) by the Planck relation, $E = hv$, in which h is Planck's constant (6.63×10^{-34} joule second). Hence the superconductor can absorb electromagnetic energy only for frequencies at least as large as $2\Delta_0/h$.

Magnetic-flux quantization. The laws of quantum mechanics dictate that electrons have wave properties and that the properties of an electron can be summed up in what is called a wave function. If several wave functions are in phase (*i.e.,* act in unison), they are said to be coherent. The theory of superconductivity indicates that there is a single, coherent, quantum mechanical wave function that determines the behaviour of all the superconducting electrons. As a consequence, a direct relationship can be shown to exist between the velocity of these electrons and the magnetic flux (Φ) enclosed within any closed path inside the superconductor. Indeed, inasmuch as the magnetic flux arises because of the motion of the electrons, the magnetic flux can be shown to be quantized; *i.e.,* the intensity of this trapped flux can change only by units of Planck's constant divided by twice the electron charge.

When a magnetic field enters a type II superconductor (in an applied field between the lower and upper critical fields, H_{c1} and H_{c2}), it does so in the form of quantized fluxoids, each carrying one quantum of flux. These fluxoids tend to arrange themselves in regular patterns that have been detected by electron microscopy and by neutron diffraction. If a large enough current is passed through the superconductor, the fluxoids move. This motion leads to energy dissipation that can heat the superconductor and drive it into the normal state. The maximum current per unit area that a superconductor can carry without being forced into the normal state is called the critical current density (J_c). In making wire for superconducting high-field magnets, manufacturers try to fix the positions of the fluxoids by making the wire inhomogeneous in composition.

Fluxoids

Josephson currents. If two superconductors are separated by an insulating film that forms a low-resistance junction between them, it is found that Cooper pairs can tunnel from one side of the junction to the other. (This process occurs in addition to the single-particle tunneling already described.) Thus, a flow of electrons, called the Josephson current, is generated and is intimately related to the phases of the coherent quantum mechanical wave function for all the superconducting electrons on the two sides of the junction. It was predicted that several novel phenomena should be observable, and experiments have demonstrated them. These are collectively called the Josephson effect or effects.

The first of these phenomena is the passage of current through the junction in the absence of a voltage across the junction. The maximum current that can flow at zero voltage depends on the magnetic flux (Φ) passing through the junction as a result of the magnetic field generated by currents in the junction and elsewhere. The dependence of the maximum zero-voltage current on the magnetic field applied to a junction between two superconductors is shown in Figure 51.

A second type of Josephson effect is an oscillating current resulting from a relation between the voltage across the junction and the frequency (v) of the currents associated with Cooper pairs passing through the junction. The frequency (v) of this Josephson current is given by $v = 2eV/h$, where e is the charge of the electron. Thus, the frequency increases by 4.84×10^{14} hertz (cycles per second) for each additional volt applied to the junction. This effect can be demonstrated in various ways. The voltage can be established with a source of direct-current (DC) power, for instance, and the oscillating current can be detected by the electromagnetic radiation of frequency (v) that it generates. Another method is to expose the junction to radiation of another frequency (v') generated externally. It is found that a graph of the DC current versus voltage has current steps at values of the voltage corresponding to Josephson frequencies that are integral multiples (n) of the external frequency ($v = nv'$); that is, $V = nhv'/2e$. The observation of current steps of this type has made it possible to measure h/e with far greater precision than by any other method and has therefore contributed to a knowledge of the fundamental constants of nature.

Oscillating currents

The Josephson effect has been used in the invention of novel devices for extremely high-sensitivity measurements of currents, voltages, and magnetic fields.

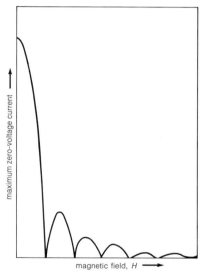

Figure 51: Maximum zero-voltage (Josephson) current passing through a junction by Cooper-pair tunneling as a function of magnetic field.

HIGHER-TEMPERATURE SUPERCONDUCTIVITY

Ever since Kamerlingh Onnes discovered that mercury becomes superconducting at temperatures less than 4 K, scientists have been searching for superconducting materials with higher transition temperatures. Until 1986 a compound of niobium and germanium (Nb_3Ge) had the highest known transition temperature, 23 K, less than a 20-degree increase in 75 years. Most researchers expected that the next increase in transition temperature would be found in a similar metallic alloy and that the rise would be only one or two degrees. In 1986, however, the Swiss physicist Karl Alex Müller and his West German associate, Johannes Georg Bednorz, discovered, after a three-year search among metal oxides, a material that had an unprecedentedly high transition temperature of about 30 K. They were awarded the Nobel Prize for Physics in 1987, and their discovery immediately stimulated groups of investigators in China, Japan, and the United States to produce superconducting oxides with even higher transition temperatures.

These high-temperature superconductors are ceramics. They contain lanthanum, yttrium, or another of the rare-earth elements or bismuth or thallium; usually barium or strontium (both alkaline-earth elements); copper; and oxygen. Other atomic species can sometimes be introduced by chemical substitution while retaining the high-T_c properties. The superconducting transition temperatures of some of the high-T_c materials are listed in Table 10. The value 134 K is the highest known T_c value. The compounds given in the table are members of the major families of high-T_c superconductors. Within each family, only the subscripts (i.e., stoichiometry) vary from one compound to another. The compounds listed have the highest observed superconducting transition temperature in their respective families. Samples in the families containing bismuth or thallium always exhibit a great deal of atomic disorder, with atoms in the "wrong" crystallographic sites and with impurity phases. It is possible that such disorder is required to make these compounds thermodynamically stable.

Table 10: Transition Temperatures of Some High-T_c Superconductors

compound	T_c (K)
$Nd_{1.85}Ce_{0.15}CuO_4$	24
$La_{1.85}Sr_{0.15}CuO_4$	40
$YBa_2Cu_3O_7$	92
$Bi_2Sr_2Ca_2Cu_3O_{10}$	110
$Tl_2Ba_2Ca_2Cu_3O_{10}$	127
$Hg_2Ba_2Ca_2Cu_3O_8$	134

The compounds have crystal structures containing planes of Cu and O atoms, and some also have chains of Cu and O atoms. The roles played by these planes and chains have come under intense investigation. Varying the oxygen content or the heat treatment of the materials dramatically changes their transition temperatures, critical magnetic fields, and other properties. Single crystals of the high-temperature superconductors are very anisotropic—i.e., their properties associated with a direction, such as the critical fields or the critical current density, are highly dependent on the angle between that direction and the rows of atoms in the crystal.

If the number of superconducting electrons per unit volume is locally disturbed by an applied force (typically electric or magnetic), this disturbance propagates for a certain distance in the material; the distance is called the superconducting coherence length (or Ginzburg-Landau coherence length), ξ. If a material has a superconducting region and a normal region, many of the superconducting properties disappear gradually—over a distance ξ—upon traveling from the former to the latter region. In the pure (i.e., undoped) classic superconductors ξ is on the order of a few thousand angstroms, but in the high-T_c superconductors it is on the order of 1 to 10 angstroms. The small size of ξ affects the thermodynamic and electromagnetic properties of the high-T_c superconductors. For example, it is responsible for the cusp shape of the specific heat curve near T_c that was mentioned above. It is also responsible for the ability of the high-T_c superconductors to remain superconducting in extraordinarily large fields—on the order of 1,000,000 gauss (100 teslas)—at low temperatures.

The high-T_c superconductors are type II superconductors. They exhibit zero resistance, strong diamagnetism, the Meissner effect, magnetic flux quantization, the Josephson effects, an electromagnetic penetration depth, an energy gap for the superconducting electrons, and the characteristic temperature dependences of the specific heat and the thermal conductivity that are described above. Therefore, it is clear that the conduction electrons in these materials form the Cooper pairs used to explain superconductivity in the BCS theory. Thus, the central conclusions of the BCS theory are demonstrated. Indeed, that theory guided Bednorz and Müller in their search for high-temperature superconductors. It is not known, however, why the transition temperatures of these oxides are so high. It was generally believed that the members of a Cooper pair are bound together because of interactions between the electrons and the lattice vibrations (phonons), but it is un-

likely that these interactions are strong enough to explain transition temperatures as high as 90 K. Most experts believe that interactions among the electrons generate high-temperature superconductivity. The details of this interaction are difficult to treat theoretically because the motions of the electrons are strongly correlated with each other and because magnetic phenomena play an important part in determining the microscopic properties of these materials. These strong correlations and magnetic properties may be responsible for unusual temperature dependencies of the electric resistivity ρ and Hall coefficient R_H in the normal state (i.e., above T_c). (For a discussion of the Hall effect, see ELECTRICITY AND MAGNETISM: *Magnetism: Magnetic forces*.) It is observed that at temperatures above T_c the electric resistivity, although higher for superconductors than for typical metals in the normal state, is roughly proportional to the temperature T, an unusually weak temperature dependence. Measurements of R_H show it to be significantly temperature-dependent in the normal state (sometimes proportional to $1/T$) rather than being roughly independent of T, which is the case for ordinary materials.

Films of the new materials can carry currents in the superconducting state that are large enough to be of importance in making many devices. Possible applications of the high-temperature superconductors in thin-film or bulk form include the construction of computer parts (logic devices, memory elements, switches, and interconnects), oscillators, amplifiers, particle accelerators, highly sensitive devices for measuring magnetic fields, voltages, or currents, magnets for medical magnetic-imaging devices, magnetic energy-storage systems, levitated passenger trains for high-speed travel, motors, generators, transformers, and transmission lines. The principal advantages of these superconducting devices would be their low power dissipation, high operating speed, and extreme sensitivity.

Equipment made with the high-temperature superconductors would also be more economical to operate because such materials can be cooled with inexpensive liquid nitrogen (boiling point, 77 K) rather than with costly liquid helium (boiling point, 4.2 K). The ceramics have problems, however, which must be overcome before useful devices can be made from them. These problems include brittleness, instabilities of the materials in some chemical environments, and a tendency for impurities to segregate at surfaces and grain boundaries, where they interfere with the flow of high currents in the superconducting state.

(Donald M. Ginsberg)

Applications of high-temperature superconductors

Superfluidity

The phenomenon of superfluidity has so far been directly observed only in the liquid forms of the two stable isotopes of helium, ^4He and ^3He, both of which remain liquid under their own vapour pressure down to the lowest temperatures reached thus far. In the case of the more abundant isotope, ^4He, superfluidity occurs at temperatures below the so-called lambda transition, which is 2.17 K. It is so named because the graph of the specific heat versus the temperature near this point has a shape resembling the Greek letter lambda. For ^3He, superfluidity is observed only at temperatures far closer to absolute zero, below 3×10^{-3} K. It is believed that superfluidity may occur in some other systems, such as neutron stars, but the evidence in these cases is much less direct.

The most spectacular signature of the transition of liquid ^4He into the superfluid phase is the sudden onset of the ability to flow without apparent friction through capillaries so small that any ordinary liquid (including ^4He itself above the lambda transition) would be clamped by its viscosity; thus, a vessel that was "helium-tight" in the so-called normal phase (i.e., above the lambda temperature) might suddenly spring leaks below it. Related phenomena observed in the superfluid phase include the ability to sustain persistent currents in a ring-shaped container; the phenomenon of film creep, in which the liquid flows without apparent friction up and over the side of a bucket containing it; and a thermal conductivity that is millions of times its value in the normal phase and greater than that of the best metallic conductors. Another property is

Superfluid phenomena

less spectacular but is extremely significant for an understanding of the superfluid phase: if the liquid is cooled through the lambda transition in a bucket that is slowly rotating, then, as the temperature decreases toward absolute zero, the liquid appears gradually to come to rest with respect to the laboratory even though the bucket continues to rotate. This nonrotation effect is completely reversible; the apparent velocity of rotation depends only on the temperature and not on the history of the system. Most of these phenomena also have been observed in the superfluid phase of liquid ^{3}He, though in somewhat less spectacular form.

It is thought that there is a close connection between the phenomena of superfluidity and superconductivity; indeed, from a phenomenological point of view superconductivity is simply superfluidity occurring in an electrically charged system. Thus, the frictionless flow of superfluid ^{4}He through narrow capillaries parallels the frictionless carrying of electric current by the electrons in a superconductor, and the ability of helium to sustain circulating mass currents in a ring-shaped container is closely analogous to the persistence of electric currents in a superconducting ring. Less obviously, it turns out that the nonrotation effect is the exact analogue of the Meissner effect in superconductors (see above *Superconductivity*). Many other characteristic features of superconductivity, such as the existence of vortices and the Josephson effect, have been observed in the superfluid phases of both ^{4}He and ^{3}He.

The accepted theoretical understanding of superfluidity (or superconductivity) is based on the idea that an extremely large number of atoms (or electrons) show identical, and moreover essentially quantum mechanical, behaviour; that is to say, the system is described by a single, coherent, quantum mechanical wave function. A single electron in an atom cannot rotate around the nucleus in any arbitrary orbit; rather, quantum mechanics requires that it rotate in such a way that its angular momentum is quantized so as to be a multiple (including zero) of $h/2\pi$, where h is Planck's constant. This is the origin of, for example, the phenomenon of atomic diamagnetism. Similarly, a single atom (or molecule) placed in a ring-shaped container is allowed by quantum mechanics to travel around the ring with only certain definite velocities, including zero. In an ordinary liquid such as water, the thermal disorder ensures that the atoms (or molecules) are distributed over the different (quantized) states available to them in such a way that the average velocity is not quantized; thus, when the container rotates and the liquid is given sufficient time to come into equilibrium, it rotates along with the container in accordance with everyday experience.

In a superfluid system the situation is quite different. The simpler case is that of ^{4}He, a liquid consisting of atoms that have total spin angular momentum equal to zero and whose distribution between their possible states is therefore believed to be governed by a principle known as Bose statistics. A gas of such atoms without interactions between them would undergo, at some temperature T_0, a phenomenon known as Bose condensation; below T_0 a finite fraction of all the atoms occupy a single state, normally that of lowest energy, and this fraction increases toward one as the temperature falls toward absolute zero. These atoms are said to be condensed. It is widely believed

Bose condensation

that a similar phenomenon should also occur for a liquid such as ^{4}He, in which the interaction between atoms is quite important, and that the lambda transition of ^{4}He is just the onset of Bose condensation. (The reason that this phenomenon is not seen in other systems of spin-zero atoms such as neon-22 is simply that, as the temperature is lowered, freezing occurs first.) If this is so, then, for temperatures below the lambda transition, a finite fraction of all the atoms must decide cooperatively which one of the possible quantized states they will all occupy. In particular, if the container is rotating at a sufficiently slow speed, these condensed atoms will occupy the nonrotating state—*i.e.,* they will be at rest with respect to the laboratory—while the rest will behave normally and will distribute themselves in such a way that on average they rotate with the container. As a result, as the temperature is lowered and the fraction of condensed atoms increases, the liquid will appear gradually to come to rest with respect to the laboratory (or, more accurately, to the fixed stars). Similarly, when the liquid is flowing through a small capillary, the condensed atoms cannot be scattered by the walls one at a time since they are forced by Bose statistics to occupy the same state. They must be scattered, if at all, simultaneously. Since this process is extremely improbable, the liquid, or more precisely the condensed fraction of it, flows without any apparent friction. The other characteristic manifestations of superfluidity can be explained along similar lines.

The idea of Bose condensation is not directly applicable to liquid ^{3}He, because ^{3}He atoms have spin angular momentum equal to $1/2$ (in units of $h/2\pi$) and their distribution among states is therefore believed to be governed by a different principle, known as Fermi statistics. It is believed, however, that in the superfluid phase of ^{3}He the atoms, like the electrons in a superconductor (see above *Superconductivity*), pair off to form Cooper pairs—a sort of quasimolecular complex—which have integral spin and therefore effectively obey Bose rather than Fermi statistics. In particular, as soon as the Cooper pairs are formed, they undergo a sort of Bose condensation, and subsequently the arguments given above for ^{4}He apply equally to them. As in the case of the electrons in superconductors, a finite energy, the so-called energy gap Δ, is necessary to break up the pairs (or at least most of them), and as a result the thermodynamics of superfluid ^{3}He is quite similar to that of superconductors. There is one important difference between the two cases. Whereas in a classic superconductor the electrons pair off with opposite spins and zero total angular momentum, making the internal structure of the Cooper pairs rather featureless, in ^{3}He the atoms pair with parallel spins and nonzero total angular momentum, so that the internal structure of the pairs is much richer and more interesting. One manifestation of this is that there are three superfluid phases of liquid ^{3}He, called A, B, and A_1, which are distinguished by the different internal structures of the Cooper pairs. The B phase is in most respects similar to a classic superconductor, whereas the A (and A_1) phase is strongly anisotropic in its properties and has an energy gap that actually vanishes for some directions of motion. As a result, some of the superfluid properties of the A and A_1 phases are markedly different from those of ^{4}He or ^{3}He-B and are indeed unique among known physical systems.   (Anthony J. Leggett)

Superfluid phases of ^{3}He

HIGH-PRESSURE PHENOMENA

Matter undergoes significant changes in physical, chemical, and structural characteristics when subjected to high pressure. Pressure thus serves as a versatile tool in materials research, and it is especially important in the investigation of the rocks and minerals that form the deep interior of the Earth and other planets. Pressure, defined as a force applied to an area, is a thermochemical variable that induces physical and chemical changes comparable to the more familiar effects of temperature. Liquid water, for example, transforms to solid ice when cooled to temperatures below 0° C (32° F), but ice can also be

produced at room temperature by compressing water to pressures roughly 10,000 times above atmospheric pressure. Similarly, water converts to its gaseous form at high temperature or at low pressure.

In spite of the superficial similarity between temperature and pressure, these two variables are fundamentally different in the ways they affect a material's internal energy. Temperature variations reflect changes in the kinetic energy and thus in the entropy of vibrating atoms. Increased pressure, on the other hand, alters the electron interaction energy of atomic bonds by forcing atoms closer together in a smaller volume. Pressure thus serves as a powerful probe of atomic interactions and chemical bonding. Furthermore, pressure is an important tool for synthesizing dense structures, including superhard materials, novel solidified gases and liquids, and mineral-like phases suspected to occur deep within the Earth and other planets.

Numerous units for measuring pressure have been introduced and, at times, are confused in the literature. The atmosphere (atm; approximately 1.034 kilograms per square centimetre [14.7 pounds per square inch], equivalent to the weight of about 760 millimetres [30 inches] of mercury) and the bar (equivalent to one kilogram per square centimetre) are often cited. Coincidently, these units are almost identical (1 bar = 0.987 atm). The pascal, defined as one newton per square metre (1 Pa = 0.00001 bar), is the official SI (Système International d'Unités) unit of pressure. Nevertheless, the pascal has not gained universal acceptance among high-pressure researchers, perhaps because of the awkward necessity of using the gigapascal (1 GPa = 10,000 bars) and terapascal (1 TPa = 10,000,000 bars) in describing high-pressure results.

In everyday experience, greater-than-ambient pressures are encountered in, for example, pressure cookers (about 1.5 atm), pneumatic automobile and truck tires (usually 2 to 3 atm), and steam systems (up to 20 atm). In the context of materials research, however, "high pressure" usually refers to pressures in the range of thousands to millions of atmospheres.

Studies of matter under high pressure are especially important in a planetary context. Objects in the deepest trench of the Pacific Ocean are subjected to about 0.1 GPa (roughly 1,000 atm), equivalent to the pressure beneath a three-kilometre column of rock. The pressure at the centre of the Earth exceeds 300 GPa, and pressures inside the largest planets—Saturn and Jupiter—are estimated to be roughly 2 and 10 TPa, respectively. At the upper extreme, pressures inside stars may exceed 1,000,000,000 TPa.

Producing high pressure

Scientists study materials at high pressure by confining samples in specially designed machines that apply a force to the sample area. Prior to 1900 these studies were conducted in rather crude iron or steel cylinders, usually with relatively inefficient screw seals. Maximum laboratory pressures were limited to about 0.3 GPa, and explosions of the cylinders were a common and sometimes injurious occurrence. Dramatic improvements in high-pressure apparatuses and measuring techniques were introduced by the American physicist Percy Williams Bridgman of Harvard University in Cambridge, Mass. In 1905 Bridgman discovered a method of packing pressurized samples, including gases and liquids, in such a way that the sealing gasket always experienced a higher pressure than the sample under study, thereby confining the sample and reducing the risk of experimental failure. Bridgman not only routinely attained pressures above 30,000 atm, but he also was able to study fluids and other difficult samples.

LARGE-VOLUME APPARATUSES

Sustained high pressures and temperatures are now commonly produced in massive presses that focus large forces (up to thousands of tons) through two or more strong

anvils to compress a sample. The simplest of these devices, introduced by Bridgman in the 1930s, employs two tapered anvils that squeeze the sample like a vise (see Figure 52). Although capable of very high pressures—in excess of 50 GPa in designs with sufficient lateral anvil support—the axial force of the squeezer tends to deform samples into extremely flattened, highly strained disks.

The piston-in-cylinder design, in use for more than a century, incorporates a strong metal or carbide piston that is rammed into a sample-confining cylinder. In principle, the piston can be quite long, so a piston-cylinder design can accommodate a much larger volume of sample than the squeezer, depending on the dimensions of the sample-holding cylinder. These devices are rarely used at pressures above about 10 GPa owing to the likelihood of lateral failure (namely, explosive bursting) of the metal cylinder.

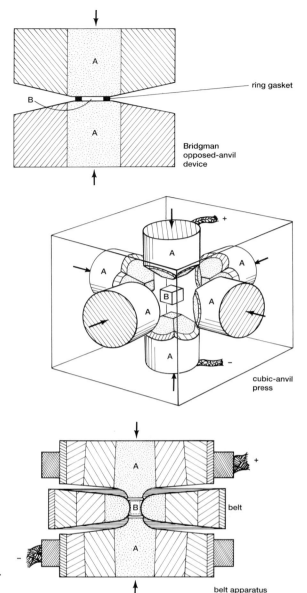

Figure 52: *High-pressure apparatuses.*
In each device, (A) anvils of carbide (stippled) and steel compress (B) a sample. Electric leads (+ and −) provide heating capability.

Adapted from A.A. Giardini and J.E. Tydings, "Diamond Synthesis: Observations on the Mechanism of Formation," *The American Mineralogist,* vol. 47, Nov.–Dec. 1962, pp. 1393–1412, fig. 1 (a & e); copyright by the Mineralogical Society of America

The belt apparatus, invented in 1954 by the scientist Tracy Hall of the General Electric Company for use in the company's diamond-making program, incorporates features of both opposed-anvil and piston-cylinder designs (see Figure 52). Two highly tapered pistonlike anvils compress a sample that is confined in a torus, much like a cylinder open at both ends. Hundreds of belt-type devices are in use worldwide in diamond synthesis.

Many high-pressure researchers now employ split-sphere or multianvil devices, which compress a sample uniformly from all sides. Versions with six anvils that press against the six faces of a cube-shaped sample (see Figure 52) or with eight anvils that compress an octahedral sample are in widespread use. Unlike the simple squeezer, piston-cylinder, and belt apparatuses, multianvil devices can compress a sample uniformly from all sides, while achieving a pressure range with an upper limit of at least 30 GPa. All these types of high-pressure apparatuses can be fitted with a resistance heater, typically a sample-surrounding cylinder of graphite or another electrically conducting heating element, for studies at temperatures up to 2,000° C.

THE DIAMOND-ANVIL CELL

The diamond-anvil pressure cell, in which two gem-quality diamonds apply a force to the sample, revolutionized high-pressure research (see Figure 53). The diamond-anvil cell was invented in 1958 almost simultaneously by workers at the National Bureau of Standards in Washington, D.C., and at the University of Chicago. The diamond-cell design represented a logical outgrowth of Bridgman's simple squeezer, but it had one significant advantage over all other high-pressure apparatuses. Diamond, while extremely strong, is also transparent to many kinds of electromagnetic radiation, including gamma rays, X rays, visible light, and much of the infrared and ultraviolet region. The diamond cell thus provided the first opportunity for high-pressure researchers to observe visually the effects of pressure, and it allowed convenient access for many kinds of experimental techniques, notably X-ray diffraction, Mössbauer (gamma-ray), infrared, and Raman spectroscopies, and other optical spectroscopies.

The utility of the diamond cell was greatly enhanced when Alvin Van Valkenburg, one of the original diamond-cell inventors at the National Bureau of Standards, placed a thin metal foil gasket between the two diamond-anvil faces. Liquids and other fluid samples could thus be confined in a sample chamber defined by the cylindrical gasket wall and flat diamond ends. In 1963 Van Valkenburg became the first person to observe water, alcohol, and other liquids crystallize at high pressure. The gasketed geometry also permitted for the first time X-ray and optical studies of uncrushed single crystals that were hydrostatically pressurized by a fluid medium.

The diamond-anvil cell holds all records for sustained high pressures. The 100 GPa (megabar) mark was surpassed in December 1975 by the geophysicists Ho-kwang Mao and Peter M. Bell, both of the Geophysical Laboratory of the Carnegie Institution of Washington, in Washington, D.C., where they subsequently attained diamond-cell pressures of approximately 300 GPa. Heating of diamond-cell samples, with both resistance heaters and lasers, has extended accessible pressure-temperature conditions to those that prevail in most of the solid Earth.

The highest transient laboratory pressures are generated with high-velocity projectiles that induce extreme shock pressures (which often reach many millions of atmospheres) for times on the order of one microsecond. Shock waves generated by explosions or gas-propelled projectiles induce dramatic changes in physical properties, as well as rapid polymorphic transformations. Carefully timed intense pulses of X rays or laser light can be used to probe these transient environments. While dynamic high-pressure studies are limited by the difficulty of making precise measurements in such short time periods, these shock techniques have provided insights into changes in atomic structure and properties that occur at extreme conditions. Explosive shock compression has also become an important tool for the synthesis of microcrystalline diamond, which is employed in the polishing of gemstones and other hard materials.

Physical and chemical effects of high pressure

The principal effect of high pressure, observed in all materials, is a reduction in volume and a corresponding shortening of mean interatomic distances. Coincident with these structural modifications are numerous changes, often dramatic, in physical properties.

In four decades of high-pressure research, Bridgman, whose work was honoured by the 1946 Nobel Prize for Physics, documented effects of pressure on electric conductivity, thermal conductivity, viscosity, melting, reaction kinetics, and other material properties. Pressure was found to induce both continuous and discontinuous changes in matter. Bridgman and others observed smoothly varying trends in properties such as electric conductivity or volume versus pressure for most materials. Some substances, however, displayed sharp, reproducible discontinuities in these properties at specific pressures. Dramatic sudden drops in the electric resistance and volume of bismuth, lead, and other metals were carefully documented and provided

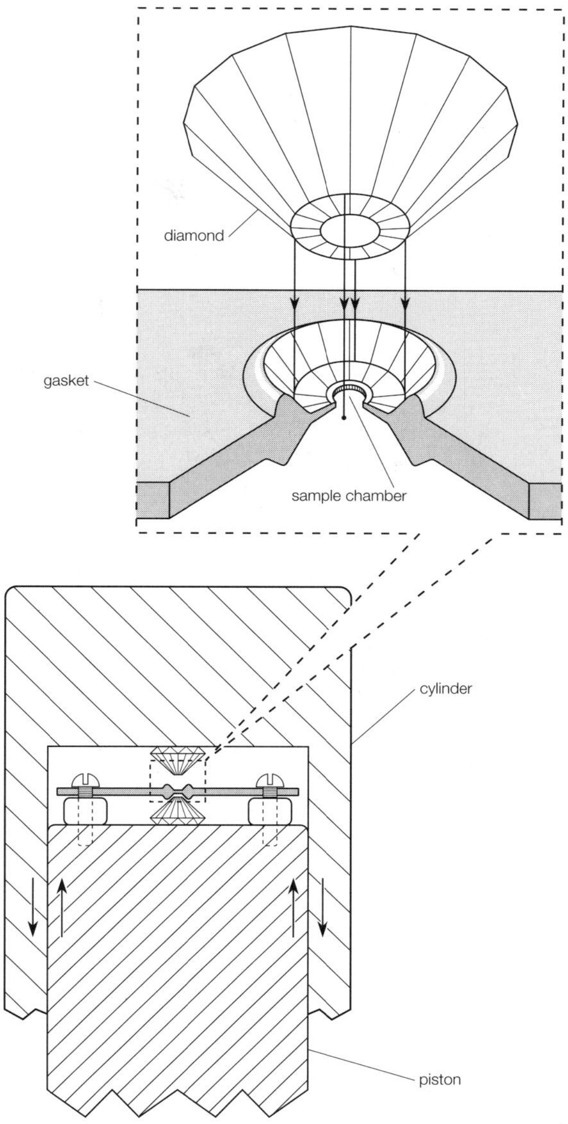

Figure 53: The diamond-anvil cell and gasket.
From H.K. Mao and P.M. Bell, "Design of the Diamond-Window, High-Pressure Apparatus for Cryogenic Experiments," *Annual Report of the Director, Geophysical Laboratory,* 1978–79; reprinted from Papers from the Geophysical Laboratory, *Carnegie Institution of Washington Year Book 78*

Bridgman with a useful internal pressure standard for his experiments. These experiments also demonstrated the effectiveness of pressure for studying continuous changes in properties (under uniform compression) and discontinuous changes (phase transitions).

PHASE TRANSITIONS

Under sufficiently high pressure, every material is expected to undergo structural transformations to denser, more closely packed atomic arrangements. At room temperature, for example, all gases solidify at pressures not greater than about 15 GPa. Molecular solids like water ice (H_2O) and carbon tetrachloride (CCl_4) often undergo a series of structural transitions, characterized by successively denser arrangements of molecular units.

A different transition mode is observed in oxides, silicates, and other types of ionic compounds that comprise most rock-forming minerals. In these materials, metal or semimetal atoms such as magnesium (Mg) or silicon (Si) are surrounded by regular tetrahedral or octahedral arrangements of four or six oxygen (O) atoms, respectively. High-pressure phase transitions of such minerals often involve a structural rearrangement that increases the number of oxygen atoms around each central cation. The common mineral quartz (SiO_2), for example, contains four-coordinated silicon at low pressure, but it transforms to the dense stishovite form with six-coordinated silicon at about 8 GPa. Similarly, the pyroxene mineral with formula MgSiO₃ at room pressure contains magnesium and silicon in six- and four-coordination, respectively, but the pyroxene transforms to the perovskite structure with eight-coordinated magnesium and six-coordinated silicon above 25 GPa. Each of these high-pressure phase transitions results in a denser structure with increased packing efficiency of atoms.

High-pressure metallization

The British scientist J.D. Bernal predicted in 1928 that all matter should ultimately become metallic at sufficient pressure, as the forced overlap of electron orbitals induces electron delocalization. High-pressure transformations from insulator to metal were first observed in iodine, silicon, germanium, and other elements by the American chemist Harry G. Drickamer and his coworkers at the University of Illinois at Urbana-Champaign in the early 1960s. Subsequently, metallization has been documented in several more elements (including the gases xenon and oxygen), as well as in numerous molecular, ionic, and covalent chemical compounds. The effort to metallize the element hydrogen at a predicted pressure of several million atmospheres remains a significant challenge in experimental physics.

COMPRESSION

High-pressure X-ray crystallographic studies of atomic structure reveal three principal compression mechanisms in solids: bond compression, bond-angle bending, and intermolecular compression; they are illustrated in Figure 54. Bond compression—*i.e.,* the shortening of interatomic distances—occurs to some extent in all compounds at high pressure. The magnitude of this effect has been shown both theoretically and empirically to be related to bond strength. Strong covalent carbon-carbon bonds in diamond experience the lowest percentage of compression: roughly 0.07 percent per GPa. Similarly, ionic bonds between highly charged cations and anions, such as bonds between

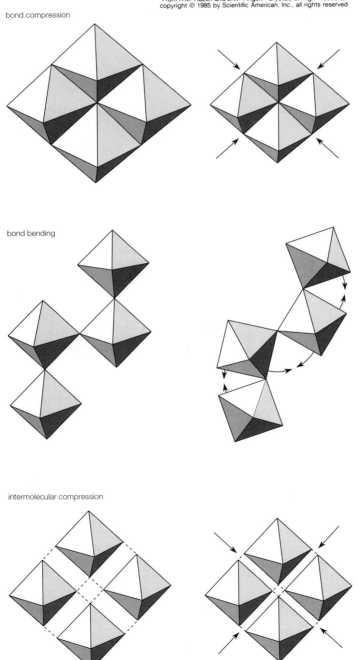

bond compression

bond bending

intermolecular compression

Figure 54: Three compression mechanisms in crystals.

Si⁴⁺ and O²⁻ in silicates, are relatively incompressible (less than 0.2 percent per GPa). Relatively weak bonds in alkali halides, on the other hand, display bond compressibilities that often exceed 5.0 percent per GPa.

Many common materials display different bonding characteristics in different directions; this occurs notably in layered compounds (*e.g.,* graphite and layered silicates such as micas) and in chain compounds (*e.g.,* many polymeric compounds and chain silicates, including some varieties of asbestos). The strong dependence of bond compression on bond strength thus commonly leads to anisotropies—that is, significant differences in compression in different crystal directions. In many layered-structure silicates, such as mica, in which relatively strong and rigid layers containing magnesium-oxygen, aluminum-oxygen, and silicon-oxygen bonds alternate with weaker layers containing alkali cations, compressibility is five times greater perpendicular to the layers than within the layers. This differential compressibility and the associated stresses that develop in a high-pressure geologic environment contribute to the development of dramatic layered textures in mica-rich rocks such as schist.

Many common ionic compounds, including the rock-forming minerals quartz, feldspar, garnet, zeolite, and perovskite (the high-pressure $MgSiO_3$ form of which is thought to be the Earth's most abundant mineral), are composed of corner-linked clusters—or frameworks—of atomic polyhedrons. A polyhedron consists of a central cation, typically silicon or aluminum in common minerals, surrounded by a regular tetrahedron or octahedron of four or six oxygen atoms, respectively. In framework structures every oxygen atom is bonded to two tetrahedral or octahedral cations, resulting in a three-dimensional polyhedral network. In these materials significant compression can occur by bending the metal-oxygen-metal bond angles between the polyhedrons. The volume change resulting from this bending, and the associated collapse of interpolyhedral spaces, is typically an order of magnitude greater than compression due to bond-length changes alone. Framework structures, consequently, are often much more compressible than structures with only edge- or face-sharing polyhedrons, whose compression is attributable predominantly to bond shortening.

Molecular solids—including ice, solidified gases such as solid oxygen (O_2), hydrogen (H_2), and methane (CH_4), and virtually all organic compounds—consist of an array of discrete, rigid molecules that are linked to one another by weak hydrogen bonds and van der Waals forces. Compression in these materials generally occurs by large decreases in intermolecular distances (often approaching 10 percent per GPa), in contrast to minimal intramolecular compression. Differences in the intermolecular versus intramolecular compression mechanisms lead in some cases to significantly anisotropic compression. Graphite, the low-pressure layered form of elemental carbon in which the "molecules" are continuous two-dimensional sheets, exhibits perhaps the most extreme example of this phenomenon. Carbon-carbon bonds within graphite layers compress only 0.07 percent per GPa (similar to C-C bond compression in diamond), while interlayer compression, dominated by van der Waals forces acting between carbon sheets, is approximately 45 times greater.

Anisotropic compression of graphite (margin note)

EFFECTS ON ELECTRIC AND MAGNETIC PROPERTIES

The measurement of electric and magnetic properties of materials in a high-pressure environment entails considerable experimental difficulties, especially those associated with attaching leads to pressurized samples or detecting small signals from the experiment. Nevertheless, electric conductivities of numerous materials at high pressures have been documented. The principal classes of solids—insulators, semiconductors, metals, and superconductors—are distinguished on the basis of electric conductivity and its variation with temperature (see above *Solid state*). Insulators, which include most rock-forming oxides and silicates, have been investigated extensively by geophysicists concerned primarily with the behaviour and properties of deep-earth rocks and minerals at extreme conditions. Indeed, it was once hoped that laboratory constraints on

such properties could be tied to known values of the Earth's electric and magnetic properties and thus constrain the composition and temperature gradients of Earth models. It appears, however, that small variations in mineral composition (*e.g.,* the ratio of ferrous to ferric iron) as well as defect properties can play a role orders of magnitude greater than that of pressure alone.

Properties of semiconductors are highly sensitive to pressure, because small changes in structure can result in large changes in electronic properties. The metallizations of silicon and germanium, which are accompanied by an orders-of-magnitude increase in electric conductivity, represent extreme cases of such changes. While simple metals display a general trend of increased conductivity with increased pressure, there are many exceptions. Calcium and strontium exhibit maxima in electric conductivity at 30 and 4 GPa, respectively, while barium and arsenic display both maxima and minima with increasing pressure. Ionic conductors, on the other hand, generally experience decreased electric conductivity at high pressure owing to the collapse of ion pathways.

Pressure has been found to be a sensitive probe of the effects of structure on superconductivity, because the structural changes brought about by pressure often have a significant effect on the critical temperature. In simple metals, pressure tends to decrease the critical temperature, eventually suppressing superconductivity altogether. In some organic superconductors, on the other hand, superconductivity appears only at high pressure (and temperatures near absolute zero). In several of the layered copper-oxide high-temperature superconductors, pressure has a strong positive effect on critical temperature; this phenomenon led to the synthesis of new varieties of superconductors in which smaller cations are used to mimic the structural effect of pressure.

Effects on superconductors (margin note)

The first measurements of magnetic properties at high pressure were conducted on samples in a diamond-anvil cell using Mössbauer spectroscopy, which is a technique that can probe the coupling of a magnetic field with the nuclear magnetic dipole. High-pressure ferromagnetic-to-paramagnetic transitions were documented in iron metal and in magnetite (Fe_3O_4), while Curie temperatures (*i.e.,* the temperature above which the ferromagnetic properties of a material cease to exist) in several metallic elements were found to shift slightly. Subsequent research has employed high-pressure devices constructed of nonmagnetic beryllium-copper alloys, which were developed for research on samples subjected to strong magnetic fields.

Applications

DIAMOND MAKING

While modest pressures (less than 1,000 atm) have long been used in the manufacture of plastics, in the synthesis of chromium dioxide for magnetic recording tape, and in the growth of large, high-quality quartz crystals, the principal application of high-pressure materials technology lies in the synthesis of diamond and other superhard abrasives. Approximately 100 tons of synthetic diamond are produced each year—a weight comparable to the total amount of diamond mined since biblical times. For centuries diamonds had been identified only as an unusual mineral found in river gravels; scientists had no clear idea about their mode of origin until the late 1860s, when South African miners found diamond embedded in its native matrix, the high-pressure volcanic rock called kimberlite. Efforts to make diamond by subjecting graphitic carbon to high pressure began shortly after that historic discovery.

Prior to the work of Bridgman, sufficient laboratory pressures for driving the graphite-to-diamond transition had not been achieved. Bridgman's opposed-anvil device demonstrated that the necessary pressures could be sustained, but high temperatures were required to overcome the kinetic barrier to the transformation. Following World War II, several industrial laboratories, including Allmanna Svenska Elektriska Aktiebolaget (ASEA) in Sweden and Norton Company and General Electric in the United States, undertook major efforts to develop a commercial process. Diamond was first synthesized in a reproducible, commercially viable experiment in December 1954, when Tracy Hall, working for General Electric, subjected a mixture of iron sulfide and carbon to approximately 6 GPa and 1,500° C in a belt-type apparatus. General Electric employees soon standardized the processes and discovered that a melted ferrous metal, which acts as a catalyst, is essential for diamond growth at these conditions.

EARTH SCIENCE

Synthesis of stishovite

Diamond-making techniques have been embraced by Earth scientists in their efforts to simulate conditions in the Earth's deep interior. Of special significance were the high-pressure syntheses of two new forms of silicates. In 1960 Sergei Stishov, while at the Institute of High-Pressure Physics in Moscow, subjected ordinary beach sand (composed of the mineral quartz SiO_2) to more than 8 GPa of pressure and high temperatures. The form of silica that he produced was approximately 62 percent denser than quartz and was the first known high-pressure compound to contain silicon in six-coordination rather than the four-coordination found in virtually all crustal minerals. The natural occurrence of this new synthetic material was confirmed within a few weeks by careful examination of shocked material from Meteor Crater, Ariz., U.S. The mineral was named stishovite.

In 1974 a second high-pressure discovery revolutionized geologists' understanding of deep-earth mineralogy when Lin-gun Liu of the Australian National University used a diamond-anvil cell to synthesize silicate perovskite, a dense form of the common mineral enstatite, $MgSiO_3$. Subsequent studies by Liu revealed that many of the minerals believed to constitute the deep interior of the Earth transform to the perovskite structure at lower mantle conditions—an observation that led him to propose that silicate perovskite is the Earth's most abundant mineral, perhaps accounting for more than half of the planet's volume.

(Robert M. Hazen)

Science Year
in Review

Contents

The Year in Science: An Overview

by Robert P. Crease

If science is "the art of the soluble," in the words of Nobel laureate Sir Peter Medawar, this would be difficult to prove on the basis of the events of 1993. Bitter controversies sprang up over the Superconducting Super Collider (SSC), cloning, experimental ethics, dinosaurs, "gay genes," mammographs, and numerous other issues. Science seemed to raise more questions than it answered.

Ordinarily, controversies in science are expected to be about interpretation of data and the reliability of methods. What was remarkable about the controversies of the past year, however, was how many other kinds there were, each with numerous variants.

Big Science controversies. With the scale of scientific projects steadily increasing, more and more concerns arise about the value of such projects; the larger a project, the more public resources society must commit to it and the fewer are left over for other scientific and nonscientific undertakings. Big Science projects were once the exclusive purview of physics; by 1994 practically every field had them, along with their concomitant controversies. Physics still led the pack, however, and the biggest Big Science controversy of the past year involved the SSC, the largest pure research project attempted. The SSC came with a price tag of $8 billion–$12 billion (depending on whose estimate you believed) and had been in planning and construction for a dozen years. In June 1993 the U.S. House of Representatives voted against it. Critics accused project managers of incompetence, while supporters complained of oppressive oversight practices and unfair accusations. In September the U.S. Senate voted for it, but in October the House prevailed and the project was killed with some 24 km (15 mi) of tunnel dug and $2 billion spent. The decision effectively marked the end of the postwar era of close partnership between science, industry, and government and gave Europe the chance to gain leadership in high-energy physics. Russian physicists committed to the SSC signed up to work at CERN, the pan-European physics center in Geneva (which was planning its own large-scale accelerator), while U.S. physicists began negotiating terms of their own participation at CERN.

ROBERT P. CREASE *is an Assistant Professor of Science at the State University of New York at Stony Brook and Historian at the Brookhaven National Laboratory, Upton, N.Y. He is also author of* The Play of Nature: Experimentation as Performance *(1993).*

Big Science controversies occurred in other fields as well. Critics attacked the value of the $2.7 billion Advanced Neutron Source proposed for Oak Ridge (Tenn.) National Laboratory, a facility to be used mainly by condensed-matter physicists. The Women's Health Initiative, which at $625 million was the largest clinical study ever undertaken by the U.S. National Institutes of Health (NIH), was attacked by a panel of medical experts for being too ambitious, unlikely to stay within budget, and poorly thought out.

Another kind of Big Science controversy arose over placement of the "B factory," a $170 million high-energy physics facility designed to produce the B particle, analysis of which holds important clues about why there seems to be more matter than antimatter. Competing for the site were Cornell University, Ithaca, N.Y., and the Stanford Linear Accelerator Facility in California. In what many regarded as a highly political decision, U.S. Pres. Bill Clinton gave the project to the latter, in an electorally important state that was suffering from a sluggish economy. The risks of Big Science projects were dramatized in August when the $1 billion Mars Observer satellite, the first to visit Mars in 17 years, was totally lost, failing to transmit radio signals just before its scheduled rendezvous with the planet.

If these projects had come cheap, no controversy would have arisen; no one doubted the basic value of studying subatomic particles, condensed-matter physics, women's health, the reason for matter, and Mars. Rather, these controversies emerged in connection with the risks and expense of the experiments needed to generate such knowledge.

Ethics controversies. Ethics controversies, too, arise in all fields of science. Front-page examples of 1993 involved cloning, postmenopausal motherhood, experimentation on uninformed subjects, and scientific misconduct.

Cloning procedures, used on mammals for years, have been subject to a simmering ethical debate that until 1993 had a slightly frivolous aura, thanks to treatment of the kind it received in Woody Allen's film *Sleeper*. The stakes of the debate suddenly rose in October when scientists at George Washington University, Washington, D.C., actually cloned a human embryo. Though the embryos died, the possibility realized by the work is now everlasting. Hailed by some as a way of boosting the embryo supply in fertility clinics, the feat was savagely attacked by others

277

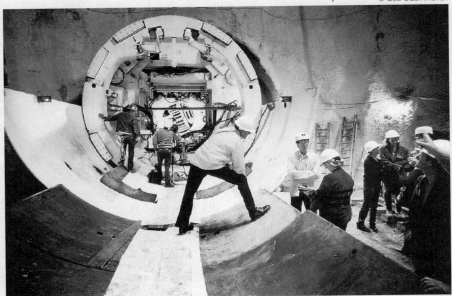

The biggest Big Science controversy of the past year involved the Superconducting Super Collider. After about 24 km (15 mi) of tunnel had been dug in Texas and $2 billion spent for the SSC, the project was canceled by the U.S. Congress in October 1993.

as tampering with nature, devaluing individuality, and potentially leading to "designer babies."

The birth of twins to a 59-year-old British woman on Christmas day, the pregnancy of a 61-year-old Italian, and the birth to a 53-year-old American of her own daughter's implanted child (her own grandchild), among other events, raised issues of the use and abuse of reproductive technology. Critics said that it made motherhood a technological rather than biological process and that it was wrong for postmenopausal women to assume the demands of motherhood. France's minister of health, a physician, called such pregnancies "immoral" and sought to ban the use of "medically assisted procreation techniques" on postmenopausal women. Advocates admitted the greater risks of late motherhood but pointed out that no new fundamental ethical issues are raised by such pregnancies that have not already been involved in standard in vitro fertilization methods; they also noted the hypocrisy of the fact that similar questions have never been raised for late fatherhood, and, given several biblical references to late pregnancies, called for more humility before stones were cast.

Variants of these controversies occurred in Great Britain and Italy, involving implantation of white women's eggs in black women and the announcement by a University of Edinburgh researcher of a method to produce test-tube babies from eggs of aborted fetuses. This is possible because 10-week old female fetuses have already produced six million–seven million eggs, all they will ever make. An egg can be removed from one and implanted into an adult woman, where it can mature and be fertilized. Critics were horrified by the specter of a child

whose mother is a dead fetus and spoke darkly of "fetus farming"; others hailed the benefits to infertile couples and spoke of the right to bear children. In commenting on these cases, the *Economist* magazine observed that the technologies in question had been created in response to social needs and pressures and that while art holds a mirror up to nature, "science holds the mirror up to society . . . smashing the mirror is not the solution."

Another explosive reaction greeted disclosure of a number of experiments involving radiation exposure on more than 800 civilians—including prisoners, pregnant women, the retarded, and terminally ill cancer patients—from 1945 to 1975. Issues raised included "informed consent," adequate knowledge of risk, and judgment by contemporary research standards. The U.S. Department of Energy (whose precursor agency, the U.S. Atomic Energy Commission, had largely supported the studies) opened an investigation. A few individuals tried to argue that the violation of ethical standards involved was small by the standards of the time—but that clearly could not be said about a secret test involving radiation exposure that was conducted in the former Soviet Union in 1954 and whose existence became public during the year. To test the fighting effectiveness of troops after a nuclear attack, the Soviet military exploded an atomic bomb near 45,000 Red Army troops, who were then ordered to stage a mock battle in the flaming, highly radioactive debris.

The issue of misconduct was a contentious one in 1993. The U.S. Office of Research Integrity gave up or lost its four biggest cases, including one against HIV (human immunodeficiency virus) codiscoverer Robert C. Gallo. In December, in a case involving

278

two University of Hong Kong researchers, the world's first legal verdict declaring a scientist guilty of plagiarism was handed down. Even heroes of the history of science were tainted. Charles Coulomb, renowned pioneer of modern physics and discoverer of the law of electrostatic forces between two charged objects, came under suspicion when two historians from the University of Oldenburg, Germany, reconstructing his equipment, could not repeat the experiment on which he based the law and implied that he had fudged the data. Other science historians said Coulomb's results might have been due to other factors and noted that experimental skill just may have played a role.

Is scientific misconduct rare or rampant? A study of that, based on questionnaires prepared by investigators at the Acadia Institute, Bar Harbor, Maine, and the University of Minnesota, was itself controversial. The results led the researchers to conclude that scientific misconduct was more widespread than commonly believed. The study was rejected by *Science* and was eventually published in *The American Scientist;* several critics wondered whether some of the reported actions involved fell more into the category of sleaze (unpraiseworthy behavior that is not criminal) rather than misconduct.

Imaging science. Each year the plots of several movies turn on a villainous scientist or group of scientists, or villainous technology. The past year's crop included the record-breaking blockbuster *Jurassic Park*. Continuing a recent trend, the scientist-villains of that movie were biotechnologists rather than the nuclear or rocket scientists of previous years; its plot involved a theme park stocked with dinosaurs that had been created through the extraction and cloning of dinosaur DNA found in blood samples of mosquitoes preserved in amber.

Even scientific institutions were swept up in the attention generated by the movie. When the Nobel committee announced its selection of Kary B. Mullis, inventor of the polymerase chain reaction (PCR; a revolutionary technique allowing rapid reproduction of tiny DNA segments in huge quantities) as co-winner of the chemistry prize, it specifically mentioned that the technique had already inspired creators of "the very popular film *Jurassic Park*" (whose scientists used PCR in their cloning). The American Museum of Natural History in New York City held an exhibition entitled "The Dinosaurs of Jurassic Park," and the large crowds that attended it seemed more interested in film clips than in fossils—prompting science wag Roger L. Welsch, in *Natural History,* to propose a new scientific field dedicated to the study of the public image of fossils: "ethnobonology." But a number of scientists expressed concern about the movie's message, and editorials appeared in journals from *Science* to *Genetic Engineering News.* Stephen Jay Gould, reviewing the movie and book in *The New York Review of Books,* was troubled that the Museum of Natural History had succumbed to dinomania, stating, "We will ultimately lose if authentic fossils are not primary, and cultural artifacts derivative." Others said the movie tapped the traditional, almost mythic, fear of scientists as amoral technocrats who unleash deadly forces beyond their control—Frankensteins whose interference with nature produces disastrous results.

A variant of disputes involving the image of science involves the fairness and accuracy of science journalism. During the past year an exceptionally vitriolic example arose over AIDS coverage by *The Sunday Times*, one of Great Britain's most profitable newspapers. *The Times* claimed that HIV does not cause AIDS ("AIDS: The Plague That Never Was," ran one headline), contrary to the almost unanimous view of the scientific community, and conducted a self-styled "campaign" against "myths" promulgated by science journals such as *Nature.* That magazine, in turn, took the unprecedented step of devoting space each issue to reporting and critiquing the AIDS coverage in *The Sunday Times*. The controversy raised issues of press freedom and irresponsibility, the ethics of reporting about research into terminal illnesses, and the effect of what former British prime minister Baroness Thatcher called "the oxygen of publicity" on controversies.

The United States had its own version of such a controversy when *Rolling Stone* in December published a clarification of an article it had featured the previous year suggesting that Hilary Koprowski, now with Philadelphia's Thomas Jefferson University, had introduced AIDS into the human population during

Postmenopausal motherhood was a major ethics controversy during the past year. Giuseppina Maganuco (below with her husband, Angelo, and baby daughter, Anna Maria) was 54 when she gave birth.

Luciano Amendola—Sipa Press

A scene from the motion picture Jurassic Park *shows scientists (played by Jeff Goldblum, far left; Laura Dern, second from right; and Sam Neill, far right) conferring with the developer of the Jurassic-era theme park (Richard Attenborough). During recent years the plots of many movies have featured science and technology being put to villainous or, at best, irresponsible uses.*

the 1950s via a contaminated polio vaccine. After Koprowski sued the magazine, *Rolling Stone*'s editors said in their clarification that they "never intended to suggest . . . that there is any scientific proof, nor do they know of any scientific proof" of that hypothesis.

Silly as such incidents seem, the image of science is no laughing matter—a point underscored by several bomb attacks carried out against researchers in 1993. During the fall, British researchers were targets of an animal-rights group, whose 34 letter bombs injured seven. Letter bombs seriously injured two U.S. scientists in June—one a University of California geneticist, the other a computer scientist at Yale University; the FBI was hunting a serial bomber believed to have attacked university and technical sites at least 12 times in 15 years.

Genetics. Another set of controversies during the past year centered on genetics. The "gay gene" dispute erupted over a study published in a July issue of *Science,* directed by a geneticist at the National Cancer Institute, Bethesda, Md., linking a genetic marker to homosexual orientation (researchers studying lesbians suggested in March that genes influence female sexual orientation as well). This ignited another version of the "nature versus nurture" debate over the respective roles of culture, family, hormones, and genes in determining sexual orientation—as well as over the value of the study itself, which was purely statistical and based on a small sample (40 pairs of homosexual brothers). Another genetics and behavior controversy arose over a study by Dutch researchers who said they had detected a link between a gene and a certain type of disease in which men commit violent acts.

In November the U.S. Food and Drug Administration (FDA) sparked protests when it approved a genetically engineered drug aimed at increasing milk production in cows; antibiotechnology campaigner Jeremy Rifkin declared it "the beginning of food politics in this country" and promised to press his

attack to the "final battleground" of "grocery stores, restaurants, and convenience stores."

Genetic screening, mandated by several states for various diseases, was condemned as misguided by a panel of experts convened by the Institute of Medicine, who said such screening has few benefits and is subject to abuse. A screening program in certain Orthodox Jewish communities named Dor Yeshorim ("the generation of the righteous"), aimed at couples considering marriage, stirred controversy when it expanded its targets beyond Tay-Sachs (a degenerative neurological disorder) to several other diseases as well.

Humor was wrung from the topic of genetic screening by a Broadway play that opened in October. The plot of *The Twilight of the Golds* involved a couple in the not-too-distant future who make the (scientifically improbable) discovery through a prenatal test that their child will be homosexual and then face the decision about whether to abort.

Science and the environment. Politics played a role in controversies involving science and the environment. The U.S. Congress authorized a five-year, $65 million research program to examine the health effects of electromagnetic fields (EMF). Public fears about the issue were dramatically illustrated in January when a man said on a national television talk show that his wife's use of a cellular car phone had caused her fatal brain cancer. Dixy Lee Ray, former chairwoman of the U.S. Atomic Energy Commission, and others charged that dangers of global warming are small and complained of an "ozone orthodoxy," in which politics rather than science motivates research. Politics was also involved in assessing the danger posed by the Russian submarine *Komsomolets,* which sank 480 km (300 mi) off the Norwegian coast in 1989 carrying a nuclear reactor and two nuclear torpedoes and was leaking plutonium from its perch about 1.6 km (one mile) deep on the ocean floor in North Atlantic fishing grounds. Some Russian scientists claimed that the danger to fishing was potentially catastrophic, while a team of Western scientists concluded the risk was minimal. Western scientists claimed the Russians were maximizing the threat to attract Western cleanup funds, while some Russians claimed the U.S. was downplaying the issue to hide its own nuclear spillage sins.

Biodiversity controversies of 1993 included a unique variant: the year came within a hairbreadth of witnessing the first deliberate extinction of a species in history, the smallpox virus. Following a recommendation by the World Health Organization, the last remaining smallpox virus stocks were scheduled to be destroyed on Dec. 31, 1993. As the day of execution approached, however, some scientists had second thoughts. "Hawks" argued that the virus was too expensive and dangerous to keep, while "doves" argued that the virus has not been mapped genetically or understood adequately and might be invaluable in yet-unforeseen ways for future virology studies. The doves prevailed, and the virus was granted a last-minute reprieve.

A bizarre environmental issue was raised by plans announced by a California company to launch a 1.6-km-long orbiting illuminated billboard 290 km (180 mi) above the Earth; its estimated brightness would rival that of the Moon. The scheme sparked a dispute over growing threats to astronomical observation, the commercialization of space, the desecration of nature, and "light pollution" of the nighttime environment; in July a bill prohibiting space advertising was introduced into both houses of Congress.

Other controversies. The abovementioned disputes represent only a tiny fraction of the spectrum of the types of scientific controversies that arose during the past year. It is impossible to resist mentioning a few others in passing. Drug studies were controversial, with conflicting reports about the value of the AIDS medication azidothymidine (AZT) and the retraction of major parts of a paper about another promising AIDS treatment. The emergence of the eight Biosphere 2 "voyagers" from their $150 million, two-year "experiment," following revelations that their colony outside Tucson, Ariz., had not been as self-contained as claimed, raised questions about patronage of ideologically based science. In the category of science and religion, noted British scientist Hermann Bondi inspired a heated series of letters in *Nature* when he wrote that "the human mind is singularly liable to be mistaken on religious issues."

A screening controversy erupted when the National Cancer Institute ended its recommendation that women under 50 have regular mammograms after it found a lack of statistically significant evidence that this procedure reduces deaths for such women (by contrast, evidence was abundant that deaths were reduced for women over 50). Debates involv-

ing psychiatry, with enormous legal ramifications, erupted concerning the suggestibility of the very young as witnesses and the reliability of adult memories of childhood sexual abuse recalled years later or evoked by therapists. In the category of pseudo-science controversies, there was the charge, lodged by protesters outside the Jet Propulsion Laboratory two days after the laboratory was devastated by loss of contact with the Mars Observer (*see* above), that the National Aeronautics and Space Administration had deliberately engineered the blackout to cover up evidence of extraterrestrials on Mars.

Even the past year's humor was controversial. In August *Science* legitimized an existing tradition of science wit by publishing a map of the Y (male) chromosome compiled by a female researcher at the University of California at San Francisco. The map located the genetic position of behaviors such as "channel flipping," "air guitar," and "inability to express affection over the phone." Not everyone laughed. One critic said that scientists who did something similar for the X chromosome "would be out of jobs and without grant support," and another that the map "constitutes grounds for a sex-harassment suit."

Triumphs of 1993. On the frontiers of the sciences, professors are often at each other's throats. Still, focusing on controversies provides a distorted view of the year in science. Sometimes controversies are falsely created or magnified by the (usually laudable) journalistic impulse to seek out views on both sides of an issue. Even when a consensus or definitive experimental result exists, a dissenting voice can always be found; as Martin Gardner once remarked, "It is always possible to find someone unable to perform an experiment."

Moreover, 1993 did have numerous and significant triumphs—as one will also find in the articles that follow. In December the most complex repair work ever performed in space was executed on the $1.6 billion Hubble Space Telescope when it was affixed with corrective lenses, fitted with new gyroscopes, solar panels, and cameras, and released from the space shuttle *Endeavour*'s cargo bay. Also in December, the $1.4 billion Princeton Tokamak Fusion Test Reactor was tested and produced bursts of up to six megawatts for three-quarters of a second, a major step on the way to fusion power. In March the Keck Telescope, after eight years of construction, achieved its first 10-day observing run, while in August came the formal inauguration of the Very Long Baseline Array (VLBA), the world's longest scientific instrument, comprising 10 telescopes spread out over 8,000 km (5,000 mi).

In June Princeton University mathematician Andrew Wiles announced a proof of a theorem, for which French mathematician Pierre de Fermat noted in a book margin he had devised a proof 350 years ago but which had remained unsolved ever since. Even more astonishing was the fact that Wiles's solution of "Fermat's Last Theorem" was not an isolated solution to the puzzle but merely one corollary of a powerful mathematical apparatus that he had developed.

And a list of dramatic successes of 1993 can hardly be complete without mention of the well-publicized 9½-hour operation that took place in a Manassas, Va., hospital in June in which a severed penis—which had been cut off with a 20-cm (8-in) kitchen carving knife, hurled from a moving car into a field of tall grass, found, packed in ice, and returned to its owner—was successfully reattached by new microsurgery techniques.

But even those successes were accompanied by questions. Was it worth $700 million to fix the Hubble, or would the money have been better spent improving conventional telescopes? What will be the characteristics of the plasma in the Princeton reactor, and will they help or hinder progress toward controlled fusion power, which has been much slower than anticipated? In regard to Wiles's proof, was it the same one Fermat had? Did Fermat really have one, erroneously think he had one, or know he did not have one and was being malicious or ironic in suggesting he had? And, following the penis-reat-

tachment operation, surgeons made plans for testing to answer questions about the ability of a reattached penis to regain normal sexual functioning. Each success in science, it seemed, is but a prelude to a new set of questions.

The art of inquiry. If true, Medawar's remark that science is the art of the soluble makes it difficult to envision what else scientific controversies could be about other than the reliability of methods or the interpretation of data. But even the survey above of the types of controversies found in 1993 alone reveals many other kinds, each with numerous permutations and variations.

Rather than the art of the soluble, science might be better defined as the art of inquiry. Then it would be clearer how a spectrum of kinds of controversies can arise, not just involving methods and data interpretation but also concerning such issues as the value, selection, and management of inquiries; the ethics of the means or ends of inquiries; the environmental impact of the means or ends of inquiries; and the image and reporting of inquiries. Not all of these are "soluble" in the sense of having definitive answers, but they involve judgment and deliberation and, therefore, risk.

A good inquiry raises more questions than it answers. By that criterion 1993 was a banner year in science.

Bursts of up to six megawatts, the highest output of energy yet achieved by nuclear fusion, were generated in December 1993 in Princeton University's Tokamak Fusion Test Reactor.

Anthropology

Soul-searching about the discipline, a focus on genetic research, and concern about human origins dominated anthropology during the past year. The questions of a changing discipline and its possible fragmentation continued to command considerable attention. While few spectacular fossils appeared, Lucy was finally dated, and fuel was added to continuing debates on the origins of modern humans and the peopling of the Americas. Applied (practical) anthropology continued to expand its role in modern-day anthropology, and two new publications drew considerable interest.

The future of anthropology. The discussions of whether anthropology continues to be a holistic discipline made up of related subfields or has become so specialized that former ties between the subfields no longer exist continued during the year. While overwhelming sentiment appeared to be with those who argued that the holism of the field is anthropology's major strength and that integration must be maintained, the topics being discussed occasioned much soul-searching within all areas of the discipline. Recently the suggestion surfaced that anthropology has become polarized into two main bodies, one oriented toward biology and the other toward culture. From another quarter came the suggestion that applied anthropology should be added to the list of major subfields making up the discipline. While all this debate raised the possibility of a fragmentation of anthropology in the United States, the British were moving steadily toward integrating the major subfields.

The future of anthropology was at the center of discussions at a recent conference sponsored by the Wenner-Gren Foundation for Anthropological Research. Citing the changing milieus of anthropology, the conference report proposed that the future of anthropology would be determined by its ability and willingness to engage in multidisciplinary research, focus on critical societal issues, and engage in international work. Despite serious threats to the discipline such as specialization, the possible fragmentation of the field, and the fact that its central concepts and methodology are being taken over by others without anthropologists' involvement, the report concluded that the enduring and important questions asked by anthropology in a world torn by racial and ethnic conflict emphasize its continuing significance.

Fossils and mitochondrial Eve. After 20 years anthropologists determined the age of Lucy, thanks to the work of geologist Robert Walter. This human ancestor, a member of the species *Australopithecus afarensis,* was discovered in Ethiopia in 1974 and was described by Donald Johanson in 1978. The dating of Lucy, set at 3,180,000 years, was made possible by a technique that focused on associated volcanic deposits at fossil localities and used a laser to melt single sand grains from volcanic ash. Actual dates were determined by measurement of the proportion of potassium and argon isotopes in the sand grains. Paleoanthropologists know that *A. afarensis* occupied East Africa for at least 700,000 years. As to how many African fossils belong to that species, Tim White and other researchers from the U.S., Belgium, and Ethiopia reported on 3.4 million-year-old fossils from Ethiopia that provided ample evidence that *A. afarensis* actually was a single, diverse primate species that ranged across what is now Ethiopia and Tanzania.

A skeleton discovered by Italian scientists near Altamura, Italy, was tentatively identified as a pre-Neanderthal, possibly as much as 400,000 years old. It appeared to be a major discovery because of its completeness. It might help to shed light on the origins of the Neanderthal and help resolve the problem of whether there were two species of Neanderthal or one. Thus far, only its characteristics had provided the clues as to its age and evolutionary status. Some features of the skeleton appeared to be classic Neanderthal, while the ridges over the eye sockets, vaulting of the skull, and face width were apparently less so. Scholars would have to wait for more precise dating before accepting the fossil, and it would have to be removed from its calcium sheath and extensively examined before all the questions could be answered.

"Should we walk upright? Should we continue to live in trees? Should we try to make things? Decisions, decisions!"

Sidney Harris

On a related note, Israeli, British, and Australian paleoanthropologists provided additional evidence that modern humans and Neanderthals coexisted in Israel some 100,000 years ago. Recently developed mass-spectrometric uranium-series dating was used to determine the age of ancestral cows' or oxen's teeth found at the sites along with human remains. Results confirmed previous dates provided by electron spin resonance.

Kenyapithecus and a skull located on Java also caused some stir during the past year. The discovery of an approximately 15 million-year-old East African mandible by Brenda Benefit and Monte McCrossin supported the idea that *Kenyapithecus* could be ancestral to apes and humans. For years, arguments had raged as to whether the species was ancestral to apes and humans or represented a separate line leading only to orangutans.

Donald Tyler reported on a skull discovered near Sangiran, Java, Indon., that he originally calculated to be 1.4 million years old. This would push African migration into East Asia back by about half a million years. According to Tyler, the skull shows marked similarity to two 1.6 million-year-old *Homo erectus* specimens found in Kenya. Not everyone agreed with Tyler's conclusions. Collaborator Sastrohamijoyo Sartono insisted that the true age of the fossil was between 500,000 and 700,000 years, and C. Loring Brace questioned the supposed African structure of the skull.

A more recent reanalysis of Indonesian fossils by Carl Swisher and Garniss Curtis dated hominids on Java to 1.6 million years ago. The oldest fossil, a child's skullcap found at Perning in 1936, was dated at 1.8 million years old, according to Curtis. These findings seemed to support Tyler and call into question our perspective on hominid evolution.

Despite the proclamation of Milford Wolpoff that the concept of "mitochondrial Eve" had been discredited, the debate over the origins of modern humans showed few signs of dying out very soon. Mitochondrial Eve was the brainchild of Allan Wilson, who used DNA research to back his suggestion that all modern humans can trace their maternal ancestry to a woman who lived in Africa 200,000 years ago. Supporters of this idea hold that humans evolved relatively recently in Africa and fanned out across the world to replace earlier hominids. In direct opposition to this hypothesis is the regional continuity theory, which holds that humans evolved gradually over a much longer period in many different parts of the world. Alan Templeton, focusing on the statistical interpretations of the genetic data and flaws in the original Eve analysis, questioned the single-source idea, geographic origin, and time frame for the appearance of modern humans as proposed in the Eve hypothesis.

In the latest exchange on the issue, David Frayer, Wolpoff, Alan Thorne, Fred Smith, and Geoffrey Pope concluded that on the basis of fossil evidence, Eve must be rejected in favor of the multiregional model. They insisted that modern humans can be described neither by a single genetic incident nor as an event that appeared in diverse areas of the world simultaneously, and they conceded that the disproof of Eve did not mean that the multiregional theory was proved, only that it was the most plausible explanation at the moment.

Using data that mirrored that of Wilson and his followers, Maryellen Ruvolo presented new data that supported his estimate as to when Eve lived. Her studies of a diverse group of modern humans indicated that the groups were closely related and evolved recently from a common ancestor. Her findings did not resolve the debate over whether modern humans first evolved in Asia or Africa. Luigi Luca Cavalli-Sforza, in collaboration with Kenneth and Judith Kidd, presented data on that issue that showed more diversity in nuclear DNA in Africans than in other people, a finding consistent with the African origin hypothesis.

In other developments in physical anthropology, Henry Harpending and Alan Rogers devised a new statistical method for analyzing mitochondrial DNA in order to reveal the history of modern human populations. Basing their work on John Maynard Smith's idea that modern humans evolved from very isolated precursor populations, Harpending and Rogers related the distribution of genetic variation to the size of the group. They concluded that a dramatic decrease in human population occurred some 65,000 years ago, after which it made a dramatic comeback through a series of "population explosions." If this was proved valid, it would falsify the out-of-Africa hypothesis for the origins of modern humans.

Peopling the Americas. Probably nothing had caused as much discussion or the creation of as many controversial theories among U.S. anthropologists as the origin of the first Americans and whether they came in one or multiple waves. Ever since the first fluted point was discovered at Clovis, N.M., the debate had raged as to whether those who made it were the first to cross the Bering land bridge between Siberia and Alaska or whether there were others who came earlier. Current theories held that the first humans came over the land bridge to the Western Hemisphere between 12,000 and 20,000 years ago. New data and reinterpretations fueled the debates.

Ellen Conghlin reported on a site in northern Alaska that dated back to between 9,700 and 11,700 years ago and indicated the presence of a Paleo-Indian culture. Reported by Michael Kunz as possibly the oldest habitation site yet found in North America (or at least the best documented), the discovery would cause problems for many theories about the peopling of the New World. Kunz reported that the inhabitants of the Mesa site were different from other Paleo-Indian groups of Alaska but similar to those found farther south. This conclusion cast doubt on the single-migration theory.

Reexamining the Paleo-Indian data of central Alaska in light of recent redating of the land bridge and other sites, John F. Hoffecker, W. Roger Powers, and Ted Goebel concluded that Beringia, a now-submerged landmass that connected Asia and North America, was settled 12,000 to 11,000 years ago. The researchers also suggested that it was probably colonized in response to climate and vegetation changes, as opposed to the widely held belief that changing sea levels or continental ice masses caused its colonization.

Some genetic researchers concluded that all present-day American Indians can trace their descent to one of four maternal lineages that originated in Asia, confirming the long-held belief that the first Americans originated there. Some new studies supported the notion that the first Americans arrived in Alaska well before the Clovis people. This conclusion was based on the genetic analyses of living Alaskan natives and Paleo-Indian remains. Antonio Torroni and Douglas Wallace reported that their mitochondrial DNA analyses indicated that there had been at least two waves of Indian settlers, while Anne Stone, Mark Stoneking, Robert Ferrell, and Andrew Merriwether confirmed the four-lineage conclusion. Other genetic studies tended to reinforce the notion that the Americas were colonized in waves sometime before 12,000 years ago (Amerinds out of Asia, followed by NaDene and lastly by Eskimo-Aleuts). However, on the basis of her study of Amerinds, Connie Kolman argued that her gene data did not support the multiple-waves theory.

Anthropology of war. At a time when ethnic and racial conflicts were occurring in many parts of the world, it came as no surprise that anthropologists should renew their interest in war. While the results of these new studies produced varied explanations as to why people go to war, some patterns emerged. Brian Ferguson suggested that people go to war because they perceive it to be less costly and more beneficial than not going to war. Ferguson and Neil Whitehead proposed that violent conflicts tend to arise in areas they call "tribal zones," areas where organized political states encounter less-organized groups. These are areas affected by the proximity of state systems but not under the administration of the state. People in such circumstances either cooperate, flee, or resist the state. All three options lead to violence. Using historical examples and cases from many parts of the world, these scholars concluded that people do not fight wars out of some innate

Spearpoint found in Alaska at a site as old as 9,700 to 11,700 years provides evidence for the theory that two distinct prehistoric peoples migrated from Siberia across the Bering land bridge to the Americas.

fierceness but because they exist in areas where increased social organization leads to increased levels of warfare. Leda Cosmides and John Tooby suggested that war is related to getting women, a position shared by Napoleon Chagnon. Ferguson and Marvin Harris argued that scarce food and land are more immediate and powerful incentives for war.

Other developments. The activities of applied anthropology continued to generate interest and attention. In forensic anthropology William Maple's work in identifying dead bodies commanded considerable interest, particularly his investigations of the remains of U.S. Pres. Zachary Taylor and those of Russia's last royal family. Military archaeologist Douglas Scott and his colleagues continued to generate interest in their research on the Battle of the Little Bighorn. Scott planned to use accelerator mass spectrometry for analyzing the chemistry of the old bones at the site to determine what Custer's men ate in their final weeks, separate the officers from enlisted men, and perhaps even separate different companies. Applied anthropology was also active in research and education concerning AIDS and in programs aimed at improving human services.

A couple of publications captured considerable attention this past year. In *Reading National Geographic*, authors Catherine Lutz and Jane Collins examined the history, philosophy, and political agendas that have shaped the *National Geographic* magazine and influenced the views and attitudes of its readers. They concluded that the *National Geographic* is one of the primary means by which Americans learn about other cultures.

Ruth Behar produced an unusual ethnography based on her work with a Mexican peasant in *Translated Woman: Crossing the Border with Esperanza's Story*. Behar's ethnography was not so much a revelation of Esperanza's story but a performance of it.

Even more interesting was the author's questioning of her own life as a result of her encounter with Esperanza. The result was not one life story but two, each a reflection of the other. Inserting herself into the narrative, Behar considerably expanded the reflective tradition prevalent among feminist anthropologists.

—Larry L. Naylor

See also Feature Article: THE PALEOLITHIC HEALTH CLUB.

Archaeology

Archaeology is one of the four major fields of anthropology. Recent debates in the discipline have centered on the relative utility and theoretical foundations of maintaining the "four-field" approach to the study of anthropology. One group calls for splitting the discipline into separate and independent fields, each with its own theoretical and practical foundations. Departments of the four major fields—sociocultural anthropology, archaeology, human biology, and linguistics—would each be separate from one another. Each discipline would be free to develop its own body of theory and practice, borrowing from the others and from other fields only specific methods and techniques, as archaeologists sometimes now borrow specific techniques from, for example, geography, geology, and botany.

Another group maintains that the most appropriate location for the fields is under the umbrella of anthropology. They feel that the four-field approach gives the discipline its legitimate claim to being "the study of human beings." Those on this side of the argument agree that four-field anthropology is growing at a rate that makes it nearly impossible for practitioners of one field to maintain more than cursory knowledge of specific theoretical advances in most of the others. Nonetheless, these scholars all agree that the theoretical foundations of anthropology should continue to anchor the four fields, so that a body of basic theory unifies the discipline, even as each subdiscipline constructs a foundation to guide its practice.

This debate will continue. Meanwhile, some examples of how archaeology and other fields can successfully interact to address important anthropological problems are discussed below. The first example is a recent reexamination of the origins and ancestry of Neanderthals and modern-looking humans and how biological anthropology relies on archaeology and some very modern physics to address old problems. The second example shows how archaeology and linguistics can give voices to ancient cultures and bring an urgency and humanity to long-lost civilizations.

Neanderthals and modern humans in the Levant. One of the most enduring puzzles in anthropology is the place of Neanderthals in human evolution. Work in Europe suggested a relatively simple solution: Neanderthals were on a side branch of the direct line of human descent and represented an interesting but specialized adaptation to cold conditions in Europe but nowhere else. Material culture in Europe supported this interpretation, as Neanderthal remains seemed to be associated with Middle Paleolithic Mousterian stone tools. Later, modern-looking human remains seemed to be associated with more complex and dynamic technologies that began about 35,000 to 40,000 years ago with the Upper Paleolithic Aurignacian culture.

The traditional interpretation was that Neanderthals, with their more primitive technology, were supplanted and disappeared after the advent of modern-looking humans about 40,000 years ago. However, problems with this scenario emerged early and gave rise to questions such as: Were Neanderthals ancestors of modern humans? Were Neanderthals replaced by modern humans, or were they assimilated into modern human populations? Where did modern humans originate, and what were the circumstances of their evolution? These questions remain, and different answers form the bases of modern debates between proponents of "Out of Africa" and "Multiregional" models of the origins of *Homo sapiens*.

Essentially the same biological and archaeological data are used to support each model. Some of the most important, but also some of the most puzzling, data come from the Middle East. Human skeletal remains were excavated in the 1920s and 1930s from several caves in the Levant (the area at the eastern end of the Mediterranean Sea), near the Sea of Galilee in Israel. Robust Neanderthal-like remains came from Tabun Cave, and more modern-looking gracile (slender) remains came from Qafzeh and Skhul caves. Neanderthal remains were also excavated from Shanidar and Amud caves in the 1950s and 1960s. Stone tools from all these caves were similarly primitive, and no clear relation in regard to the geologic strata in which they were found was established between the two different human groups. The stone tools and stratigraphic contexts suggested that the skeletal remains were approximately the same ages, but the European model proposed that the Neanderthals had to be older than the gracile forms.

Biological anthropologists and archaeologists proposed several different scenarios to account for these nebulous data, but the lack of adequate dating techniques became the major obstacle to solving this important puzzle. The remains are all older than 40,000 years, which is the practical limit of radiocarbon dating, but they are too young and in the wrong kinds of sediments for uranium-thorium or potassium-argon methods, which are accurate only for remains older than 500,000 years.

A recent project was designed to address this question. By means of excavations at Kebara Cave and also through careful analyses of the contexts of skeletal remains in the region, Ofer Bar-Yosef (Harvard University) and Bernard Vandermeersch (University of Bordeaux, France) tested the hypothesis that Neanderthal-like forms were older than more gracile humans. They used electron spin resonance and thermoluminesence to date the sediments containing many of the human remains. These dating techniques corroborated their careful examination and reconstruction of the stratigraphy of Kebara, Qafzeh, Skhul, Amud, and other caves. In addition,

Stephen Weiner (Weizmann Institute, Reḥovot, Israel), Paul Goldberg (University of Texas), and Bar-Yosef mapped the distribution of minerals in the sediments of Kebara Cave to show that skeletal remains were found in their original contexts and had not been disturbed and mixed, as some had suggested to account for the seeming contemporaneity of the two kinds of human remains.

These studies revealed that the stratigraphic relations of the skeletal remains and dated materials in Kebara and other caves in the Levant are highly reliable and that they did not confirm the neat correlation between biology and culture perceived in Europe. Gracile humans were older than the Neanderthals and had been in the region for at least 100,000 years and probably for as many as 200,000 years. Neanderthals entered the Levant about 60,-

Three-dimensional grid at Kebara Cave (above) near the eastern shore of the Mediterranean Sea helps researchers assign ages to the objects found in the cave. Hearth remains found on the floor in the middle of the cave (left) reveal that the Neanderthal inhabitants of Kebara used their living spaces in ways similar to those of modern-looking humans.

000 years ago. Both groups used similar stone tools until about 45,000 years ago. Modern-looking humans and Neanderthals coexisted in this small area in the Levant for nearly 20,000 years. Whether they interacted with each other remains unknown.

It is possible that Neanderthals came into the region when severe Arcticlike conditions prevailed in southeastern Europe. Colder conditions in the Levant may have suited the Neanderthals but would have pushed the gracile humans, adapted for warmth, back into Africa and the Arabian Peninsula. Wave after wave of cold weather may have resulted in waves of robust and gracile peoples moving back and forth across the same territory, so that only one group at a time was in the Levant. However, even if they did not meet each other, they would have been aware of each others' presence.

Other interesting archaeological and biological evidence came from the work of Bar-Yosef and his co-workers in Kebara Cave. Much of this evidence indicates that although the biological differences were great and consistent, the archaeological similarities between Neanderthals and modern-looking humans in the region were remarkable. For example, the distributions of stone tools, bones, and other debris around hearths and against the back walls of Kebara Cave suggest that Neanderthal groups used their living spaces in ways similar to those of modern-looking humans. Both groups also used similar tools and tool-making technologies. Both seemed to have selected the best material for long-term tools and local poorer material for expedient tools. In addition, both groups deliberately buried their dead in excavated burial pits. Such pits have been found in Qafzeh, Skhul, Amud, and Kebara caves.

Both groups made and used perforated marine shells and red hematite stains, suggestive of symbolic behaviors that most likely required language skills. Until recently, human language was considered possible only in modern *Homo sapiens*. However, the hyoid bone preserved in an adult Neanderthal male skeleton in Kebara Cave shows that its vocal tract resembled that of modern humans and suggests that Neanderthals were capable of articulate human speech. One final similarity was the lack of change in stone-tool technology used by both groups for more than 50,000 years. In fact, very little change in stone-tool technology was evident anywhere in the world for more than one million years prior to about 45,000 years ago.

At the end of the Middle Paleolithic Period, an unprecedented era of change and innovation occurred between 45,000 and 40,000 years ago in the Levant and somewhat later in Europe. This period of 5,000 years marks the emergence of distinctly human culture. It is characterized by rapid change in stone tools and by the advent of different kinds of tool technologies from region to region. Some argue that it was also the beginning of human self-consciousness and the first time people used objects to display relative status in human societies. All these changes signify the beginning of the Upper Paleolithic, when increasing change and innovation became the hallmarks of human culture.

Neanderthals disappeared from the archaeological record about 40,000 years ago in the Levant and about 35,000 years ago in Europe. No one knows what happened to them. Recent advances in genetic studies may soon provide clues as to how many, if any, Neanderthal genes contributed to Upper Paleolithic human populations and, perhaps, how many persist in modern humans. But, as Bar-Yosef and Vandermeersch argue, "Phylogeny cannot explain the cultural revolution that ushered in the Upper Paleolithic age. To solve that problem, scholars must infer changes in human behavior from the subtle traces of the physical record"—in other words, through archaeology. Biological evidence, no matter how exact and specific, cannot provide all the keys to understanding past human behavior. Archaeology is able to approach these questions, but solutions are most likely to come from collaborations of archaeologists, biological anthropologists, and a host of other specialists operating, at least for the most part, under the aegis of anthropological theories.

The decipherment of pre-Mayan hieroglyphic writing. The earliest civilization in Mesoamerica (Mexico and Central America) is called Olmec, and it lasted for 700 years between 1200 and 500 BC. The later Mayan civilization began about AD 450 and lasted until the European conquests of the 1500s. Between these two civilizations was a relatively poorly known culture called Epi-Olmec. Recent archaeological and linguistic studies have illuminated much about this tradition and have provided insights into a few of its personalities and customs. John Justeson (State University of New York at Albany) and Terrence Kaufman (University of Pittsburgh, Pa.) deciphered part of the 2,000-year-old Epi-Olmec script and provided the oldest readable texts in the Americas.

The breakthrough took two years and was made possible by the discovery in 1986 of Stela 1 from La Mojarra, Veracruz, Mexico. This delicately carved four-ton rock slab contained multiple columns of text with enough glyphs (symbolic figures or characters) to allow cross-checking with nine other known Epi-Olmec texts. The most important of these was the Tuxtla Statuette, a small ducklike human figure. Justeson and Kaufman found that most Epi-Olmec glyphs are either syllabograms, which represent syllables, or logograms, which represent words. Using picture symbols and clues from Mayan texts, they deciphered about 80% of the La Mojarra glyphs. The stela tells of the ascent to supreme power and the rule of Harvest Mountain Lord. His rise took 5,256 days (14.4 solar years) on the Venus cycle calendar, as described on the stela. The Venus cycle calendar was used by Maya and other Mesoamerican groups, and this work confirmed its use prior to AD 450. One Venus cycle is 584 days, the time it takes the planet Venus to again occupy the same position in the sky relative to the Sun.

The text tells how a young Harvest Mountain Lord leads an army to battle on a day of the first described Venus cycle. He ascended to supreme power on the same day exactly nine Venus cycles later. The event is marked by several rituals, including the Harvest Mountain Lord drawing blood from his penis. Glyphs depicting this specific ritual were some of the first keys to unlocking the meaning of other glyphs in the Epi-Olmec script. Harvest Mountain Lord went on to fight other battles, the most important of which was the defeat of his brother-in-law. This appeared to cement his power, and the stela depicts his "payment" of ritual objects to various supporters to maintain his realm. Chiefdom-style coalition building such as that depicted on the La Mojarra stela is thought to have developed into the late Epi-Olmec and later Mayan authoritarian system of rule, where supreme power was inherited rather than gained through battles and coalitions.

Justeson and Kaufman also found that Epi-Olmec language is the ancestor to four languages in the Mixe-Zoquean family spoken in south-central Mexico. The Epi-Olmec script is closely related to Mayan hieroglyphic writing and appears to be its ancestor as well. The recent decipherment is only a beginning, and the two authors called for more archaeological and linguistic fieldwork to continue the process. A review of existing Epi-Olmec monuments, the search for additional monuments in archaeological contexts, and the study of Mixe-Zoquean languages

are all expected to contribute to the unfolding story of the Harvest Mountain Lord and other people in the Epi-Olmec and early Mayan world. Such studies will undoubtedly lead to the decipherment of earlier Olmec texts as well, giving voice to perhaps 3,000 years of once-mute archaeological remains in the New World.

—James D. Wilde

Architecture and civil engineering

Economic vitality, prevailing social values, and regional emphasis determine the types of structures society builds. Various swings and fads in aesthetic values and taste affect the styles in which many structures are built. New technological developments can be used to generate innovative forms, be made to conform to popular taste, previous styles, or be distorted and abused in a misunderstanding of their true potential.

The continued economic slowdown in Europe and the United States resulted in a decrease in commercial construction and, consequently, a relative increase in publicly funded work. National and regional governmental agencies built new offices for ever expanding bureaucracies, added museums and law courts, and responded to the unfortunate need for more prisons. Roads, bridges, tunnels, air and rail terminals, flood-control and water-supply systems, and waste-facility works were added in response to expanding populations, while existing infrastructures continued to deteriorate as a result of stringent budgets. In the United States alone, more than 118,500 highway bridges were deemed to be structurally deficient, according to the Department of Transportation.

East facade of Israel's new Supreme Court building, designed by Ram Karmi and Ada Karmi-Melamede, is penetrated by a massive stone wall that slices through the structure in an east-west arc.

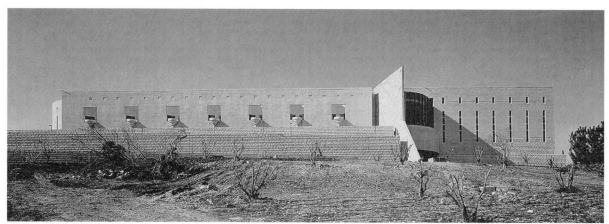

Richard Bryant—ARCAID

Office building designed for IBM Corp. by T.R. Hamzah & Yeang Sdn. Bhd. rises 15 stories in Shah Alam, Malaysia. A landscaped berm at the base insulates the bottom three stories from the tropical morning sun.

Architecture. Judiciary buildings, courts, and religious edifices are among the buildings that project an image of how a society perceives itself. The U.S. government elected to utilize stylized symbols of past cultures for the new Federal Judiciary Building in Washington, D.C., designed by Edward Larrabee Barnes/John M.Y. Lee and Partners. In what has been called a blend of Classicism and Modernism, symmetry, scale, and formalism were combined to achieve dignity. The building's style and proportions were carefully chosen to blend with the adjacent Federal-style Union Station and U.S. Post Office.

While the U.S. chose to reinterpret classicism, Israel's new Supreme Court building, designed by Ram Karmi and Ada Karmi-Melamede, exploited the uniqueness of its site and experimented with forms to achieve a quiet, timeless majesty. The building is separated into different functional volumes for the library, courtrooms, and a judges' area that surrounds a private courtyard. A pedestrian walkway leading to the Knesset (parliament) pierces the complex in a north-south direction. A massive, symbolic, stone wall slices through in an east-west arc creating a great foyer in front of the law courts. The wall then straightens before continuing on to separate the library from the judges' complex and eventually terminates after penetrating through the east facade.

A modest 15-story office building built for IBM Corp. in Shah Alam, Malaysia, is an outstanding example of an environmentally sensitive building, deriving its quiet beauty from expressing the inherent truths of its being. The tower's form evolved from a rational response to the effects of the tropical sun, along with respect and regard for the needs of the building's occupants. The richness of its circular form comes from the skillfully blended articulation of recessed windows, louvers, indented garden terraces, and balconies that form an exterior climbing helix and from a vertical exterior service core. Humanely, the architect Ken Yeang provided natural light and ventilation in the elevator lobbies, stair shafts, and rest rooms.

The new, elegant 55-story aluminum-and-glass-clad tower of DG Bank in Frankfurt, Germany, designed by the U.S. firm of Kohn Pedersen Fox Associates, PC, is an example of the current version of the type of high-rise office building that was built worldwide in large numbers during the late 1980s. While the texture of the lower part of the tower is more suited to its surroundings and the overall

DG Bank in Frankfurt, Germany, designed by the U.S. firm of Kohn Pedersen Fox Associates, PC, is a 55-story tower clad in aluminum and glass. It resembles many of the high-rise towers built since the late 1980s.

290

Undulating, eccentric three-hinged trusses hover over the curving tracks of London's new Waterloo terminal, designed by Nicholas Grimshaw & Partners.

massing slightly more playful than most of its predecessors, windows remain sealed and the fringes on top owe more to an attempt to create interest than to function. Frank Gehry's tortured forms for an eight-story commercial office in a historic area of Prague is an example of the use of shock values that can also produce elegant spaces. Its plastic shapes, undulating columns, and distorted turrets can be perceived as either clashing with its neighbors or respecting them by expressing them in a new idiom.

Several noteworthy museums were built, including a formalistic gem in Nîmes, France, by Norman Foster and an archaeological museum in Montreal by Dan S. Hanganu/Provencher, Roy. Japan continued to be the source of small, exquisite, environmentally sensitive specialty museums. A squid museum that includes a garden and a raised observation platform to permit visitors to view the glowing mollusks in the bay was designed by Heneghan and Dagfinnsdottir in Namerikawa. Tadao Ando created a "Forest of Tombs" museum that permits visitors to view the ancient Iwabari burial mounds at Kamoto-Gun.

With large airports forced to locate at considerable distances from city centers, the high-speed train continued its expansion as a rational alternative for medium-distance travel in Europe. Train stations have become an architectural phoenix, rising from their turn-of-the-century forms in new contemporary shapes. Two of the most dramatic are the Waterloo terminal on the English side of the Channel Tunnel and the station at Lyon, France. France's commitment to high-speed rail travel and quality design is exemplified by Santiago Calatrava's dramatic skeletal

concrete rib cage that covers the 500-m (1,640-ft)-long platform in Lyon. Nicholas Grimshaw & Partners, designers of the Waterloo terminal, had to cope with most of the functions of an airport, including customs control, yet the crowning form of the complex is the train shed. Three-hinged trusses that undulate in three dimensions hover over the curving tracks. Daylight streams through the glass that covers the larger segment of the eccentric trusses' span and lines the underside of the shorter one-third, creating a breathtaking space that is eminently suited to its function.

Large-scale affordable housing, despite being an ongoing architectural problem, generally continued to elude successful solutions in inner-city urban environments. The current perception is that the failures of past housing projects were due to their destruction of the surrounding urban fabric and the dissociation from society felt by their residents, encapsulated in isolated high-rise compartments strung along dank empty corridors. As one effort to achieve a better solution, Renzo Piano's 220-unit Rue de Meaux project in Paris reinterprets century-old traditions. Its six- and seven-story mass surrounds a large, tree-filled center garden. Its outer facade maintains the existing street lines and incorporates small shops. Each of the repetitive elevator and stair cores serves only two apartments per floor, eliminating the need for corridors and permitting floor-through apartments to have cross-ventilation and views of both the public street and private garden.

Continued recognition of the inherent value and beauty of old structures led to an increase in the number of renovations and alterations that adopted historic buildings for new uses while maintaining their original beauty. One of the finest examples of the merits of this approach was the rehabilitation of the Bradbury Building in Los Angeles. The architects, Brenda Levin and Associates, brought this former office building up to modern code requirements, introduced stores in the lower level, and integrated the building with an adjacent parking garage, all while maintaining and enhancing the original Chicago School ambience of its skylit center court with its exposed ironwork balconies and stairs.

A summary of developments and trends would not be complete without recognition of a small but influential group of architects who are constantly questioning established values. Their work was marked by such innovations as destabilizing right angles (such as in Peter Eisenman's Greater Columbus [Ohio] Convention Center), plasticizing shapes (as in Gehry's structures), and reinterpreting traditional proportions to the delight of some architectural critics and the dismay of others.

Civil engineering. Knowing there will always be one more river to cross, engineers continued to find newer and better ways to do so. The cabled-stayed bridge continued to gain popularity for medium spans. A 490-m (1,608-ft)-span cable-stayed bridge

will form a dramatic link in the 16-km (10-m)-long connection between Denmark and Sweden that began during the past year. The $2 billion project will include a sunken-tube tunnel and an artificial island. Longer spans remained under the domain of the suspension bridge. For example, the just-completed 850-m (2,787-ft)-span Askoy suspension bridge near Bergen, Norway, became the longest span in Scandinavia.

In the U.S., Iowa acquired its first cable-stayed bridge. Its single 100-m (325-ft) tower supports spans of 200 m (660 ft) and 125 m (405 ft) over the Mississippi River. Just north of St. Louis, Mo., another cable-stayed bridge was completed. The new 10-lane-wide Clark Bridge, designed by Hanson Engineers Inc., has a 398-m (1,306-ft)-long cable-stayed section. The bridge that caused the most controversy remained on the drawing boards. James Carpenter's poetic design for a V-mast cable-stayed crossing of the Mississippi at St. Paul, Minn., also features a curved split deck. The proposal received worldwide critical acclaim, but many in St. Paul did not like its futuristic image and voiced their desire for a more conventional structure, thus postponing construction and putting the final bridge form in doubt.

In a $500 million fight against time and tide, work was progressing on a pair of giant flood-control gates

Drawing reveals the V-mast cable-stayed bridge proposed by James Carpenter to cross the Mississippi River at St. Paul, Minn. Along with its unique mast, the bridge would feature a curved split deck.

at the entrance to the New Waterway ship canal located downstream from Rotterdam, Neth. A pair of 250-m (820-ft)-long, 22-m (72-ft)-deep gates will swing on a ball-and-socket joint that is 10 m (33 ft) in diameter in order to close the canal against tidal surges that often have flooded the lowlands.

Borings for a 1,250-m (4,100-ft)-long twin highway tunnel in Tennessee's Cumberland Gap National Historical Park were completed. All tunnels, however, are not bored through mountains. An immersed tunnel crossing Boston Harbor had 98-m (320-ft)-long 8,000-ton twin-tube steel sections that were lined with concrete and sunk onto a dredged bed 17 m (55 ft) below the surface. The world's first floating tunnel was being planned. It will be tethered to the bottom of Norway's 250-m-deep, 1,190-m (3,900-ft)-wide Hogsfjord near Stavanger.

For pure size, little can compare to the immensity of today's offshore oil rigs. In the Gulf of Mexico 210 km (130 mi) offshore from New Orleans, La., Shell Oil Co. built a $1,250,000,000 drilling platform. Its 22.8-sq m (245-sq ft), 13.7-m (45-ft)-deep deck floats on 22.6-m (74-ft)-diameter steel drums that are secured by twelve 71-cm (28-in)-diameter pipe tendons anchored 871 m (2,857 ft) below to a foundation held in place by 12 piles, each of which is 114 m (375 ft) long and 213 cm (84 in) in diameter and weighs 260 tons.

China continued with its plan to build the world's tallest building in Chungking (Chongqinq). At 457.5 m (1,500 ft), the office tower will contain hotel accommodations on its upper floors. Despite being 14 m (46 ft) taller than the Sears Tower in Chicago, it will be only a fraction of the size of a modern oil rig. Another of the more intriguing engineering feats under study was a $4 billion pipeline under the Arabian Sea that would link the gas fields in Oman to India.

Highways can be far more complicated engineering undertakings than motorists might realize. The Colorado Department of Transportation received the year's Outstanding Civil Engineering Achievement Award from the American Society of Civil Engineers for the recently completed 20.1-km (12.5-mi)-long Glenwood Canyon Highway. The $500 million project included 39 bridges and viaducts, cantilevered roadways, and a twin 1,220-m (4,000-ft)-long rock-reinforced tunnel where each vehicle is tracked on computers throughout its passage.

—David Guise

Astronomy

From the smallest objects in the solar system to evidence for the existence of unseen dark matter, the past year was one marked by interesting discoveries in astronomy.

Solar system. In addition to the nine planets that circle the Sun, there are millions of much smaller objects in the solar system. During the past year some of the most noteworthy discoveries involved these bodies.

Comets are chunks of ice, rock, and dust that are a few kilometers in diameter. The vast majority of them orbit the Sun in the outer "deep freeze," beyond the outer planets. Because of their small size, they reflect only a tiny amount of the feeble sunlight that reaches them, and so they are rarely seen. However, gravitational interactions sometimes disturb their orbits and send about a dozen comets each year into the inner solar system, where they follow a long elliptical orbit around the Sun. As a comet nears the Sun, its ices begin to sublimate, producing a tail of gas and dust. Jupiter, being the most massive planet, can have a significant gravitational influence on a comet. For example, if a comet passes close to Jupiter, the size of its orbit can be considerably reduced, with the result that the comet returns to the Sun every few years or decades. Halley's Comet is a famous example of these short-period comets.

During the past year, planetary astronomers made a remarkable discovery. On March 24, 1993, astronomers Eugene and Carolyn Shoemaker, David Levy, and Philippe Bendjoya discovered a new comet with the 0.46-m Schmidt camera at the Palomar Observatory in California. The photographic image was not round and fuzzy as expected, but instead it looked like a short streak. Jim Scotti was asked to take a closer look with the 0.91-m telescope at the Kitt Peak National Observatory in Arizona. His image showed that the streak was made up of a string of "minicomets." Observations in the months that followed showed that there were at least 22 separate objects moving in a line. From these observations Brian G. Marsden was able to compute the orbit of the objects. The results indicated that on July 7, 1992, the comet had come as close as 20,000 km (12,400 mi) to the cloud tops of Jupiter. At that distance a comet would be broken apart by the tidal forces of Jupiter's strong gravity. The 22 separate fragments were produced by that encounter. Observations by the Hubble Space Telescope showed that each fragment was no more than 4 km (2.5 mi) in diameter.

Marsden's calculations also revealed that the path of the comet fragments had been radically altered from that of the original comet. They were now orbiting Jupiter rather than the Sun. This orbit is very long and narrow—so narrow, in fact, that when the comet returns to Jupiter in July 1994, it will hit the planet. The fragments are expected to strike Jupiter one by one from July 16 to 21. Astronomers have known for a long time that comets must occasionally strike the planets, but this will be the first time any-

Jane Luu, University of California, Berkeley, and David Jewitt, University of Hawaii

Comet Shoemaker-Levy 9, discovered by astronomers in March 1993, formed an image that resembled a short streak rather than the expected round and fuzzy shape. Later observations revealed the reason for this—the comet's nucleus consisted of a string of "minicomets" moving in a line; astronomers concluded that the comet's close encounter with Jupiter in 1992 had broken the nucleus into these fragments.

one has been able to watch the event. Unfortunately, the impact site will be on the night side of Jupiter and out of view from Earth. However, at a speed of 60 km (37 mi) per second and an impact energy of 250,000 megatons of TNT per fragment, some planetwide effects may be seen. No one is precisely certain what the impact will be like. It seems likely that atmospheric shock waves will move across the face of the planet. A considerable effort will be made to monitor this historic event in July 1994.

Diagonal trail reveals the path of asteroid 1993 KA$_2$. In May 1993 the tiny asteroid came within 140,000 km (86,800 mi) of the Earth. This was the closest approach yet recorded for an asteroid or comet.

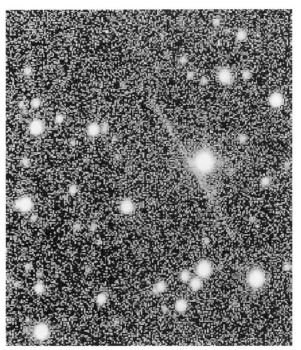

Image courtesy of James V. Scotti

In the early 1950s U.S. astronomer Gerard P. Kuiper predicted the existence of a large number of comets orbiting the Sun beyond Neptune. These comets would move in a flattened disk that lies in the same plane as the orbits of the planets. This proposed region has become known as Kuiper's belt, and it has been suggested as the source of most short-period comets. Ordinary comets at distances beyond Neptune's orbit would be nearly undetectable, even with modern telescopes, and so for many years Kuiper's idea remained only a suggestion. Recently, however, astronomers Jane X. Luu and David Jewitt began searching with the 2.2-m telescope on Mauna Kea in Hawaii. In August 1992 they discovered an exceedingly faint (magnitude 23.5), slow-moving, starlike object. Its motion revealed that this object, now designated as 1992 QB$_1$, is orbiting the Sun at a distance of more than 40 astronomical units (AU; one AU equals 150 million km, or 93 million mi). For a comet to be seen at that distance, it must have a diameter of 200 km (125 mi), much larger than the typical comet.

In March 1993 this same research team discovered a second example, designated 1993 FW, orbiting the Sun at about 50 AU. In September they found two more of these objects at 33.3 and 35.4 AU, just beyond the orbit of Neptune. A few days later Iwan P. Williams, Alan Fitzsimmons, and Donald O'Ceallaigh discovered two more with the 2.5-m Isaac Newton Telescope at La Palma in the Canary Islands. Thus, it appears that the Kuiper belt has at last been detected. Astronomers suspect that these newfound objects are among the largest members of the Kuiper-belt comets.

Asteroids are rocky objects measuring up to 1,000 km (620 mi) in diameter. The vast majority of the several thousand cataloged asteroids orbit between Mars and Jupiter. However, it is known that a few (the exact number is unknown) have more elliptical

Supernova 1993J (arrow) was discovered by amateur astronomer Francisco García of Spain in a spiral arm of M81 galaxy.

orbits that take them inside the orbit of the Earth. These asteroids, therefore, could collide with the Earth. Such an impact, even from a small asteroid, could have devastating effects. It is now widely believed that a collision with a 10-km (6.2-mi) asteroid 65 million years ago brought about the extinction of the dinosaurs and many other creatures. That impact placed vast quantities of dust and smoke into the atmosphere that blocked the sunlight for at least a year. This had a disastrous effect on plant life and the entire food chain. In 1993 the Earth barely missed a similar collision with a smaller asteroid. On May 21 Tom Gehrels detected an asteroid on several images obtained with a 0.9-m telescope at Kitt Peak. Its orbit, calculated by Brian Marsden, showed that this asteroid, designated as 1993 KA$_2$, missed the Earth by only 140,000 km (86,800 mi). This is a far closer approach than that of any previously recorded asteroid or comet. The asteroid is only 5 to 10 m (16.5 to 33 ft) in diameter and has an elongated orbit that carries it inside the orbit of Venus to almost the orbit of Jupiter.

Stars. M81 is a bright, relatively nearby galaxy located in the sky near the Big Dipper. It is a favorite object for amateur astronomers. On March 28, 1993, one such amateur, Francisco García of Spain, noticed a 12th-magnitude star not far from the nucleus of M81. He had not seen this star two nights earlier. García had discovered a supernova, now designated SN 1993J, in a spiral arm of the galaxy. A supernova is the huge explosion of a massive star. At its peak a supernova can be as bright as the combined light of 100 billion Suns.

About a dozen supernovas are discovered each year in other galaxies. Despite this frequency, astronomers are relatively ignorant of their workings because the vast distances to these galaxies make the supernovas faint and difficult to study. Therefore, the discovery of a supernova in a nearby galaxy

like M81 (11 million light-years distant) is extremely important. Because of this proximity, it was possible to identify the progenitor star on older photographs. This was only the third time that such an identification could be made. The star that exploded appears to have been a red supergiant, just the type of star predicted by current supernova theories. SN 1993J was the closest supernova since 1987, when one exploded in the Large Magellanic Cloud (170,000 light-years distant).

SN 1993J was carefully studied by ground-based observatories and orbiting astronomical telescopes. During the first few days of outburst, the light spectrum showed strong lines of hydrogen gas, and the star's brightness peaked. It faded for about a week and then brightened again, reaching a second maximum. Astronomers believe they understand the cause of this behavior. The first rise was due to the explosion itself and the hot expanding shell of debris. Because of the large distance to the supernova, the debris cloud was not resolved; that is, it appeared starlike, even in large telescopes. As this shell expanded, it cooled, causing the supernova to appear to dim. However, the supernova also produced large numbers of new atomic nuclei, including radioactive nickel. The nickel nuclei decayed by emitting gamma rays that scattered through the debris cloud. The interaction with the matter in the cloud converted the gamma rays to visible light. Early in the expansion of the debris, the cloud was so dense that this light was unable to escape. As the expansion proceeded, the cloud thinned, and the light from the nickel decay was able to reach the Earth. This produced the second peak.

The Advanced Satellite for Cosmology and Astrophysics (ASCA), a joint venture of the U.S. and Japan, detected strong emission of X-rays from the supernova. It is believed that the X-rays were produced when material ejected from the blast collided with cold interstellar gas. Much of this gas may have originated from the progenitor star itself. Supergiant stars, like the progenitor, are luminous, and the pressure of their light is known to generate strong winds that over the life of the star can drive a significant amount of its outer layers into interstellar space.

Globular star clusters contain 100,000–one million stars bound together by their mutual gravity. Each star orbits the center of mass of the cluster. Guido De Marchi and Francesco Paresce used the Faint Object Camera of the Hubble Space Telescope to image the central portions of M15, a relatively nearby globular cluster. In addition to the numerous ordinary stars, their images revealed 15 stars with surface temperatures of approximately 30,000° C (54,000° F). These stars are tightly bunched near the cluster's center. They are also less luminous than other stars in the cluster that have the same temperature. This indicates that they are small.

These stars could be white dwarfs, the final stages in the lives of low-mass stars like our Sun. However, it was not clear why white dwarfs should be found congregated at the cluster's center rather than being spread out evenly throughout the cluster. De Marchi and Paresce proposed an intriguing idea. It has long been known that globular clusters provide the environment for strong gravitational interactions between stars because the average distance between stars is much less there than in most of the galaxy. As stars pass near each other in their orbits, there is a transfer of momentum from the more massive star to the less massive one. The result of this transfer is that the massive stars will tend to "sink" toward the cluster's center. De Marchi and Paresce theorized that some of the close, near-miss, interactions may also strip away the extended atmospheres of massive giant stars. After several such interactions, the giants would settle into orbits near the cluster's center with only their hot central cores intact. It may be these hot naked stellar cores that De Marchi and Paresce detected. Unlike white dwarfs, these cores are still the sites of fusion reactions. To confirm these ideas, they will use the Hubble Telescope again to analyze the light of one of these stars spectroscopically. Also, if this scenario is correct, a search of other clusters with the Hubble Telescope should reveal the same kinds of stellar cores.

Galactic astronomy. The Milky Way is seen as a hazy band of faint stars that extends across the sky. It is a galaxy of hundreds of billions of stars, of which our Sun is just one. Because of the Sun's interior position in the galaxy, it is difficult for astronomers to gain an overall impression of the Milky Way. Recent discoveries reveal that the Milky Way may be in the act of colliding with another galaxy. The Milky Way has two small satellite galaxies, the Large Magellanic Cloud (LMC) and the Small Magellanic Cloud

(SMC). For many years astronomers have known that the LMC displays a faint tail of stars and gas about 100° long in the sky. It is called the Magellanic stream. Because the LMC is only 170,000 light-years away (the disk of the Milky Way is only 100,000 light-years across), it has been suspected that the stream is due to the gravitational tidal effects of the Milky Way on the LMC. Recently, Douglas N.C. Lin, Burton F. Jones, and Arnold R. Klemola made careful measurements of the motion of the LMC with respect to background objects. Their measurements had to be corrected for the effects of the Earth's motion and the rotation of the Milky Way. The results indicate that the LMC is moving across our line of sight at more than 200 km per second on a path that will eventually cause it to collide with our galaxy. The Magellanic stream consists of stars and gas that have been pulled from the LMC by tidal forces. The eventual collision will cause the LMC to merge with the Milky Way.

The motion of the LMC indicates the strength of the gravitational field of the Milky Way. This in turn allowed Lin and his collaborators to estimate the mass of our galaxy as at least 600 billion solar masses. The visible matter in our galaxy accounts for only 100 billion solar masses. Therefore, this becomes one more piece of evidence that most of the matter in the Milky Way is in the form of dark matter.

Extragalactic astronomy. In recent years there has been growing evidence that more than 90% of the mass of the universe is unseen. This has been determined from the rotation rates of galaxies, the orbital motion of binary galaxies, and the motions of galaxies in clusters. In all of these cases, the amount of visible matter is insufficient to provide the gravitational force required for preventing these systems from flying apart. Approximately 10 times more matter is needed for the maintenance of stability. Possible explanations for this unseen dark matter have generally fallen into two categories: previously unknown subatomic particles, and large numbers of low-mass stars and brown dwarfs (objects more massive than planets but not massive enough to produce nuclear fusion reactions).

The rotation of the Milky Way galaxy indicates that the 100 billion solar masses of visible stars and gas must be immersed in a much more massive halo of dark matter. Recently, an attempt was made to test the second theory, namely that the halo is composed of dark massive compact halo objects (MACHOs). Three research groups undertook a search for these objects: a U.S.-Australian group led by Charles Alcock, a U.S.-Polish team led by Bodhan Paczynski, and a French group headed by Michel Spiro.

Whatever these objects are, there must be hundreds of billions of them in the halo of the Milky Way. As they move through space, they should on

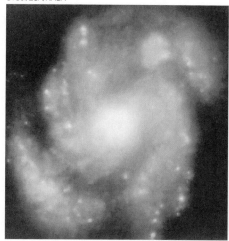 

Blurred photograph of the core of spiral galaxy M100 at the far left was taken by the Wide-Field Planetary Camera of the Hubble Space Telescope in November 1993, just before U.S. space shuttle astronauts repaired the Hubble's flawed optics. At the near left is the much sharper image of the same region produced a month later by the new Wide-Field Planetary Camera installed by the astronauts.

occasion pass in front of a more distant object, as viewed from Earth. Because the probability of such an alignment is so small, many thousands of distant objects must be monitored to catch a single event. Until recently, the proper technology was unavailable for such a project. Charged-coupled-device (CCD) detectors and inexpensive computer hardware now make this project practical. A rich background star field to be viewed through the halo is needed. For example, Alcock's group was monitoring rich star fields in the Large Magellanic Cloud.

These groups were actually looking not for an occultation of the background star but rather for the gravitational effect on the light from the background star. Einstein's General Theory of Relativity predicts that the path light follows is affected by gravity. In 1986 Paczynski noted that if a MACHO were to pass between the star and the Earth, the MACHO's gravitational field would act like a magnifying glass, concentrating light and making the star appear to brighten. He was able to calculate the size of this effect and show that its detection was possible. The brightening and dimming of starlight due to a MACHO's gravitational field has a predictable, symmetrical pattern that helps to distinguish it from the changes of ordinary variable stars.

In 1993 all three research teams claimed that they had detected these microlensing events. The Alcock team had monitored 1.8 million stars for a year before the first detection. They and the French team were able to show that the star did not change color during the event. This is unlike the behavior of known variable stars but was expected from a microlensing event. As of early 1994, it was still too early to know if MACHOs had actually been discovered. The exact masses of the lensing objects that had been detected were not well established. They could be as massive as the Sun, which would remove them from the category of dark matter. As more

observations are collected and statistics improve, the question may be answered.

More than 20 years ago Earth satellites launched by the U.S. to detect the gamma-ray emission from nuclear testing discovered instead bursts of gamma rays from deep space. These bursts may last for only a few seconds and never were seen to be repeated from the same location in the sky. None of these "gamma-ray bursters" has been identified with a visible object.

In 1991 the U.S. National Aeronautics and Space Administration (NASA) launched the Compton Gamma Ray Observatory satellite hoping to solve the mystery of the gamma-ray bursters. Were these objects located within our own galaxy or outside at much greater distances? The question is crucial, for it weighs heavily on the matter of the energy production of these sources. By 1993 the Compton observatory had detected more than 600 bursts, and the mystery had deepened. Many astronomers had expected the bursters to be located within our Milky Way galaxy, which would make the required energy production more reasonable. If this were the case, then the Compton observatory data would show the burst sites concentrated toward the galactic center, just as the stars are. However, the results revealed a completely random distribution on the sky. This strongly argues that they are extragalactic in nature. If these bursts are coming from objects in other galaxies, then a typical burst of a few seconds emits a thousand times the total energy output of the Sun in 10 billion years. Astronomer Stan Woosley suggested scenarios involving colliding neutron stars or the collapse of a massive star to form a black hole. (*See* Feature Article: NEW EYES ON THE GAMMA-RAY SKY.)

As 1993 ended, the successful repair of the Hubble Space Telescope promised exciting discoveries in the year ahead.

—Ronald H. Kaitchuck

Chemistry

Many of the advances made in chemistry during the past year were directed toward solving practical problems. Researchers developed ceramic materials with record-high superconducting transition temperatures, devised new methods for converting methane into useful chemicals, and moved individual atoms around on a surface in order to build a container for electrons. Other achievements included several novel battery designs, a cholesterol-lowering agent made from cellulose, and the complete laboratory synthesis of a promising immune suppressant.

Inorganic chemistry

During the past year chemists pursued the promise of boron neutron capture as an anticancer therapy, made molecules that are the atomic-scale equivalents of rigid rods and capillary tubes, and explored the question of how many atoms it takes to make a metal. Researchers reported record-high critical temperatures for new mercury-containing superconducting ceramics, and a still-living Nobel laureate in chemistry was honored with an element named for him.

Naming of new elements. By international agreement the naming of newly created elements is formally the province of the Inorganic Nomenclature Commission of the International Union of Pure and Applied Chemistry (IUPAC). In practice, however, that group has always accepted the names that were proposed by the discoverers, provided that the reported chemical and nuclear properties of the new element were confirmed by an independent research group. This corroborative process, however, can result in lengthy delays. For example, element 106 (which has 106 protons in its nucleus) was initially synthesized in 1974 by Albert Ghiorso and his team at the Lawrence Berkeley Laboratory in California, but the data from their experiments were not confirmed until late 1993, when a second Berkeley group was able to fuse californium-249 nuclei with oxygen-18 nuclei to generate a small amount of element $^{263}106$. The product of the reaction is characterized by a half-life of 0.9 second and decays by the emission of alpha particles (helium-4 nuclei) to element $^{259}104$ and then to nobelium-255.

Thus, after a period of 20 years, the original discoverers of element 106 were able to propose that it be named seaborgium after the 1951 chemistry Nobel laureate Glenn T. Seaborg and that the chemical symbol be Sg. The proposal is somewhat unusual since its adoption would mark the first time that an element had been named for a living chemist, but it is also appropriate since the 82-year-old Seaborg has been a seminal figure in the area of transuranium chemistry.

Lawrence Berkeley Laboratory, University of California

Octogenarian nuclear chemist Glenn T. Seaborg points to the position on the periodic table of element 106, which was named seaborgium (Sg) in his honor.

In 1993 controversy continued over the naming of some of the remaining unnamed heavy elements. In essence, the literature contains a number of competing, but sometimes unsubstantiated, claims for the first successful synthesis of elements 102 through 109 by the nuclear chemistry groups at Dubna, Russia, Darmstadt, Germany, and Berkeley, Calif. The Transfermium Working Group, a joint committee of IUPAC and the International Union of Pure and Applied Physics (IUPAP), was attempting to resolve the various claims for priority by critically reassessing the scientific data. In some cases the evidence was quite clear. For example, the initial preparations of elements 107, 108, and 109 were ascribed to the Darmstadt group, who proposed nielsbohrium (Ns), hassium (Hs), and meitnerium (Mt) for their elements. Similarly, the Berkeley claim for element 106 was found to be solid. The greatest difficulties were centered on elements 104 and 105, for which the committee proposed that the Dubna and Berkeley groups share the honors. The suggestion was vociferously assailed by the Berkeley group.

298

Boron neutron-capture therapy. In the subdiscipline of bioinorganic chemistry, an intriguing set of experiments was just getting under way. The ultimate goal of the research is to take medical advantage of the nuclear reaction between thermal (slow-moving) neutrons (n) and the boron isotope of mass 10 (^{10}B). This reaction, $n + {^{10}B} \rightarrow {^4He} + {^7Li}$, liberates approximately 2.8 million electron volts of energy, which is primarily carried off as kinetic energy by the helium-4 and lithium-7 nuclei. The energetic products of the reaction dissipate their energy in collisions with nearby molecules, which results in bond disruption within those molecules. In solids and liquids the distances traveled by the helium and lithium atoms are limited to about one cell diameter; thus, an appropriately placed boron atom ultimately could kill a targeted cancer cell while leaving the surrounding normal cells unaffected.

Since ^{10}B nuclei are some 1,000 to 10,000 times more reactive with thermal neutrons than, for example, the hydrogen, carbon, nitrogen, and oxygen nuclei commonly found in living tissue, the strategy behind the experiments is to develop a methodology by which boron cluster compounds, primarily $C_2B_{10}H_{12}$ derivatives, can be incorporated within or adjacent to the nuclei of tumor cells. Ideally, the boron compounds would be covalently attached to biochemicals that are preferentially taken up by fast-growing cancers but not used appreciably by normal cells, thus loading the undesirable cells with ^{10}B. Irradiation of the patient with epithermal neutrons (neutrons with slightly higher kinetic energies than those of thermal neutrons), which are much less damaging than the normally used gamma irradiation, would then result in the destruction of essentially only the malignant cells.

The process outlined above is called boron neutron-capture therapy (BNCT). The essence of the procedure was successfully tested by Hiroshi Hatanaka of Kosei-Nenkin Hospital, Osaka, Japan, who initially employed $B_{12}H_{11}SH^{2-}$ as the boron compound. He was able to gain remission and, in some cases, apparent cure of patients stricken with malignant glioblastoma multiforme, a type of brain tumor. At present, the major difficulties associated with the method involve the development of appropriate systems for the selective delivery of the boron compounds to the malignant cells. Earlier studies examined a number of potential carriers, including boron-containing amino acids, modified monoclonal antibodies, artificial membrane-enclosed vesicles called liposomes, and ring-shaped molecules called porphyrins, but more recent research has focused on the synthesis of boron-containing nucleotides and nucleosides, the molecular building blocks of genetic material. As of early 1994, clinical trials of the efficacy of BNCT against certain types of glioma and melanoma were either in progress or about to start in several countries.

Organosilicon chemistry. One of the interesting questions in organosilicon chemistry can be stated as follows: Given that silicon is directly below carbon in the periodic table, why are not their chemistries more similar? Part of the difference between the two is that carbon readily forms strong multiple bonds, whereas the larger silicon atoms do so only with great reluctance. Although compounds with more reactive silicon multiple bonds had been previously reported, the first exceptionally stable compound of this type, a silaallene, $R_2Si{=}C{=}CR_2$, in which R is a very bulky alkyl group, was generated only during the past year by Robert West's group at the University of Wisconsin. The air- and water-stable 1-silaallene is by far the most stable, least reactive multiply bonded silicon compound known.

Another difference between carbon and silicon is that carbon forms carbocations, R_3C^+ (R is a generalized atom or group), relatively easily in solution and in the solid phase. These reactive carbocations are characterized by a 120° bond angle between the ligands and by a planar arrangement of the bonds to central carbon atom. Curiously, the larger silicon atoms do form the corresponding silylium ions, R_3Si^+, in the gas phase, but despite numerous attempts free R_3Si^+ cations have never been shown to exist in condensed phases of matter. Instead, in solids and liquids there has always been a fourth group interacting with the silicon atom. In the past year papers reported the closest approaches to a planar, triply bonded silicon cation yet achieved. Joseph B. Lambert of Northwestern University, Evanston, Ill., determined that the $C{-}Si{-}C$ bond angles of $(C_2H_5)_3Si^+(C_6F_5)_4B^-$ were 114°, but in this compound there was a slight interaction with a solvent molecule. Christopher Reed of the University of Southern California measured $C{-}Si{-}C$ bond angles of 117° in $[CH(CH_3)_2]_3Si^+B_{11}Br_6H_6C^-$. In this case a residual interaction existed between the silicon atom and one of the bromine atoms in the anion. On the basis of nuclear magnetic resonance data, a $[Si(CH_3)_3]_3Si^+$ cation synthesized by Lambert may well be the most planar silyl cation known, although the X-ray crystallography data remain to be reported.

Syntheses of small molecules. Successful preparations of small molecules that were reported in 1993 include the formation of the interesting dihydrogen trioxide, HOOOH, which Bozo Plesnicar of the University of Ljubljana, Slovenia, generated by reacting ozone with 2-ethylanthrahydroquinone. Although compounds like CF_3OOOCF_3 that contain three oxygen atoms in a row had been known for some time, this was the first report of the parent hydride. Karl Christe of Rocketdyne, a division of Rockwell International Corp., Canoga Park, Calif., proved conclusively that the reaction of osmium tetroxide (OsO$_4$) with krypton difluoride (KrF$_2$) in anhydrous hydrofluoric acid (HF) yields *cis*-OsO$_2$F$_4$ rather than the OsOF$_6$ that had been previously claimed. The weakest possible chemical bond, that found in the helium "molecule" He$_2$, was characterized by Clayton Giese, W. Ronald Gentry, and co-workers of the University of Minnesota at a small fraction of a degree above absolute zero. The average distance between the helium atoms is about 25 times the distance found in more normal bonds (see *Physical chemistry*, below). The square planar anion Cu(CF$_3$)$_4^-$ was examined crystallographically by Dieter Naumann of the University of Cologne, Germany; the species is of interest because it is a rare example of a stable trivalent copper salt.

The addition of gaseous cyanogen, (CN)$_2$, to a working carbon arc was shown by Andreas Hirsch of the University of Tübingen, Germany, to result in the formation of compounds made of linear chains of atoms; for example, N≡C–C≡C–C≡C –C≡C–C≡C–C≡C–C≡C–C≡C–C≡N. This rigid molecule can be compared to a stirring rod or a

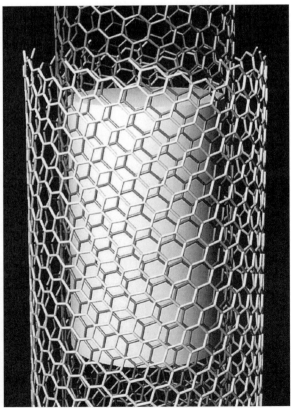

Nested nanotubes made of carbon atoms bonded in hexagonal arrays, with a mass of material drawn up inside the inner tube, are modeled in a computer-generated image. Researchers in Japan reported making such structures in 1993.

P.M. Ajayan and Sumio Iijima, NEC Corporation, Tsukuba, Japan

swizzle stick that has been constructed on the scale of individual atoms, a scale sometimes referred to as nanoscale (where distances are typically measured in nanometers [nm], or billionths of a meter). Other nanoscale objects that have been fabricated recently include molecular bowls, dishes, beakers, shuttles, iron wires, and soda straws. P.M. Ajayan and Sumio Iijima of the NEC Fundamental Research Laboratory, Tsukuba, Japan, formed the last from carbon nanotubes that were generated in carbon arcs. The nanotubes are cylinders of bonded carbon atoms that can be hundreds of angstroms long, yet only eight angstroms across. (An angstrom is a ten-billionth of a meter; *i.e.*, 0.1 nm.) The walls of the cylinders are carbon atoms arranged in hexagonal arrays, and the caps are carbon atoms situated in pentagons. Since the latter are more reactive than the former, addition of a reactive metal such as lead removes the ends of the tubes but leaves the walls untouched. To complete the analogy of the straw, once the end of the tube has been removed, the metal atoms can be drawn up inside the tube by capillary action.

Another example of a nanoscale object is the molecular "switch" constructed by Jean-Marie Lehn of Louis Pasteur University, Strasbourg, France (*see* Figure). As illustrated, the switch on the left is "off" in that the dication, a ruthenium-based complex, will not luminesce (shine) when exposed to light. If the right-hand portion of the dication, however, is reduced to the dihydrogen species shown on the right, the luminescence of the molecule is turned "on."

Organometallic chemistry. Much of the research in organometallic chemistry is driven by the need to transform plentiful organic compounds (petrochemicals) into more useful chemical intermediates. A more contemporary concern is the desire to move toward using more environmentally benign solvents in industry than the chlorocarbons commonly employed currently. As an example, methane (CH$_4$) is the most abundant and the cheapest hydrocarbon, with estimated reserves approaching the equivalent of 1.5 trillion bbl of oil. Methane, however, is also the most unreactive hydrocarbon, and generally it is burned to produce heat or, if the distances to a market are too great, it is simply flared where it is extracted. During the past year two processes were revealed that offer the potential for economical oxidation of methane. The first, by Catalytica, Inc., Mountain View, Calif., employs mercuric salts as the catalyst and generates methyl alcohol (CH$_3$OH) in about 40% yield from CH$_4$ and oxygen (O$_2$). The second, by researchers at the University of Minnesota, involves oxidation of CH$_4$ over a platinum or rhodium surface to give syngas (a mixture of carbon monoxide [CO] and hydrogen [H$_2$] that is commonly employed to generate larger organic molecules) in approximately 90% yield (see *Organic chemistry*, below).

switch "off"   switch "on"

Other studies have investigated the possibilities of using carbon dioxide (CO_2) as a chemical feedstock. In one report, by Walter Leitner of the University of Jena, Germany, the reaction of CO_2 with H_2 to give formic acid (HCO_2H) in aqueous solutions was examined. The catalyst employed was fairly unique in that it was a water-soluble rhodium-based catalyst. Clifford Kubiak of Purdue University, West Lafayette, Ind., demonstrated the activation by light of CO_2 in the presence of a nickel trimer, $Ni_3(dppm)_3I_2$ (dppm is bis[diphenylphosphino]methane), and generated alkyldicarboxylates from reactions with cyclohexene. George G. Stanley of Louisiana State University published the details of a new, more efficient catalyst for the liquid-phase hydroformulation of olefins. The reaction, which converts 1-alkenes to aldehydes, is the single most important homogeneous catalytic organometallic industrial process.

Advanced materials. The emphasis in advanced materials is upon producing new solids and surfaces with properties that are superior to those of materials currently available. For example, automobiles would require far less fuel if their internal-combustion engines were able to run at higher temperatures. For this purpose, however, new lightweight, strong ceramics are needed. In 1993 Isuzu Motors Ltd. was testing a prototype ceramic engine that operates at 850° C (1,560° F) rather than the conventional 250° C (480° F). In this engine the pistons and cylinders are fabricated from silicon nitride and aluminum titanium oxide.

Supercomputers are limited to the speed at which electrons flow through wires and to the operating speed of their components, which are mostly silicon. For some applications even the largest computers are too slow. Recent experiments showed that if the silicon is doped (made impure) with small amounts of germanium, the speed at which the semiconductor devices operate can be increased near that of devices made of inherently much faster, but much less oxidatively stable, gallium arsenide.

Long-range efforts in the area of advanced computers are focused on replacing electrical circuitry with optical circuitry. For the endeavor to be successful, an entirely new array of light-generating solids must be developed. In particular it will be necessary to double the frequency of light at will, a process that, in essence, would convert red light to blue. Materials that can achieve such effects are said to have nonlinear optical (NLO) properties, and new compounds with NLO attributes far superior to any currently available must to be developed if optical computing and data storage are to become a reality. In the past year many research groups explored the potential of a variety of solids for use as NLO materials. (*See* Feature Article: COMPUTING WITH LIGHT.)

A question of interest to many solid-state chemists and materials scientists is: At what point do the properties of a cluster of atoms become indistinguishable from those of the bulk metal or compound? It is clear, for example, that the properties of an isolated gold atom are very different from those of a gold atom located in the midst of a gold ingot. Similarly, in a small iridium-containing cluster molecule such as $Ir_4(CO)_{12}$ the properties of the Ir_4 core are measurably different from those of metallic iridium, and the question above thus can be reduced to one of how many atoms it takes to make a metal.

The evidence accumulated from a study by Dieter Fenske of the University of Karlsruhe, Germany, on $Cu_{146}Se_{73}[P(C_6H_5)_3]_{30}$ indicates that the properties of this large cluster are like those found in bulk copper selenide (Cu_2Se). An examination by scanning tunneling microscopy and X-ray photoelectron spectroscopy of $Au_{55}[P(C_6H_5)_3]_{12}Cl_6$ and nanometer-sized gold particles by C.N.R. Rao of the Indian Institute of Science led to the conclusion that the properties of the Au_{55} cluster (which is 1.4 nm in diameter) are best described as those of a molecular species but that the properties of the 4-nm-diameter gold particles have crossed the threshold and are very similar to those of the bulk metal.

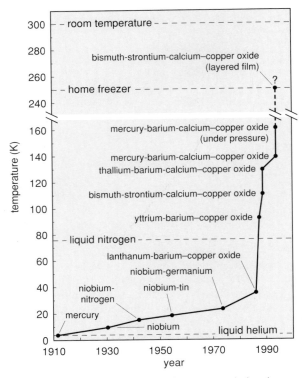

Critical temperatures for superconductors soared after the discovery of copper oxide-based ceramics in the late 1980s. In 1993 new records in the 130–150 K range were established with mercury-containing formulations, while a less certain observation of 250 K was reported for a layered film.

At temperatures below a characteristic critical temperature, superconducting materials transport electricity without resistive losses (heating). Superconductors are already important to society because they have revolutionized magnet technology. The superconducting magnets found in most magnetic resonance imaging (MRI) devices used for medical diagnosis operate below about 18 K, which requires the use of expensive liquid helium (boiling point 4 K) as the cooling agent. (To convert kelvins to degrees Celsius, subtract 273; thus, 18 K = −255° C. To convert Celsius to Fahrenheit, multiply by 1.8 and add 32.) In the late 1980s copper oxide-based ceramic superconductors were discovered. Some can operate at temperatures in the vicinity of 100 K, which means that they can be cooled with much cheaper liquid nitrogen (boiling point 77 K). These so-called high-temperature superconductors, however, are very brittle and thus difficult to mold into electrical components such as coil windings and electrical cables, and it was only in the past year that it proved possible to make cables from them that can carry the levels of current (around 2,000 amp) that are required by commercial utility companies. High-temperature superconductors also were deployed in

acoustic transducers for submarines during the past year.

After a prolonged period of research in which the maximum critical temperature for superconductors was not increased, several research groups found that adding mercury to copper oxide formulations raised the critical temperature above 130 K at normal atmospheric pressure and above 150 K at very high pressures.

The most astonishing report of the past year, however, was that of Michel Laguës of the National Center for Scientific Research, Paris, who showed that portions of a film synthesized by sequential addition of layers of bismuth, strontium, calcium, and copper atoms to a strontium titanate substrate appeared to have a critical temperature near 250 K, a temperature normally found in domestic freezers and easily achieved with conventional refrigeration equipment. If the results are substantiated and if the material can be formed into conductive wires and coils, the compound will revolutionize the way electric power is used and transported.

—John A. Morrison

Organic chemistry

There is a natural ebb and flow to the popularity of subdisciplines in organic chemistry. The 1960s were the heyday of physical organic chemistry, the 1970s saw the flowering of organic synthesis, and the 1980s witnessed the emergence of bioorganic chemistry. All these fields have continued to advance, but indications are that the 1990s may well be the decade of polymer chemistry. After a long time out of favor, organic polymer chemistry again has been generating great excitement among scientists, as evidenced by the variety of developments that were reported in the past year.

Polymers. Robert M. Waymouth and Geoffrey W. Coates of Stanford University succeeded in preparing from simple precursors the first polymer that has a right-left handedness to it because of the arrangement of substituent groups attached to the polymer chain (see 1). As a result of this handedness, the polymer has potentially useful optical properties not seen in typical nonhanded polymers. The two chemists prepared the polymer, poly(methylene-1,3-cyclopentane), abbreviated PCMP, by using an optically active zirconium-containing catalyst to polymerize 1,5-hexadiene. Possible uses of PCMP are in separations technology and in specialized optical applications.

The industrial synthesis of diamond by heating graphite to 2,500° C (4,500° F) at ultrahigh pressure has been carried out for nearly 40 years. In 1993 Patricia A. Bianconi and her students at Pennsylvania State University reported their discovery of a potentially much easier method for making diamond. They found that heating the organic polymer poly(phenylcarbyne) (see 2) to a temperature of only 1,000° C (1,800° F) at atmospheric pressure yields a gritty black powder with a hardness approaching that of microcrystalline diamond. Should further work confirm the identity of the product, the method has potential applications for obtaining thin-film diamond coatings.

Antibodies are a group of complex biological polymers (biopolymers) that are produced by an organism's immune system and are able to recognize molecules that are foreign to the organism by virtue of their characteristic shapes. Attempting to mimic this kind of molecular recognition, Klaus Mosbach and his colleagues at the University of Lund, Sweden, developed a process called molecular imprinting to create antibody-like shape-selective recognition sites in simple synthetic polymers. In essence, the process is a chemical version of the lost-wax process used by artists to cast metal objects. A polymer "cast" is prepared in the presence of a template molecule, which is then removed by extraction. Left behind in the resultant polymer are cavities whose shapes complement those of the template molecule in the same way that a glove complements a hand. When the polymer is then exposed to a mixture of many different compounds, it specifically absorbs into its cavities only those molecules having the shape of the template molecule, thereby making possible an exquisitely sensitive molecular-assay method.

Bioorganic chemistry. The nucleic acids DNA and RNA have evolved over billions of years to code and pass on an organism's genetic information. It thus seems reasonable to assume that their structures would be so highly optimized by now that few improvements could be made. Surprisingly, however, a group of synthetic DNA mimics prepared by Michael Egholm and Ole Buchardt of the University of Copenhagen, Peter Nielsen of the Panum Institute,

3 rapamycin

Copenhagen, and Rolf Berg of the Riso National Laboratory, Roskilde, Den., may indeed be a substantial improvement on the natural material, at least for certain pharmaceutical purposes. Called peptide nucleic acids (PNAs), these DNA mimics are a chemical hybrid of proteins and nucleic acids. Like DNA, the synthetic PNA molecules encode their message in a sequence of molecules called bases that are strung along a chemical backbone. For PNAs, however, the chemical backbone is made of amino acid units linked in a linear chain—the basic structure of proteins—rather than the sugar and phosphate units that make up the backbone of nucleic acids. Preliminary indications are that PNAs not only are more stable in cells than their natural DNA counterparts but also bind to natural DNA some 50–100 times more tightly that natural DNA binds to itself. These properties could make possible the synthesis of pharmaceutical agents that are able to seek out and bind to specific sequences in a DNA strand and thereby block the action of unwanted genes.

Another kind of molecular modification of natural biopolymers was carried out by Samuel H. Gellman and Gregory P. Dado of the University of Wisconsin. The researchers designed and synthesized a peptide (a small protein) that is able to switch back and forth reversibly between α-helix and β-sheet conformations—two characteristic structures that the amino acid chains of proteins can assume when they fold into their natural three-dimensional shapes. Which conformation the peptide assumes depends on whether the units of the amino acid methionine in the peptide are in their oxidized or reduced forms. Such control of protein-folding structure could in principle lead to corresponding control of protein function.

Synthesis of complex molecules. Rapamycin (see 3), a naturally occurring metabolic product of a fungus, has been under intense scrutiny in recent years because of its ability to suppress the human

303

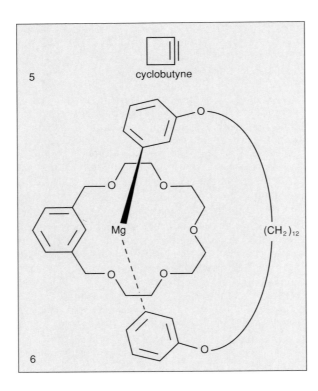

4

cyclobutyne

5

6

immune system following organ-transplant surgery. Synthetic work on rapamycin culminated in the past year in a complete laboratory synthesis of the substance, carried out by Kyriacos C. Nicolaou and a research team at the Scripps Research Institute, La Jolla, Calif., and the University of California at San Diego. Although the successful synthesis would not replace the fermentation method currently used to obtain the drug, it opened the way for preparation of simpler rapamycin analogues that may find use as pharmaceutical agents.

Proteins and nucleic acids have long been made routinely by automated synthesizers, but the carbo-hydrates (*i.e.,* polysaccharides, which are polymers of simple sugar molecules) have proved much more difficult to prepare. In 1993 researchers at Yale University led by Samuel J. Danishefsky reported the development of a new technique of polysaccharide synthesis that could form the basis of an automated carbohydrate synthesizer. In the new technique a sugar unit in the form of a glycal—a sugar molecule with a carbon-carbon double bond in the ring—is first attached to a solid support. The glycal is then activated (made reactive) at the site of the double bond, and another glycal is linked to it. In a similar fashion additional glycals are attached, gradually building up a chain of sugar units.

Buckminsterfullerene (C_{60}), a molecule comprising 60 carbon atoms bonded into a geometry resembling that of a soccer ball, and AIDS inhibitors, compounds that interfere with the virus (HIV-1) that causes AIDS, have been among the hottest topics to hit organic chemistry in recent years. The two topics came together unexpectedly in 1993 when George L. Kenyon and Simon H. Friedman of the University of California at San Francisco prepared a water-soluble derivative of C_{60} (*see* 4) that shows a substantial ability to inhibit the growth of the AIDS virus. Kenyon postulated that the large C_{60} molecule plugs up the active site of a key enzyme of the virus, HIV-1 protease, like a cork in a bottle, thereby disrupting its function as a biological catalyst.

Unusual molecules. Most chemists would have predicted that cyclobutyne (*see* 5) would be far too unstable to exist because of the strain induced by the forcing of triply bonded carbon atoms to adopt bond angles of 90° rather than their preferred 180°. Nevertheless, Richard D. Adams and co-workers at the University of South Carolina pulled a major surprise when they used the stabilizing influence of three osmium atoms to prepare the first stable complex of cyclobutyne. Future work will concentrate on freeing the pure cyclobutyne from the metal atoms.

Other work reported in the past year on unusual molecules included preparation of the first example of an organometallic catenane, a molecular structure containing two rings that are interlocked like links in a chain. Friedrich Bickelhaupt and his colleagues at the Free University of Amsterdam were able to thread a magnesium-atom–tipped "needle" through a large preformed ring and then tie off the thread to make a second ring (see 6). Although work on such unusual structures is driven purely by curiosity and may have no obvious applications, it is always of interest to see what extraordinary molecules chemists can devise and make.

Methane conversion. For at least 70 years the holy grail of researchers in the field of synthetic fuels has been the development of a practical method for converting cheap and abundant methane gas (CH_4) into more easily transported liquid fuels or chemical feedstocks. Two new possibilities were reported in 1993. One group of researchers, headed by Roy A. Periana of Catalytica Inc., Mountain View, Calif., uses mercuric ions to catalyze the conversion of methane to methyl alcohol (CH_3OH) in yields as high as 43%. The key step in the process is the reaction of mercuric sulfate with methane at 180° C (360° F) to yield methylmercurous bisulfate. Further reaction of the product with sulfuric acid and water gives methyl alcohol. A second group, comprising Lanny D. Schmidt and Daniel A. Hickman of the University of Minnesota, uses a direct catalytic oxidation of methane with oxygen over a platinum or rhodium surface to yield a mixture of carbon monoxide and hydrogen gas. The gas mixture can then be converted into methyl alcohol by well-established chemical methods.

—John E. McMurry

Physical chemistry

Researchers in the past year used a tiny quantum electron "corral" to verify visually the predictions of quantum theory regarding the behavior of electrons confined to a very small space. The ability of chemists to work with ever smaller amounts of material advanced with the discovery that magnetic resonance could be detected optically from single molecules of a compound embedded in a host material. Progress was made in understanding how biological patterns, such as those found in animal hide coloration, may result directly from chemical interactions. The detection of helium "molecules" in a beam of helium atoms resurrected the old question of how to decide when a molecule is so unstable as not to merit the name.

Constructing a quantum corral. Students taking a course in physical chemistry learn that when electrons are confined to a very small region of space,

the electron density, that is, the likelihood of finding the electron, will vary from place to place in a predictable way. In particular, confinement in a circular two-dimensional box should result in smooth ripples in the electron density similar to those caused by a stone dropped into a pool of water. Rather than moving outward like ripples in a pond, however, the electron waves remain stationary. Whereas scientists had been able to predict from quantum theory what the size and spacing of these standing waves of electron density should be, until the past year they had not been able to see the waves directly.

That situation changed when Michael F. Crommie, Christopher P. Lutz, and Donald M. Eigler of the IBM Almaden Research Center, San Jose, Calif., built a quantum corral that beautifully verified the predictions of quantum theory. The researchers used the tip of a scanning tunneling microscope (STM) to nudge 48 individual iron atoms into a circle on the surface of a piece of copper metal, "fencing" off an area with a diameter of about 140 angstroms (Å; 14 billionths of a meter). The iron atoms caused the electrons on the surface of the copper to remain within this atomic-scale corral. The researchers then used the same STM to sense the electron density inside the corral while keeping the sample at a temperature close to absolute zero to minimize atomic vibrations. What they found was a pattern of waves with the same spacing and heights predicted by quantum theory.

The IBM experiment was more than just a visually striking validation of the predictions of theory. Making designer quantum-confinement structures that tune the electronic properties of materials has become an increasingly important topic in modern microelectronics. The demonstration suggested that manipulation of individual atoms on a surface may be a practical way to build such structures and to engineer useful electronic behavior for a new generation of electronic devices. (See Year in Review: PHYSICS: *Condensed-matter physics*.)

Spectroscopy on single molecules. Magnetic resonance spectroscopy is frequently used to probe the shape of a molecule and its interactions with the molecules that surround it. In crystalline materials all the molecules are in the same environment. However, in disordered or amorphous materials, which include well-known substances such as glasses and exotic new materials such as amorphous silicon, the situation is more complicated. Many different possible chemical environments exist in a given sample, rendering the magnetic resonance spectra less sharp and more difficult to interpret. A path out of this dilemma was suggested by experiments, carried out by two European research groups, in which spectra were taken from single molecules added as an impurity to a host material.

One study was by J. Köhler, J.A.J.M. Disselhorst, M.C.J.M. Donckers, E.J.J. Groenen, J. Schmidt, and W.E. Moerner of the University of Leiden, Neth., while the second study was by J. Wachtrup and C. von Borczyskowski of the Free University of Berlin and J. Bernard, M. Orrit, and R. Brown of the University of Bordeaux, France. Both groups studied the molecule pentacene, which was embedded as an impurity in crystals of *para*-terphenyl. They bombarded the chilled sample with laser light tuned to a specific frequency that excited just one pentacene molecule; the excitation was to a state in which two electrons are unpaired such that their spins no longer cancel. With modern instrumentation the researchers were able to measure the lower frequency fluorescence light radiated back by this one molecule as it returned to its ground state with paired electron spins. When the sample was simultaneously subjected to microwaves, the intensity of the fluorescence changed owing to electron-spin transitions, resulting in an electron spin resonance spectrum.

The experiments were remarkable in that they detected signals from just one molecule out of the many billions of billions present in the sample. They also offered the prospect of getting spectra of crystalline quality from amorphous substances, information that could significantly advance scientists' understanding of such materials.

Oscillating reactions and biological patterns. A popular lecture demonstration in chemistry is an oscillating reaction. In such a reaction the color of a solution changes back and forth in a regular manner. If the solution of reactants is prepared as a thin layer and is not stirred, beautiful patterns form, usually in the form of rotating spiral waves that move out from a center. If the concentrations of the reactants are not quite right, the periodic behavior becomes erratic and unpredictable.

Kenneth Showalter, Jonathan Masere, and Valery Petrov of West Virginia University and Vilmos Gaspar, a visitor from Kossuth University, Debrecen, Hung., showed for the first time that one can keep such a chemical system in stable oscillation and avoid chaotic behavior by continuously adjusting the concentrations of key chemicals in a feedback loop. They pumped solutions of the components of the well-known Belousov-Zhabotinsky (BZ) oscillating reaction (named after its Soviet discoverers)—malonic acid, cerium sulfate, and sodium bromate—into a tank. They could follow the chemical concentrations in the oscillating reaction by monitoring the voltage of an electrode in the solution. The voltage measurements were then used to alter the flow rates of cerium and bromate solutions to make the system exhibit either stable oscillations or chaotic behavior. Other experiments by Oliver Steinbock and Stefan C. Müller of the Max Planck Institute, Dortmund, Germany, and Vladimir Zykov of the Institute of Control Sciences, Moscow, showed that patterns in the BZ reaction can be controlled by periodic illumination of the solution.

In the 1950s the British mathematician Alan Turing speculated that biological patterns such as the stripes on a zebra or the spots on a Dalmatian dog have their origins in stable variations in the concentrations of chemicals caused by the interplay of the rate of chemical reactions themselves and the rate of diffusion of the reactants together. Evidence for such Turing patterns in closed chemical systems—those, like living systems, that do not have chemical concentration gradients imposed on them from some external source—has been difficult to find. In 1993, however, transient Turing patterns were observed by Istvan Lenyel, Sandor Kadar, and Irving Epstein of Brandeis University, Waltham, Mass., in a gradientless chlorite-iodide-malonic acid reaction system.

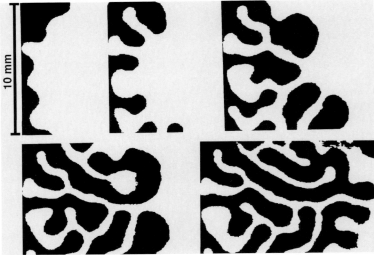

A sequence of images made over a three-hour period (left to right, top to bottom) follows the progress of a pattern-forming reaction in a gel continuously fed a nonequilibrium mixture of reagents. The reaction was initiated with intense ultraviolet light at the left boundary. In contrast to Turing patterns, which are regular and emerge spontaneously everywhere, patterns such as the one illustrated are highly irregular, and they develop locally and then spread to fill space.

Kyoung J. Lee, W.D. McCormick, Qi Ouyang, and Harry L. Swinney, University of Texas, Austin

The patterns, which consist of spots, stripes, or both, required about 25 minutes to form and lasted for 10–30 minutes.

It also appears that stationary patterns can be formed in chemical media by other than Turing mechanisms. Kyoung J. Lee, Qi Ouyang, William D. McCormick, and Harry L. Swinney of the University of Texas at Austin, in collaboration with John Pearson of the Los Alamos (N.M.) National Laboratory, discovered a second mechanism for such patterns. They used ultraviolet light to initiate pattern formation in a gel containing a nonequilibrium mixture of ferrocyanide, sulfite, and iodate. In contrast to the regular arrays of hexagons and stripes that emerge everywhere spontaneously in Turing patterns, the new patterns are highly irregular, and they develop locally and then spread to form a stable pattern, reminiscent of crystal growth. The researchers observed stationary patterns of stripes as well as self-replicating changing patterns of spots, which could be reproduced by a computer simulation of reacting and diffusing chemicals.

Although much remains to be done to establish a general theory of chemical pattern formation, the ability to establish patterns and control chaotic behavior may have a variety of important applications, including the operation of solid-state lasers and the control of potentially fatal heart fibrillations, rapid irregular contractions of the heart muscle.

When is a molecule not a molecule? Chemists are used to thinking of atoms being held together in molecules by strong bonding forces. But what happens if the forces holding atoms together are weak? In such cases how does one recognize a molecule as having a true existence?

Theoreticians have long been interested in van der Waals atomic complexes. It has become recognized, particularly through the work of William Klemperer of Harvard University, that almost any two atoms that are brought close to each other will stick by means of van der Waals forces. These forces arise from the small perturbations induced in the electron cloud that surrounds an atom by the presence of the other atom, but they are by nature extremely weak. Hence, the "molecule" that is formed is held together so tenuously that any small input of energy, such as the light of a laser used to investigate it, is enough to make it fly apart.

The strength of the forces that bind such atom pairs together decreases as the atoms get smaller and the electron cloud less deformable. The ultimate example of a van der Waals atomic complex is the helium dimer, He_2, and for many years chemists thought that it was too unstable to be observable. The situation changed when Fei Luo, Geunsik Kim, George C. McBane, Clayton F. Giese, and W. Ronald Gentry of the University of Minnesota observed the He_2^+ ion by mass spectrometry from a supercooled, supersonic helium beam. The effective temperature of the helium in the beam is low enough (a tiny fraction of a degree above absolute zero) that the He_2 molecule can form and be detected by ionization. The two helium atoms are held together so weakly that they spend more time apart than close together. The average separation distance of the helium atoms is 55 Å (5.5 billionths of a meter), roughly 25 times the spacing of the atoms in a normal molecule. So, while the He_2 molecule does appear to exist, whether it qualifies as a molecule in the normal sense of the word is a matter of debate.

—Philip R. Watson

Applied chemistry

New battery designs, new food products, photographic film that needs no chemical processing, and progress on a family of highly branched polymers called dendrimers numbered among the newsworthy developments of the past year in applied chemistry. While the purported phenomenon of cold fusion remained a topic of research and controversy in some scientific circles, the development of controlled nuclear fusion took a significant step forward with the announcement of a record power output from an experimental fusion reactor.

Cold fusion. In 1989 B. Stanley Pons of the University of Utah and Martin Fleischmann of the University of Southampton, England, announced a simple, tabletop electrochemical process for producing room-temperature, or cold, nuclear fusion. Although announced at a press conference outside the normal peer-review process and without the descriptive detail characteristic of scientific reports, their highly controversial "discovery" nevertheless was hailed by some as a potential source of virtually limitless energy and the greatest scientific event of recent decades. In the succeeding weeks, months, and years, however, scientists around the world obtained conflicting results in their own attempts to detect the heat, neutrons, and hydrogen isotope tritium (hydrogen-3) that Pons and Fleischmann cited as evidence that fusion was actually occurring.

As was the case in 1991, no unanimity on the reality of cold fusion had been reached by the end of 1992 (see *1994 Yearbook of Science and the Future* Year in Review: CHEMISTRY: *Applied chemistry*). Despite dismissive articles in mainstream science journals and fading scientific and media interest, the issue refused to die. The year 1993 saw the publication of science writer Gary Taubes's well-received *Bad Science*, hailed as a "definitive" account of events in the cold-fusion saga from early 1989 through early 1992. As evidenced by the book's subtitle, *The Short Life and Weird Times of Cold Fusion*, Taubes considered cold fusion dead and buried. Yet the quest for cold fusion continued in some quarters, and the scientific community still remained sharply polarized between the skeptical majority, who considered it a case of "pathological science," and a minority of cold-fusion supporters.

Since the early 1990s the focus of cold-fusion research has shifted to Japan and, to a lesser extent, Russia and Italy. The third International Conference on Cold Fusion, supported by seven Japanese physical societies, was held in Nagoya in late 1992 and was attended by some 350 participants from 16 countries. More than 70 Japanese companies, universities, and institutions were represented. Despite the relative lack of interest in the alleged phenomenon in the U.S., more than 50 scientific representatives from U.S. corporations and federal laboratories participated. Electrochemist John O'Mara Bockris, a cold-fusion advocate from Texas A&M University, reported that "a thousand researchers work on cold fusion worldwide. The Japanese put in $50 million, [and] the Russians have 27 research institutes. A new field has been born that calls for new theoretical work on conditions for nuclear reactions in solids." Like the Japanese, he disliked the term *cold fusion,* preferring the phrase *chemically stimulated nuclear reactions.*

In the May 3, 1993, issue of the peer-reviewed journal *Physics Letters A,* Pons and Fleischmann, who were working in France at the European facility of the Institute of Minoru Research Advancement (IMRA), funded by Technova, an affiliate of Toyota, published a new calorimetric study of their cold-fusion apparatus. They claimed that continuous temperature measurements showed that about four times more heat energy is produced than can be accounted for by the input of electric current. Contrary to their initial 1989 report, which mistakenly claimed evidence for production of neutrons and tritium, they did not invoke any nuclear reaction, yet they suggested that ordinary chemical explanations for their results "must be excluded." Predictably, advocates of cold fusion hailed the report as additional evidence of the reality of the phenomenon, while mainline scientific skeptics, citing lack of proper controls and calibrations, found nothing new in it.

As 1993 ended, a fourth cold-fusion conference took place in December on Maui, Hawaii. Also in December the University of Utah, which had previously supported cold-fusion research with public funds, licensed its exclusive patent rights for an amount in the "low six figures" to ENECO, a Salt Lake City firm specializing in research on alternative energy sources. Richard Koehn, vice president for research at the university, stated that ENECO will "try to explore any commercial value that they may believe the technology has." According to ENECO

president Fred Jaeger, the company would be able to work closely with Pons and Fleischmann, whose relationship with the university had been strained since 1990.

Nuclear fusion. In 1989, the same year as that of the initial cold-fusion announcements, chemists Robert J. Beuhler, Jr., Gerhart Friedlander, and Lewis Friedman of Brookhaven National Laboratory, Upton, N.Y., reported that their bombardment of a deuterium-loaded target with clusters of heavy water (deuterium oxide) molecules resulted in what they called cluster impact fusion (deuterium, or hydrogen-2, is a heavy isotope of hydrogen), and they applied for a patent on the process (see *1991* and *1993 Yearbook of Science and the Future* Year in Review: CHEMISTRY: *Applied chemistry*). In contrast to Pons and Fleischmann, Brookhaven researchers were cautious and tentative in their claims. In 1993 they published what amounted to a retraction, attributing the alleged fusion to "small ion impurities." Friedman's comment could be applied to the cold-fusion controversy: "The paper is the end of the story. When you get a result that appears to be spectacular and is supported by a large body of circumstantial evidence, there is some tendency to want to believe that it's really there. You have an obligation to prove it one way or the other."

The big story in controlled nuclear fusion for 1993, however, was the record power level of 6.4 million w (6.4 MW) attained in December in Princeton University's 15-m-high, 12-m-diameter Tokamak Fusion Test Reactor. The previous record power output was the attainment of 1.7 MW at the Joint European Torus (JET) nuclear research center in Culham, England, in 1991 (see *1993 Yearbook of Science and the Future* Year in Review: CHEMISTRY: *Applied chemistry*). Both experiments involved heating magnetically confined mixtures of the two heavy hydrogen isotopes—deuterium (D) and tritium (T)—but, whereas the experiment at JET used a 9:1 D-T ratio, the one at Princeton used a more powerful 1:1 D-T ratio, similar to that projected for commercial fusion reactors of the future. The deuterium and tritium were fused at 300 million degrees C (about 540 million degrees F) to form helium-4 nuclei (20% of the fusion energy) and neutrons (80% of the fusion energy). In a commercial fusion power plant, the neutrons would be used to generate heat to drive turbines. Princeton's experiment lasted only five seconds, with a one-second burst of fusion power.

The Princeton scientists hoped to increase the output in 1994 to 10 MW, enough to power about 3,000 homes but still less than half the 24 MW required for the reactor to be self-sustaining. They also intended to study ways for saving heat from the plasma and the effect of the resulting helium nuclei and to find the best materials for the reactor. A one billion-watt (1-GW) International Thermonuclear Experimental Reactor (ITER), currently planned by the U.S., Japan, Russia, and Europe as the next fusion reactor prototype, will generate its magnetic field with superconducting magnets, which require less power input than conventional magnets.

New batteries. Both the revolution in portable consumer electronic products and environmental concerns, which make development of electric vehicles desirable, have continued to stimulate research around the world on new types of compact, high-performance, rechargeable batteries (*see* Feature Article: THE REBIRTH OF ELECTRIC VEHICLES). Chemists Dharmasena Peramunage and Stuart Licht of Clark University, Worcester, Mass., developed a lightweight aluminum-and-sulfur–based aqueous battery with a high energy-storage capacity per unit weight. Sulfur is inexpensive and low in weight but is normally an insulator. The Clark University chemists found that interfacing it with a saturated aqueous potassium polysulfide (K_2S_4) solution makes it a conductor. Their new battery, consisting of a solid sulfur cathode, polysulfide interface, and aluminum anode, produces 1.3 v. The polysulfide anion (S_4^{2-}) accepts electrons to form S_3^{2-} ions, which react with sulfur to regenerate S_4^{2-} ions.

According to Licht, "Sulfur and aluminum are wonderful chemicals for batteries. . . . They're both plentiful, cheap, lightweight, environmentally safe, and easy to work with. Lead-acid and nickel-cadmium [batteries] pose environmental problems, and they're heavy, so a car can't go far between recharges. Both sodium and lithium batteries explode if water touches them. And sodium-sulfur batteries operate above 600° F [316° C], with safety and cost constraints."

By contrast, the sulfur-aluminum battery operates at room temperature. Its energy density of 220 w-hr/kg (100 w-hr/lb), seven times that of present lead-acid storage batteries, provides, according to Licht, "enough energy per pound to move a car several hundred miles before recharging—much farther than the 80 miles now possible with other batteries." Licht admitted, "We're only in the beginning stages, building tiny experimental cells. There's a long way to go before our battery reaches the marketplace."

Chemists Jean-Marie Tarascon and Dominique Guyomard of Bell Communications Research (Bellcore), Red Bank, N.J., developed a new, experimental rechargeable battery whose electrodes function as "sponges" for lithium ions, which migrate between a lithium-manganese oxide ($Li_{1+x}Mn_2O_4$) electrode and a carbon anode (graphite). Called a "rocking chair" battery because of the back-and-forth motion of the lithium ions during charging and discharging, it is said to be safer, longer lasting, and potentially cheaper to manufacture than other lithium batter-

ies. The experimental version yields three times the energy of the most popular type of rechargeable battery, the nickel-cadmium cell, which, along with the lead-acid battery, it may replace in numerous applications. After being recharged 1,000–2,000 times in tests, it still retained 90–65% of its capacity. It operates at 3.7 v, 3 times higher than nickel-cadmium cells and 1.5 times higher than nickel-metal hydride cells. Because a standard electrolyte would be degraded at the high voltage (4.3 v) needed in the charging cycle, the Bellcore chemists developed an electrolyte stable up to 5 v—a proprietary mixture of organic liquids and a lithium salt that can function at temperatures between −20° and 55° C (−4° and 131° F). The battery is lighter than nickel-cadmium cells and is free of cadmium's toxicity.

Commercial batteries based on the new design could be used by telephone companies to provide continuous, reliable backup power for electronic components in remote outdoor locations where the service lifetime of lead-acid batteries is shortened by lack of temperature control. Tarascon intended to downsize the new battery to a rechargeable microbattery that could power a single computer chip, which would retain its memory during a power failure. Lithium batteries can potentially outperform other batteries in terms of power and longevity, but safety concerns have limited their commercial uses. Because of its high reactivity, lithium may explosively short-circuit cells with liquid electrolytes.

Among the difficulties inherent in the search for new lithium batteries have been the electrolyte's electrical resistance (which may exclude high-power applications such as electric vehicles) and its changes in volume and composition during charging and discharging. Highly conductive solid glasses may crack, while more durable rubbery polymers have been poor conductors. In the search for more highly conducting and more stable electrolytes, physical chemists C. Austen Angell, Chui Liu, and E. Sanchez of Arizona State University developed a new class of electrolytes combining the high conductivity of glassy materials with the flexibility of rubbery polymers. They reversed the process for making "salt-in-polymer" electrolytes. Rather than dissolving a small amount of salt (ionic compound) in the polymers, they dissolved a small amount of poly(propylene oxide) and poly(ethylene oxide) polymers in a low-melting-point "cocktail" of lithium salts. The resulting "polymer-in-salt" electrolyte readily conducts lithium ions, and its consistency (resembling rubber cement) is elastic enough to withstand volume changes during discharging and charging. Because of its greater salt content, at room temperature the electrolyte is 1,000 times more conductive than previously developed materials. Angell's next step is to determine how well the new electrolyte performs in a prototype battery.

Dendrimers. Dendrimers (from *dendron,* Greek for "tree," and *polymer*) are new types of polymers that have highly branched, usually curved structures with internal architectures that, for example, may be used to contain drugs, herbicides, pesticides, cosmetics, catalysts, fragrances, or other substances to be released slowly as required. Unlike linear polymers, which consist of entangled single chains of molecules having only two end groups per chain, multibranched dendrimers provide many functional end groups per molecule. Also, whereas other polymers vary in size and weight from one molecule to another, dendrimers possess precisely defined structures and can be produced in very uniform batches. Because their syntheses are difficult, however, they have been prepared only in relatively small amounts. According to Bert W. Meijer of the Eindhoven (Neth.) University of Technology, "It's not the individual steps in the synthesis where the problem lies, so much as the many times the reactions have to be done on the same molecule without encountering any defects." Nevertheless, the Dutch chemical firm DSM recently began preparing dendrimers in multikilogram lots to be sent to laboratories around the world in the hope that these versatile substances could be available commercially by the end of the century.

Meijer and Ellen M.M. de Brabander-van den Berg prepared poly(propylenimine) dendrimers with 64 functional groups, subsequently produced by DSM, by repetitively reacting 1,4-diaminobutane with acrylonitrile and hydrogenating the product. Italian chemists Vincenzo Balzani of the University of Bologna, Sebastiano Campagna of the University of Messina, and Gianfranco Denti of the University of Pisa prepared a 1,090-atom dendrimer containing 22 atoms of ruthenium, a platinum-group metal; the molecule was believed to be the largest transition-metal complex of its kind ever made (*see* Figure). Timothy M. Miller, Thomas X. Neenan, and co-workers at AT&T Bell Laboratories, Murray Hill, N.J., synthesized polyaryl ether dendrimers that may prove to have useful properties quite distinct from those of their linear-chain counterparts. Chemists Jeffrey S. Moore and Zhifu Xu of the University of Michigan prepared a dendrimer comprising 127 monomer units with the formula $C_{1398}H_{1278}$ and a molecular mass of 18,054 daltons, which is the largest known pure hydrocarbon (compound of carbon and hydrogen). According to Moore, "Nature has

$\vcenter{\hbox{—}} = $ [pyridine–pyridine structure]

$\vcenter{\hbox{U}} = $ [pyridine–pyrazine–pyridine structure]

Ru = ruthenium atom

1,090-atom dendritic complex

spent a great deal of time controlling the structure of macromolecules. If we can do that too, there's a possibility we will be able to do many of the same things that nature has done."

Dry photographic film. Scientists at the Xerox Research Centre of Canada, Mississauga, Ont., devised a photographic film that contains no silver halide and requires no developing chemicals, and Xerox Corp. founded VerdePrint Technologies to introduce it, beginning in 1994, under the trade name VerdeFilm to the $1.8 billion-per-year U.S. graphics industry. The film is a sheet of aluminized Mylar polyester with a layer of a heat-sensitive polymer, about one micrometer (0.00004 in) thick, in which selenium particles are embedded. It is photosensitive only when subjected to an electric charge, and therefore, unlike conventional, silver-halide-based film, it can be casually exposed to light without effect. When charged in a special Xerox machine, however, and exposed to light and then developed by gentle heating, an image appears. VerdeFilm was intended for commercial printers' high-resolution, black-and-white intermediate master images used for magazines, catalogs, and posters. Xerox had no plans for color or consumer versions of VerdeFilm.

The film's trade name is intended to imply a "green" or environmentally friendly technology that completely avoids the costs and wastewater-disposal problems of developers, fixers, and dissolved silver salts associated with conventional film. Because the embedded selenium cannot escape from the resin, the state of California classified VerdeFilm as "casually disposable." Nevertheless, VerdePrint Technologies plans to collect all exposed film to recycle the selenium.

Food products. Because high cholesterol levels in the blood are a major risk factor for heart disease and stroke, scientists have been searching for ways to lower cholesterol levels. Pharmaceutical scientist Jennifer B. Dressman of the University of Michigan, chemist Stephen W. Tobey of Dow Chemical Co., Midland, Mich., and co-workers developed a cellulose-derived food additive that lowers cholesterol levels to a greater extent—an average of 23% for total cholesterol and of 30% for low-density lipoprotein (LDL, so-called bad cholesterol)—than do current drugs on the market without the toxic side effects associated with those drugs. The new compound, a high-molecular-mass hydroxypropylmethylcellulose (HPMC), which Dow was expected to license to a pharmaceutical company for marketing, is an inexpensive substance derived from cellulose extracted from wood pulp. Some HPMC products are already being marketed as additives to thicken cheesecakes, puddings, and other food products, and they are used as tablet coatings, controlled-release agents, and binders in pharmaceutical products.

Jeffrey S. Moore, University of Illinois, Urbana-Champaign

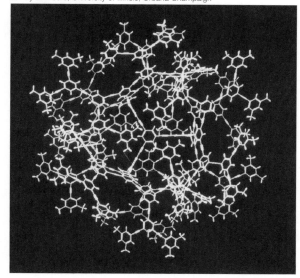

Computer-generated image depicts the skeleton of a giant hydrocarbon molecule, a dendrimer, made of 1,134 carbon atoms, to which are bonded 1,146 hydrogen atoms. The chemists who synthesized the structure also made a larger one with the formula $C_{1398}H_{1278}$.

Ding Ming and Göran Hellekant of the University of Wisconsin isolated a potential new sweetener in the form of a supersweet protein from the Nigerian vine plant *Pantadiplandra brazzeana*. The plant makes the novel molecule in an edible reddish fruit slightly larger than a grape. The 52-amino-acid protein, which the Wisconsin biochemists named brazzein, bears little resemblance to other sweet proteins, is 2,000 times as sweet as sugar, and is stable toward heat, acidity, and alkalinity.

Anniversaries. The year 1993 marked several anniversaries related to applied chemistry. In 1493, 500 years ago, Philippus Aureolus Theophrastus Bombastus von Hohenheim, who called himself Paracelsus and who championed the application of chemistry to medicine (iatrochemistry), was born in Einsiedeln, Switz. In 1743, 250 years ago, Antoine-Laurent Lavoisier, the founder of modern chemistry, was born in Paris. On April 19, 1943, 50 years ago, chemist Albert Hofmann of the Swiss chemical firm Sandoz serendipitously discovered the psychedelic properties of lysergic acid diethylamide (LSD), which he had derived from alkaloids formed in ergot, a fungal infection of rye. After accidentally ingesting a tiny amount of the substance, Hofmann experienced a terrifying bicycle ride home from his laboratory—the first "acid trip." LSD's early promise as an aid to mental processes and for the treatment of mental diseases was never fulfilled, and it is best known as the preferred recreational drug of the 1960s.

—George B. Kauffman

311

Defense research

With the continued winding down of the Cold War, as exemplified by the agreement in January 1994 by Presidents Bill Clinton of the United States and Boris Yeltsin of Russia to cease aiming their nuclear missiles at each other's country, the trend in defense research accelerated toward finding "dual-use" technologies. These are technologies that are capable of meeting national defense needs but also are applicable to consumer and industrial products in an increasingly competitive international marketplace.

ARPA. A focal point of this effort within the military establishment was the U.S. Department of Defense's own internal "think tank," the Advanced Research Projects Agency (ARPA), in Arlington, Va. Of its annual research budget of nearly $2 billion, more than 70% was for research to support dual-use programs. ARPA, founded in the 1950s to enable the U.S. to keep pace in critical military technologies, was the source of such programs as the Strategic Defense Initiative—the so-called Star Wars antimissile defense system—and in recent years efforts to develop smaller and more powerful electronic integrated circuits. (During the administrations of Presidents Ronald Reagan and George Bush, the agency was known as the Defense Advanced Research Projects Agency to emphasize its military responsibilities, but the Clinton administration restored its original name to recognize its civilian role.)

ARPA's efforts in defense research, particularly in electronics technology, have become analogous to the way the U.S. National Science Foundation (NSF) supports basic scientific research. Like the NSF, ARPA has no internal research facilities of its own and thus no fixed infrastructure to resist change. Every year about 20% of ARPA's projects are completed in order to make room for new projects aimed at what agency executives call "technology surprises." The U.S. was surprised—and embarrassed—by the Soviet spacecraft Sputnik in 1957, and ARPA's charter was to prevent that from happening again.

By 1994 ARPA had begun focusing on electronics technologies to produce smaller, lighter, and more mobile information systems both for military purposes and to enhance the competitiveness of U.S. electronics firms. An example was the High Definition Systems (HDS) program, which ARPA's Electronic Systems Technology Office said "focuses on getting information out of computers and databases and into people's minds." Among the new display technologies being investigated were flat-panel and helmet-mounted displays using liquid crystals, electroluminescence, plasma, and cold cathodes. Recent successes included the development of a liquid crystal display (LCD) with a diagonal measurement of 11.1 cm (4.4 in) containing 20,000 elements,

used in the horizon-situation indicator of the U.S. Air Force's F-15 fighter aircraft; a 6 million-pixel (picture element) LCD; a full-color, plasma-type panel measuring 48 cm (19 in) diagonally; a color 10 × 13-cm (4 × 5-in) electroluminescent panel; and a digital color mirror with more than 20 million moving parts.

Another ARPA research program was known as Microelectromechanical Systems (MEMS), which involved such technologies as embedded microsystems, microdynamic systems, and conformal electronics for mobile information systems. Embedded microsystems were used in signal processing to minimize energy dissipation and increase the computing power that could be supported by small batteries. Microdynamical devices included microsensors and actuators, micromechanical accelerometers, miniature analytical instruments, mass data storage devices, miniature mass spectrometers, thermopneumatic microvalves, and micropumps. Potential applications included distributed unattended microsensors for ground surveillance, unobtrusive biomedical sensors, and personal inertial guidance units to complement existing navigation systems that used the space-based Global Positioning System (GPS). Conformal electronics involved packaging technologies that enabled the electronic components to conform to, rather than to dictate, the shape of the system in which they were installed. An example was the use of radar antennae embedded in the wings and fuselages of aircraft.

Another electronics research program under way at ARPA involved microwave and millimeter-wave monolithic integrated circuits (MMICs). These were solid-state circuits that either amplified received signals and sent them to the digital-processing portion of a system or transformed digital information into microwave signals to be transmitted by an antenna. Hardware development began in May 1988 on devices using improved gallium arsenide (GaAs) material, and by 1994 more than 80 chip types had been fabricated and demonstrated. In the Gulf war MMIC devices were used in antiradiation missiles that homed in on enemy radars and missile sites and in terrain-following radars for allied forces.

As electronics devices became increasingly complex, research began to integrate the functions in ever more dense devices. An ARPA program was launched to go beyond current applications-specific integrated circuits (ASICs) to what were becoming known as applications-specific electronic modules (ASEMs). One facet of this effort was developing multichip module (MCM) technology for digital systems operating at clock rates from 100 MHz (millions of cycles per second) to several GHz (gigahertz; billions of cycles per second). (The clock rate is the rate at which bits or words are transferred from

A scientist at the Armstrong Laboratory at Wright-Patterson Air Force Base in Ohio examines a test pattern on a liquid crystal display being developed to project images on the visors of pilots' helmets. Such displays are expected to reduce pilot workload by providing improved visibility of critical data.

one internal element of a computer to another.) With MCMs, bare chips were interconnected via a common substrate instead of being packaged individually in single-chip carriers. ARPA estimated that MCM technology offered the potential of 10–100-fold improvements in density, a reduction in electrical power requirements by a factor of two to three, and a 10-fold improvement in reliability. By integrating the chips in MCMs, the researchers hoped to be able to mix analog and digital chips in the same packages.

Transfers from DMSP. An example of transferring already existing military technology to civilian needs was the U.S. government decision to make available data from the Defense Meteorological Satellite Program (DMSP). Those data became accessible to civilian users upon request to the U.S. government and were expected to give meteorologists new abilities to detect and track tropical storms as well as to measure rain rate over land in order to generate alerts of severe weather conditions.

The military services, with their pressing battle-field requirements for up-to-the-minute knowledge of the weather, had been in the forefront of low-cost, transportable ground-weather stations ever since meteorological satellites were developed in the early 1960s. But acquiring the data from the satellites was only the first step. Powerful new real-time, interactive, computing techniques were needed to analyze the data quickly and accurately enough to enable meteorologists to issue timely warnings.

Weather satellites initially provided only relatively low-resolution, wide-area images in the visible and infrared portions of the electromagnetic spectrum to measure cloud cover, rainfall, and temperature. The advent of microwave imagery in the DMSP program in June 1987 added a new dimension to permit forecasters to measure critical wind speeds over ocean surfaces. The spaceborne microwave imager could see through the cloud cover and look at the sea surface. Since stronger winds produced rougher seas, by measuring the ocean roughness (actually

the amount of sea foam blown off by ocean waves), analysts could determine surface wind speeds.

The U.S. Air Force used to do this almost solely with a fleet of WC-130 Hercules "hurricane hunter" aircraft, but new spaceborne sensors provided significant improvements. They were not constrained by the cloud cover or limited to observing winds along a narrow flight path. Also, this technique did not put air crews at risk. Instead, the meteorological data were recorded onboard the spacecraft and periodically transmitted in the form of raw voltages to ground receiver sites for subsequent analysis and distribution to users. The Joint Typhoon Warning Center at Guam, for example, began receiving daily transmissions to help formulate typhoon warnings that were disseminated for use throughout the greater Asia Pacific region.

Until 1992 this information was restricted to U.S. and allied military forces. By 1994, however, in an opportunity that paralleled the growing worldwide commercial use of positional data from the U.S. Defense Department's GPS navigation satellites, meteorologic agencies of other governments were able to gain access to DMSP data. Beginning in 1993 with the United Kingdom, several countries obtained U.S. government approval to receive the data in real time. The governments of Pacific Rim countries, including Australia, showed particular interest in DMSP capabilities for efforts to anticipate tropical storms, measure rainfall over land, and provide severe thunderstorm warnings.

This technology also delivered something that analysts had long wanted: data fusion. By color-coding wind, temperature, and rainfall data on computer screens to highlight the critical data, the system enabled the analysts to visualize the information in ways that were never before possible. Air traffic safety—and efficiency—could be improved by these new techniques. Aircraft could be rerouted around storms, thus reducing the possibilities of accidents and also improving fuel efficiency.

313

Infrared sensors. Infrared sensors (IR) similar to those used in the DMSP were available for the computerized weapons of the future as well as for a variety of civilian purposes, such as law enforcement, interception of illegal drug trafficking, and space-based resource surveys and meteorology. Two reasons were cited for the increasing popularity of IR: the increasing vulnerability of aircraft, tanks, and other weapons to enemy electronic surveillance and jamming, and technological improvements that promised to erase IR's inherent deficiencies and drive down costs to the point where civilian users could afford them. IR sensors had one big advantage: they were passive. That meant that, unlike radar, they did not radiate telltale electromagnetic signals that an enemy could home in on with electronic jammers or antiradiation weapons.

Offsetting this advantage—at least until recent months—were a host of disadvantages. IR sensors operated in a portion of the electromagnetic spectrum next to the one used by the human eyeball. Humans cannot see through clouds, and neither could IR sensors. "They [the IR sensors] work great against a blue sky," commented one researcher. For military aircraft, that shortcoming limited them to dogfights with other aircraft—and then only at high altitudes.

As a result, the near-infrared (NIR) portion of the electromagnetic spectrum, just above human vision, was being exploited for new cost-effective solutions to long-standing law-enforcement problems. A recent example was a series of field tests conducted in September 1993 in Florida that used a new Kodak digital infrared camera to find drug smugglers in the area around Palm Beach, Miami, and Fort Lauderdale. The images, using reflected light from stroboscopes operating just above the range of human vision, were downloaded in real time to an Apple laptop computer. The computer operators viewed images on a screen, while the images were simultaneously stored on a hard disk. The black-and-white still images were taken at a peak frequency just above 800 nanometers (nm; or billionths of a meter), and, because the strobes also operated above 800 nm, the suspects did not know they were under surveillance by law-enforcement personnel.

It was expected that in the future these images could be downloaded again to a central computer via modems and wireless communications links. The net result would be to coordinate law-enforcement efforts through the use of advanced but affordable technology. The camera in the Florida tests used mechanical cooling to drive the cost down to $8,500, including battery pack, considerably less expensive than the cryogenically cooled cameras operating in the higher infrared wavelengths.

The U.S. Army, in particular, was enthusiastic about infrared sensors for tanks. The original silicon infrared sensors were being supplemented by more sensitive focal-plane arrays made of mercury-cadmium-telluride. The U.S. Air Force's Rome Laboratory at Griffiss Air Force Base, New York, began developing the IR sensors of the future, using platinum and iridium silicides, for upgrades to the B-52 bomber and perhaps later for the B-2 stealth bomber.

HUDs. Another spin-off of military technology to law-enforcement applications occurred in August 1993 with the first production deliveries of a vehicle-mounted head-up display (HUD) able to give police officers the same kind of up-to-the-second information that military fighter pilots had depended on for years. The new HUD, called DataVision by its manufacturer, General Motors Hughes Electronics, generated a "virtual image" that appeared to hover beyond the windshield. This image could be any alphanumeric or pictorial information, such as a suspected criminal's license plate number, instructions from a dispatcher, or description of stolen property. All of this information would be instantly available, even during a high-speed chase.

For fighter pilots HUDs were used to present crucial information on a transparent viewscreen (called a combiner) so that they would not have to look down to read their instruments. "Looking down for information can cause a momentary loss of visual contact with the outside world, which can be changing very rapidly," explained Joseph Smalanskas, DataVision marketing manager at Hughes. "The HUD can provide drivers with information from the vehicle's computer, MDT [mobile data terminal], radar surveillance camera or other sensors, displayed on a combiner mounted on the windshield where they can read it without taking their eyes off the road or a suspect."

HUDs for automobiles were not new. General Motors Corp. had long supplied less sophisticated versions as an option on several Oldsmobile and Pontiac models. The motorist would see an image that appeared to be about 3.3 m (11 ft) away displaying such information as speed, fuel, engine temperature, headlights, high beams, and turn signals. The image, generated by a liquid crystal display, provided the equivalent of 12 lines of 40 characters each of alphanumeric data and appeared to float in front of the vehicle at about the distance the driver's eyes would normally be focused for driving. What was new was that the law-enforcement HUD interfaced with a variety of existing police equipment—infrared sensors for night vision, laser and radar speed monitors, and mobile communications—and integrated the resulting data into a comprehensible display. Furthermore, the HUDs were expected to interface with future technologies, such as the satellite navigation terminals being developed under the U.S. government's intelligent vehicle highway systems (IVHS) program, computer voice-recognition devices, and various image-enhancement and recognition systems based on those used by the military.

This was just the beginning, however, according to Smalanskas, who envisioned the entire fleet of some 300,000 law-enforcement vehicles in the U.S. tied into a single network for communications and display by the year 2000. He estimated that vision-enhancement systems and navigation aids derived from IVHS would be ready to be tied into the network by the end of 1994, collision-avoidance sensors by 1995, voice recognition by 1996, and vehicle-identification sensors by 1997.

—John Rhea

Earth sciences

In a year marked by extremes in weather in North America, the most extensive blizzard in the eastern United States in the 20th century struck that region in March 1993, and heavy rainfall in the central U.S. caused catastrophic summer flooding. Geophysicists continued their efforts to predict the time and location of severe, potentially destructive earthquakes, while other geologists focused on the role of terrestrial impacts in mass extinctions.

Atmospheric sciences

During the past year there continued to be considerable interest in environmental issues involving the atmosphere, including potential climate change associated with human input of carbon dioxide and other trace gases. Extreme weather also was frequently newsworthy during the year. Improved observational capabilities continued to be developed, and results were reported from measurement experiments conducted in earlier years.

Extreme weather. During March 12–15, 1993, the most widespread blizzard of the 20th century in the eastern United States occurred. The surface pressure of this intense winter storm was the lowest ever recorded at cities such as Columbia, S.C., and Richmond, Va. Snowfall exceeded one meter (39 in) at some sites in the Appalachian Mountains. In early 1994 much of the eastern two-thirds of the U.S. and Canada experienced their coldest weather in years.

During June and July 1993 rainfall of 30–45 cm (12–18 in) across many areas of the Midwest and east-central Great Plains resulted in catastrophic flooding of portions of the Mississippi and Missouri rivers and their tributaries. More than 41,000 sq km (15,830 sq mi) of farmland were flooded, and crop losses exceeded $5 billion. On the Indian subcontinent during July and early August, some of the worst flooding of the century occurred. Up to 12,000 lives were lost in Nepal owing to heavy rainfall.

Observational capabilities. The U.S. National Weather Service continued to modernize its measurement and forecasting capability in 1993. Early in the year a $41 million contract was awarded to PRC Inc. of McLean, Va., to develop the Advanced Weather Interactive Processing System, which would consist of a weather service forecast office workstation and associated communications network. Installation of Doppler radars (WSR-88D radars) and automated surface observation systems (ASOS) mostly at or near airports continued. The radars provide high-resolution images of rain and snow, as well as indicating the speed and direction of the wind in the lower atmosphere. ASOS supplies continuous surface weather observations and reduces the time required for weather service personnel to make measurements of current weather. A capability to monitor temperature profiles of the lower atmosphere by using a radio acoustic sounding system was developed by the U.S. National Oceanic and At-

In the aftermath of the most widespread blizzard of the 20th century in the eastern U.S., pedestrians struggle through heavy snowdrifts in New York City in March 1993. Snowfall in some places in the Appalachian Mountains exceeded one meter (39 in).

© Ron Haviv—Saba

mospheric Administration (NOAA) Forecast Systems Laboratory in Boulder, Colo. Through measurement of the speed of sound as it propagates upward to about 2 km (1.2 mi), the atmospheric temperature up to that altitude can be determined. This capability was expected to be added to the wind profiling network that NOAA established in the central U.S. and at other selected locations throughout the country. These wind profilers continuously monitor winds at intervals ranging from several hundred meters to about 10 km (6.2 mi).

Meteorologic satellite capability was also to be added in 1993, but there were failures at inserting these observational platforms into orbit and in maintaining contact with them once they were in space. The $100 million NOAA-13 polar orbiter was launched in August 1993, but communications with it were lost after several days. In October the $228 million NOAA Landsat 6 satellite disappeared in space shortly after its launch. To minimize the loss of geostationary satellite imagery, NOAA and the European Organization for the Exploitation of Meteorological Satellites (Eumetsat) signed a long-term agreement for a mutual backup of capabilities. If such a satellite should fail, NOAA and Eumetsat would reposition their satellites to provide replacement coverage.

The U.S. National Center for Atmospheric Research (NCAR) purchased its first new research aircraft in nearly a decade. The four-engine Lockheed C-130 turboprop, which was obtained as surplus from the U.S. Department of Defense, was being outfitted to provide a wide range of atmospheric measurements.

Field programs. To test theories and to develop new insight into atmospheric processes, it is necessary to conduct field measurement programs. For this reason, a network of 61 automated weather stations was established in Antarctica. During the 1993–94 field season, one goal of the network was to study the near-hurricane-velocity surface wind that persists for long periods of time in western Antarctica and is associated with cold drainage flow off the ice cap.

The Tropical Ocean Global Atmosphere (TOGA) Coupled Ocean-Atmospheric Response Experiment (COARE) ended an intense four-month operating period in late February 1993. A major goal of TOGA COARE, whose field project was directed from Townsville, Australia, was to improve the understanding of air-sea interactions in a region of the western Pacific Ocean. These interactions appeared to be critical to the initiation of an El Niño. An El Niño occurs when anomalously warm tropical ocean surface conditions develop in the equatorial Pacific Ocean west of South America, with associated major effects on the global weather pattern.

Results from the Atlantic Stratocumulus Transition Experiment field program in the Azores and Madeira islands in the Atlantic Ocean, involving more than 300 scientists, continued to be analyzed during the year. This program monitored the behavior of stratocumulus and trade-wind cumulus clouds, which are known to strongly influence the potential effect of human-generated greenhouse gases on climate.

The collapse of the Soviet Union permitted new field experiment opportunities. Research scientists

Flooded fields isolate a village in Nepal during the summer of 1993. Heavy rainfall in late July and early August resulted in some of the worst flooding of the century and the loss of about 12,000 lives.

A Lockheed C-130 turboprop, the first new research aircraft purchased by the U.S. National Center for Atmospheric Research in almost a decade, was equipped with instruments such as millimeter-wavelength radar, spectral radiometers, and aerosol-particle probes in order to provide a wide range of atmospheric measurements.

from the U.S. and Russia visited several sites in Siberia to investigate what was found to be water vapor plumes rising from the ocean around Bennett Island in the Laptev (Siberian) Sea. In Norilsk, Siberia, Russian and U.S. scientists were planning to study radioactive contamination from former Soviet defense activities.

In the upper portion of the Earth's atmosphere, the U.S. National Aeronautics and Space Administration (NASA) began the Thermosphere-Ionosphere-Mesosphere Energetics and Dynamics program in order to investigate the region between 60 and 180 km (37 and 112 mi) above the surface. This atmospheric layer is too high for balloons but too low for long-term Earth-orbiting satellites, so NASA planned to use small expendable satellites.

Huge flashes of light lasting for $1/30$ of a second, extending upward about 40 km (25 mi) into the Earth's upper atmosphere, and having a width of about 10 km were seen from an airplane flying over thunderstorms in the Midwest. Walter Lyons documented more than 600 of these events as viewed from a surface location in eastern Colorado, where he found them detectable only by image-intensified video cameras and, therefore, seldom visible with normal human night vision. These electrical discharges upward from cumulonimbus clouds could be threatening to space shuttle orbital insertions and reentries.

Computing capabilities. The use of numerical weather prediction and global circulation models requires large amounts of computer memory and storage and central processing time. Until several years ago, atmospheric scientists who required these extensive computational resources needed access to supercomputing centers. The introduction of high-performance workstations, however, substantially lessened the need for centralized supercomputing.

Bill Buzbee of NCAR summarized major trends in atmospheric science. They included the migration of calculations from the supercomputers to the powerful microprocessors, the growth in the use of parallel processing on both shared-memory supercomputers and massively parallel systems, the requirement for large and efficient mass storage capability, and the use of high-speed networks to exploit national data networks. As of early 1994 NCAR stored 35 terabytes (trillion bytes) of data on its system, while the U.S. National Science Foundation computer network could transmit 45 million bits of data per second. These computers provided improved capabilities for visualizing weather and climate and for understanding atmospheric processes.

Ozone depletion. During the past year, there was continued concern regarding low concentrations of ozone in the stratosphere, particularly in polar latitudes. Referred to as the ozone hole when it occurs over the Antarctic during the Southern Hemisphere spring, this depletion permits potentially life-damaging high-energy ultraviolet radiation to reach the Earth's surface. Since the Sun shines obliquely in Antarctica, the radiation is not strong, but the concern becomes greater when the depleted regions of ozone move toward the equator, over Australia, or over other populated areas. The cause of the lower concentrations has been attributed to human-generated chlorofluorocarbons (CFCs) as well as to the isolation of the stratosphere over Antarctica from the atmosphere farther north; this isolation permits the ozone-depletion chemistry to occur unimpeded by mixing with northern air.

In September 1992 ozone depletion in the Southern Hemisphere was the largest on record and covered an area of 23 million sq km (8.9 million sq mi), as reported by NASA scientists at the Goddard Space Flight Center. During February 1993 even the Northern Hemisphere polar regions experienced reduced concentrations, with reductions from the long-term average of more than 20% for a region extending from the Atlantic east to the Ural Mountains and north to the polar circle. James Kerr and Charles T. McElroy reported in *Science* that between 1989 and 1993 ultraviolet radiation over Toronto rose by 5.3% every winter and by nearly 2% every summer as a result of reduced stratospheric ozone levels. At least some of this depletion, however, resulted from a natural chemical reaction associated with the Mt. Pinatubo volcanic eruption in 1991.

As a substitute for CFCs, the material hydrochlorofluorocarbon (HCFC-22) was being used for refrigeration, air-conditioning, and foam. Unlike CFCs, less of this chemical reaches the stratosphere because it is destroyed by reaction with hydroxyl radicals in the troposphere, the lowest part of the Earth's atmosphere.

Air pollution. The quality of the air and the clarity of the atmosphere remained a major area of interest in 1993. The Grand Canyon Commission, comprising governors or their representatives from most of the states in the western U.S., began developing a plan to protect and improve visibility in several national parks in the southern Great Basin.

In Colorado the U.S. Forest Service, the Environmental Protection Agency, and the Colorado Department of Health documented visibility impairment at Mount Zirkel Wilderness Area, apparently predominantly due to two power plants in the vicinity. In 1993 the U.S. National Academy of Science released a report entitled "Protecting Visibility in National Parks and Wilderness Areas," which highlighted the recent interest in this topic.

Climate change. The most attention in atmospheric science continued to be directed toward potential long-term climate changes as a result of human input into the atmosphere of the so-called greenhouse gases of carbon dioxide, methane, and CFCs. A total of $1.5 billion was budgeted for 1994 for the U.S. Global Change Research Program to study this issue.

The search for evidence of a persistent warming and for past climate variations continued. Jonathan Kahl and associates at U.S. and Russian laboratories, using data from 27,000 temperature profiles, reported no evidence of warming over the Arctic Ocean during the past 40 years. This finding was contrary to the simulated response of general circulation models (GCMs) to increases of greenhouse gases. In contrast, Raymond Bradley and associates at the University of Massachusetts and NOAA's Environmental Research Laboratory discovered increases in surface temperature over the last few decades in areas from longitude 62° W to 162° W and from latitude 70° N to 83° N.

Satellite observations analyzed by scientists at the University of Alabama at Huntsville and at NASA's Marshall Space Flight Center indicated that the global-averaged lower tropospheric temperatures remained slightly below the 1979–93 average, perhaps in part a continued response to the June 1991 eruption of Mt. Pinatubo. This volcano lofted a plume of ash more than 14,900 m (49,000 ft) high into the atmosphere, which resulted in global cooling because a greater percentage of incoming solar radiation was reflected back out into space.

On longer time scales, remarkable rapid climate fluctuations were documented. Climate records collected as part of the joint European Greenland Ice-Core Project revealed that the weather pattern in the North Atlantic region was able to reorganize itself, perhaps on time scales as short as a few decades. Their data suggested that the relatively stable climate during the last several thousand years may be the exception rather than the rule. This record shows that even during the last interglacial period, of about 115,000–125,000 years ago, at which time the climate was apparently similar to, but slightly warmer than, the present, severe cold periods began rapidly and lasted from decades to centuries.

Gordon Bonan and associates at NCAR used a GCM to show that the presence of the far northern forests results in winter temperatures about 12° C (21.6° F) warmer in the Arctic and 2° C (3.6° F) higher at the equator than would occur without these trees. These dark spruce and fir forests absorb up to three times the solar radiation that would be absorbed if those regions were deforested and replaced by tundra.

The GCMs themselves were also receiving increased scrutiny. Beth Chertock of NOAA's Wave Propagation Laboratory and Yogesh Sud of NASA's Goddard Space Flight Center, for example, compared global seven-year satellite-based records of ocean surface solar irradiance with GCM results and found discrepancies of 60 watts per meter squared and more at various geographic locations. Such results raised serious concerns regarding the use of GCMs as predictive tools.

Policy makers nonetheless continued to work toward a reduction of greenhouse gas inputs. In late 1993 U.S. Pres. Bill Clinton's "Climate Change Action Plan" was released. Designed to fulfill the UN Framework Convention on Climate Change that was signed by U.S. Pres. George Bush at the 1992 Rio de Janeiro "Earth Summit," the plan called for the U.S. to reduce greenhouse gas emissions to 1990 levels by the year 2000. This was to be accomplished by the promotion of energy efficiency, the planting of trees, the subsidization of public transit, and a reduction in industrial emissions of greenhouse gases.

—Roger A. Pielke

Geologic sciences

Gaps in the fossil record, the role of catastrophic terrestrial impacts on mass extinctions, and the occurrence of earthquakes on previously unrecognized faults were among the major subjects of interest and research during the past year.

Geology and geochemistry. *Paleontology.* Charles Darwin was at pains to account for the apparent lack of continuity of the organic diversity, which, according to his theory of adaptive modification through natural selection, had arisen gradually in unbroken lines of descent. He maintained that if the entire record of life was available, it would reveal the continuity that his theory demanded. The "gaps" in the record resulted, he insisted, from accidents of preservation, and he devoted an entire chapter of the *Origin of Species* in support of this contention.

Darwin pointed out that paleontological collections contain but a meager sample of the plants and animals that have lived on Earth because only a small portion of the Earth's surface has been explored by paleontologists. Also, because of the contingencies of preservation, it cannot be expected that all the missing portions of the record will ever be recovered. No soft-bodied organisms can be preserved, and bones and shells will decay unless they are quickly buried. Even those remains that are buried and preserved may ultimately be lost when the rocks that contain them are elevated and destroyed by erosion. Darwin believed that the record of terrestrial organisms is especially poor because areas where sediments in which they are likely to be buried are rare. The accumulation of all sediments is intermittent, and there are, consequently, periods in which no organic remains are preserved. Darwin did, however, hold out the hope that continued geologic exploration would serve to fill many of the gaps in the record.

A particularly puzzling feature of the fossil record for Darwin was that although the theory of natural selection compelled him to suppose that allied species are descended from single progenitors, the sedimentary rocks lying below the lowest of fossil-bearing zones known at the time of the publication of the *Origin of Species* in 1859 appeared to be devoid of any evidence of life other than phosphate nodules and traces of carbon that Darwin believed to be of organic origin. Several eminent contemporaries of Darwin, including the geologist Roderick Murchison, were convinced that in the sudden appearance of plant and animal remains in the lowest known fossil-bearing strata was revealed the dawn of life on Earth.

Plainly, like any historical record, the record of life on Earth is incomplete. The question for paleontologists has been whether it is complete enough to give a true picture of the development of plants and animals. Creationists have pointed to the "gaps" in the fossil record as irrefutable evidence that the hypothesis of evolution and the theory that Darwin proposed to explain it are false. Evolutionary paleontologists have at the same time become increasingly reluctant to dismiss every apparent discontinuity as an accident of preservation. As early as 1942 the renowned paleontologist George Gaylord Simpson observed that after nearly a century of intense paleontological exploration, the major gaps in the fossil record remained, and that it was no longer satisfactory to impute them entirely to chance. The 1972 proposal of Niles Eldredge and Stephen Jay Gould that evolution proceeded by occasional rapid episodes of speciation rather than by the gradual and steady accumulation of small differences was strongly conditioned by an unyieldingly discontinuous fossil record.

Darwin's conviction that life existed on Earth long before the oldest fossil-bearing rocks known in his day were deposited has been fully vindicated by the recovery of abundant evidence of life dating from as early as 3.5 billion years ago. Hiroshi Ohmoto of Pennsylvania State University and his colleagues reported in 1993, for example, that analysis of the sulfur isotope composition of pyrite grains recovered from the 3.4 billion-year-old Barberton Greenstone belt of South Africa showed that the grains were formed by the bacterial reduction of sulfates from seawater. The presence of bacteria that remove the oxygen from sulfur compounds indicates that the oceans were rich in sulfates at this early date and that the atmosphere already contained an appreciable amount of free oxygen.

The much later appearance of a vast variety of complex multicellular organisms, which Murchison saw as evidence of the beginning of life, is now thought to mark a period of explosive evolutionary activity. Jack Sepkoski of the University of Chicago was quoted in *Science* as saying, "Virtually every phylum of [marine invertebrate] animals comes in, plus things that can't be related to modern forms. They're the fastest rates of evolution we ever see." The episode that Sepkoski describes in such dramatic terms has been thought to have begun early in the Cambrian Period about 570 million years ago and to have lasted from 20 million to 40 million years. Recent dating of volcanic rocks from Siberia by Samuel Bowring of the Massachusetts Institute of Technology and his colleagues revealed, however, that the evolutionary explosion may have begun about 533 million years ago, suggesting that it may have lasted only from 5 million to 10 million years.

If this unique burst of evolutionary activity was confined to so brief an interval of geologic time, then its explanation becomes even more difficult. It has been suggested that only at the beginning of this period had atmospheric oxygen reached a concentration capable of supporting the activity of multicellular organisms. Andrew Knoll of Harvard University pointed out, however, that the remains of multicellular organisms have been found in rocks dating almost 575 million years ago, before the beginning of the Cambrian evolutionary explosion. Other researchers believe that it was necessary for organisms to reach some minimum level of complexity before they could begin to adapt to the great variety of environmental circumstances with which they were confronted. Joseph Kirschvink of the California Institute of Technology proposed an ingenious explanation that rests upon paleomagnetic and geologic data that suggest that coincident with the evolutionary explosion, the Earth's crustal motions were undergoing a period of fundamental change during which the tectonic plates constituting the crust slipped in unison about the interior. Kirschvink suggests that the resulting rapid shifts in climate might have induced an evolutionary burst.

Light has recently been shed upon one of those early Cambrian animals that paleontologists have failed to relate to any recent form. The small conical structures assigned to the genus *Volborthella* found in the lower Cambrian rocks of North America and Europe have generally been regarded as the complete skeletons of individual animals. Philip Signor and Dallas Ryan of the University of California at Davis questioned this interpretation. They described a fossil from the lower Cambrian Harkless formation in eastern California that consists of several of the conical structures arrayed in a bilaterally symmetrical pattern, suggesting that they were the parts of a larger animal. The authors noted that although this fossil contributes to the understanding of the structure and ecology of *Volborthella*, it brings scientists no closer to an understanding of its evolutionary history.

Mass extinctions. A possible cause of discontinuities in the fossil record that was discounted not only by Darwin but also by most 20th-century geologists and paleontologists until little more than a decade ago is the occurrence of catastrophic physical events. Since Luis Alvarez and his colleagues suggested in the early 1980s that a collision between an asteroid and the Earth caused a mass extinction at the end of the Cretaceous Period about 65 million years ago, geologists and paleontologists have increasingly invoked not only asteroid impacts but such other events as violent and widespread volcanic eruptions in their attempts to explain mass extinctions.

Virgil Sharpton of the Lunar and Planetary Institute, Houston, Texas, and his colleagues concluded from a continuing study of gravity data that the Chicxulub impact structure in Mexico may be significantly larger than the 180 km (112 mi) in diameter estimated on the basis of earlier studies. According to the authors, the structure consists of three concentric rings and parts of a fourth, a pattern that has been observed in the largest impact landforms on the planets of the inner solar system. If the incomplete and indistinct outer ring marks the rim of the crater—and not every geophysicist is willing to grant that it does—then the structure may be up to 300 km (186 mi) in diameter. The impact of an extraterrestrial object sufficient to produce such an immense crater would have to be eight times as powerful as that previously calculated. Studies continued to point to the Chicxulub impact as a significant factor in the great extinction that ended the Cretaceous.

Nevertheless, paleontologists were far from agreement about the role of the impact of terrestrial objects in mass extinctions. William Clemens of the University of California at Berkeley, whose conclusion that some dinosaurs were capable of surviving in cold climates cast doubt upon the view that it was a prolonged, impact-induced winter that led to their extinction, raised the most perplexing question about mass extinctions. In *Science* he said, "The real questions is, How did the others—how did any animal—manage to survive? [Impact theorists] have got to come up with a hypothesis that puts equal weight on survival. So many of these catastrophists want to kill the dinosaurs, they forget the rest of the biota. Birds, mammals, and amphibians managed to survive, and that tells you that there is something wrong with most of these hypothetical horrors."

G.A. Izett of the U.S. Geological Survey and his colleagues reported that grains of the impact-generated mineral sanidine have yielded a date of 73.8 ($\pm$ 0.3) million years ago for the formation of the Manson impact structure in Iowa. This puts the time of impact some nine million years earlier than the date of 64 million to 65 million years ago reported in a previous study, which suggested that the impact might have been one of a number of asteroid collisions with the Earth at the end of the Cretaceous Period. It now appears that the Manson impact was too early to have contributed to the great extinction that marked Cretaceous-Tertiary transition.

Analyses of microfossils revealed that across the Cretaceous-Tertiary boundary the surface-to-deep-water gradient of ^{12}C and ^{13}C, two stable isotopes of carbon, is markedly different from, and even the reverse of, the pattern characteristic of other times. This curious anomaly has generally been regarded as evidence of an interruption of primary organic production following a destructive impact. Linda Ivany and Ross Salawitch of Harvard University maintained, however, that in addition to such an interruption, the burning of 25% of the terrestrial biomass is necessary to account for the inferred gradients of the carbon isotopes in seawater. Their work lent support to earlier suggestions that widespread wildfires might have contributed to the dramatic extinction that occurred 65 million years ago.

Meanwhile, the search for new impact structures continued. Steinar Thor Gudlaugsson of the University of Oslo, Norway, reported, for example, that seismic profiles in the Barents Sea revealed the presence of a large structure with the morphological and structural features of an impact crater. The author estimated that the structure, which is 39 km (24 mi) in diameter, was formed by the impact of an asteroid or comet measuring between 0.7 and 2.5 km (0.4 and 1.5 mi) in diameter. Although no drilling was undertaken in the vicinity of the structure, seismic and stratigraphic comparisons suggested that the impact occurred in Jurassic or early Cretaceous time, some 150 million years ago.

Although perhaps not of immediate relevance to the problem of the geologic and paleontological consequences of collisions between the Earth and comets and asteroids, the predicted collision between the periodic comet Shoemaker-Levy 9 and Jupiter was bound to attract the attention of earth scientists. According to the calculations of Zdenek Sekanina of the Jet Propulsion Laboratory in Pasadena, Calif., even if the comet strikes the far side of the planet, secondary phenomena triggered by the explosion of kilometer-sized fragments will be visible from the Earth.

Paleontology and the dating of rocks. Although methods of radioactive dating have improved substantially during the past few decades, fossil correlation continues to play a significant role in the dating of sedimentary rocks. Robert Gastaldo of Auburn (Ala.) University and his colleagues reported, for example, that plant fossils established a Mississippian age (360 million–320 million years ago) for a formation in Alabama, indicating that the deformation of the southern Appalachians took place later than that of the northern Appalachians (400 million–360 million years ago). According to Gastaldo and his colleagues, this finding will require a complete reevaluation of the tectonic history of the southern Appalachians.

Despite this indispensable role of paleontology in the determination of the age of geologic events, and the intense interest in the history of life for its own sake, Warren Allmon of the Paleontological Research Institution in Ithaca, N.Y., felt compelled to write a commentary entitled "In Defense of Paleontology" in the November 1993 issue of *Geotimes*. He pointed out that in several universities teaching positions vacated by paleontologists were filled by geologists, and in some academic departments consideration was being given to dropping paleontology as a required course. Allmon made a strong case for the continuing importance of paleontology.

Uniformitarian principle. The uniformitarian principle, the dictum that the present is the key to the past, induces geologists to observe processes now in operation as an aid to interpreting geologic history. Stephen Boss and A. Conrad Neumann of the University of North Carolina took advantage of a rare opportunity to study the effects of a major hurricane upon features that might be preserved in the geologic record. The northern quadrant of Hurricane Andrew in August 1992 passed over the well-studied reefs, shoals, and low-lying islands of northern Great Bahama Bank. A survey taken seven weeks after the passage of Andrew showed that the positions and dimensions of sandbanks were unchanged relative to the underlying bedrock features and that reef communities were little disturbed. These findings were consistent with the meteorologic data, which shows that although sustained winds of 225 km/h (140 mph) in southern Florida placed Andrew among the most destructive of Atlantic hurricanes, it had weakened as it passed over the Grand Bahama Bank. The authors concluded that factors such as intensity, size, and duration, which vary over relatively short distances, will influence the geologically significant effects of a hurricane.

Kam-biu Liu and Miriam Fearn of Louisiana State University found geologic evidence of Frederick, a hurricane that struck the Alabama coast in 1979, in the form of a distinct sand layer deposited in the sediments of a freshwater lake as storm-generated waves swept over the sand barrier that separates the lake from the Gulf of Mexico. Cores taken from the center of the lake indicated, moreover, that five other major hurricanes had struck this stretch of the Gulf coast within the last 3,000 years.

Difficulties in the application of the uniformitarian principle arise when structures that appear to be identical are shown to have different causes. For many years a "frosted" surface on sand grains was taken as unequivocal evidence that they had been transported by the wind. It was later found that chemical etching could produce the same frosted appearance. The difficulty was resolved when it was found that the surfaces produced by the two different agents could be distinguished from one another when viewed through an electron microscope.

—David B. Kitts

Geophysics. During the past year destructive earthquakes occurred in Japan, Guam, India, Oregon, and southern California. The disastrous Northridge earthquake brought further evidence of the accelerating seismic cycle in southern California, as well as new insights into the area's seismic vulnerability.

Earthquakes and volcanoes. Six volcanologists and three tourists were killed during a sudden eruption of Galeros Volcano in Colombia on Jan. 14, 1993. A violent eruption of Mayon Volcano in the Philippines on February 2 killed more than 70 people and sent ash clouds more than 5 km (3 mi) into the air. Large eruptions also occurred in Russia (Sheveluch, Klyuchevskoy, and Bezymianny volcanoes on the Kamchatka Peninsula), Chile (Lascar Volcano), and Japan (Mt. Unzen).

On July 12, 1993, a magnitude-7.8 earthquake occurred in the northern Sea of Japan off the southwestern coast of Hokkaido. Damage from the earthquake and associated tsunami (seismic ocean wave) was concentrated in coastal Hokkaido and nearby Okushiri Island, but damage also occurred as far away as coastal areas of Russia and Korea. Although the area near the earthquake's epicenter was sparsely populated, more than 190 people were killed in the disaster, and damage estimates exceeded $600 million. Strong shaking lasted more than one minute, and ground acceleration probably exceeded amplitudes of 0.5 g in the epicentral area. (The acceleration of gravity, g, is the measure of ground shaking preferred by engineers and seismologists who study damaging earthquakes, because it can be easily related to the forces induced in man-made structures by shaking.) Shaking caused some landsliding and liquefaction, but most of the casualties and damage were caused by the tsunami, which struck five minutes after the earthquake and reached heights of more than 30 m (100 ft) along the southern coast of Okushiri. Massive 4.5-m (15-ft)- high concrete walls, designed to protect coastal areas from tsunamis, were largely ineffective.

The 1993 earthquake apparently filled a seismic gap in a zone of earthquakes that trends north-south through the eastern Sea of Japan. The aftershock zone, which in most cases delineates the slip area of a main shock (the area in which displacement along the fault plane takes place), extended approximately 150 km (95 mi) between the 1940 Shakotan and 1983 Japan Sea earthquake zones. The overall faulting mechanisms of all these large earthquakes (inferred from a combination of seismic, geologic, and geodetic data) were consistent with convergence of tectonic plates between the Japan Sea and mainland Japan. Faulting in the 1993 event, however, showed some interesting complexity. Inversions of long-period teleseismic waves (those recorded far from the epicenter of the earthquake), which reflect the "average" faulting mechanism, were consistent with subduction (descent of one tectonic plate under another) on a shallow plane dipping toward the east, but higher-frequency data from the early part of the rupture favored subduction on a westward-dipping plane. The lack of a well-developed zone of deep earthquakes suggests that subduction in this area may be very young (unlike, for example, the eastern coast of Japan, where the Pacific Plate has been subducting westward beneath the island for more than 100 million years). This spatial and temporal complexity may be revealing something fundamental about the early stages of a young subduction zone, before a consistent pattern of subduction is established.

On August 8 a magnitude-8.1 earthquake occurred off the southern coast of the island of Guam in the Pacific Ocean, the largest tremor to strike U.S. territory since the great 1964 Alaskan earthquake. Faulting was apparently related to northwestward subduction of the Pacific Plate beneath the Philip-

A man sits in front of his ruined house in a village in central India. A magnitude-6.4 earthquake struck the region on September 30, killing more than 9,700 people and destroying the city of Killari and more than 20 villages.

pines Plate in the Marianas Trench. Early estimates placed the focus of the earthquake near Guam at a depth of 70 km (43.5 mi). Strong shaking on Guam lasted for more than one minute and probably exceeded 0.3 g locally. Damage exceeded $100 million, consisting mostly of shaking damage to public buildings and hotels designed in accordance with modern U.S. standards. Severe damage due to ground failure occurred in the port area on the western side of the island, an area that is built on soft natural alluvium and artificial fill (most of the island is hard rock or firm soil).

On September 30 a magnitude-6.4 earthquake struck central India. This earthquake was extremely destructive for its moderate size; more than 9,700 people were killed, the city of Killari and more than 20 villages were destroyed, and more than 120,-000 people were left homeless. Several factors contributed to the devastation: the shallow focus of the earthquake, poor construction (primarily stone and mud), and the high population density concentrated in villages in lowland areas, where soft soils can amplify shaking. Remarkably, there was little evidence of historical seismicity in the area, and postearthquake investigations revealed no geologic evidence of prehistoric faulting such as fault scarps or other near-surface deformations. (A fault scarp is a steep cliff formed by movement along one side of a fault). Seismologists speculated that the earthquake may have been related to the filling of a nearby reservoir; several recent earthquakes in India, including a large one near Koyna in 1976, have been associated with new reservoirs.

Two moderate earthquakes occurred in Oregon in 1993, and they also demonstrated some of the problems that can happen when earthquakes occur in areas where they are not expected. The magnitude-5.6 Scott's Mills earthquake occurred 40 km (25 mi) south-southeast of Portland on March 25, and a magnitude-5.7 quake struck 25 km (15.5 mi) west-northwest of Klamath Falls on September 20. Separated by six months and more than 300 km (185 mi), the two earthquakes were probably not structurally related. But they shared a similar tectonic setting, eastward subduction beneath the Cascade Range, which was reflected in volcanism and geothermal activity, and they would ultimately have to be related to this tectonism. There was significant damage, especially to unreinforced brick buildings, causing authorities to reevaluate and upgrade seismic zoning in Oregon.

A magnitude-4.8 earthquake on November 14 near Parkfield in central California caused excitement among research seismologists who were trying to understand the fundamental physical processes of earthquake generation and fault propagation. Because of the relatively regular occurrence during the past century of magnitude-6 earthquakes there, the Parkfield segment of the San Andreas Fault system became the most heavily instrumented and studied fault in the world—a virtual seismological laboratory. As a possible foreshock, the November earthquake generated the highest alert level since observations began in earnest at Parkfield more than a decade earlier, but the anticipated magnitude-6 earthquake did not occur.

Northridge earthquake. On Jan. 17, 1994, at 4:31 AM, a magnitude-6.6 earthquake struck the San Fernando Valley northwest of downtown Los Angeles. The Northridge earthquake killed more than 61 people, and by early February, when damage estimates exceeded $30 billion, it had surpassed 1992's Hurricane Andrew to become the costliest natural disaster in U.S. history. By many estimates the toll would have been much greater if the tremor had occurred during heavy commuting time or during school and business hours.

The Northridge earthquake occurred in a zone of active and complex tectonics, where the strike-slip regime of the San Andreas Fault system, which defines the boundary between the North American Plate and the Pacific Plate in central and southern California, is interrupted by the compressional regime of the Transverse Ranges. (In strike-slip faulting, two crustal blocks slip horizontally, parallel to the Earth's surface; in compressional faulting, the slip has a large vertical component, with one crustal block sliding up and over another.) The area has been extensively studied and instrumented, especially since 1971, when the magnitude-6.5 San Fernando earthquake (64 deaths, approximately $510 million damage) ushered in the modern era of engineering seismology. Thus, it provided rich new data for scientists and engineers.

As with any large earthquake, the best understanding of faulting deep in the Earth is achieved indirectly, from sparse and distant measurements made at the Earth's surface. The arrival times, polarities, and amplitudes of seismic phases can be modeled to give locations of the main shock and its aftershocks as well as the amount and direction of slip, while measurements of displacements of the Earth's surface can help identify the faulting mechanism. Because the Northridge earthquake occurred on a previously unmapped fault and the fault plane did not break the Earth's surface, these indirect observations were all that were available to seismologists in this case.

Faulting apparently began to occur at a depth of 18 km (11 mi) beneath the Northridge neighborhood and then ruptured toward the north-northeast under the Santa Susanna Mountains along a south-dipping 40° plane with the southern block overriding the northern block. This reverse-faulting mechanism was

Part of the Northridge Meadows apartment building collapsed during the magnitude-6.6 earthquake that struck the San Fernando Valley near downtown Los Angeles on Jan. 17, 1994 (right); 16 residents of the building were killed. Many highways in the area were also extensively damaged, including Interstate 5 (below), where a police officer on a motorcycle was killed.

consistent with the known pattern of deformation in the area: north-south compression and shortening across the San Fernando Valley. Although many shallow aftershocks occurred, their pattern suggested that faulting in the main shock stopped near a depth of 5 km (3 mi), consistent with the lack of an observed surface break.

Interestingly, the Northridge Fault plane may have partially underlapped part of the 1971 San Fernando Fault plane and renewed seismicity on the old plane. Although both earthquakes reflected the same compressional deformation, the San Fernando plane dipped northward and broke the surface near Sylmar and San Fernando, south of the north edge of the Northridge plane. Taken together, the seismic and geodetic data suggested that the Northridge earthquake might have had an usually high stress drop for a California earthquake, as much as 5 m (16.5 ft) of slip on a fault plane measuring 10 × 7 km (6.2 × 4.4 mi).

Ground shaking in the Northridge earthquake appears to have been much greater than expected for an earthquake of its size, perhaps a reflection of the high stress drop. The main shock and largest aftershocks were well recorded by arrays of strong-motion

seismographs operated by the U.S. Geological Survey, the State of California Strong-Motion Instrumentation Program, and the University of Southern California. (Shaking near a large earthquake will saturate or even damage conventional seismographs that are designed to record and locate smaller earthquakes. Strong-motion seismographs are low-sensitivity instruments that are specially designed to record very strong shaking.) Records of the Northridge quake from these instruments revealed that ground shaking at some sites was two to three times greater than predicted (on the basis of the historical instrumental dataset for an earthquake of comparable size). A few strong-motion records were especially noteworthy, showing complexity in the duration of the main shock stress release, and sustained ground motions greater than 1 g. Damage to a wide range of buildings, from houses and apartment buildings to major lifelines such as hospitals and expressways (especially Interstates 5 and 10), was extensive especially in the light of lessons that had been learned in the San Fernando earthquake. Sixteen people were killed when a three-story apartment building collapsed in Northridge. When it was built, this structure met current building codes, which did not require plywood shear bracing for three-story wood-frame buildings. After its collapse, authorities were considering requiring similar buildings to be fitted with such bracing. Although one- and two-story wood-frame houses generally withstood the quake, hillside houses built with irregular designs and construction techniques were conspicuously vulnerable to damage.

There was no short-term prediction of the Northridge earthquake, and its precise location surprised seismologists. Like the 1987 Whittier Narrows earthquake near Los Angeles, Northridge occurred on a previously unrecognized low-angle fault. As seismologists added more and more instruments in southern California and obtained increasingly precise earthquake locations, they were finding that the earthquakes generally fail to line up on linear structures, as they do in more "well-organized" seismic zones. Consequently, seismologists speculated that it may be possible to have a magnitude-6.5 quake virtually anywhere in the Los Angeles area. The possible locations of even larger earthquakes remained a topic of intense research interest.

—Charles S. Mueller

Hydrologic sciences

During 1993 summer floods in the upper Mississippi River basin in the United States and December floods along a number of rivers in Western Europe focused attention on the economic and societal impacts of infrequent, high-volume flows within river channels. Preliminary damage estimates suggested that the floods on the upper Mississippi and its tributaries would be the costliest in the history of the U.S. From a scientific perspective the summer floods provided valuable insight into the factors that lead to floods of extreme magnitude. Two of the important goals in the hydrologic sciences are an improved understanding of the many processes that interact to determine the magnitude of a flood and improved methodologies for predicting the likelihood of such extreme hydrologic events.

Hydrology. River flows have been monitored on a routine basis at a number of stations in the Mississippi River basin. In some cases these data extend back to the 19th century. Measurements have included both the volume of flow in the river channel and the river stage. River stage is a measure of the water level in the river. The severity of the 1993 flood was highlighted by comparison with the historical record. Peak discharges exceeded the 10-year recurrence interval at 154 stream-flow gauging stations in the area affected by the floods. The peak discharge corresponding to a 10-year recurrence interval is exceeded, on average, only once every 10 years. At 46 gauging stations peak flows exceeded those estimated

to have a 100-year recurrence interval. Discharges exceeded the previous peak discharge on record at 42 gauging stations. On August 1 the river stage on the Mississippi River at St. Louis, Mo., exceeded the maximum stage that had been recorded in the previous 132 years by more than 1.8 m (6 ft).

The summer floods were also remarkable for their duration. At St. Louis the Mississippi River was above flood stage for more than 10 weeks. The volume of flow in the river channel, totaled over a number of consecutive days, provided another measure of the duration of flooding. The total volume of flow at St. Louis exceeded the previous maximum values for periods equal to 15, 30, 60, and 90 consecutive days.

The floods in the Upper Mississippi valley were not solely due to heavy summer rainfall. Instead, they were the consequence of a series of meteorologic and hydrologic events that developed over time. Moist antecedent conditions in the area started in July 1992. Six months of above-normal precipitation preceded the summer floods. This precipitation saturated the soil zone, leaving little capacity to store additional water at or near the ground surface. After mid-May 1993 a persistent mid-level circulation pattern in the atmosphere supported the repeated development of cyclonic storms and intense convective systems in the upper Midwest. This unusual excess in summer rainfall quickly found its way to stream channels that ultimately fed the larger rivers in the watershed. The persistence of the weather patterns amplified the severity and duration of the flooding.

Ken Potter and his colleagues at the University of Wisconsin tackled the important question of how rare the 1993 floods may be. This issue is important for the assessment of the risk associated with future events, for the design of flood-control structures, and in land-use planning. The researchers pointed out that it was difficult to provide an accurate estimate of the recurrence interval for the 1993 flood. Recurrence intervals are estimated on the basis of a statistical analysis of historical flow records, tied to an assumption of a model that describes the probability of observing a given discharge volume in the river channel. Long-term modifications in the basin could mean that records of stream discharge recorded over many tens of years are no longer representative of present-day conditions. For example, the loss of wetlands and the channelization of streams have the potential to increase the severity of flooding. Changes in agricultural practices that have occurred in the Midwest over the decades may play a role in influencing the potential for flooding. Research is needed to develop a quantitative understanding of how changes in the landscape and in land use may affect the potential for flooding and how these factors should be integrated into the methodologies used to estimate return periods for extreme flooding events.

Earth Observation Satellite Company, Lanham, Md.

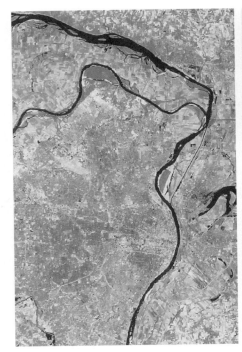 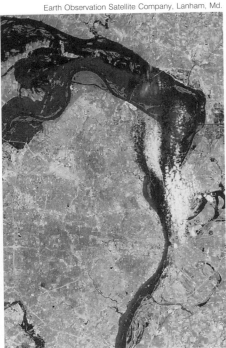

Images of the St. Louis, Mo., area obtained by Landsat satellites reveal the contrast between the drought year of 1988 (near right) and the flood year of 1993 (far right). Shown in the images is the confluence of the Mississippi (from upper left to bottom) and Missouri (extending left from the Mississippi) rivers in July 1988 and July 1993. St. Louis lies to the south of the confluence, where the flooding was the most extensive.

Water balance studies and investigations of the links between surface water and groundwater quality provided important insights into hydrologic behavior. The value of these types of studies extended beyond the local area of the study, as they provided information that was representative of hydrologically similar settings over a much broader geographic region.

Lance Lesack of Simon Fraser University, Burnaby, B.C., writing in the journal *Water Resources Research*, reported the results of a study to characterize hydrologic properties and nutrient export from a rain forest water catchment in the Central Amazon basin. This study was unique in that measurements were made to evaluate three runoff components: base flow runoff, storm flow runoff, and subsurface outflow through deep tropical soils. Base flow runoff is the volume of flow in a stream channel after the higher peak discharges from a storm event have dissipated. Through comparison of these hydrologic pathways, it was possible to examine their roles in controlling the total export of nutrients and major ions such as calcium or sulfate from a catchment-scale basin (approximately 23 ha [57 ac] in size). Estimates of nutrient and major ion export are used as indicators of rates of chemical weathering in tropical soils and for evaluation of the nutrient-retention characteristics of the catchment. Total rainfall during the one-year study was 287 cm (113 in), of which 165 cm (65 in) and 4.1 cm (1.6 in) left the catchment by streamflow and subsurface outflow, respectively. The balance of the rainfall in the catchment was either added to storage in the soil zone or returned to the atmosphere by evaporation and transpiration by vegetation (evapotranspiration). Subsurface outflow and changes in soil water storage during the year were equivalent in magnitude to the storm water flow that left the catchment. Evapotranspiration estimates based on water balance calculations were significantly less than values previously reported for similar catchments in the central Amazon, although they were within the range of the measurement error for values calculated on the basis of micrometeorological techniques. Micrometeorological techniques apply equations to estimate evapotranspiration given measurements of variables such as temperature, wind speed, and relative humidity.

Lesack found that base flow discharge accounted for 92% of the water outflow from the basin, making it the dominant pathway for solute export. Storm flow discharges represented 5% of the total water outflow but accounted for up to 25% of the nutrient and major ion exports. Subsurface outflow accounted for 2.5% of the total water export and up to 5% of the solute export from the catchment. It is noteworthy that the export of most solutes was substantially less than the amounts previously reported for comparable catchments in the Amazon basin. Lesack suggested the possibilities that the larger quantities reported prior to his study were due to earlier methodological problems with water sampling and chemical analysis.

Agricultural chemicals found in both surface water and groundwater have been used as chemical tracers to enhance understanding of the pathways through which these contaminants move in the biosphere.

326

Widespread river flooding occurred in the Midwest in 1993 when heavy summer rains fell on already saturated ground. The Mississippi River poured into downtown Davenport, Iowa, (top) and overran railroad tracks near Quincy, Ill. (left). A highway near Chesterfield, Mo., is covered by water from the Missouri River (above).

Atrazine is a widely used herbicide commonly present as a contaminant in both surface water and ground-water. Its presence in the water cycle indicates that it is both mobile and persistent in the biosphere. Paul Squillace and several colleagues at the U.S. Geological Survey reported on a study that identified the principal sources of atrazine and its metabolite deethylatrazine in the Cedar River in Iowa. Their study focused on a 116-km (72-mi) reach of the Cedar River. Data were collected during a period in September when the river was in a base flow condition. Thus, groundwater was the primary source of water in the river, rather than water that originated as runoff from precipitation. The researchers found that tributaries to the Cedar River, although they aggregated almost all of the discharge from tile drains in agricultural fields, contributed only about 25% of the increased load of atrazine and deethylatrazine between sampling sites. Approximately 75% of the increased load originated along the main river channel itself. This increase could not be attributed to the removal by desorption of those chemicals from sediments forming the river bed. They concluded on the basis of several lines of evidence that the alluvial aquifer bounding the stream channel provided the main source of atrazine and deethylatrazine in the river.

The atrazine carried into the river by groundwater entered via two different pathways. Atrazine and deethylatrazine that originated as bank flow storage provided larger concentrations to the river during early base flow conditions. Bank flow storage occurs when water flows into the alluvial aquifer from the river when the river is at a high stage (for example, during spring runoff). This water subsequently discharges to the river when the river stage declines. Atrazine levels in the river were normally higher during spring runoff. Following depletion of bank flow storage, stable and smaller concentrations of atrazine entered the river from groundwater that originated in areas distant from the river. Baseflow concentrations of atrazine and deethylatrazine were both on the order of 0.15 micrograms per liter, with values up to three times higher when bank flow storage contributed a significant component to the flow in the river.

Atrazine and other agricultural chemicals were also carried into the Mississippi River during the floods of 1993. Scientists from the U.S. Geological Survey reported that while the flow in the Mississippi River was at record levels, concentrations of atrazine were similar to maximum concentrations measured during normal flow conditions in earlier years. Surprisingly, the large volume of flow in the river did not dilute herbicide concentrations. Instead, the concentrations were normal for that time of year. The record flows, combined with normal concentration levels, imply that the total amount of atrazine carried into the river by the floodwaters was as much as 50% larger than values measured in previous years.

—Leslie Smith

Oceanography. In 1993 the World Ocean Circulation Experiment (WOCE) neared the midpoint of its 1990–97 program of observations intended to span entire ocean basins. Planning for WOCE began in the early 1980s when researchers realized that changes in ocean circulation might hold the key to predicting climate. One example of the new results that were emerging from the experiment related to the Pacificwide distribution of carbon-14.

Cosmic rays from space continually convert a very small amount of the stable isotope carbon-12 present in the atmosphere into the radioactive

L'Europe, a new vessel for France's Institute for Marine Research, was launched in late 1993. A catamaran design was chosen for the ship to provide both stability and convenience when scientific instruments are lowered into the water. Among L'Europe's missions will be the study of fisheries resources and echo-sounding operations.

isotope ^{14}C. The half-life of ^{14}C—the time it takes half the atoms in a given sample to decay—is about 5,730 years. A buried or otherwise isolated sample of carbon that has been out of contact with the atmosphere for several thousand years thus will have much less ^{14}C than a sample in contact with the atmosphere. The age of the isolated sample can be determined through measurement of its ^{14}C content. Oceanographers use ^{14}C measurements to determine the time that waters below the surface of the ocean have been away from the atmosphere. Some of the most interesting WOCE results of the past year concerned such measurements in the Pacific Ocean.

On the basis of ^{14}C content, researchers believe that the deep water of the northern Pacific has been away from the atmosphere for about 1,500 years. This water is a mixture of water that was last at the surface around Antarctica or even farther away in the far North Atlantic. The traditional view of Pacific deep circulation is that the oldest water (the water below the surface for the longest time) is to be found deep in the northwestern corner of the Pacific, but ^{14}C measurements by WOCE during the year surprisingly changed this picture. The oldest Pacific waters were found at depths of thousands of meters (but not at the bottom) in two east-west transpacific bands about 1,000 km (620 mi) wide, one on either side of the equator. The water in the very northern part of the Pacific is not the oldest; its ^{14}C content suggested that it had been in contact with the atmosphere more recently than that in the transpacific bands.

The term El Niño refers to a recurring event in which the cold, nutrient-rich waters off the western coast of South America are replaced by warmer, relatively nutrient-poor water, with consequent catastrophic failure of coastal fisheries. Researchers gradually realized that El Niño is but one part of a Pacificwide pattern of oceanic and atmospheric change now called the El Niño/Southern Oscillation (ENSO). Predicting ENSO events is of global economic importance. A number of researchers had successfully predicted the 1986 and 1991 events, but predictions made in the fall of 1993 ranged widely, from another El Niño to an abnormally cold eastern Pacific.

One problem in developing predictive El Niño models has been that, because ENSO events typically occur only once or twice a decade, historical meteorologic records cover a fairly small number of events. Typically, ENSO events include abnormally intense rainfall at equatorial Pacific islands. During the year researchers reported that the concentration of the isotope oxygen-18 in a core of coral grown over the previous 96 years at an island in the western Pacific mirrors the index of rainfall over the central Pacific. The condensation of water vapor during atmospheric convection preferentially separates out oxygen isotopes of different weight into the rainfall; consequently, the ^{18}O content of the ocean surface water and, therefore, of corals growing in it is lower during times of abnormally intense rainfall. The coral record may actually be a better measure of rainfall averaged over the tropical Pacific than would be an island rain-gauge record because ocean currents cause the ^{18}O content of the coral to reflect rainfall conditions over a broad region rather than just where the coral grows. Such work was expected to allow researchers to look back over many more ENSO events to determine if their frequency and duration have changed over time.

Relaxation of Cold War tensions provided oceanographers with an unexpected new source of data. They gained access to the U.S. Navy's global acoustic undersea surveillance system, originally designed to detect and track submarines, in order to listen for signals as diverse as whale vocalizations and seafloor volcanoes and earthquakes. The global coverage afforded by this system would provide whale researchers with a basin-scale picture of numbers and locations of whales at any given time. Earth scientists would enjoy greatly increased ability to monitor seismic activity under the ocean, particularly the frequent but relatively low-level activity that is believed to occur along with volcanism at ocean-ridge crests, the sites of seafloor spreading.

Seafloor earthquakes sometimes generate extremely destructive ocean waves called tsunamis. Because seismic waves travel faster through the Earth's crust than do the water waves of the tsunami, researchers who monitor the world for earthquakes on the seafloor or near the coast often can warn coastal residents of a possible tsunami several hours or more in advance. But they cannot tell with certainty whether a particular earthquake has, in fact, generated a large tsunami.

In 1993 researchers suggested that the traditional measure of earthquake intensity underestimates the size of those earthquakes that release their energy relatively slowly and thus have hidden potential for generating tsunamis. They argued that the Nicaraguan earthquake of Sept. 2, 1992, which generated only mild ground motions at the coast but was followed by large tsunami waves, was one such slow earthquake, and they noted similar historical occurrences around the Pacific. Their work suggested that a change in the way earthquakes are monitored could provide more certain tsunami warnings than are presently available.

—Myrl C. Hendershott

See also Feature Articles: CALLING NATURE'S BLUFF: THE SECRET WORLD OF CLIFFS; THE NEW SUBMERSIBLES.

Electronics and information sciences

New and faster microprocessors, computers small enough to be held in one's hand, and high-speed fiber-optic networks were among the significant developments in electronics and information sciences during the past year. Computers, telephones, and television were coming together to develop the "data superhighway" of the future.

Communications systems

Countries throughout the world were recognizing that communications technologies would propel them into the information age and toward the 21st century. During the past year billions of dollars were committed to the enhancement of communications infrastructure; the world was being laced with fiber-optic cable, copper was being utilized in previously unimagined ways, and wireless systems were proliferating.

However, it was not technologies alone that were driving the world forward; just as important were the affiliations taking place between dissimilar companies and industries. The slow but steady movement toward competition throughout the world permitted these technologies to be effectively utilized. In Europe and Asia private companies were competing with firms that until recently had been government monopolies. In the U.S. such companies as Metropolitan Fiber Systems, Inc., and Teleport Communications Group were installing their equipment in telephone company central offices. In some parts of the world radio communications were being seen as viable replacements for wired communications. Cable television companies were getting into the telephone business, and telephone companies were entering the cable TV business. AT&T, the largest provider of long-distance service in the U.S., purchased McCaw Cellular Communications Inc., the country's largest provider of cellular communications. Companies whose main business was telephones were bidding for movie studios.

All of these enterprises utilized one or more of the three transmission media: copper, fiber optics, and wireless. In every case it was electronics of one sort or another that allowed these transmission media to function.

Copper. Most of the developed countries in the world were laced with twisted pairs of copper wires that formed the foundation of telecommunications systems. However, without the sophisticated coding that is applied to the signals being transmitted, the capacity of these copper pairs was restricted and (it was thought) certainly could not carry the immense bandwidth required by television. Because of this, in much of the urban U.S. cable TV companies built an overlay network of coaxial cable—a cable consisting of a tube of flexible conductor forming one-half the pair and a single conductor down the center forming the other half. As of 1994 about 62% of the residences in the U.S. received cable TV.

Recently, however, it was determined that complex coding schemes could be implemented that would allow vast quantities of data to be transmitted accurately for up to 4.8 km (3 mi) on plain twisted-pair copper wire. One such scheme was known by the acronym ADSL (asymmetrical digital subscriber line), and tests were under way in many parts of the world to determine whether copper pair might do the job of coaxial cable. In one such trial (for Bell Atlantic Corp.), an ADSL system transmitted a 1.5-Mbps (megabit per second) channel to the home and a 16-Kbps (kilobit per second) channel from the home. (One megabit equals 1,000,000 bits, and one kilobit equals 1,000 bits.) It was likely that these speeds would be increased in the future.

Additionally, TV pictures could be "compressed" to require less bandwidth. Since the background of a particular TV picture changes only slightly from frame to frame, why, then, is a huge amount of electromagnetic spectrum used to transmit this background over and over again? Keeping the same background (compressing it) would result in significant savings.

Another transmission technology based on copper wire was ISDN (integrated services digital network). Though it had been developed for more than a decade, ISDN was less than a major market success. In fact, it had often been described as a solution in search of a problem. Indeed, many still wondered whether its capabilities had not been surpassed by other technologies. Basic-rate ISDN (there was also a faster primary-rate ISDN) provided two 64-Kbps voice channels and one 16-Kbps data channel over a single pair of wires. Of course, in order to utilize this service, central offices would have to be specially equipped, and equipment on the customer's premises—terminals—also would have to be of a special type. However, by 1994 ISDN did seem to be moving ahead. In the U.S., central offices were increasingly able to accommodate it, as was also the case in Europe.

One other transmission technology had given copper a new lease on life. This was called HDSL (high bit rate digital subscriber line) and was an outgrowth of ISDN. It permitted telephone companies to transmit information at 144 Kbps over standard, or even substandard, copper lines.

Thus, copper was no longer seen as a dying transmission medium. Those millions of kilometers of copper pair were still of great value.

A worker produces fiber-optic cable at an AT&T factory in Atlanta, Ga. Sales of cable and other fiber-optic components were expected to increase during the 1990s.

Fiber. Fiber optics continued to be the "transmission medium of choice." By transmitting information over hair-thin strands of glass instead of copper conductors and by using light instead of electricity, transmission capability was increased by orders of magnitude. Indeed, by 1994 there were transmission systems operating at rates of gigabits (billions of bits) per second, and entire networks were operating at many megabits per second (Mbps). For example, a fiber-optic network that ran at 622 Mbps was established between the University of Wisconsin at Madison and the University of Illinois at Urbana-Champaign. At 622 Mbps, approximately 13 million words, or 530 million bits, could be transmitted in less than one second. Sending the same amount of information from a home computer at the typical speed of 2,400 bits per second would take more than two and a half days.

Fiber-optic networks, although usually operating at slower speeds than mentioned above, were increasing in number. The U.S. Federal Communications Commission (FCC) estimated that the seven operating Bell companies had deployed 8.8 million km (5.5 million mi) of fiber and the long-distance interexchange carriers an additional 3.9 million km (2.4 million mi).

This trend toward fiber was not unique to the U.S. Countries throughout the world were deploying fiber at a rapid rate, and consortiums were covering the floor of both the Atlantic and Pacific oceans with fiber cables.

One of the most newsworthy of the cables was to be known as FLAG (fiber-optic link around the globe). It would land at 13 countries and dependencies: the U.K., Gibraltar, Italy, Egypt, Saudi Arabia, India, Indonesia, Singapore, Malaysia, Hong Kong, South Korea, Japan, and Spain. The length of the cable would be nearly 29,000 km (18,000 mi), and the entire capacity would be handled by four strands of fiber. Current plans called for operation at 5 Gbps, significantly higher than the highest rates now being offered commercially.

What had made this increased speed possible? Was the chemical composition of the glass so much better than that of the previous decade? Better, yes, but not that much better. The greatest advances in speed capability had to do not with the glass itself but with the electronics at each end of the system. An obvious advantage of this was that as improvements were achieved and speeds were increased, it was only the electronics—not the fiber itself—that needed to be replaced.

There had been, however, significant improvements in glass. One was dispersion-shifted fiber. Standard fiber had very good (low) attenuation characteristics with light at a wavelength of 1,550 nm (nanometers); that is, the light waves did not become weaker. However, when operated at that frequency, the light pulses were rapidly spread out—that is, dispersed. At a wavelength of 1,300 nm, this dispersion dropped to an almost negligible level, but the attenuation was unacceptably high. Dispersion-shifted fiber captured the best of these two characteristics; such fiber had a structure that changed the zero-dispersion wavelength from 1,300 to 1,550 nm while retaining the low attenuation characteristics.

331

This combination allowed longer spans between amplifiers and provided higher transmission speeds.

Even with dispersion-shifted fiber, a signal could be transmitted only so far before it had to be amplified. In past years an attenuated optical signal had to be regenerated to retain its integrity. Unfortunately, regenerative repeaters required complex and expensive electronics and would operate only with a particular prescribed coding structure. Such a system, good though it may have been, was obviously inflexible. However, an optical amplifier was introduced that utilized a short length of fiber that had been doped with the element erbium. In addition to the electronics, it used a laser-diode "pump" that supplied additional energy into the fiber. Although its operation was extremely complex, its results were not; a signal utilizing virtually any coding structure could be transmitted, amplified, transmitted, amplified, etc., with little signal deterioration. In fact, experiments indicated a boost in transmission range by a factor of nearly 100.

It is impressive to discuss the tremendous speeds that can be achieved with optical fiber, but what is the method or the structure of these transmissions? The method that seemed to be preferred by 1994 was called asynchronous transfer mode (ATM). ATM was a packet-switching technology. A "packet," or "bundle," of information was transmitted from origin to destination through the network. Additional packets were likely to take different routes. The packets moved in fixed-length, 53-byte cells. (One byte equals eight bits.) All broadband services (whether audio, data, imaging, or radio) were digitized, placed into a series of these cells, and then transmitted across the network.

This system was not unlike a railroad network. The intelligence (cargo) was loaded into the cars of the train, and the train left for its destination. Additional cargo (information) was loaded into waiting trains, and the trains made their way across the network. Except in this case the "trains" arrived at their destination less than one millisecond after they had departed.

Wireless. Advances in the field of wireless communications were, if anything, even more remarkable than those for fiber or copper. Cellular communications, only 10 years old, achieved its 11 millionth subscriber in the U.S. during the past year. Progress was no less amazing in other parts of the world. In fact, the transmission technique that seemed to be achieving the greatest deployment had its origin in Europe. This system, GSM (global system for mobile communications), could be imported to the U.S. to compete with the three systems currently deployed there.

The first of the three U.S. systems was analog, identified by the letters FDMA (frequency division multiple access). It was the original cellular system and in 1994 was used by close to 100% of U.S. cellular subscribers. The second was digital, identified as TDMA (time division multiple access). This had been regarded as the standard digital system for the U.S., but more recently yet another digital system made its appearance. This system, CDMA (code division multiple access), in most applications employed a technology known as spread spectrum—an offshoot of military communications systems. As of early 1994 no single method had been selected, and indeed there seemed to be equal support for TDMA and CDMA.

Although the preferred technology for cellular communications had yet to be determined, researchers were pursuing the next wireless system—a personal communications system. As presently envisioned, cells would be much smaller, and there would be many more of them. Telephone handsets would be shirt-pocket size, and a user would be able to reach anyone, anyplace, at any time because the myriad of cells all would be connected to the public switched-telephone network. Such systems were still in the formative stage, and although it was generally agreed that they would not be used in moving vehicles, there was little agreement on other aspects of their design, use, or application.

The wireless technology that had captured the imagination of people throughout the world was the system identified as LEO—low Earth orbit. In this system (one should say systems, because several were in the development stage), constellations of satellites (as few as 66, as many as 840) would be deployed at altitudes of approximately 700 km (435 mi). These satellites would not be geostationary—that is, remain over the same part of the Earth at all times. Rather they would constantly, one after another, appear at one horizon and drop over the other. In order for the system to be successful, however, at least one satellite would have to be in sight at any given time.

The system was based on the cellular principle, with a user's communications taking place with one satellite (cell site) until it started dropping over the horizon. At that time, a handoff would take place to a better-situated satellite. It should be noted that a handoff would take place not because a user had moved beyond the range of a cell site but because a cell site had moved beyond the range of a user.

The advantage of such a system was that a person anywhere in the world would always be able to communicate with anyone else in the world, at any time. The question was whether there was significant demand for such a system. Several companies were saying that there was, and they were making plans to launch such satellites.

—Robert E. Stoffels

Computers and computer science

During the past year manufacturers introduced a new type of computer. Small enough to be carried everywhere and powerful enough to perform basic computing chores, these computers also had radio communication capabilities. Computer manufacturers also introduced faster, more powerful versions of conventional computers.

Software manufacturers announced major new versions of the basic software that controls a computer. One particular operating system, announced by Microsoft Corp., will make it possible for personal computers to be used in new ways.

For many years computer scientists have investigated ways to encrypt data—keep the contents of a message secret as it travels from one computer to another. During the past year the government endorsed a new data-encryption scheme that keeps message contents protected but also makes it possible for law-enforcement agencies to examine messages when authorized.

Faster processors for personal computers. A central processing unit (CPU) forms the heart of a computer. The CPU contains electronic circuitry to perform arithmetic operations such as addition and subtraction as well as electronic circuitry for operations such as comparisons needed to execute a program. In most modern computers the CPU consists of a single integrated circuit, usually called a microprocessor. Although a CPU can perform complex arithmetic and logical operations at high speeds, it fits onto a small piece of silicon approximately one centimeter (0.4 in) square.

When IBM Corp. first introduced its personal computer, it chose to use the 8088 microprocessor sold by Intel Corp. Later, Intel designed the 8086 as a replacement. Because IBM's personal computer design is widely accepted, Intel's microprocessor became a standard for all personal computers. During the following years Intel produced a series of faster, more powerful microprocessors, the Intel 286, Intel 386, and Intel 486 models. As of 1994 the firm held an 85% share of the microprocessor market.

During the past year Intel introduced two versions of a new, faster microprocessor named the Pentium™. The high-speed version operates at 66 million cps (cycles per second), while the slower version operates at 60 million cps. Because the high-speed version costs more, manufacturers that use the Pentium microprocessor in their computers must choose either lower cost or higher speed. Computer specialists use a scale known as SPECint92 as one measure of microprocessor performance. The fastest Pentium processor achieves a SPECint92 rating of 64.5. To understand the significance of the Pentium, one must compare it with existing processors.

For example, some personal computers use an Intel 486 processor that operates at 33 million cps. Such a processor achieves a SPECint92 rating of only 18.2. Other personal computers use a faster Intel 486 processor that operates at 66 million cps. Such processors perform fewer computations per cycle than the new Pentium and consequently achieve a SPECint92 rating of 32.4. Thus, the new Pentium processor performs 2 to 3.5 times faster than processors currently used in personal computers.

The SPECint92 rating assesses the speed at which a processor performs arithmetic with integer values. For applications that move large quantities of data or perform computations involving fractional values, the Pentium can operate 5 to 10 times faster than older Intel processors. It contains several features that make such performance possible. To achieve dramatic increases in speed, the Pentium requires significantly more electronic circuitry than its predecessors. The active electronic element used in a microprocessor is a transistor. Each Pentium contains approximately 3.1 million transistors, nearly three times as many as the Intel 486 processor.

Various manufacturers responded to Intel's new microprocessor. IBM, Apple Computer Inc., and Motorola Inc. together designed a new microprocessor

Powered by more than three million transistors, the Pentium™ microprocessor, introduced by Intel Corp., can operate 5 to 10 times faster than previous Intel models for applications that move large quantities of data.

Intel® Corporation

The pen-operated EO personal computer developed by AT&T is the first portable computer to offer telephone and fax capabilities. It can also communicate with other computers through cellular telephone connections.

known as the PowerPC, which they expected to be competitive with the Pentium. IBM also began developing new personal computers that would use the PowerPC. To encourage other manufacturers to choose the PowerPC, IBM set its initial price lower than the price of the Pentium.

New handheld computers. A new type of computer small enough to fit in a person's hand and light enough to be carried anywhere reached the market during the past year. Despite its small size, it is sophisticated enough to handle such office tasks as sending or receiving a fax or communicating via electronic mail.

Handheld computers use hardware in new ways. For example, although the handheld computer has a screen to display output, it is much smaller than a conventional screen. Consequently, these computers perform one activity at a time, and information is displayed only when needed. Instead of having large, cumbersome keyboards, some of the new computers allow users to select items from a menu or to write on the screen by using a long pointed stylus that resembles a pencil with no point. The computer senses when the stylus touches the screen and when it moves.

Called personal digital assistants or personal communicators, these small computers offer a variety of services to an individual. For example, most have a calendar program that allows a person to schedule

appointments. A person can use a stylus to look through a menu system, select a time, fill in details, and enter an appointment. Later the user can ask the computer to display all appointments for a given day or to emit an audible tone when it is time for the next appointment.

Perhaps the most dramatic new idea underlying the design of the new computers is portability. Each handheld computer has the ability to communicate with other computers. Manufacturers expect that in the future the handheld computers will be able to communicate through digital data networks. However, the models introduced during the past year used conventional cellular telephone connections, which enabled them to communicate with other computers or conventional fax machines. For example, a user can create a message on the screen, enter the telephone number of a fax machine, and have the handheld computer send the message as a fax. Similarly, a handheld computer can receive a fax and display the message on the screen.

Each of the new computers offers features that distinguish it from the others. For example, the EO Personal Communicator produced by AT&T was the first portable computer to include telephone and fax capabilities. The Newton MessagePad computer from Apple contains software that recognizes handwriting. It allows a user to write answers or messages on the screen with a stylus, and then attempts to process the handwriting and recognize individual characters. General Magic also designed a handheld computer and chose Sony Corp. and Motorola to manufacture the hardware. In addition, General Magic was working on software that would simplify sending and receiving electronic mail.

New operating system software. An operating system is a complex computer program that each computer needs in order to control basic processing, handle input and output, and provide access to files on disk as well as communication with other computers. Part of the operating system remains resident in the computer's memory. When a user requests an application program, the operating system fetches the application from a disk, loads it into the memory, and runs the application. After a user finishes with an application, the operating system waits for the user to select another application.

Because part of the operating system remains in a computer's memory at all times, application programs do not need to have copies of the code built into them. Instead, an application calls on functions in the operating system to perform tasks such as reading keystrokes from a keyboard or writing a file onto a disk. Because the set of functions in a given operating system differs from sets in other operating systems, an application program must be written to work with a specific operating system.

During the past year Microsoft, the largest producer of software for personal computers, introduced a major new operating system called Windows NT. The new system is significant for two reasons. First, much of the software written for personal computers is designed to work with Microsoft operating systems. If the industry follows the same pattern as it has in the past, both owners of personal computers and companies that produce software for personal computers will begin using the new system. Second, because Windows NT provides new functionality not found in its predecessors, it will allow personal computers to run software previously available only on larger, more sophisticated computers.

The most important new function that Windows NT provides is called preemptive scheduling. Preemptive scheduling was invented for large computers that serve many users at the same time. By using preemptive scheduling, an operating system can allow multiple programs to run simultaneously. The operating system switches the processor among the programs so rapidly that it gives the illusion that each program is running continuously.

Support for multiple simultaneous programs is important for three reasons. First, it allows a user to perform multiple tasks at the same time. For example, suppose a user needs to print a document and use a spreadsheet application. If a system supports multiple programs, printing can proceed at the same time the user runs the spreadsheet application. Second, support for multiple programs will permit a personal computer to run communication programs while the user runs other programs. For example, with Windows NT a personal computer will be able to run a program that receives electronic mail while the user edits a document. Third, support for mul-

tiple programs will permit a personal computer to run software that is currently available only on more powerful computers called servers. For example, computers connected to a network use a server and special operating system software in order to allow other computers to share their files simultaneously. Windows NT permits any computer to offer file-sharing services.

A new data-encryption mechanism. Because many people use computers to store information, privacy and security have become important issues. Individuals who want to keep information confidential seek privacy; anyone who does not want information altered seeks security. For example, an employee can choose to keep his or her salary private by refusing to release the information to others. An organization can keep its computers and data-storage facilities secure to prevent unauthorized access or changes to the information they contain.

Computer networks make the task of ensuring privacy and security more difficult because they provide electronic access to an organization's computers and allow computers to transmit information from one computer to another. Transmitting information across a computer network increases the risk of unauthorized access because the network as well as both the sending and the receiving computer must be protected.

Networks that transfer messages across shared communications media are especially vulnerable to eavesdropping. For example, a computer network can consist of a single cable to which many computers are attached. The computers cooperate by taking turns in using the shared cable to send messages. Because each message sent across the wire identifies the destination computer, the network hardware can

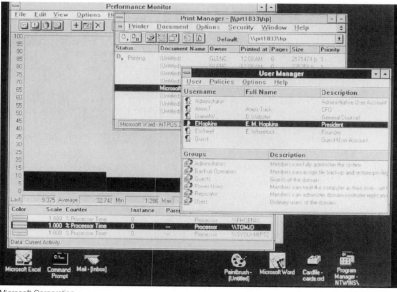

Microsoft Corporation

Windows NT, a new operating system developed by Microsoft Corp. for personal computers, allows multiple programs to run simultaneously. The 32-bit system can operate existing DOS and Windows software.

ensure that the intended recipient receives the message. However, because all computers are attached to a shared wire, it is possible to program a computer to make a copy of each message transmitted regardless of the intended recipient. One does not need sophisticated computer hardware to eavesdrop on a network and observe all messages—an inexpensive personal computer can be programmed to perform the task. Therefore, any computer attached to a network that uses shared media can compromise the privacy of all information transferred across the network.

To help achieve privacy, computer scientists have devised a variety of techniques. Although the details vary, most techniques employ the same general approach used by the military for centuries: a message is encrypted (coded) so that it cannot be understood by anyone except by the intended recipient. Successful encryption requires that the sender and recipient agree on an encryption method. Before transmitting a message across a network, the sending computer encrypts it by translating the message into a coded form. Once the message has been received, the destination computer reverses the encryption process to obtain the original message. If an eavesdropper obtains a copy of a message, the encryption makes interpreting the message difficult or impossible.

The codes that computers use to encrypt data must be more complex than the codes that people invented to encrypt messages before computers were available. For example, a simple method of encrypting a message substitutes one letter in place of another and then rearranges the order of words. Although such an encryption makes most messages unintelligible to a person, it does not suffice for use with computers because a computer can break the code quickly by trying many possible substitutions and rearrangements.

Instead of substituting individual letters or digits and then rearranging the order, codes used with computers treat the characters of a message like a series of numbers. To encode a message, a computer applies a mathematical function to the numbers, using such operations as multiplication, addition, and division. The mathematical operations must be carefully chosen so that the recipient can reverse them to reproduce the original message. Because the mathematical operations scramble the message well, the encoded form does not resemble the original in any way. Because so many combinations of mathematical functions exist, the code cannot be broken easily; a computer requires many years to try all possible combinations.

The National Institute of Standards and Technology devised an encoding scheme that uses mathematical functions to encrypt data. Called the Data Encryption Standard (DES), the scheme requires both the sender and receiver to know a large number that is kept secret. The number is called a key and is used by the mathematical function to encrypt information.

Originally, digital encryption techniques were designed to protect data, such as a document sent from one computer to another. However, because modern telephone systems also use digital transmission, the same techniques used to encrypt data can be used to encrypt voice communication. During the past year AT&T introduced a product that used the DES technique to encrypt digitized voice messages sent between two telephones. Such a device can be used to keep a telephone conversation private because anyone who wiretaps the telephone line can neither interpret the data nor reconstruct the voice.

The U.S. government became concerned about the widespread use of encryption, especially as it applies to telephone conversations. Federal law allows a court to issue a warrant that authorizes a law-enforcement agency to use wiretapping to investigate serious criminal activities for which other methods of investigation are likely to fail. The government was concerned that criminals would use encryption to prevent law-enforcement agencies from understanding criminal communication.

To solve the problem, the government proposed using a new encryption technology known as the Clipper chip. Manufactured by Mykro Tronics Inc., the system operates like most other encryption technologies except that it contains a special provision to allow authorized wiretapping. Like other encryption mechanisms, the Clipper chip allows the sender and receiver to choose a key in order to encode data. In addition, each individual Clipper chip has both a unique serial number and a special number called a unit key built into the chip when it is manufactured. Separately, the serial number and unit key cannot be used for wiretapping. However, when used together, the two special numbers are sufficient to decode any message the Clipper chip encodes no matter which key the sender and receiver have chosen for encryption.

To guarantee that only authorized law-enforcement agencies can wiretap encrypted communication, each of two separate groups in the federal government, appointed by the U.S. attorney general, will hold one of the special numbers for a Clipper chip. When a court authorizes wiretapping for a particular Clipper chip, both groups will reveal their number, which the law-enforcement agency can then use to wiretap any communications from that particular chip. During the year AT&T announced that it would begin using the Clipper technology in its telephone security device, making it possible for law-enforcement agencies to monitor criminal activities.

—Douglas E. Comer

Electronics

An intriguing element of the U.S. presidential campaign of Bill Clinton and Al Gore was their reference to the construction of an "electronic highway." It is being built to connect various electronic technologies and to allow them to exchange information at rapid speeds. While most people continue to slog along on electronic secondary roads, the outline of the new highway system is already making its appearance.

One element of that future highway system is the teleputer. Its name is a contraction derived from the interconnection of computers, telephones, and television. Historically, the three elements of this future highway developed separately, but by 1994 they were coming together to form the information system of the future. This convergence of technologies was made possible by the fact that all of them thrive on the same electronic fuel. That fuel consists of a series of pulses that convey information down the electronic highway at the posted speed limit of 300,000 km (186,000 mi) per second, the speed of light. Furthermore, the new electronic road surface consists of fiber-optic cables that allow vast amounts of information to travel from point of origin to final destination. In technical terms, the fiber-optic cables have a wide bandwidth, which makes the electronic highway akin to a multilane expressway.

However, just as with conventional highways, the exit ramps of the electronic system are bottlenecks. The twisted copper-wire exit ramps, which connect customers to the highway, slow down the communications. However, these antiquated ramps, according to the telephone companies that build them, will soon be replaced with fiber-optic cables so that the electronic exit ramp speed can be increased.

What can be expected from the electronic highway? For one thing, electronic banking will assume ever greater proportions of a person's total banking activities. Banking will increasingly be done by phone. A patent was issued to Online Resources and Communication Corp. in McLean, Va., for a system through which customers could do all their banking transactions at home. The customer enters the system by means of a "smart card," much in the manner in which current automatic teller machines are accessed. The patent covers transactions such as pay-per-view television, home shopping, interactive video games, securities trading, and many other services available through telephones, computers, or other terminals.

A second result of the electronic highway is new telecommuting systems that will make it possible for employees to work at home. Through these systems they will have full access to the computers at their workplace. Electronic mail will be sent not only through on-line services such as Internet but also to anyone anywhere in the world who has a television set or telephone.

Many people will be using little magic boxes that tie them to the electronic highway no matter where they are and when they want to be connected. During the year a new breed of handheld computers began making its appearance (*see* Computers and computer science, above).

International developments. Throughout much of Europe, economic recession was the cause of a lackluster year for sales in 1993. In particular, the U.K. and Germany slowed down the growth of the information technology market, while Italy, France, and Spain prevented it from slipping even further by posting positive growth rates.

Online ScreenPhone 220™, developed by the Online Resources and Communications Corp., combines a standard telephone with the visual features of an automatic teller machine. It makes it possible for owners to do their banking at home.

Online Resources and Communications Corporation, McLean, Va.

"Excuse me, I'm lost. Can you direct me to the information superhighway?"

Growth in 1994 was expected primarily in software, with an increasing demand for local area networks and system-management software. Moreover, increased demand for consulting services was expected. Finally, the report predicted a growing demand for ink-jets and a sustained growth in the laser printer segment of the market.

The Italian firm Società Finanziara Telefonica per Azioni of Rome and Bell Atlantic Corp. were planning a joint venture to develop new multimedia services. They intended to produce a technology that would enable the transmission of audiovisual programs over ordinary telephone networks. Both companies planned to develop the special videocassette recorders needed for such a transmission. The service would also allow customers to call up individual programs as desired. Britain installed its first broadband data communications highway. Developed by the British Telecommunications Plc, the system was designed to connect major business centers in England, Wales, Northern Ireland, and Scotland.

At the Systems '93 trade show in Munich, Germany, Russia introduced a computer that is a product of its formerly top-secret laboratories. A parallel-processing supercomputer, it executes one billion floating-point operations per second. (In floating-point calculations, numbers are expressed as integers multiplied by the root raised to an integral power; thus, 0.0087 becomes 87×10^{-4}.) Its power consumption is 500 w. All of this computing power fits within a $56 \times 45 \times 20$-cm ($22 \times 18 \times 8$-in) space. Dubbed Multicon, it was expected to be priced at $\frac{1}{30}$ to $\frac{1}{20}$ the cost of a comparable supercomputer. The Centre of Computing Image Processing (CCIP) in Moscow, which developed Multicon, revealed that computers using the Multicon technology have been used in the Russian space station *Mir*.

The Taiwanese government planned to promote computers and peripheral equipment in an industrial park to be established near the U.S.-Mexican border. It was hoped that this would offset the expected negative impact of the North American Free Trade Agreement upon Taiwan's exports. Some 80% of Taiwan's exports overlapped with those from Mexico. Nine of Taiwan's semiconductor manufacturers were investing more than $4 billion in the construction of new foundries. This would result in a fivefold expansion of the nation's present production capacity within the next three years.

Automotive applications. Several major car rental companies established electronic ties to government computers to check the driving records of potential car renters. The check could be completed in about five seconds for those with clean records. For others the checking process took about 10 seconds. As a result of these checks, about 10% of the applications were being refused.

American Flywheel Systems Inc. (AFS), a company based in Bellevue, Wash., obtained a patent for an electromechanical device that, it was claimed by the company, could deliver electrical power up to six times as long between recharging as those of conventional batteries that used chemicals. The company, in the face of much skepticism, reached an agreement with Honeywell Inc., which agreed to build a working model within the next two years.

The AFS device is powered by a flywheel that uses magnets to create electricity. The flywheel is set spinning by household electrical current. Once it has been set in motion, it can continue to spin for a considerable length of time. The electricity generated by the flywheel is fed to the car's electric motor, which in turn propels the car. Feasibility studies show that such a car would have a range from about 475 to 950 km (300 to 600 mi) on a single charge. This compares favorably with more conventional electrical propulsion systems, which average 130–160 km (75–100 mi) with conventional batteries.

Noise Cancellation Technologies Inc. of Stamford, Conn., and the New York City Transit Authority began a six-month study of four buses equipped with electronic mufflers. The muffler works on the principle of producing antinoise in response to the muffler's noise. To visualize this process, one should picture two waves traveling simultaneously. While one of them undergoes a maximum upward displacement, the second one undergoes a maximum downward displacement. The net sum of the two displacements is zero. In the language of the engineer, the two waves are 180° out of phase and thus cancel each other.

Besides making its cars more powerful for the coming year, the Ford Motor Co. added an improved electronic onboard technician in the form of a powerful computer. The new unit operates 20% faster and has 66% more memory than the unit it replaced. It features a flash erasable electrically programmable read-only memory chip (flash-EEPROM), which allows the computer to be reprogrammed without the need to replace it, as was the case in former years. The computer remembers all of the car's intermittent errors and faults, and it is capable of monitoring all pollution-control equipment.

Medical electronics. The accurate measurement of a person's blood pressure is a vital concern, especially during crisis periods such as are encountered in a hospital operating or emergency room. While existing monitoring devices are accurate, they have some drawbacks. Of the two types existing, the invasive monitor, which uses a catheter inserted in one of a patient's arteries, can cause blood clotting and consequent complications. The noninvasive monitor gives readings only intermittently, thus possibly missing an important and dramatic change in a patient's blood pressure. In response to these problems, several nonintrusive devices that measure blood pressure continuously were introduced in recent months. They use infrared, ultrasound, or piezoelectric sensors. One such device using piezoelectric sensors is manufactured by the Biosyss Corp. of Braintree, Mass. It consists of three parts. A wristband containing a module measures the palpable pulse in an artery near the wrist. The module contains piezoelectrical sensors that are sensitive to the changing pressure created by the pulsating artery. The sensors convert the changing pressure to voltage pulses, which are then fed to a bedside computer. Its screen displays the pulse as a wave on the computer's monitor, and it provides a numerical display of the patient's blood pressure. The manufacturer claims that the device is nearly as accurate as an invasive monitor, with a margin of error of between five and seven millimeters of mercury. It is capable of measuring a diastolic pressure as low as 40 and a systolic pressure as low as 85.

A new biofeedback system to help reduce pain in a patient by having that patient associate pleasant images with a stage of increasing relaxation was developed during the year. The patient is connected to a computer by sensors that measure heartbeat, body temperature, and blood pressure. The computer analyzes the physiological data and determines what particular scene would be most appropriate to be sent to a video screen by means of a laser disc player. It was found that certain images, such as the view and sound of a waterfall and the view of a beautiful sunset, relax patients. It is hoped that eventually the patients will be able to recall for themselves these images and thus reduce their often stress-related pain. The system was being used by about 20 medical centers.

New products. It has been estimated that about 8 out of 10 people who own videocassette recorders cannot program them. That statistic probably is a reflection of the sheer fright many encounter as they try to understand the proper operating procedures from often badly written instruction manuals. Help is on the way. A device, the VCR Voice Programmer, made by a company in Canoga Park, Calif., will allow the programming of the VCR directly by means of a user's voice. To use the device, a user must first train it to recognize his or her particular voice pattern. It is claimed that this can be done within 15 minutes. The device contains patented computer chips that use artificial intelligence and fuzzy logic. The latter allows the computer to work with imprecise terms. The device's limited vocabulary contains standard terms such as *fast forward, stop,* and *play.* To tape a particular show on a particular TV channel, for instance the MacNeil/Lehrer NewsHour, one would say, "MacNeil, 13," if one resides in the New York City area. Next one would say, "Monday 7 PM." To watch the tape, one would tell the machine to "rewind" and then "play." Commercials can be eliminated with the command "zap."

Parents who are frustrated by the inability to curtail the amount of sex and violence so often seen by their teenage children can now turn to electronics for help. Technology is available that will automatically block out any programs that the parents deem inappropriate for watching by their children. The cost of this electronic moralist is about $5 per set. An unused portion of the television signal is used to send a special rating code for each show. For instance, V could be used for denoting violence, L for obscene language, and N for nudity. The watchful eye of the new electronic gadget then would simply block programs that had any or all of these ratings.

—Franz J. Monssen

Information systems and services

As it meets the challenges of the future, the U.S. Library of Congress has a special responsibility to ensure that the application of the new information technologies will not widen the gap between the information-rich and the information-poor, between the affluent and the destitute in society. It must enable the U.S. to take full advantage of the country's investment in libraries, information services, and the people who provide these services.

Recognizing that the key to the future progress of the U.S. depends upon convenient and rapid access to organized information, the Library of Congress issued a strategic plan that outlined its mission and future objectives, which are: (1) to support the Congress of the U.S. by providing its members with relevant information as it addresses issues of national and international importance; (2) to promote the cultural and intellectual heritage of the U.S. by reinforcing the link between libraries and education through the presentation of lectures, symposia, concerts, and other public programs; (3) to expand bibliographic control over all parts of its collection, and to make this collection more accessible to Americans in every state; (4) to modernize the library's management and support activities so as to encourage and sustain efficiency, flexibility, and innovation; (5) to further the development of the "electronic library" by improving existing electronic information services to members of Congress and inaugurating such services to the rest of the nation and its libraries.

However, because of budget cuts, the Library of Congress has had to curtail services unrelated to its principal priorities and objectives. It suspended its interlibrary loan program to foreign libraries as a result of lack of funds to cover the program's cost. It also closed the National Translation Center, which functioned as an international depository and referral center and helped users locate unpublished translations of foreign-language literature in the sciences.

U.S. information systems. Many federal government departments operated computer-based bulletin boards to better serve residents of the nation. The Economic Bulletin Board, operated by the Department of Commerce, enabled users to obtain the latest government statistical information from the Bureau of Labor Statistics, Bureau of the Census, the Federal Reserve Board, and other federal agencies by employing a simplified menu interface that helped retrieve desired data files and related press releases. The Department of Labor operated an electronic bulletin board with information about consumer and producer prices, employment and unemployment statistics, job safety and health regulations, and a nationwide listing of federal job opportunities. The service was free, and anyone with a computer modem and communications software could use it by dialing 1-800-597-1221.

The National Criminal Justice Reference Service (NCJRS) is the largest criminal justice information network in the world. Its specialized clearinghouses have been staffed by information specialists who provide a wide range of reference, referral, and distribution services. The NCJRS electronic bulletin board was made available as a free service to state and local criminal justice professionals. The Bureau of Justice Assistance Clearinghouse kept justice professionals informed about criminal justice programs and products. The National Victim Center provided relevant information to criminologists, researchers, and individual crime victims. Specialists in the Bureau of Justice Statistics Clearinghouse answered requests by researchers seeking crime and criminal

justice data, performed database searches, and provided statistical information packages and other related products and services. In essence, all branches of the NCJRS worked to improve criminal justice and the criminal justice system.

Produced by the American Psychological Association, the ClinPSYC database, on CD-ROM (compact disc read-only memory), contained records selected to meet the specialized needs of clinical psychologists and social workers, hospitals and mental health centers, schools of social work, and university departments of psychology. Included were U.S. and international journal articles on the assessment, treatment, and prevention of psychological and related physical disorders. Each of the approximately 222,500 records, dated from 1980 to the present, contained a bibliographic citation, index terms, and an informative abstract summarizing the source document. The search software that was included utilized user-friendly interfaces and allowed for quick access to the data files by means of the controlled psychological vocabulary.

The Institute of Electrical and Electronics Engineers (IEEE) is the world's largest technical society, with a membership of more than 274,000 people in 150 countries. Each year the society held approximately 300 technical conferences throughout the world and published an estimated one-quarter of the world's literature in computing, electronics, and electrical engineering. To make this literature more readily available, the Institute created a document-delivery service called Ask*IEEE, which allowed members and nonmembers to order scientific and technical articles that had been published in journals, magazines, and conference proceedings. The price of the delivered article covered all fees, including copyrights.

QUAKELINE was developed by the National Center for Earthquake Engineering Research as an on-line index to nearly 20,000 items of information related to earthquake hazards and related topics. The Federal Emergency Management Agency (FEMA) provided additional funds to the center so that it could serve as a research and information resource for special projects conducted by FEMA.

The telephone book white pages went on-line through CompuServe. This on-line version was much larger than the printed pages and supported enhanced search capabilities. The database contained 80 million entries, each with a name, address, telephone number, and length of residence. If the exact name and address were known, a simple search would retrieve the phone number. One could also search on the phone number and retrieve the name and address. If only the surname and the state, city, or zip code were known, Phone*File would list and display all the names that matched. But one should be aware that there were more than 30,000 people named Smith residing in New York state.

On a less serious side, the National Information Services Corp. published a CD-ROM that contained 25,000 jokes, anecdotes, and funny quotations. These humorous items were gathered from various published sources and were organized into more than 1,000 subject headings for easy retrieval and use by people making speeches and presentations.

International information systems. The Vatican Archives were founded in 1611 by Pope Paul V as a repository of the day-to-day proceedings of church government; the correspondence of bishops, popes, and kings; and papal pronouncements on the authority of the church and the pope. These records document the history of the Holy See and its worldwide interests from the 9th to the early 20th century. Thanks to grants from the National Endowment for the Humanities and Getty Grant Program, some 1,450 descriptions of records in the Vatican Archives plus 550 histories of the agencies that produced, received, or archived them were transcribed onto an electronic database and made available for study and searching through the Research Libraries Information Network.

Teikoku Databank (TDB), a large Japanese information service organization, was founded in Tokyo in 1900. The organization, with its many reporters and offices throughout Japan, collected and provided financial information about Japanese companies. However, until recently, all those who wanted to examine the financial history of a Japanese company had to be able to read Japanese. This situation changed with the advent of TDB's COSMOS2 electronic database, which provided U.S. organizations with English-language financial information on 200,-000 large and small Japanese companies. A TDB subsidiary was located in New York City to service users of the English-language database.

The Arab Medical Information Network produced a bibliographic database of Arabic medical literature and related materials. Additional databases provided a referral information system for Arab medical personnel and organizations, statistical data on the health of patients, and information about the medical welfare situation in various Arab countries.

The English Poetry Full Text Database, produced by Chadwyck-Healy Ltd., filled two CD-ROMs and contained 64,000 poems by 680 poets. Included were many forgotten or ignored poets, whose works were thus made accessible to readers and scholars. The first disc contained the writings of poets up to the end of the 18th century, and the second held the works of 19th-century poets. Also included on the CD-ROM were computer programs that offered a choice of search procedures, a user-friendly interface, a guide to changing patterns of word use and vocabulary styles, and programs for computing different stylistic and linguistic analyses.

Research. NYSERNet is a not-for-profit corporation whose mission is to advance science, technology, and education by providing electronic access to information and encouraging collaboration between the network affiliates. It received grants from the Apple Computer Corp. and the J.M. Kaplan Fund in support of Project GAIN (Global Access Information Network). The project studied the effect of linking rural libraries to Internet, a high-speed telecommunications network, which could in turn link those communities to a global information environment. Using Internet, the connected libraries were able to exchange electronic mail with users throughout the world and tap into remote databases. Syracuse (N.Y.) University's School of Information Studies monitored the project and studied how the libraries benefited when they used the computers and telecommunications network to achieve a renewed sense of community by organizing electronic town hall meetings and disseminating information from the government and from various groups in the community.

The National Library of Medicine awarded a three-year High Performance Computing and Communications Contract to a consortium of nine West Virginia institutions headed by the West Virginia University Research Corp. The award, which was part of the federal government's efforts to apply advanced technologies to improve health-care services, enabled the consortium to apply advanced networking technologies to the delivery of health services in both rural and urban areas of West Virginia and evaluate them.

Wayne State University Library System, Detroit, Mich., received a grant from the U.S. Department of Education to create machine-readable records of the manuscript and oral history collections housed in the Walter P. Reuther Archives of Labor and Urban Affairs. These archives were established in 1960, and they held the most important collection concerning the history of the North American labor movement. Previously, the only access to this material had been by means of printed guides. The conversion to computer-stored records provided users with faster and more convenient access to the files, which were now searchable by names, subject categories, and key words in the document.

The Research Libraries Group, which sponsors the American Literary Materials Project, was awarded a grant by the National Endowment for the Humanities to develop a national database of information about primary materials in American literature. Materials such as manuscripts, typescripts, and correspondence have always been difficult or even impossible to locate. The first stage of the project identified research materials related to an initial list of 125 U.S. authors and developed methodologies for surveying, describing, and cataloging them so that they could be made available throughout the Research Library Information Network.

—Harold Borko

Satellite systems

Earth applications satellites consist of three broad classes: communications, Earth observation, and navigation. These automated civil and military spacecraft are designed, built, launched, and operated by nations, groups of nations, and commercial firms.

Communications satellites. This largest class of commercial satellites continued to grow in number, complexity, and performance during the year. More than 200 countries currently relied on some 200 of these satellites for domestic, regional, and global links and for defense communications, direct broadcast services, and mobile communications. In 1994 satellite communications were expected to become a $15 billion-per-year business. International newspapers and periodicals regularly used satellites to beam copy directly to printing plants throughout the world. *Time,* for example, sent many different versions of the magazine to its 10 printing plants for mail distribution within 24 hours.

The commercial cooperative International Telecommunications Satellite Organization (Intelsat), the major provider of global transoceanic telephone and television services, operated 19 satellites positioned in Clarke (geostationary) orbits. (In a geostationary orbit a satellite travels from west to east at such a speed that it remains fixed over a given place on the Earth's equator at an altitude of approximately 35,900 km [22,300 mi]. In October 1993 the first of the new Intelsat VII satellites was successfully launched. Eight more were on order. Each Intelsat VII could accommodate 75,000 telephone calls and two TV channels, a 20% increase in capacity. To provide additional capacity, Intelsat signed an agreement to lease up to three geostationary Express satellites, as demand required, from Informkosmos of Russia. During 1993 Intelsat also expanded its digital video service offerings. These included a compressed broadcast video service at 6.6 megabits per second and a high-definition television (HDTV) service at rates of 45 and 60 megabits per second.

The rapid evolution of mobile satellite systems continued as the International Maritime Satellite Organization (Inmarsat) completed final design and acceptance testing of its new briefcase-sized Inmarsat M transceiver terminals that could be used for land mobile services. Inmarsat also planned for a successor to its Inmarsat M in the form of a miniature handheld transceiver known as the Inmarsat P. Two land mobile satellite systems were scheduled for launch in 1994 by the American Mobile Satellite Corp. (AMSC) and Telesat Mobile Inc. (TMI). AMSC would provide service primarily to the U.S. and its coastal waters, while TMI would provide service primarily to Canada and its coastal waters. These satellite systems used a Clarke orbit and employed extremely high power to reach small receivers in mobile vehicles.

Plans proceeded for new mobile systems in low- and medium-altitude Earth orbit to transmit voice messages and store and forward data. These systems included the Gonets system (Russia), the Orbcomm system (U.S.), the Leo One system (Mexico/U.S.), Vitasat (U.S.), Afristar (U.S.), and Starsys (U.S./Europe). The first to provide messaging services was expected to be Orbcomm, which planned to launch and deploy satellites in 1994.

Direct-broadcast satellite (DBS) services proved to be another area where great change occurred. The first high-powered DBS made by Hughes Aircraft Co., owned by DirecTv and United States Satellite Broadcasting (USSB), was launched on Dec. 17, 1993, from Kourou, French Guiana. It was expected that in the spring of 1994, the DBS would begin providing entertainment and news programming directly to homes equipped with low-cost, 65-cm-diameter very small-aperture terminal (VSAT) antennae in the U.S. and Canada. Meanwhile, on July 22, 1993, Spain launched DBS Hispasat 1B into a Clarke orbit on an Ariane 44L booster rocket. This satellite, which would carry television programming and telephone traffic for the Iberian Peninsula and the Canary Islands, was declared operational in October. On Nov. 19, 1993, Mexico's DBS Solidaridad 1 also was launched successfully. This satellite was designed to provide telephone, television, and data services for Mexico, Central America, the Caribbean, and the Spanish-speaking nations of South America. It was the first DBS over the Americas to mount transponders for three different frequencies: C-band, K-band, and L-band (for mobile communications). (A transponder receives a signal on one wavelength and then transmits the signal on another frequency.)

In East Asia the transition continued from the Japanese DBS service provided by the BS-3 satellite to a fully commercial operation to be provided by the Nippon (or N-Star) satellite that was being built for launch in the mid-1990s. This DBS system was to provide digital HDTV services and broadcast its signals to small 35-mm flat-plate antennae.

Earth observation satellites. This category includes meteorological (weather), Earth resources, and military early-warning-surveillance and reconnaissance satellites.

Weather satellites. Continuous global weather observations were obtained during the past year from U.S., European, and Japanese weather satellites in

DBS-1, North America's first high-powered direct-broadcast satellite, was launched by an Arianespace rocket from Kourou, French Guiana, on Dec. 17, 1993. The satellite was made by Hughes Aircraft Co.

high-altitude geostationary orbits and from U.S., Russian, and Chinese satellites in lower-altitude polar or near-polar orbits. Images and other meteorological data transmitted by these satellites benefited many economic sectors, including energy, construction, agriculture, fishing, and the transport and service industries.

Europe's Meteosat weather satellite system maintained complete weather coverage over the continent, with three operational Meteosats positioned in Clarke orbits as Europe's contribution to the World Weather Watch Global Observation System (other participants were the U.S., Russia, and Japan). Late in the year the 13-nation European Space Agency (ESA) began to transfer the operation of the Meteosat program to the 16-nation Eumetsat organization at Darmstadt, Germany. Composed of the meteorolog-

ical agencies of European governments, Eumetsat was created in 1986 to finance and manage the operational Meteosat system. Meanwhile, on Nov. 19, 1993, Meteosat 6 was placed in orbit, with Mexico's Solidaridad 1 riding the same launcher.

The U.S. National Oceanic and Atmospheric Administration (NOAA) operated two meteorological Geostationary Operational Environmental Satellites (GOES—similar to Europe's Meteosats) in Clarke orbits above North America and at least two operational NOAA weather satellites in low-altitude polar orbits. To replace a failing GOES-East, the U.S. leased Meteosat 3 from Eumetsat and moved it westward to cover the east coast of the U.S. and the Caribbean.

Earth-resources satellites. This class of remote-sensing spacecraft observed the Earth and transmitted images in various bands. Among other applications, they provided information on changes in the physical, chemical, and biological processes in the Earth's ecosystem and the influence of human activity on these systems.

The Franco-U.S. (Centre National d'Études Spatiales-National Aeronautics and Space Administration) Topex/Poseidon oceanographic polar-orbiting satellite continued to perform its ocean-mapping mission and assay activity in the oceans. This effort has proved valuable in understanding ocean current circulation and heat transport.

Other Earth-monitoring satellites equipped with imaging scanners, such as the French Satellite pour Observation de la Terre (SPOT) and U.S. Landsat vehicles, furnished imagery of significant commercial value. France and the European Union shared costs of temporarily activating the SPOT 1 satellite in the spring and summer in order to help monitor agricultural programs and crop production. Other SPOT and Landsat vehicles contributed images that were important in assessing damage caused by river flooding in the U.S. Midwest and Western Europe as well as by wildfires that swept southern California and for planning recovery operations afterward. The SPOT 3 satellite was successfully launched into polar orbit on Sept. 25, 1993. Landsat 6, launched on October 5, fell into the Pacific Ocean when the booster rocket malfunctioned. That loss placed the Landsat image distributor in a precarious competitive business position, with SPOT Image positioned to take advantage of the expanding commercial imagery market.

Elsewhere, China and Brazil agreed on a joint project to build and launch a remote-sensing satellite. Brazil's Ministry of Science and Technology planned to construct the spacecraft, which China was scheduled to launch in 1996. On Sept. 20, 1993, the Indian Space Research Organization (ISRO) launched a remote-sensing satellite, IRS-1E, into the wrong orbit when its four-stage Indian Polar Satellite

The European environmental resource satellite ERS-1, shown here in an artist's drawing, has supplied valuable data about the Earth's surface and atmosphere.

Launch Vehicle malfunctioned after liftoff from the Sriharikota Launch Center.

Military reconnaissance/surveillance satellites. Reconnaissance satellites provide optical and radar images of the Earth and monitor electronic emissions of terrestrial and airborne communications and radar systems. "Early-warning" surveillance satellites are equipped with infrared sensors that detect missiles within moments of their launch from land or sea, while other sensors record nuclear explosions above ground or in space. In a peacekeeping role, these U.S. and Russian spacecraft monitor compliance with international treaties and furnish warning of imminent hostilities. Reconnaissance/surveillance spacecraft normally operate in low-altitude polar orbits, highly elliptical Molniya (Northern Hemisphere-loitering) orbits, and geostationary orbits.

Both Russia and the U.S. continued to operate all forms of instrumented reconnaissance and surveillance satellites. With the end of the Cold War, however, these programs began to be reduced significantly in size and scope. Western European governments, on the other hand, expanded efforts to develop and acquire images from reconnaissance satellites. On April 27, 1993, the 10-nation Western European Union (WEU) signed a reconnaissance satellite agreement with France. In exchange for financial support, France and its project partners, Italy and Spain, would provide to the WEU optical images of the Earth obtained from Helios spy satellites. The first of these satellites, scheduled for launch in mid-1994, would transmit images to a space control center in Torrejon, Spain.

Navigation satellites. Both the U.S. and Russia continued to operate navigation satellites in high-altitude Earth orbits. Signals from these military satellites permitted those with receivers on Earth to determine their geographic position, altitude, and velocity with a high degree of accuracy. Almost identical twins, the U.S. Global Positioning System (GPS) and Russia's Global Navigation Satellite System (GLONASS) each consisted of 21 active satellites and three spares. The GPS became fully operational in 1993, while GLONASS was to become operational in 1995. Because of the enormous commercial benefits that signals from these vehicles provided in increasing the efficiency of air and surface transportation, significant changes occurred in civil exploitation of these military satellite systems during the year.

Although signals from the GPS satellites are encrypted to prevent their accurate use by potential U.S. adversaries, commercial users demanded the more precise unencrypted signals. Therefore, the U.S. Coast Guard and the Federal Aviation Administration (FAA) rebroadcast differentially "corrected" GPS signals in selected areas. Moreover, in 1993 a U.S. commercial firm began marketing a similar service. It allowed users to determine their location or track vehicles to within a few meters of actual position by using a combination of signals from GPS satellites and local FM radio stations.

—F.C. Durant III; R. Cargill Hall
See also Feature Article: Computing with Light.

Meteosat 6, a weather satellite of the European Space Agency, waits to be checked out in a test cell. The satellite was placed in orbit on Nov. 19, 1993.

Energy

The past year brought few surprises in the energy industry. Certainly there were no developments even remotely as striking as the oil crises of the 1970s, which inspired significant rapid shifts not only in the world oil markets but in other energy sectors as well. Nor were there major accidents that would inspire a rethinking of current technologies, as did the nuclear power plant accidents at Chernobyl in the Soviet Union in 1986 and at Three Mile Island in Pennsylvania in 1979. Although the year was not one of sensational developments, a broad array of changes was occurring in the energy industry, largely as continuations of trends of the previous several years. Some of these trends addressed underlying long-term challenges that could flare up in future years. In particular, energy-related environmental degradation and increasing world dependence on oil from the Middle East remained as intractable as ever.

Energy and the environment. As with many industrial activities, energy production and use can affect the environment significantly. One environmental concern that transcends national boundaries and has broad implications for all aspects of energy supply and use is global climate change. At the "Earth Summit" in Rio de Janeiro in June 1992, most of the world's nations agreed to try to limit emissions of carbon dioxide (CO_2)—produced by the combustion of fossil fuels and the major contributor to potential climate change—to the levels of 1990 by the year 2000. During the year many nations grappled with how best to meet that goal. International climate-change talks continued in August 1993 in Geneva, with a new focus on meeting national goals while encouraging "joint implementation"—cooperative efforts between countries (or entities within them such as electric utilities) to reduce "greenhouse" gas emissions. In the United States an intense national debate occurred concerning the merits of a broad-based energy tax, which could encourage some reductions in energy use and help in meeting CO_2 goals. After extensive discussion the U.S. Congress decided that the costs of this approach outweighed the benefits. In October 1993 U.S. Pres. Bill Clinton announced his Climate Change Action Plan, with a variety of initiatives across a broad range of energy activities, including spurring private-sector adoption of energy-efficient technologies, encouraging the use of natural gas (a fuel that emits less carbon dioxide per unit of energy than either oil or coal), assisting electric utilities in developing methods of reducing emissions of greenhouse gases, accelerating commercial deployment of renewable energy sources, and reducing emissions of natural gas (the second most significant greenhouse gas, after carbon dioxide) from distribution systems and coal mines.

Another energy-related environmental concern of widespread interest is acid deposition. Acid deposition can have serious, but generally local or regional, consequences, including water acidification, fish losses, forest damage and decline, reduced visibility, and both direct and indirect human health effects. The precursors of acid deposition, sulfur dioxide (SO_2) and nitrogen oxides (NO_x), are emitted in fossil-fuel combustion. Of the estimated 23 million tons of SO_2 emitted in the U.S. in 1987, more than two-thirds stemmed from electric utilities.

Emissions of major pollutants from fossil-fuel plants could be greatly reduced by technologies already developed. While these technologies were widely used in industrialized nations, some areas were just beginning to address energy-related environmental protection challenges. For example, SO_2 deposition in Poland was several times higher than in Western Europe, and in China limited environmental controls on coal consumption have resulted in high levels of acid precipitation and of particulate matter in the atmosphere. As part of an effort to introduce U.S. pollution-control technologies in Eastern Europe, the U.S. Department of Energy (DOE), provided funding for a variety of clean-coal projects in Krakow, Poland. The projects ranged from introducing briquetting technology in order to reduce emissions from household stoves to promoting more efficient district heating operations to installing particulate-collections devices.

In the U.S., efforts continued to further control the environmental impact of fossil-fuel use in electricity generation. One notable development was the U.S. Environmental Protection Agency's (EPA's) first-ever auction of "pollution allowances," a market-based approach to pollution control. As authorized by the Clean Air Act Amendments of 1990 (CAAA), the EPA sold at auction the rights to emit SO_2. In an emissions trading market authorized by the CAAA, several utilities also traded between themselves the rights to emit SO_2. One intended benefit of this novel approach to environmental control was that it allowed market forces to determine the combination of technologies that reduce SO_2 emissions at the lowest cost. In contrast to specifying a particular type of emission-control technology to be used (such as scrubbers on all coal plants) or allowable emissions rates for any particular power plant, the CAAA approach allowed utilities to employ any of a variety of methods, including adding scrubbers, using coal with a lower sulfur content, cofiring with natural gas, and retiring high-emissions plants.

Radioactive-waste-disposal issues continued to receive considerable attention during the past year. In contrast to the environmental challenges of fossil-fuel combustion involving large volumes of SO_2, CO_2, NO_x, and coal ash, the environmental challenges of nuclear plants involved relatively small volumes of materials with sometimes high levels of radioactivity. Efforts to find suitable sites and to develop facilities for waste disposal were proceeding far more slowly than originally anticipated because of a combination of political, economic, institutional, and technical challenges. For example, DOE, which was to be responsible for the permanent disposal of commercial spent nuclear fuel beginning no later than Jan. 31, 1998, planned to spend the next several years evaluating whether Yucca Mountain, Nevada, would be a suitable site for a permanent repository. Contingent on a favorable evaluation, DOE intended to construct the facility by 2010. However, many experts (including the Nuclear Waste Technical Review Board) viewed DOE's schedule as optimistic. The state of Nevada was critical of the efforts to site the facility within the state and raised regulatory and legal challenges. In the absence of a permanent repository, DOE was pursuing the development of a temporary facility, called monitored retrievable storage.

Until DOE could accept the commercial spent fuel, that fuel was to be held primarily in water-filled pools within each nuclear power plant's reactor building. However, commercial reactor-fuel pools were typically not designed to hold the entire amount of spent fuel generated over the lifetime of a plant. According to recent DOE surveys, 28 operating reactors—about 25% of all nuclear power plants—would have inadequate storage capacity by the end of the year 2000. Although measures such as reracking of spent fuel assemblies (decreasing the spacing between the assemblies) extend somewhat the capacity of fuel pools, independent spent-fuel storage installations would be needed at a growing number of plants in order to continue operations. Such dry-storage facilities had been built or were being planned at several plants, but some states were reluctant to allow them, noting that such facilities could become permanent if DOE waste-disposal efforts remained unsuccessful.

Evolving structure of the electric power industry. Worldwide consumption of electricity, with its ease of use and versatility, grew rapidly during the past decade. For example, consumption in North America and Western Europe increased by about one third between 1982 and 1991. Consumption grew even more rapidly in less developed countries during this same period. For example, consumption nearly doubled in India and China and grew by about 50% in Central and South America and Africa.

As the pace of electricity development continued, there were improvements in the primary generation technologies, leading to cleaner, more efficient production. Perhaps even more important was a shift in the planning, development, and operation of electric power systems. During the past decade the electric power industries in many countries underwent significant structural changes. One aspect of this change was the growth of competition as nonutility organizations began to design, build, and operate power plants, eroding the traditional monopoly of electric utilities. In the U.S. this competition was encouraged by the Public Utility Regulatory Policy Act of 1978 and further stimulated by the Energy Policy Act of 1992. As the nonutility generation market grew, electric utilities typically were the purchasers of this competitively supplied power, which they then sold to retail consumers. However, large industrial consumers increasingly were seeking direct access to competitive supplies through utility-transmission networks and made some limited advances in doing so during the past year.

Continuing a decade-long trend, competitively acquired supplies supplanted the construction of power plants for utilities in many areas. For example, a several-year effort in California to solicit bids to supply a total of 1,340 MW to the state's three private utilities ended in 1993. That solicitation reportedly drew 386 bids totaling 17,981 MW from 186 different suppliers. The forthcoming awarding and implementation of the contracts could largely determine new power plant construction in California through the rest of the decade.

The growth of generation competition continued outside the U.S., as well. For example, nonutility power development was reported in many countries in 1993, including China, South Korea, the Philippines, India, the United Kingdom, Greece, The Netherlands, Portugal, Russia, Slovakia, Argentina, Peru, and Panama.

Another related structural change was occurring in many countries that had government-owned utilities. Efforts to increase private-sector involvement in the electric power industry had recently accelerated in many of these nations, beginning with the 1990 privatization of the state-owned Central Electricity Generating Board in the United Kingdom and continuing with the 1992 sale of Argentina's state-owned utility. In 1993 Electrobras, Brazil's state-owned electric utility, announced that several power plants under construction would be sold to the private sector or completed in joint ventures with private enterprises. Electrobras was also expected to announce the sale of two major regional utilities by the year's end. Other privatization efforts, at various stages, were continuing in many countries, including Pakistan, Bolivia, Turkey, Australia, and New Zealand.

World oil markets. Petroleum remained the leading commodity in international trade in 1993. The flow of crude oil between nations averaged nearly 30 MBD (million barrels per day) during the past year. World petroleum production in 1993 was at about the same level as the all-time high of more than 60 MBD reached in the late 1970s. However, the relative stability in total world crude oil consumption masked substantial underlying regional changes. A 10% decline among industrialized nations during the past 15 years and a drop in the former Soviet Union since 1989 countered large increases in the less developed countries.

In contrast to the relative stability of total consumption, world oil prices fluctuated greatly during the past two decades. Substantial declines took place during the past two years. Adjusted for inflation, 1993 prices, which dropped sharply at year's end, declined to about half of their 1990 levels and to less than one-third of the highs reached in the early 1980s.

Until its dissolution in 1991, the Soviet Union was the world's largest oil producer. However, production had undergone a sharp decline since the highs of about 12 MBD in 1987 and 1988. By 1993 poor management of oil resources in the former Soviet Union, including lack of exploration, a shortage of spare parts, and declining drilling, had reduced production to about 7 MBD. This collapse was accompanied by similar drops in consumption in the former Soviet Union and also in Central and Eastern Europe. International efforts were made to

Workers construct high-voltage power lines on mountainous terrain in China. Consumption of electricity in China nearly doubled between 1982 and 1991.

Sovfoto/Eastfoto

revive Russia's oil industry. For example, the U.S. announced a $2 billion loan package for oil and gas equipment intended to help return to production 35,000 idle wells.

While the amount of oil produced by OPEC increased slightly during the past decade, at 25 MBD it remained well below the maximum production of more than 31 MBD reached in 1978. Despite intensive exploration efforts throughout the world during the past decade, OPEC nations continued to hold the great majority of the nearly one trillion barrels of world crude oil reserves, with Saudi Arabia alone accounting for more than 25% of the total.

Expanding natural gas use. With its relative abundance, favorable emissions characteristics, and well-established technologies for production, delivery, and use, natural gas remained a fuel of choice during the past year. Worldwide natural gas consumption had soared in the past two decades from about 43 tcf (trillion cubic feet) in 1973 to about 70 tcf in 1992. As with oil, worldwide consumption totals masked dramatic underlying shifts in regional natural gas production. For example, in the U.S. fluctuating prices had had a strong impact on natural gas consumption since the 1970s. Owing to rapid price increases in the 1970s and early 1980s, consumption dropped from 22 tcf in 1972 to 16 tcf in 1986. Since 1984, however, inflation-adjusted prices at the wellhead had fallen to about half their peak, with a corresponding increase in demand to 20 tcf in 1992.

Natural gas reserves were highly concentrated, as was the case with oil. However, they were primarily in the former Soviet Union rather than in the Middle East. For example, while Saudi Arabia held over 25% of the world's oil reserves, it had less than 5% of the natural gas reserves. In contrast, while the former Soviet Union held about 6% of world oil reserves, it had about 40% of natural gas reserves.

Another difference between oil and natural gas reserves was their relative magnitude, with natural gas appearing to be far more abundant. For example, at current consumption rates, world oil reserves represent about 16 years of use, while natural gas reserves represent about 60 years of use. Technologies continued to be developed enabling more economical deeper wells, horizontal drilling, in-field development, and wells farther offshore in deeper water, all of which could increase reserves.

New energy technologies. Research, development, and commercialization continued on a broad range of energy technologies during 1993. While there were a number of interesting and useful developments holding both near- and long-term promise, there were no unanticipated breakthroughs in basic research or demonstrations of new technologies likely to revolutionize the energy industry. There was, however, continuing progress in a wide range of areas.

Construction crews work on a section of a natural gas pipeline near Brest in Belarus. Worldwide natural gas consumption rose from 43 trillion cubic feet (tcf) in 1973 to more than 70 tcf in 1992.

In a development likely to have a long-term impact, DOE began two major shifts in energy research funding. One was an effort to focus increasingly on activities with strong private-sector support. Many of DOE's programs were increasingly geared to fostering collaboration between industry and the federal government and to transferring technologies developed in DOE's national laboratories by means of cooperative research-and-development agreements. A second shift was in the choice of technologies, a move toward renewable energy efficiency and natural gas. For example, the federal budget for solar energy increased by 36% to nearly $250 million in fiscal year 1994. Shipments of photovoltaic devices in the U.S. had increased steadily since the early 1980s, averaging 13% growth since 1988, although the total supply remained a very small fraction of electricity supplies. Several utilities instituted or continued programs using such devices to provide power to customers at remote locations as a cost-effective alternative to building expensive distribution lines. In 1992 a record 15.6 MW of photovoltaic devices were shipped, most of which were for export markets. The leading renewable source for electricity remained hydroelectricity, a largely mature technology. About 13% of the total installed generating capacity in the U.S. was hydroelectric.

Considerable progress continued to be made in improving the efficiency of electricity-consuming devices and appliances. These technologies ranged from compact fluorescent lamps that were smaller, lighter, brighter, and less expensive than their earlier counterparts to integrated steelmaking processes that greatly reduced the need for coking coal. Many electric utilities continued to use new energy-efficient technologies to reduce the need for adding new generating plants, investing about $2 billion in such technologies in 1993. The largest utility program to date was announced in 1993 by Canada's Hydro-Quebec, which planned to invest about $2.4 billion through 2000 on energy-efficient technologies. Hydro-Quebec expected its program to reduce its capacity needs by 5,400 MW through use of such technologies as an advanced residential thermostat, which would be placed in 1.1 million households that used electric heat. Energy-efficient technologies for commercial and industrial customers would also be promoted.

Despite the relative maturity of natural gas technologies, a variety of research activities held considerable promise. Among them were advanced drilling systems for different types of gas reservoirs and high-efficiency consumption equipment such as advanced aeroderivative turbines for electric power system use. Efforts to develop nuclear power and fossil-fuel technologies that had demonstrated commercial interest also continued. For example, the nuclear power industry was preparing designs for the next generation of light-water reactors. Outside the U.S. some orders for new plants were announced in 1993. These plants were designed to make use of a variety of technical advances, including digital control systems and simpler designs requiring fewer pumps, valves, and motors.

DOE announced the winners of the fifth, and possibly final, round of the Clean Coal Technology Program. The goal of the multiyear $6 billion program, jointly funded by the U.S. government and by industry, was to promote highly efficient and clean advanced coal technologies. The winners of the fifth round included the following: a 480-MW, $780 million power plant in which coal with a high sulfur content would be gasified, cleaned, and then burned in a combustion turbine that exhausted into a steam generator; a $146 million project to add a gas turbine to an existing coal power plant, creating a 62-MW combined-cycle plant; a $375 million pressurized circulating fluidized-bed power plant with an advanced hot-gas cleanup system; a $37 million project to develop a diesel engine system that could use a coal-water slurry; and an $825 million demonstration of an integrated power-production/steelmaking process that eliminated the need to produce coke. Each project was expected to convert about 45% of the energy in coal into electricity, well in excess of the roughly 33% typical of conventional plants.

As in past years, substantial funding was devoted to researching the distant but, if successful, revolutionary prospect of nuclear-fusion power. In the U.S. alone, federal funding of fusion research during the past decades totaled billions of dollars, with more than $300 million added in 1993. Tangible progress was made in December with a successful experiment at the Tokamak Fusion Test Reactor (TFTR) to fuel briefly a fusion reaction using a mixture of deuterium (^{2}H) and tritium (^{3}H). Previous fusion experiments at TFTR and at the Joint European Torus had used deuterium alone or with small amounts of tritium in the fuel mix, producing a less-energetic reaction. Despite the successful experiment, the goal of commercial fusion power remained a few decades distant at best, with many more technical challenges to be met. Among them were the fundamental challenges of creating a reaction energetic enough to be self-sustaining and to produce more energy than would be consumed in starting the reaction and, if that was accomplished, of developing an economically attractive design for a commercial plant. Because of the high costs of fusion research, international collaboration was increasingly viewed as a necessity in the long-term effort to develop commercial fusion power.

Automotive transportation remained the leading use of oil, accounting for more than 40% of consumption in the U.S. during the past year. One notable development that could affect future oil consumption was a multiyear federal "clean car" initiative announced by President Clinton. Under that program, DOE was working with the U.S. automotive industry to promote cleaner, more efficient vehicles. Already during the past two decades, automotive technology had improved greatly, and this initiative would be based on those gains. Between the early 1970s and the mid-1980s, the average fuel economy of new automobiles in the U.S. doubled from 14 to 28 mi per gal, as mandated by federal corporate average fuel economy (CAFE) standards, and it had since remained constant. Harmful emissions had also been considerably reduced. The next-generation car might employ any of a variety of propulsion technologies being investigated, including electric motors fed by flywheels or chemical batteries, advanced internal combustion engines, or hybrid systems integrating advanced electric vehicle technology with advanced, high-efficiency engines or fuel cells.

—Robin K. Roy

See also Feature Article: The Rebirth of Electric Vehicles.

Environment

Six environmental issues seemed to be of paramount importance during the past year. There were many anomalous weather events worldwide, and catastrophic flooding in particular attracted a great deal of attention. Crime, violence, war, and aggressive behavior in general became part of the environ-

ment for an increasing proportion of the world's population. There was a growing awareness among experts on energy that the world energy market had become dangerously unstable and that there might be an explosive growth in energy prices beginning about 1997. If this happened, there would be a wide variety of surprising consequences, many of which would threaten the very fabric of modern civilization because of their effects on, for example, transportation, the economic survivability of metropolitan areas, agriculture, and the chemical industry. Penetrating and philosophical reexaminations of the very foundations of agricultural strategy were appearing in quantity. An agonizing reappraisal of strategy and tactics was under way among the most visionary resource managers.

All these issues have ramifications and implications that affect many other fields, from atmospheric sciences to city planning and medicine. The concern here will be to focus on a systemic overview of these issues, with particular emphasis on their environmental aspects. This type of overview is appropriate in that another important event of the year was the assembling of a new international network of scholars interested in applying the methods and approach of systems science to large-scale societal problems.

Flooding. During the year there was serious flooding in many parts of the world. In North America flooding occurred in a large triangle of land, with the southern corner near St. Louis, Mo. This flood was so unusual that it came to be referred to as a one-in-500-year flood. Late in the year there was serious flooding in several European countries, including France, Germany, Belgium, and The Netherlands. This flood was regarded as the worst in Europe in about 70 years. What does science have to say about possible root causes for these events?

One explanation concerns the role of the eruption of Mt. Pinatubo in the Philippines. Major volcanic eruptions have left clear "footprints" in historical weather records. Depressions in temperature for all recorded sites are clear for the years 1784 (after Mt. Asama in Japan and Skaptar Jökul in Iceland), 1817 (after Mt. Tambora in Indonesia), and 1836 (after Cosegüina in Nicaragua). The pattern for precipitation is more complex. For example, in 1836 precipitation in Baltimore, Md., was 185% of that in 1834, and 1836 was one of the four highest precipitation years for Baltimore in the 19th century. However, in 1836 the amount of rainfall in Charleston, S.C., was only 60% of what it had been in 1834. At New York City and Philadelphia, the altered climate produced no significant impact on precipitation. Thus, it appears that major volcanic eruptions do not increase precipitation everywhere. Rather, they alter the movement patterns of jet streams and wind systems, thereby changing the distribution of rainfall.

The eruption of Mt. Pinatubo, therefore, could have produced catastrophic flooding in some places but relative drought in others.

James C. Knox studied the history of the relationship between flooding and climate during the last several thousand years. He concluded that large increases in the magnitude of floods can be produced by remarkably small changes in climate. Excess rainfall in summer results from slow-moving cold fronts colliding with moist and unstable tropic-derived air masses. This may be the mechanism connecting the eruption of Mt. Pinatubo to the flooding at various places in the world during 1993. There has been a much greater likelihood of large floods in the period from 3,300 years ago to the present than there was from 5,000 to 3,300 years ago. The earlier period was warm and dry, with precipitation on average 15% less than in the recent period and July temperatures averaging at least 0.5° C (0.9° F) warmer. The surprising point here is the extraordinary sensitivity of the probability of serious flooding to small changes in mean temperature.

People living in floodplains have been lulled into a state of false security by recent, relatively flood-free history. Throughout most of its history, the Earth has been far less climatically stable than it has been in recent times. A recent article by GRIP (the Greenland Ice Core Project) concluded that, given the history of the last 150,000 years, the past 8,000 years have been strangely stable.

Natural climate changes due to geophysical phenomena, including volcanic eruptions and planetary glaciation cycles, are only part of the causation for flooding. The other part relates to land-management practices, particularly with respect to deforestation. Several years ago James E. King wrote of the long-run vegetation history of Illinois and noted that massive conversion of native forests and prairies to intensive agriculture occurred in the middle of the 19th century. Throughout the world and all through history, this pattern has been associated with subsequent flooding. The reason was discovered by Frank H. Bormann and Gene E. Likens: deforestation decreases the proportion of rainfall absorbed by the landscape and thus increases stream outflow. In a review of the effects of forest management on watershed hydrology, Bill Freedman noted that in the year after clear-cutting (removal of all trees in a stand of timber), stream outflow can be 32–40% higher than when the forest was intact.

Forests are of far more than aesthetic significance to a landscape. They have a wide variety of climatic and thermodynamic effects. A series of recent research reports have pointed out, for example, that the degree of deforestation of a landscape affects the reflectance (albedo) of the Earth's surface at night and, consequently, the outward radiation of heat.

A treeless snow- or ice-covered landscape in high latitudes during winter will be white and shiny—and highly reflective. This increased reflectivity will lower surface air temperatures on a regional scale. The net effect of forests is to stabilize all features of climate: temperature, precipitation, wind speed, evaporation, and flooding.

A phenomenon appeared during the coverage of the flood: criticism of the scientific enterprise. It was noted that publications on how to manage river basins so as to minimize the likelihood of flooding had been gathering dust on library shelves. Also, it was noted that there was a lack of integration of the flood-abatement efforts of different agencies. These themes—of inadequate historical perspective, related in part to too much emphasis on new research and not enough on analysis of previous results, and the fragmented worldview of institutions—were repeated in regard to the other issues.

Crime, violence, war, and aggression. Scientists and scholars have discovered several phenomena that shed a new light on crime, violence, war, and aggression. The statistics from several national and international agencies reveal astonishing differences in the incidence of crime in different countries. Homicide in the United States is 12 times as frequent per person as in Finland and 7 times as frequent as in Japan. Rape in the United States is 25 times as frequent per capita as in Japan. Robbery and violent theft are 147 times as frequent in the U.S. as in Japan. These huge differences do not seem to be some type of statistical artifact of data collection-and-processing procedures. Visitors to Europe and Asia notice the astonishingly peaceful character of many societies. In China one is typically surrounded by vast throngs of people. Not only is physical violence between individuals scarce, one hardly ever notices harsh words between people.

Curiously, if physicians who specialize in epidemics were given the statistics on crime but were not told what the statistics measured, they would assume they were dealing with epidemics. Only in the last two years has this view of crime as an epidemic begun to gain much visibility in the scientific community.

Several explanations for the crime in the United States seem obvious, once pointed out. For example, retail energy prices in the U.S. have always been much lower than in most other developed nations. Energy and labor can be substituted for one another as inputs to all economic activities. Therefore, any employer, given a choice between hiring one new worker or increasing the productivity of current staff by using more energy per worker, will choose the latter in areas where energy is cheap. The U.S. in 1994 was in the curious position of having used up more than half its domestic crude oil, importing more than half the crude oil it used, selling crude-oil products more cheaply relative to wages than any other country, having a severe unemployment and crime problem, and requiring huge expenditures for police and the criminal justice system. Basically, the society was being managed as if there were an embarrassing surplus of crude oil and a critical shortage of people to supply the labor force, when the opposite was true.

It is curious that people rarely note the connection between these related phenomena. The fact that connection is seldom made provides an important clue about one of the ultimate causes of environmental problems. The literature on systemic environmental problems is becoming so fragmented and scattered over thousands of professional magazines and journals that it is very difficult to perceive causal connections that actually exist. The fragmented character of the scientific literature, and of all human institutions, fosters a way of looking at real-world systems that focuses on individual puzzle pieces of very complex jigsaw puzzles rather than on the picture formed when all the pieces are fitted together.

During the last 20 years and particularly the last 5, medical research has made great strides in understanding the biological foundations for aggression and crime. Drawing on results from many research teams, Markku Linnoila and Matti Virkkunen proposed a hypothesis to connect neurotransmission within the brain, blood-sugar levels, alcohol, and violence. In their theory the driving force, or root cause, is a deficit in brain activity of the neurotransmitter chemical serotonin. This deficit precipitates a disturbance in glucose (sugar) metabolism. Low blood-glucose concentration lowers the threshold for impulsive violent behavior. Alcohol consumption causes a quick increase in serotonin release and modifies the mood-altering effects of low serotonin. However, chronic alcohol consumption intensifies the effects of low serotonin concentration. The net effect is to further increase the propensity for impulsive and violent behavior.

Another root cause of aggression in adults is drugs or other chemicals that have entered the bodies of pregnant women. For example, sex hormones prescribed to lower the likelihood of miscarriage have resulted in the child's growing up to be more aggressive.

A final cause may lie in the educational system. In their book *The Learning Gap: Why Our Schools Are Failing and What We Can Learn from Japanese and Chinese Education*, Harold W. Stevenson and James W. Stigler discovered that Asian elementary school classrooms encourage cooperative rather than highly competitive behavior. Students are eager to display what they know, and they are challenged to learn

© Lowack—Action Press/Saba

The Rhine River in Germany overflows its banks between Mainz and Koblenz. Flooding in several European countries, including France, Germany, Belgium, and The Netherlands, in late 1993 was regarded as the worst in about 70 years. Cologne in Germany was especially hard hit.

what is being taught rather than to surpass other children. Asian students strongly identify with the school and with each other. This finding is consistent with the observations made by foreign scientists working temporarily for universities in China. Many subtle devices are used to foster loyalty to the group and the institution instead of encouraging a spirit of interpersonal competitiveness. Analysts of crime have discovered that rape, for example, is less frequent where the inhabitants of a large metropolitan area all feel a sense of community with respect to one another.

From a collation of all these types of information, it is possible to hypothesize that the incidence of crime would be higher than otherwise at any time and place where one or more of the following conditions occurred: unusually low retail energy prices, an evolutionary-genetic mechanism at work increasing the incidence in the population of people with depressed serotonin activity in the brain, an increased input of chemicals into the bodies of pregnant women that resulted in a greater likelihood that their children would mature to be aggressive, and an emphasis by educational systems on competition rather than cooperation.

351

Los Angeles police officers search suspects after a crime in a commercial district. Aggression, violence, and crime were the subjects of research by many scientists during the past year.

Energy prices. A consensus was developing among energy analysts that crude-oil prices would continue to decline for a few more years but in about 1997 would begin to rise again at an astonishingly steep rate that would continue for many years. This idea is supported by computer-simulation gaming, which projects energy prices by using models that describe the history of world oil prices. The consequences of such an energy-price increase would pervade all aspects of modern society, and some of them would be astonishing and brutal. In their recent book *Cities and Automobile Dependence: An International Sourcebook*, Peter Newman and Jeffrey Kenworthy make clear one of the potential surprises from large energy-price increases. They thought it would be useful to produce a statistical compendium—in which all the numbers had been gathered in a consistent fashion—that focused on the world's major metropolitan areas. The only way they could achieve that goal was to visit all the cities and work with the government officials responsible for collating and processing the data. They made an astonishing discovery. For transporting commuters some of the world's major metropolitan areas use 12 to 16 times more energy per person per year than other metropolitan areas.

These huge differences in the energy intensiveness of processes from one metropolitan area to another have multiple causes: differences in average commuting distance due to differing degrees of urban sprawl; differences between the energy efficiency of transportation systems, as between large, energy-inefficient cars and high-technology, energy-efficient train systems; and differences in the loading of vehicles. In some cities most commuting is done with one person per car, while in others it is done with commuter trains fully loaded.

It takes little imagination to foresee the consequences to the economic sustainability of energy-inefficient cities if large increases in the world crude-oil price occur.

Agriculture. Within the last 18 months a number of remarkable critiques of conventional agriculture have appeared. Two features of this literature are particularly noteworthy. Much of it is coming not from universities but from interdisciplinary organizations that are viewing societal problems from a broad perspective, unrestricted by the increasingly intense forces operating within conventional institutions to produce ever more narrow specialization. Second, in these critiques agriculture is often used as a metaphor for the complete panoply of problems now plaguing society. The assumption is that if one has a really profound understanding as to what is wrong with agriculture and what needs to be done to solve the problems, one understands the problems of the broader society and the necessary solutions.

In this section only specific points raised in some of these critiques will be mentioned. At the end of this review, all these points will be pulled together into a synthesis, which will also draw on material from other sources.

Paul B. Thompson, Robert J. Matthews, and Eileen O. van Ravenswaay made many important points in their book *Ethics, Public Policy, and Agriculture*. They noted that continuing residue problems with antibiotics and sulfa drugs in veal calves and hogs occurred because the cost of violating government regulations is often much smaller than the cost of compliance. They also noted that government policy was tending to mask the real current financial hardships associated with farming in the U.S. Financial support from the government to farmers accounted for almost 50% of net farm income in 1986 and 1987. This is consistent with comments throughout this review that institutions increasingly address environmental problems by dealing with effects rather than causes.

The book specifically addresses the systemic character of present-day agricultural problems. For example, the reduction of chemical inputs, especially herbicides, would increase the demand for farm labor and revitalize rural communities. The central role of unrealistically low retail energy prices in generating problems in agriculture, and by implication, throughout society, was prominently mentioned.

Another new critique of agriculture, on the need to rethink industrial agriculture, came from the International Society for Ecology and Culture. Peter Goering, Helena Norberg-Hodge, and John Page—in their book *From the Ground Up: Rethinking Industrial Agriculture*—also wrote about the central role of fossil-fuel energy, particularly petroleum, in modern agriculture. For example, during the 20th century the total energy input into 0.4 ha (one acre) of corn (maize) has increased by a factor of eight. The authors believed that free trade would increase unemployment in the North as large corporations shifted their activities to exploit the cheap labor and lower environmental standards of nations in the South. They also concluded that free trade would produce a dramatic increase in global transport. This would increase the need for roads and fuel. As mentioned elsewhere in this review, that would coincide with a sudden increase in the global oil price, beginning in about 1997. These authors also noted the increasing global problem of salinization and waterlogging of irrigation schemes.

A comprehensive and profound reexamination of agriculture was produced by Judith D. Soule and Jon K. Piper of the Land Institute of Salina, Kan. Their book *Farming in Nature's Image: An Ecological Approach to Agriculture* represented the thinking of the entire group at that institute. They noted that a dominant theoretical framework in modern science is reductionism, with its underlying basic belief that the whole can be understood as the sum of its parts. The weakness in this approach is that small but cumulative effects operating over many years tend to be neglected. Economists tend to focus on benefits over a short time frame and, more generally, use a short time frame for comparing alternative policies. The consequences are pervasive. For example, the relative attractiveness of pesticides compared with integrated pest management or cultural control of pests follows from an emphasis on immediate results.

The authors also noted what they described as the omnipotence assumption—the belief that people can master nature and manipulate and improve upon it for their own ends. Modern science, they maintained, has been fundamentally concerned with fighting nature's laws. The underlying theme of the Land Institute is that agriculture should mimic nature, not fight it. Agriculture in prairies should mimic natural prairie plant communities, for example. That

would represent a move away from large acreages devoted to one annual crop, such as wheat.

Resource-management strategy and tactics. Donald Ludwig, Ray Hilborn, and Carl Walters published an important paper on resource exploitation, uncertainty, and conservation that attracted wide attention. They argued that the problem of managing natural resources is not one of managing the environment but rather one of managing people. They maintained that all resource-management problems have the same fundamental problem structure; whether the situation is a gold rush, geologic reserves of crude oil, an oceanic fishery, or the forests of a nation, there are three fundamental features of the situation in each case. First, there is the prospect of large and immediate financial gain through rapid exploitation of the resource. Second, politicians and governments invariably see it as being in their own immediate self-interests to ally themselves with the groups seeking to facilitate the process of rapid exploitation. Third, governments often come to subsidize the process of overexploitation and destruction of the resource.

The larger and more immediate the prospects for gain, the greater the political power that will be used to facilitate unlimited and ultimately destructive exploitation. The authors concluded that we should stop pretending that more research will lead to certainty concerning the status of the resource and the selection of an optimal management strategy. Rather, we should learn management strategies based on the assumption that uncertainty is an inevitable feature of any management situation. The authors noted that applied mathematics, decision theory, management science, and operations research provide a rich body of theory and methodology for managing systems in the face of uncertainty. An implication of their paper is that much scientific work on resource management has been misdirected; it was people and institutions we should have been learning to manage, not the resources.

Root causes of environmental problems. During the past year an informal international network of scholars and scientists in many fields and countries was assembled to consider how systems science might be applied to large-scale problems of society and presented to mass audiences. The group considered problems from every imaginable perspective: institutional structure; the way decisions are made; how research is conducted; and how knowledge is organized, synthesized, and used, for example. This group and the people at the Land Institute had been working completely independently and only by accident discovered each others' activities in December 1993. Both groups perceived that important causes of the ills in modern society included a fragmented worldview (shaped more by the division of responsibility and authority in institutions than by real-world processes or phenomena), a lack of historical perspective, a sense of omnipotence, and the self-serving character of many institutions.

The large international network additionally saw that a new kind of science was needed, one in which the emphasis was not on studying things or systems but rather on studying the way people think about systems. It began research to compare the relative realism and utility of different conceptual models of real-world phenomena. One important discovery was that much of science and scholarship errs in seeking explanations for present effects in very recent causes. Many effects are due to causes from 10 to 40 years in the past, particularly causes that cumulate over time.

This group also determined that many problems were being considered at too low a level of aggregation or abstraction for their true nature to be perceived. In particular, inconsistencies between pairs or among sets of policies were avoiding detection because insights from too narrow a perspective were being used in decision making. A root cause of this problem is that the way reality is viewed and decisions are made is primarily a consequence of the way all institutions are organized—so as to fragment reality into small units—and is not an appropriate response to the actual systemic, cross-disciplinary character of real-world systems. Furthermore, the structure of all institutions, particularly educational institutions, strongly programs us not to perceive problems as systemic. A few examples illustrate this.

A simple example concerns choice of transportation systems. People have become habituated to the automobile. However, it is slow; requires much land for roads and parking spaces; inefficiently uses resources, from metal and plastic to energy; generates pollution; and works against wise patterns of land use. Very high-speed, high-technology, energy-efficient, nonpolluting electric trains are obviously a superior choice and, consequently, are in use or under development in many countries. But in the U.S. the organization of government makes development difficult. Transportation departments do not have a mandate to develop electric-train systems, and energy departments do not have a mandate to deal with electricity as applied to trains. The electric-train option, therefore, simply disappears because no agency has a mandate to consider it.

A historical approach reveals that many environmental problems and decisions are linked to one another and also to one central decision. By 1974 the U.S. was first experiencing large and rapidly growing merchandise trade deficits due to the importation of crude oil. There were several possible ways of dealing with this situation. Three possibilities were to increase retail energy taxes dramatically, making them comparable to those in Europe; to impose a

high tariff on imported crude oil; or to render the problem invisible by increasing the rate of growth of the money supply. The third option was chosen. Interest rates tend to increase or decrease in response to changes in the inflation rate, and so interest rates increased along with the cost of imported crude oil. Since 1974 interest rates have tended to move up or down in response to changes in the current dollar cost of crude-oil imports. However, the prime interest rate charged by banks has typically been much higher than it was in 1972, at times up to 7½ times as great.

The effects of this large increase in prime interest rates since 1973 have pervaded society because the present value formula for evaluating all investment proposals is extremely sensitive to the discount rate, the interest rate charged by a central bank for loans of reserve funds to commercial banks and other financial intermediaries. When that rate is very low, a dollar earned 30 years in the future is significant. In such an investment environment, there is ample incentive to invest in capital items with a long useful life, such as new railway systems, tunnels, modern automobile plants and steel mills, dams, locks, bridges, ports, airports, freeway maintenance, large new buildings, educational systems, biological control of insect pests, and so on. When the discount rate is very high, there is a huge shift in the investment capital of a society toward items that it is hoped will pay off in a short time. In general, these are consumer products ranging from clothing to automobiles, though expenditures on commercial jet transports have also been included.

The consequences of this pattern of capital allocation have been catastrophic. There has been massive overinvestment in items that were not needed and massive underinvestment in items that were needed desperately. One example hints at the awesome scale of the consequences of not viewing major societal decisions from an an appropriately systemic perspective. On Dec. 19, 1993, it was reported that 700 unused commercial jet transports were parked in the desert. Assuming an average purchase cost of $50 million per airplane, this represents $35 billion that could have been invested in something else. If that money and the national capacity to produce complex high-technology vehicles had been converted to high-technology, energy-efficient trains, the U.S. would be well on the way to having complete regional train systems in all metropolitan areas, similar to those in Tokyo, Vienna, London, Paris, and Rome. The research group concluded that this misallocation of capital has occurred because of the high discount rates, which would not have been necessary if the country had shifted to an appropriate energy policy in 1974.

—Kenneth E.F. Watt

Food and agriculture

Bad weather and political upheavals caused reduced production of many significant crops. A global trade accord was finally reached, although haggling between individual nations continued. Nutritionists were devoting considerable attention to the possible health benefits.

Agriculture

Global production of several major crops—rice, wheat, and corn—dropped in 1993, prompting record high trading of these commodities in early 1994. Rising beef production pushed down cattle and beef prices. Overall, international economic growth supported farm demand. The world economic situation was predicted to improve slightly during 1994, with Japan and Western Europe showing positive but weak economic growth. In the U.S., heavy flooding in the Midwest caused a 13% drop in the index of crop production. However, beef and poultry production increased, causing a rise of almost 3% in the nation's total meat production. Overall, food prices increased for U.S. consumers but at a rate of about 1% less than that of other goods and services.

GATT. The Uruguay round of talks under the General Agreement on Tariffs and Trade (GATT) accomplished its main goal—to liberalize trade, thereby subjecting producers everywhere to more intense competition. But as 1994 began, nations continued to attempt to negotiate better deals from their trading partners before the pact went into effect on July 1, 1995.

It was a miracle that GATT survived at all, but after seven years of haggling, trade officials from 117 countries in December finally achieved a global trade agreement that slashed tariffs and reduced subsidies.

For the first time, agriculture, professional services, textiles, and investments were to be covered by international rules of fair trade. Tariffs and trade barriers were expected to tumble, thereby driving down consumer prices. New rules to prevent the dumping of goods at unfairly low prices were established. The agreement was expected to cut $300 billion a year in subsidies paid by industrialized nations to prop up their farmers and should cause prices to drop, giving less developed nations a better position in world markets.

Animal genome. Scientists at the U.S. Department of Agriculture's (USDA's) Meat Animal Research Center at Clay Center, Neb., used data from researchers throughout the world to produce genetic maps of cattle and hogs. The maps were the first step in allowing researchers to pinpoint and later control specific genes to produce desirable characteristics such as disease resistance in animals.

The work was focusing on a coordinated effort to map the genome—find the chromosomal locations of all genes—of agriculturally important animals as part of a program established by the USDA. Currently attempting to map the genome of cattle, poultry, sheep, and hogs, 51 scientists at 27 locations were developing information compatible with the human and mouse genome databases that were also being established. The work was to be coordinated internationally with other genome-mapping efforts.

Bovine somatotropin. Dairy products made from milk containing recombinant bovine somatotropin (rBST) went on sale in 1994 with USDA and independent analysts both predicting that the use of the new animal drug in dairy cows would have little overall impact on sales. Some studies had indicated that most consumers would not object to rBST, but three of the nation's largest food companies and distributors—the Kroger Co., Southland Corp., and

Stephen Crowley—The New York Times

Demonstrators outside a Washington, D.C., supermarket protest the sale of dairy products containing recombinant bovine somatotropin, a genetically engineered growth hormone given to cows to stimulate milk production. Although milk produced with the hormone was declared safe by federal agencies, many consumers feared that it was a health hazard.

Digitized images on a computer monitor, based on data provided by sensors in an airplane, reveal the amount of algae activity in catfish ponds. The rapid growth and death of blue-green algae in the ponds causes an off-flavor in the fish that makes them unsuitable for consumption.

Pathmark Stores Inc.—fearful of consumer reaction, took measures to restrict use of the drug and told distributors that they would prefer products without the hormone. However, other large food companies took no such action.

Despite sometimes stiff opposition from a small but vocal coalition of consumer and farmer groups in some states, the U.S. Food and Drug Administration (FDA) in November 1993 approved Sometribove, a drug containing rBST, for use in stimulating milk production in dairy cows. Manufactured by Monsanto Co., Sometribove was to be marketed under the name Posilac. The FDA approval marked the end of an exhaustive scientific review of the drug that began in the early 1980s.

The protein hormone somatotropin is produced by the pituitary gland of all farm animals and humans. Each species produces somatotropin with a slightly different composition. Cows produce bovine somatotropin, or bovine growth hormone, which is required for controlling normal growth processes, including normal growth and development of the mammary gland, as well as for normal milk production.

The FDA had declared in 1985 that milk and meat from cows treated with rBST were safe for human consumption, but it had not approved the hormone for commercial use on dairy farms. The American Medical Association, the National Institutes of Health, the World Health Organization, and peer-reviewed articles appearing in many science and medical journals all declared rBST safe.

Opposition to the drug was led by some farm groups, which feared that it would drive down milk prices owing to overproduction, and by some consumer groups opposed to most genetically engineered foods and drugs. Boycotts and lawsuits were expected in some states.

Ethanol. It was expected that by early summer 1994 the U.S. Environmental Protection Agency (EPA) would issue its final ruling on the role of ethanol in carrying out the provisions of the Clean Air Act Amendments of 1990 and the Energy Policy Act of 1992. The EPA's proposed rules had given ethanol a 30% share of the reformulated fuels market and resulted in plans for increased production facilities.

Ethanol is produced from starch-rich agricultural materials such as corn and sugarcane and may also be produced from cellulosic biomass materials such as wood, forage, and wastes; it is most often produced from corn. Demand for the environmentally friendly product in 1993 reached 3.8 billion liters (1 billion gallons). Ethanol is credited with playing a major role in reducing harmful carbon monoxide in Phoenix, Ariz., and Denver, Colo. As 1994 began, ethanol accounted for 8% of U.S. gasoline sales, and some analysts predicted that it would be a major competitor in the reformulated gasoline market by 1995.

Oil companies attacked the EPA's mandate on ethanol as an unfair intrusion into the marketplace, and the petroleum industry was expected to take the issue to court if the agency did not withdraw its proposed rules. As the debate raged, there were arguments that ethanol could not keep up with the demand that the 30% mandate would generate and that the fledgling industry could not compete with established industries without government assistance. Others saw the debate as a rural economic issue that could net taxpayers millions of dollars in savings as a result of reduced farm subsidies.

Health watch. A deadly protein known as ricin, found in the castor plant, has two polypeptide chains; one does the targeting, and the other does the killing. Scientists want to reengineer the protein so that it will seek out and kill only cancer cells without harming the cancer patient.

The structure of the protein, crystallized by a University of Texas researcher, was analyzed, and a three-dimensional picture of it was sent to the University of Missouri. There it was turned, sliced, and manipulated on the computer so that details less than a billionth of an inch wide were revealed.

Using crystallography and computer graphics imagery, researchers made small changes in the ricin. First, alterations were made on the computer, reengineering the molecule and calculating the effects of the changes. Data from that task were then taken into a laboratory where changes in the actual genes were made and the DNA was recoded to make the molecule behave in different ways. Although as of 1994 the research was at a very basic level, genetically engineered ricin might eventually be used to break up oil slicks or kill cancer cells.

Preliminary scientific findings revealed that supplements of glutathione may boost older people's weakening immune response. The antioxidant glutathione—one of the most abundant simple peptides in humans and other living organisms—is a common dietary supplement in Japan but is seldom used in the U.S. USDA researchers tested the peptide first in aging mice, with successful results, and then on white blood cells from both young and old people. Glutathione improved the cells' ability to divide and to produce substances that mobilize other substances involved in the immune response. It also dampened the cells' production of inflammatory substances. Glutathione's greatest effect was on the sluggish cells of the older population, boosting their function close to that of the younger people. Researchers were hoping to take the results from cell studies and test glutathione supplements in human beings. Earlier USDA studies had shown that another antioxidant, Vitamin E, helps restore older people's ability to nip germs and would-be cancers in the bud.

New products. It may not be possible to make a silk purse from a sow's ear, but a researcher at Purdue University, West Lafayette, Ind., developed a chemical process that makes silklike rayon from recycled office paper and other sources of cellulose. Industries from as far away as Japan were showing an increasing interest in the process.

An Indiana company hoped to take advantage of this cellulose-based process by making high-quality home insulation from recycled newspaper, claiming that the cellulose insulation is more effective than most fiberglass. A Tennessee firm hoped to use the technique to produce rayon yarn and said that if current research succeeded, a low-cost biodegradable rayon could be on the market within five years. A Japanese company said it would spin cellulose into cloth.

Faster and cheaper than current production methods, the process begins with cellulose, a chain of sugar molecules found in paper and wood. Rayon, which is used to produce a silklike cloth, is formed through separation of the cellulose chains and combination of them to create strong fibers. Previously, rayon could be made only from high-quality cellulose composed of very long chains. Even when researchers discovered that zinc chloride could be used to extract fiber from cellulose, the fibers were still not strong enough. But the process developed at Purdue created fiber several times stronger than previously made rayon, and it can be produced from many sources. After production, the fiber remains free of chemical residue and can be used for food or medical products. One of the chief problems with rayon is that most common manufacturing processes use toxic chemicals.

Catfish. Sensors mounted on an airplane could be a practical, economical tool to help limit off-flavor problems in farm-raised catfish. USDA scientists concluded that the imagery provided by the sensors gives reliable estimates of algae activity in catfish ponds. Rapid growth and death of blue-green algae causes sudden deterioration of water quality and the production of off-flavor compounds that are absorbed by the catfish.

Researchers were correlating images from remote-sensing equipment with mathematical calculations based on actual experiments to determine the various stages of algae growth and health. The sensors record wavelengths, which are translated into specific pigments. The color and amount of pigments indicate the type of algae present in the pond, their numbers, and their health.

—John Patrick Jordan; Patricia Brazeel Lewis

Nutrition

Continued developments in several exciting areas of research in nutrition (along with the usual amount of controversy) highlighted a productive year. Those findings most relevant to human health and well-being include: (1) the possible beneficial effects of antioxidants, including some common vitamins, on the resistance to coronary heart disease (CHD); (2) the role of an iron-rich diet in CHD; (3) neurotransmitters and appetite control; (4) energy intake and obesity; (5) molecular biology approaches to nutrition; and (6) functional foods, those in which the normal nutrient profiles have been altered so as to improve resistance to aging and disease.

Antioxidants and iron. One of the most exciting areas of nutrition research has to do with the potential health benefits of antioxidants. Research results strongly suggest that antioxidants have the ability to slow the aging process and the progression of

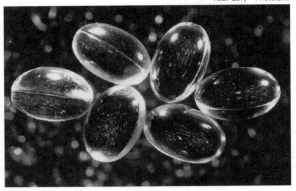

Vitamin E capsules are among the many antioxidants being used to protect people against harmful oxidation reactions in living tissue.

many aging-associated diseases, including CHD and some cancers. Oxygen is required for life but, under certain conditions, can form "active oxygen species" (AOS), which sometimes cause harmful "oxidation" reactions in living tissue. Antioxidants, as the name implies, protect tissue by reacting with AOS before damage can be done. Antioxidants prevent oxidation (in food, oxidation is called "rancidity"). They can be synthetic, such as butylated hydroxy anisol (BHA), commonly used in foods and packages; natural, such as the vitamin C in orange juice, vitamin E in corn oil, and beta-carotene in vegetables; or a combination, such as synthetic vitamin C and E, commonly taken as tablets. (Synthetic C is identical to natural C.) There are also scores of antioxidants that are not vitamins and that are found in plant materials, including vegetables, fruits, green tea, potatoes, and whole grains. Nutritionists recommend that foods rather than vitamin supplements be the primary means of increasing antioxidant intake whenever possible.

CHD has been the subject of the most intensive research on antioxidants and disease. Low-density lipoprotein (LDL) has long been recognized as a key factor in CHD. LDL carries cholesterol to the arterial wall and then deposits it to form plaque, the material responsible for the clogging of arteries. Researchers have provided substantial evidence that LDL must first undergo oxidation, under the influence of AOS, before cholesterol can be deposited. This could explain why smokers have a high risk of CHD. Smoking is known to release large amounts of AOS into the circulation and, in fact, smokers have lower levels of vitamin C in plasma and tissues. It is logical to expect that antioxidants would help to protect against damage induced by AOS and slow the rate of plaque accumulation in the arterial wall.

Some evidence has been obtained to support these ideas. It has been well established that antioxidants

slow or delay the rate of LDL oxidation. In fact, it is an established chemical principle that, in tissues or in foods, before oxidation of components can occur, the antioxidants in the system must be depleted. Other evidence supporting the idea that antioxidants help to slow plaque accumulation has been obtained in experimental animals and in epidemiological studies of human populations. Human populations with a high rate of CHD, such as those in Northern Ireland and Scotland, also have a high rate of smoking, especially among men, and a low consumption of fruits, vegetables, whole-grain cereals, and antioxidant supplements. The high risk of CHD is often blamed on the consumption of animal products by these people, which is not very high. It is tempting to speculate that increasing the intake of antioxidant supplements could reduce the prevalence of CHD in such high-risk populations and do so in a cost-effective manner.

A recently proposed hypothesis that implicated high intakes of dietary iron in CHD appeared to agree with what is known about antioxidants and CHD. It also served to illustrate the controversial debate on how best to prevent CHD and the role of the media in transmitting and interpreting nutritional information to the consumer. Researchers in Finland demonstrated that individuals with high levels of plasma ferritin (the primary iron storage form in the body) tended to have a higher risk of CHD than those with lower levels. This was an epidemiological study, the type of research that by definition cannot establish a cause-effect relationship but rather is conducted to gain clues about what variables should be studied further.

The ferritin hypothesis has some logic supporting it because iron is a strong pro-oxidant, meaning that iron works directly against antioxidants by initiating many oxidative reactions. In fact, free iron, that which is not bound to a protein like ferritin, is extremely toxic to the body, so much so that very little free iron exists at all. The body has elaborate biochemical means to keep iron sequestered and not moving about.

The ferritin hypothesis has been criticized by a number of leading scientists. They regarded the methodology for determining levels of ferritin in blood as suspect and noted that the one AOS (the hydroxyl radical) blamed for toxic effects has never been found within a living organism. Also, several studies during the year failed to confirm the original findings of the Finnish workers, including one done on the same population of Finnish men.

The role of the media in this controversy was enlightening. The original study implicating dietary iron and plasma ferritin as risk factors for CHD was widely published by the popular press and reported on by radio and television stations. It was darkly hinted by some newspapers and magazines that these findings were further evidence against eating beef. Beef, after all, is the best source of iron for most people. Several other studies were later published in the scientific literature that disagreed with the original findings, including one that reported somewhat the reverse of the first study. These studies, however, were apparently not deemed sensational enough for publication in the media.

The foregoing discussion illustrates a problem that must concern nutritionists, especially those involved in public education programs. On one hand, the widespread coverage of nutrition research is welcomed, as is the apparent interest in the subject on the part of the public. On the other hand, there is a great need for restraint on the part of reporters to wait for confirmation of results, in much the same way that scientists do, so that a single and possibly controversial study is not so widely disseminated. In this case the public interest was not served by the publicizing of erroneous results that advise people against eating meat and other sources of iron when iron deficiency and anemia are some of the most common nutritional problems. Those most susceptible to iron deficiency are pregnant women, infants, children, and menstruating women. Decreases in immune function, which can lead to increased susceptibility to diseases, and decreased work performance are the results of iron deficiency. If the deficiency continues long enough, anemia will result. Experienced during pregnancy, iron deficiency may harm the fetus. Iron deficiencies during the preschool years are a leading cause of low scholastic performance, and such deficits may not be reversible when the deficiency is cured.

Neurotransmitters. Neurotransmitters, chemicals involved in the transmission of nervous impulses, are nutrients or are synthesized from nutrients or food components. The amino acids glutamate, aspartate, glycine, and gamma-aminobutyric acid are important in nerve transmission in the brain. Levels of brain transmitters are greatly influenced by levels of transmitters in the blood; in turn, blood levels are easily influenced by diet.

Appetite-controlling and sleep-inducing neurotransmitters have been identified, and research is under way to determine the underlying mechanisms responsible for eating and sleeping disorders. Neurotransmitters may be responsible for differences in preferences for fat over carbohydrate, thereby affecting energy balance and weight gain. These factors, in turn, may contribute to the development of diabetes. Non-insulin-dependent diabetes mellitus is linked to obesity, but the mechanism is not understood. The cells of the body become resistant, for some reason, to the effects of insulin so that blood sugar control is more difficult in the obese person. Diabetes, especially the insulin-dependent type, is a risk factor for CHD, kidney disease, and blindness.

Molecular biology. Nutritionists were becoming interested in the techniques of molecular biology in an attempt to understand the relationship between nutrients and genes. Genes have long been known to affect nutrient metabolism. In the disease of iron metabolism, hemochromatosis, individuals receive defective genes from both parents and have poor regulation of iron absorption. Excessive absorption of iron occurs, and the deposition of excessive amounts of iron in tissues can lead to severe health effects, including cirrhosis of the liver, heart muscle damage, diabetes, arthritis, and, possibly, liver cancer.

The ways in which nutrients can affect gene expression are not well understood. Because genes exert influence by the synthesis of proteins (enzymes) and amino acids are nutrients used to make proteins, nutritional effects appear to be important. Indeed, without the supply of all essential amino acids in the diet—those amino acids that the body cannot make—proteins cannot be made.

Functional foods. The interface between nutrition and food science was an active area of research during the past year. Functional foods were the focus of much of this research. Functional foods, also called "nutraceuticals" or "designer foods," are formulated to improve the health of the consumer beyond the benefits provided by traditional food. Theoretically, this should be possible through a reduction of salt, fat, cholesterol, and total calories and an increase in nutrients.

Several approaches were being used to improve foods from the nutritional and health standpoints. Reductions in fat, cholesterol, calories, and salt, coupled with increases in vitamins and minerals, can substantially increase the nutrient density, or the weight of the nutrient per kilocalorie, of foods. Skim milk represents perhaps the first functional food. However, most functional foods are much more difficult to create than skim milk. Some notable advances were made in low-fat meat products, including reducing the fat content of frankfurters from 30% to as low as 3%. Although such properties of high-fat sausages as flavor and smell are difficult to duplicate in low-fat sausages, acceptability of these newer products on the part of consumers appeared to be good. Low-fat ground-beef products were being developed in part through substitution of plant materials for fat.

Augmentation of the vitamin and mineral content of foods is another approach to functional foods. Antioxidant vitamins and trace minerals are candidates as additives for creating a functional food.

—Paul Bradley Addis

See also Feature Article: THE PALEOLITHIC HEALTH CLUB.

Life sciences

Newsworthy developments in the life sciences during the past year included the recovery of fossil plant DNA as old as 40 million years, the identification of giant bacteria more than a half millimeter long, the discovery of a new species of large mammal in Vietnam, and the resolution of the three-dimensional structure of several proteins important in basic cellular processes. That mercury in dental fillings may be migrating elsewhere in the body was suggested from studies of intestinal bacteria, and an unusual steroid antibiotic was isolated from a species of shark.

Botany

Research in botany during the past year continued to emphasize plant genetics and forest-related issues. However, other areas of investigation also yielded interesting discoveries.

Plant genetics. The history of modern corn, or maize (*Zea mays*), has interested botanists for a long time. According to one theory, modern corn descended from an ancestor resembling the wild Mexican grass called teosinte. One major difference between the two is that teosinte has kernels that are surrounded by hardened fruit cases, while modern corn has exposed kernels because the parts of the fruit case do not develop very much. The fruit cases of teosinte interfere with the use of the kernels as food. Jane Dorweiler of the University of Minnesota and her associates reported locating the gene that may be responsible for the change from the encased to exposed kernels in the evolution of corn.

A leaf of the extinct tree Hymenaea protera *is preserved in amber that has been dated at 35 million–40 million years old. The amber was discovered in a mine in the Dominican Republic.*

George O. Poinar, Jr., University of California, Berkeley

Increasing numbers of genes were being identified from fossil material. An example reported during the past year came from amber deposits in the Dominican Republic. Hendrik Poinar of California Polytechnic State University and associates extracted and sequenced a gene, *rbcL,* belonging to the extinct tree *Hymenaea protera*. The amber contained fossils of organisms living 25 million–40 million years ago. This finding nearly doubled the amount of DNA recovered from fossil material that has been identified. Upon comparison of the sequence of the fossil gene with that of existing trees, the researchers concluded that this fossil tree was more closely related to the existing African tree *H. courbaril* than it was to the South American *H. oblongifolia*.

Plants respond to various wavelengths of light within and near the visible spectrum. For instance, red light is most important for photosynthesis. Plant functions related to blue light have also been known, some of them for more than a century. As of 1994, a search for some kind of cellular receptor for light had not met with much success. One approach that held some promise was the identification of a mutation that is unable to respond to blue light and the discovery of the corresponding defective gene product. This was the approach taken by Margaret Ahmad and Anthony Cashmore of the University of Pennsylvania, who reported on the isolation of such a gene, designated *hy4*, in the small plant *Arabidopsis thaliana*. The researchers verified that the normal gene, *HY4*, encodes a protein that is similar to photolases, a rare group of flavoproteins known to be a blue-light photoreceptor. They then suggested that one of the blue-light photoreceptors in *A. thaliana* is similar to one of these flavoproteins and that the mutant plants do not produce this photoreceptor.

Forests. Continued concern and controversy about tropical forest destruction was affecting research efforts to discover the extent of change. An example was a report from David Skole of the University of New Hampshire and Compton Tucker of the National Aeronautics and Space Administration Goddard Space Flight Center. They examined Landsat satellite imagery to compare deforestation and forest fragmentation in the entire Brazilian Amazon Basin. According to a computer analysis of satellite data by a geographic information system, they reported changes from 1978 to 1988. Tropical deforestation increased from 78,000 to 230,000 sq km (30,100 to 88,750 sq mi). Forest fragmentation, defined as cutting the forest into pieces too small to support certain species of wildlife, increased from 208,000 to 588,000 sq km (80,300 to 227,000 sq mi). The investigators suggested that their estimates of deforestation were lower than others had been but that, even so, they indicated a magnitude of change that would significantly affect biodiversity in the forest.

Most countries directly involved in tropical forest timber harvesting invoked short-range economic and social arguments to support this practice. Environmentalists argued that nontimber resources should be utilized instead. In a 1993 issue of the journal *Economic Botany,* Pamela Hall and Kamaljit Bawa of the University of Massachusetts reflected on the fact that the effects of utilizing nontimber resources were not known. They suggested methods for making rapid assessment of such practices and advocated the use of these in tropical forest management.

Focusing on the controversies about forestry usage in the Pacific Northwest of the U.S., Dean S. DeBell and Robert O. Curtis issued a call in the *Journal of Forestry* for forest managers to pay attention to at least four concepts: (1) Natural forest stands are dynamic because fire and other perturbations have always caused changes, even in old-growth forests. (2) There are combinations of practices that should be explored for achieving management purposes. (3) The options of natural regeneration or planting should be used in combinations suitable for different sites. (4) Extending the harvest age of stands may be a desirable option to help meet complex forestry objectives.

Such considerations may prove helpful in meeting some of the objections of opponents of public forestry practice. Major objections were to be the emphasis on timber harvest as a major management goal and the method of harvest used to meet that goal. Of the variety of harvesting techniques, foresters favored the "even-aged" methods; these typically employ planting an area that has been clear-cut, thinning periodically to improve the productivity of the remaining trees, and then clear-cutting a fairly large area. Usually all trees are removed in clear-cutting and, until recently, often the undesirable material was burned. Destruction of habitat for wildlife results from these practices, but the new growth provides a favorable habitat for some mammals and birds. Sometimes scattered seed trees are left standing.

Others were more favorable to the "uneven-aged" techniques. These typically involve selective cutting, which removes only the most mature trees or the trees in small areas. While this is more expensive than the even-aged procedures, it more adequately preserves habitat for animals, is more aesthetically pleasing, and more adequately allows for natural seeding. Strong opposition to clear-cutting in the national forests from Ohio west to Arkansas was met by decisions to decrease the number and size of the clear-cuts and to employ more selective cutting techniques. That this was a significant move is indicated by the nature of these particular forests. Unlike the "old-growth" ecosystems of the Pacific Northwest, forests in this mid-U.S. region were established in the early part of the 20th century on lands denuded

of trees. The resulting second-growth forest has been intensively managed in generally even-aged stands.

Fungi. A natural substance produced by the Pacific yew (*Taxus brevifolia*) is useful for the treatment of human cancer. This substance is called taxol, and it is now also known to be made by a fungus (*Taxomyces andreanae*) that grows in the inner bark of the yew. Andrea Stierle of Montana State University and her associates reported that they were able to isolate the fungus, grow it in a synthetic medium, and verify that it incorporates forms of acetic acid and phenylalanine as precursors to taxol production. The fungus does not produce taxol as abundantly as does its host tree, but improved methods of culturing may make it a significant source of the chemical. This will become increasingly important as the yew becomes scarcer.

Many fungi are parasites on specific plant species. The technique for getting from one plant to another involves the transport of spores, the usual reproductive structures for fungi. An unusual method for spore dispersal was reported during the year by B.A. Roy of the University of California at Davis. He found a rust fungus (*Puccinia monoica*) that infects plants of the rock cress group (*Arabis*). In the process of infection, the fungus inhibits flowering of the host plant and creates elevated clusters of infected leaves that mimic flowers of unrelated species. Visiting insects, attracted to these pseudoflowers, pick up fungal spores and inadvertently transfer them to other plants.

Two University of California at Riverside researchers were investigating the genetics of parasitism of fungi on their higher plant hosts. Stanley Freeman and Rusty J. Rodriguez reported that they had isolated a mutant gene, *path-1,* that permits a fungus to live successfully within its host without producing the usual harm associated with such a relationship. *Colletrotichum magna* is a filamentous fungus that produces a disease called anthracnose in plants of the cucumber family when it has the wild-type gene, *Path-1.* Crosses between *Path-1* and *path-1* fungi confirm that the genetic variation is due to a single gene and that infection and pathogenicity are due to separate genetic material.

Other developments. Two Swedish investigators from the University of Uppsala, working with an associate from the University of Antanarivo, Madagascar, developed a technique for staining (microtagging) the pollen of orchids in order to trace it to its destiny in the process of pollination. The pollen of orchids is transmitted in masses called pollinia by their pollinators. The investigators, L. Anders Nilsson, Elizabeth Rabakonandrianina, and Börge Pettersson, used stains to mark the pollinia of two populations of *Aerangis ellisii* in Madagascar. They studied the distribution of these by hawkmoths, noting that pollen transfers usually take place within 5 m (16 ft), are infrequent, and involve single pollen sources. Among further perceptions, they concluded that the relative rarity of actual cross-pollinations resulted in a high proportion of self-pollination (44%) and a small number of plants carrying out cross-pollination.

A large group of Brazilian researchers reported their conclusions on why popcorn pops. William da Silva of the University of Campinas and associates examined the question of why popcorn, out of all the forms of Z. *mays*, actually pops. Most reports have shown that the hull (pericarp) and starch content are important. These investigators developed techniques involving strains of normal corn and popcorn that varied in thickness of pericarp and type of starch content. They concluded that the pericarp characteristics seem to be most important for popping.

Quaking aspen (*Populus tremuloides*) is known for the obvious characteristic of trembling leaves. The species is widely distributed in woodlands across the northern U.S., the southern half of Canada, and as far north as central Alaska. It is less well known that other members of the genus also have trembling leaves, which are the result of leaf petioles that are flattened and flexible. (A petiole is the stem that supports the blade—broad, flat portion—of a leaf.) Two University of California at Davis investigators, John S. Roden and Robert W. Pearcy, examined the possibility that leaf fluttering serves to decrease leaf temperature and thus enhance leaf-related processes such as photosynthesis and water retention. Western cottonwood (*P. fremontii*) was included in their study, which involved attaching thermocouples to leaves. These researchers reported that leaf temperature is not significantly decreased in the lower canopy of a forest but was decreased as much as 2°–4° C (3.6°–7.2° F) in the crown. They concluded that this decrease would not affect the function of aspen leaves since aspens grow in cool areas. However, there may be some advantage for the western cottonwoods, which live in warm regions such as the Central Valley of California.

Cell walls are usually mentioned as an outstanding difference between the cells of plants and those of other organisms. In addition to this feature, cell walls relate to a number of important characteristics of plants and the function of the cells. Not only are plant shape and size dependent on the character of the plant's cells, but a large number of biological processes are promoted by and through the walls. Naturally, it would be of interest to botanists to determine how the constituents of these walls contribute to their functioning. The three main constituents of the primary cell wall are the polysaccharides cellulose, hemicellulose, and pectin. It is fairly well known that the first two provide the scaffolding for the wall, but

the function of pectins is not as clear. Wolf-Dieter Reiter, Clint C.S. Chapple, and Chris R. Somerville, working at Michigan State University, reasoned that the production of plants that are mutant for pectin synthesis would help clarify pectin function. With the chemical ethyl methanesulfonate, these researchers produced mutants of A. *thaliana* and were able to identify 38 mutations for cell-wall constituents. Of these, five carried a mutant gene responsible for the almost complete elimination of a constituent of pectin called L-fucose. This is a monosaccharide (simplest building block of polysaccharides). The researchers designated the mutant genes *mur1* and found the mutant plants to be variously dwarfed owing to shortened leaf petioles and stems. They also found that the cell walls were significantly weakened, thus verifying that normal pectin is involved in the strengthening of cell-wall structure.

Two Canadian scientists, C.J. Bird and J.F. Van der Meer of the Institute for Marine Bioscience in Halifax, Nova Scotia, were making a case for increased attention to taxonomy in a study of the utilization of algae for food and substances that contribute to the production of pharmaceuticals and cosmetics. While recognizing that Canada has only a small portion of the global supply of algae, they reasoned that benefits could be derived from what is available if uses of algae were investigated and negative features were better understood. They claimed that such analysis calls for more active taxonomic approaches to this difficult group of plants since many of the particularly small ones show a great deal of variability in their life histories and their responses to environmental differences. Their suggestion is significant in light of the decreasing interest in taxonomy among biologists during recent years.

—Albert J. Smith

Microbiology

During the past year a number of remarkable discoveries were made in the field of microbiology. These can be divided into the categories of general microbiology, biotechnology, medical microbiology, and ecology.

General microbiology. One of the conventional notions is that all bacteria are small. While this is usually the case, there are a number of exceptions, and an exceptionally large bacterium was recently discovered. In fact, it is the largest prokaryote (organism without a distinct cell nucleus) yet observed, with a cell volume more than a million times larger than that of an average-sized bacterium such as *Escherichia coli*. The story began in 1985 when a microorganism known as *Epulopiscium fishelsoni* was discovered in the intestinal tract of a brown surgeonfish, *Acanthurus nigrofuscus*, from the Red

Sea. It was originally thought to be a eukaryote (an organism containing a visibly evident cell nucleus) because it can attain sizes of about 600 × 80 μm (micrometers, or millionths of a meter; Figure 1). However, closer inspection of *E. fishelsoni* revealed features more typical of prokaryotes, such as the absence of a membrane surrounding the nucleoid.

Working with *E. fishelsoni* has been difficult since it has not yet been possible to cultivate the microorganism outside the surgeonfish. Recent studies by Ester R. Angert and colleagues focused on the ribosomes (large complexes of RNA and protein molecules that are sites of protein synthesis) of this organism and demonstrated that *E. fishelsoni* contains prokaryotic ribosomal ribonucleic acid (rRNA). More important, their work helped define an experimental approach in the analysis of microorganisms that defy cultivation. First, a technique known as the polymerase chain reaction (PCR) was used to copy a portion of the rRNA from about 1,000 intestinal bacteria that were predominantly *E. fishelsoni*. To demonstrate that the copied rRNA molecules were derived from *E. fishelsoni* and not from some other gut bacterium, a short oligonucleotide that binds only to the copied rRNA molecule was attached to a dye and used as a probe to determine which organism(s) in the surgeonfish gut contains the complementary sequence. The probe annealed to *E. fishelsoni* RNA, demonstrating that the PCR-copied rRNA sequence was derived from *E. fishelsoni*. It is estimated that the vast majority of existing bacterial species have never been cultivated, and this approach could help identify and enumerate this portion of the bacterial world.

The symmetrical patterns that particular clusters of cells form are often visually striking; examples include the petals of a flower and the spiral in a snail shell. Biological patterns can form by the organized growth of cells, the organized movement of cells, or both. One aspect of recent microbiological research involved determining how such patterns develop. Elena O. Budrene and Howard C. Berg discovered that when *E. coli* cells are inoculated with intermediate products of the tricarboxylic acid (TCA) cycle, such as succinate, fumarate, or malate, cells swim toward well-spaced centers, where they accumulate in large numbers to form symmetrical arrays of spots or stripes. The distribution of these aggregation centers is so regular that highly detailed stationary patterns are produced (Figures 2a and 2b on page 364). In these examples the mechanism of pattern formation is due to the secretion by some of the *E. coli* cells of a small chemical attractant (chemoattractant), aspartate and/or glutamate, which then entices distant cells into the aggregation center. Once cells are in the center, they temporarily lose their ability to move and cannot leave for a period of time, thus stabilizing

Courtesy of Esther R. Angert and Norman R. Pace, Indiana University

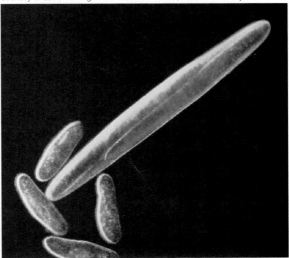

Figure 1: Epulopiscium fishelsoni, *shown next to four smaller* Paramecium *cells, is the largest known prokaryote (organism without a distinct cell nucleus). It can attain a length of about 600 micrometers.*

the pattern. The precise reason for this behavior is not known. This aggregation response is induced by environmental conditions that are potentially toxic, such as oxidative stress. Perhaps there is safety in numbers, and cells in such clumps are more protected from the toxic molecules.

Sensory transduction, the manner in which chemoattractants are sensed by cells, was also an area of intense research interest. In *E. coli*, chemoattractants are sensed with chemoreceptors, proteins in the cell membrane that register the presence of the chemoattractant by binding it and activating a cascade of events that ultimately controls the rotation of the flagella, the primary organelles of motion of the cell. By measuring concentration changes as they move, bacteria determine whether they are moving up a chemoattractant gradient. *E. coli*, for example, swims about 10–20 of its body lengths per second. By comparing current chemoreceptor occupancy with that during the previous few seconds, a cell is able to measure chemoattractant concentration over distances of many cell lengths. Using immunologic microscopy techniques, Janine Maddock and Lucille Shapiro determined that a protein chemoreceptor known as Tsr and two sensory cascade proteins, CheA and CheW, of *E. coli* are clustered in a region of the cell membrane that acts like a nose spot (a cluster of receptors for sensing chemicals in the environment). Antibodies that specifically bind the proteins of interest, in this case anti-Tsr, anti-CheA, or anti-CheW antibodies, are allowed to react with the cell to form an antibody-chemoreceptor complex. Then the unbound antibody is removed, and a

Figure 2: Escherichia coli *cells form symmetrical patterns when inoculated with intermediate products of the tricarboxylic acid cycle, such as succinate, fumarate, or malate. These cell clusters were inoculated at the center of an 8.5-cm (3.3-in)-diameter plate containing soft agar and succinate as the carbon and energy source. At the top (2a) is the pattern formed by wild E. coli after three days of incubation. Below (2b) is the pattern formed by an E. coli mutant that cannot sense the amino acid serine.*

secondary antibody that reacts with the primary antibody is added. In the example shown in Figure 3, the secondary antibody was attached to colloidal gold particles. Since gold is electron-dense, the chemoreceptor-primary antibody-secondary antibody complex is defined by the dark circles by means of transmission electron microscopy.

The reason for receptor clustering is unknown since a concentrated patch of chemoreceptor molecules will be in the path of fewer chemoattractant molecules than will be evenly dispersed chemoreceptors. Those molecules that do encounter a patch are more likely than other molecules to activate a chemoreceptor before being transported into the cell cytoplasm, where they are unable to stimulate the receptor.

Biotechnology. A drug known as taxol has shown considerable promise in the treatment of ovarian, breast, head, and neck tumors. Taxol greatly shrinks tumors in about 30% of women whose ovarian cancers have resisted other therapies. Taxol is extracted in tiny amounts from the bark of the Pacific yew tree, *Taxus brevifolia,* and other members of the genus. Considering that only 0.01% to 0.03% of the phloem (inner bark) dry weight is taxol and that a patient requires about two grams of taxol for a full regimen of cancer therapy, these slow-growing trees could be wiped out to preserve human lives. The National Cancer Institute and Bristol-Myers Squibb Co., which exclusively supply taxol, were under intense pressure to reduce the cost, about $986 per treatment cycle.

The recent discovery by Andrea Stierle and her colleagues of a fungal species that also produces taxol may save the lives of yew trees and cancer patients. Ironically enough, *Taxomyces andreanae* was isolated from the phloem of a Pacific yew in Montana. Although the amounts of taxol produced by *T. andreanae* are low, improved culturing techniques and genetic engineering are expected to improve the yield. It is not clear whether the fungus or the tree first developed the enzymes to manufacture taxol. Scientists speculated that because taxol has antifungal properties, the yew may have produced taxol to ward off parasitic fungi. Then the fungus may have acquired the gene(s) for taxol synthesis from the yew. In the long run, this discovery is expected to reduce environmental pressure on the yew and lower taxol production costs.

Medical microbiology. It appears that mercury, a toxic metal, is leaching from our tooth fillings and contaminating our bodies. Amalgam, the gray material commonly used to fill cavities in molars, contains 50% mercury. Anne Summers and Stuart Levy and their colleagues found that within two weeks after monkeys received fillings, bacteria in the monkey's intestines became resistant to mercury as well as to a variety of commonly used antibiotics such as penicillin, streptomycin, kanamycin, chloramphenicol, and tetracycline. The study suggests that the fillings release mercury vapor that is inhaled into the lungs and converted into its poisonous form, mercury ion, by enzymes in the blood. From the blood it proceeds to the liver, where it is trapped in bile and released into the intestines at concentrations that are high enough to kill sensitive bacteria. Eventually, resistant bacteria emerge that contain a protective enzyme that converts the mercury ion back to the nontoxic vapor form. The acquisition of mercury resistance along with resistance to many antibiotics suggests that the genes encoding mercury resistance are located near genes that confer resistance to the antibiotics. At present it is not clear that the con-

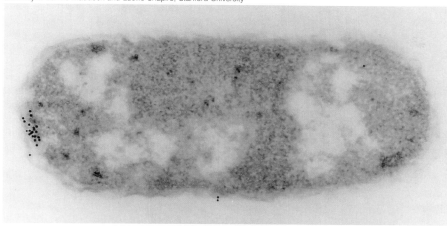

Figure 3: The black area in the electron micrograph is an Escherichia coli nose spot, revealed by the presence of colloidal gold particles that are electron-dense. The nose spot is a region on the cell membrane where a protein chemoreceptor and two sensory cascade proteins are clustered and react with antibodies that bind the proteins to form an antibody-chemoreceptor complex (see text).

centrations of mercury leaching from the amalgam fillings are sufficiently high to cause bodily harm, but people with acute sensitivities to metals should be aware of this problem.

HIV, which causes AIDS, contains RNA as its genetic component. Shortly after infection, the RNA is converted to DNA by a viral enzyme known as reverse transcriptase. During active stages of infection, the DNA is then copied into RNA by host enzymes and packaged into viral particles. During latent stages of the infection, the DNA remains inactive in host cells. HIV infection is generally followed by a burst of virus production shortly after infection and then by a prolonged period during which no disease symptoms are present. Infected, asymptomatic patients are nevertheless capable of transmitting the virus, indicating that some cells in the body harbor and continue to produce it. Using the polymerase chain reaction, which can detect as few as 1–10 HIV-infected cells present in 100,000 uninfected cells, two research groups discovered HIV in large numbers of helper T cells and macrophages in the lymphoid tissues of HIV-infected individuals. In a large proportion of these infected cells, the virus is present in a dormant (latent) state.

The vast quantities of latent virus in infected, asymptomatic individuals is alarming; cells with latent virus are not susceptible to the drugs being used to treat AIDS, which inhibit reverse transcriptase, because that step in the viral-replication process has already been completed in latently infected cells. The best opportunity for eliminating the disease with inhibitors of reverse transcriptase would be at the onset of infection, which is, unfortunately, often asymptomatic. Thus, prevention of infection remains the single most effective tool in the fight against AIDS. During the past year the World Health Organization (WHO) estimated that more than 13 million young people and adults had become infected with HIV, the majority through heterosexual intercourse. In addi-

tion, about one million children had been infected before or during birth. In some cities in Africa, as many as one out of three adults is infected.

One of the most intense areas of AIDS research involves the development of an HIV vaccine. A safe vaccine should be free of risks and side effects and should stimulate the immune system to produce specialized cells that respond quickly to inactivate the real virus. There are three basic approaches to vaccine development that have been successful with other diseases. The first strategy involves producing a vaccine from viruses that have been inactivated by means of chemical or physical treatments. This approach runs the risk that certain batches of vaccine will contain infectious viruses that were not inactivated. Many view this as an unacceptable risk with a disease as deadly as AIDS. The second strategy involves using a live but weakened (attenuated) form of the virus that can establish an infection but not cause disease. Attenuated viruses, such as those used in the polio vaccine, induce perhaps the highest levels of immunity. However, if the virus mutates to the disease-causing (virulent) form, as sometimes happens with the polio vaccine, the risks associated with using the vaccine may again be unacceptably high. A third approach involves the use of genetic engineering to mass-produce a harmless portion of the deadly virus that then serves as the vaccine. This is anticipated to be the safest approach because it does not involve production of either a virulent or an attenuated virus. Most researchers have utilized the third approach to generate an HIV vaccine, but by early 1994 it had not yet activated the immune system to a satisfactory level. In addition, only marginal success was obtained with the killed-virus method.

Recent data from experiments with a related monkey virus known as simian immunodeficiency virus (SIV) suggest that it is possible to produce a nontoxic attenuated virus that induces a strong immune response in monkeys. Ronald C. Desrosiers and his colleagues stumbled onto the approach while studying the mechanism by which SIV causes disease. In 1991 they created a mutant version of the virus in which a gene called *nef* was deleted, and they then injected this virus into six rhesus monkeys to learn how the mutation affects the course of the disease. Another group of monkeys received unaltered SIV. The monkeys that received the natural virus began dying of AIDS, while the six monkeys that received the *nef*-deleted strain remained healthy, suggesting that the *nef*-deletion rendered the virus harmless. Two and a half years later, the researchers challenged four of the monkeys vaccinated with the *nef*-deleted virus and four unvaccinated monkeys with SIV. Within 36 weeks the four unvaccinated monkeys were sick or dead, while the four that received the *nef*-deleted virus remained healthy. The vaccinated monkeys then resisted another challenge with an even higher dose of SIV. These results brightened an otherwise gloomy outlook for the production of an HIV vaccine, although such a vaccine, if it can be made from HIV, is still many years away.

Ecology. Biological invasions threaten the integrity of natural communities and the preservation of endangered species. There are many documented cases where one or a few invaders severely affected native species. Oceangoing ships carry as ballast seawater that is acquired in one port and released at subsequent ports of call. The transport by this means of entire coastal planktonic assemblages across oceanic barriers to similar habitats in distant parts of the world could make bays, estuaries, and inland waters among the most threatened ecosystems. The invasion of the Asian clam, *Potamocorbula amurensis*, in San Francisco Bay; the zebra mussel, *Dreissena polymorpha,* in the Great Lakes; and the comb jelly, *Mnemiopsis leidyi*, in the Black Sea illustrate the catastrophic impact of ballast water introductions. It has been suggested that outbreaks of toxic algae are also associated with ballast release, although it is much more difficult to correlate microbial blooms with invasion since the habitat distribution of microbes has not been as extensively studied as that of higher organisms. (*See* Feature Article: SPECIES THAT NEED NO INTRODUCTION.)

—Lawrence J. Shimkets

Molecular biology

The three-dimensional structure of proteins at a resolution on the scale of atoms can be determined at present only by analysis of the X-ray diffraction patterns produced by crystals or, for small proteins, by nuclear magnetic resonance spectroscopy of concentrated solutions. The past year was a vintage one for X-ray crystallography, and the structures of many important proteins were solved. Three of the more interesting were proteins involved in transcription, translation, and cell-to-cell signaling.

A viral RNA polymerase. Three classes of macromolecular syntheses lie at the heart of the biology of the cell: the replication of DNA (the genes), the transcription of DNA into RNA (the messages), and the translation of RNA sequences into the amino acid sequences of proteins (the cell's structural and catalytic elements). DNA replication is carried out by enzymes, *i.e.*, reaction-catalyzing proteins, known as DNA polymerases. Transcription is carried out by RNA polymerases. In both cases the chemistry required is the addition of one of the four molecular building blocks (a deoxyribonucleotide in the case of DNA, a ribonucleotide in the case of RNA) to a growing linear strand of nucleotides. The four molecular possibilities in DNA are commonly abbreviated A, G, C, and T; in RNA they are A, G, C, and U, which replaces T. Which of the four is selected as the next to be added to the strand is determined by a template strand of DNA, following the well-known base-pairing rules elaborated by James Watson and Francis Crick in 1953: A pairs with T or U, and G pairs with C.

DNA and RNA polymerases were first purified in the early 1960s. Certain features of the reactions that they catalyze were described then; these features are common to all such enzymes, regardless of source. Every polymerase needs a domain—meaning a region of the protein, which can be a contiguous stretch of amino acids or several different stretches brought together by folding the protein's amino acid chain—for binding and exposing the template strand. It needs another domain for binding the individual nucleotides that are being added to the new DNA or RNA strand. It also needs a third domain to catalyze the addition reaction and a fourth domain to bind and then release the product DNA or RNA.

The early characterization of RNA and DNA polymerases as proteins made it difficult to see how these common purposes were achieved. The first DNA polymerase to be purified, DNA polymerase I from the bacterium *Escherichia coli*, is a single large chain of amino acids (commonly termed a polypeptide). Subsequently discovered DNA polymerases were found to contain multiple polypeptide chains as subunits. Bacterial RNA polymerases have five or more such subunits, while the three types of RNA polymerase from eukaryotic cells (cells with nuclei) each contain at least 10 subunits. These complex structures present daunting problems for scientists who wish to understand in intimate detail how the enzymes work.

To the rescue, in a way, came viruses. Recall that a virus is a molecular parasite, little more than a strand of DNA or RNA wrapped in a protein coat, capable of infecting a cell and reproducing hundreds of copies of itself by subverting one or more parts of the cellular machinery for replication, transcription, and translation. Viruses that infect bacteria provided the first clues to the nature of the gene, the molecular basis of mutations, the role of messenger RNA in carrying information from the gene to the cell's protein-synthesis machinery, and the principles of self-assembly of complex protein structures. RNA-containing tumor viruses provided the first examples of reverse transcription, the process by which information in the genetic material of the virus, a strand of RNA, is copied into DNA and subsequently integrated into the DNA of host cells. Bacterial viruses and RNA tumor viruses carry or encode simpler forms of DNA and RNA polymerases, amenable to complete structural analysis.

During the past decade researchers determined the three-dimensional structure of several polymerases by means of X-ray diffraction studies of their crystallized forms. The first was a fragment of the *E. coli* DNA polymerase I, solved in 1985 in the laboratory of Thomas Steitz at Yale University. In 1992 the same laboratory described the structure of the RNA-templated DNA polymerase (reverse transcriptase) of the human immunodeficiency virus (HIV), the virus that causes AIDS. Moreover, in 1993 a group led by Rui Sousa and Bi-Cheng Wang of the University of Pittsburgh, Pa., reported the crystal structure of the RNA polymerase encoded by the bacterial virus T7. Comparison of the three polymerase structures provides considerable insight into the mechanism by which nucleic acids are synthesized.

Bacteriophage T7 is one of seven viruses infecting *E. coli* that were deemed worthy of study by Miroslav Demerec of Cold Spring Harbor (N.Y.)

Laboratory in the 1940s. Ignored for a time, T7 was eventually studied by William Summers at Yale. He found that the virus carried the gene for its own RNA polymerase and that this enzyme differed substantially from the RNA polymerase of *E. coli*. The T7 double-stranded DNA chromosome was subsequently studied exhaustively by William Studier and John Dunn of Brookhaven National Laboratory, Upton, N.Y. Among their many contributions to the molecular biology of T7, they determined the complete nucleotide sequence, 50,000 base pairs, of the T7 chromosome.

The T7 RNA polymerase is a single polypeptide containing 883 amino acids, making it the simplest known RNA polymerase. Biochemical studies showed that it shares most of the mechanistic features of the much more complex *E. coli* enzyme, such as recognizing and binding to specific nucleotide sequences (promoters) in the double-stranded DNA template, unwinding the helical template locally, initiating synthesis by joining two nucleotides, propagating synthesis by the successive addition of template-selected nucleotides, accelerating the rate of synthesis after the first nine nucleotides have been strung together, and finally terminating transcription and releasing the product RNA at specific nucleotide sequences (terminators) in the template DNA. The principal difference between T7 RNA polymerase and the *E. coli* enzyme is that the former is unregulated. Given a correct promoter sequence, the T7 enzyme binds and transcribes flat out. The *E. coli* enzyme, on the other hand, recognizes a wide range of sequences as promoters and can be either enhanced or reduced in activity at a given promoter by the binding of auxiliary proteins to the DNA nearby.

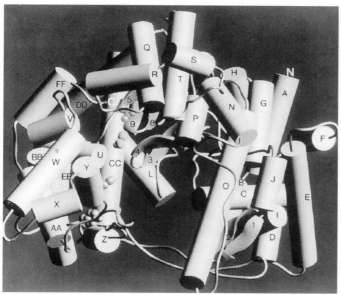

Figure 1: The crystal structure of RNA polymerase from the T7 virus is shown in a schematic representation. Cylinders correspond to characteristic structural elements of proteins called α helices, ribbonlike arrows to β sheets, and strings to random coils. The catalytic site of the enzyme is near the center, where β sheets 8 and 9 come together.

Rui Sousa, Yong Je Chung, John P. Rose, and Bi-Cheng Wang, University of Pittsburgh

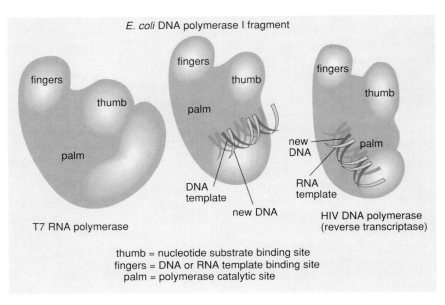

E. coli DNA polymerase I fragment

fingers

thumb

palm

T7 RNA polymerase

fingers

thumb

palm

DNA template

new DNA

fingers

thumb

new DNA

palm

RNA template

HIV DNA polymerase (reverse transcriptase)

thumb = nucleotide substrate binding site
fingers = DNA or RNA template binding site
palm = polymerase catalytic site

Figure 2: Schematic diagrams of the three polymerases for which detailed crystal structures are known reveal their remarkable similarities. Each can be thought of as having a thumb, which binds the nucleotides used to build the new strand; fingers, which bind the DNA or RNA template; and a palm, on which resides the catalytic site. The structures of the polymerases from Escherichia coli and HIV include short bound strands of nucleotides corresponding to newly synthesized products.

Studier and Dunn developed a laboratory procedure, based on transcription by T7 RNA polymerase, for the abundant expression of the products of cloned genes in *E. coli*. Sousa and colleagues applied the procedure to the T7 RNA polymerase itself, describing their first crystals of the protein in 1989 and the crystal structure at a resolution of 3.3 Å (0.33 nanometer, or billionths of a meter) in 1993. Their achievement provides the first glimpse of an RNA polymerase and represents the largest polymerase structure of any kind to be solved. A schematic representation of the structure is shown in Figure 1 on page 367. Like most enzymes, the structure comprises many small elements, represented by cylinders and flat ribbons with arrowheads that are connected by loose strings. The cylinders correspond to regions called α helices, the flat arrows to those called β sheets, and the strings to random coils. These three classes of structural element describe the path of the polypeptide backbone of the protein. The detailed structure determined by Sousa and colleagues reveals the orientation of each amino-acid side chain as well. The key parts are near the center, where β sheets 8 and 9 come together. That site is where the nucleotide to be added to the growing RNA strand is bound and the chemistry of its addition is catalyzed.

Of greater interest than the structure itself is the relationship of that structure to the two others mentioned: the fragment of DNA polymerase I and the reverse transcriptase of HIV. The former uses a double-stranded DNA template to direct the synthesis of new DNA strands; the latter uses a single-stranded RNA template to direct the synthesis of one strand of DNA, yielding a hybrid product with one DNA strand and one RNA strand. Both of these structure determinations have been refined

to include short, bound strands of nucleotides corresponding to newly synthesized products. With the positions for template binding and product location firmly assigned for these structures, it became possible to suggest corresponding locations on the T7 RNA polymerase.

The three related structures are shown schematically in Figure 2. They are remarkably similar in that each can be thought of as having a "thumb," "fingers," and a "palm." The thumb region binds the nucleotides used to build the new strand (*i.e.*, the nucleotide substrate), the fingers bind the DNA or RNA template, and the catalytic site sits on the palm. These structures provide a revealing view of central events in the life of a cell. Together with genetic experiments, in which individual amino acids in the enzymes are replaced by others, they indicate how the modules of the enzymes interact and how each functions in each step of template binding, new strand synthesis, and release of the product. Further work remains to elucidate the three-dimensional structure of the multisubunit RNA polymerases but, meanwhile, there is much to be learned from the simpler enzymes already solved.

An elongation factor for protein synthesis. The DNA and RNA polymerases are responsible for replication and transcription, respectively. The third process central to all cells is translation, in which the nucleotide sequence of messenger RNA is read, three units at a time, to guide the synthesis of the polypeptide chain that makes up protein molecules.

Translation requires a much more complicated machine than a single enzyme. The complex called the ribosome, consisting of several large RNA molecules and more than 50 different proteins, provides the workbench on which proteins are made in the cell. The ribosome has sites for binding messenger RNA and the transfer RNA molecules (tRNAs) to which amino acids are chemically bonded. Each of the 20 amino acids used to make proteins is attached to a different set of tRNA molecules. The tRNAs have exposed nucleotide triplets (groups of three consecutive nucleotides) at one end that, on the surface of the ribosome, are positioned to form hydrogen bonds (A with U, G with C) with triplets in the messenger RNA. In this way the nucleotide sequence in messenger RNA guides the positioning of the tRNAs and, therefore, the sequence of amino acids in the growing polypeptide chain. Peptide bonds are formed between the amino acids and the growing end of the protein one at a time.

Three other proteins participate in crucial steps of the process. One, called elongation factor G (EF-G), is responsible for moving the messenger RNA and the growing polypeptide chain across the surface of the ribosome. Another, elongation factor Tu (EF-Tu), delivers the tRNA that is bearing the next amino acid to be added to the surface of the ribosome. The third, elongation factor Ts (EF-Ts), interacts with EF-Tu in a way that allows EF-Tu to recycle, picking up a new amino-acid–tRNA complex after delivering one to the ribosome. The cycling of EF-Tu is controlled by the small molecule guanosine triphosphate (GTP). GTP comprises a nucleoside (a purine or pyrimidine base bound to a sugar molecule) to which is attached a chain of three phosphate groups. Removal of the trailing phosphate of GTP by hydrolysis, yielding guanosine diphosphate (GDP) and an inorganic phosphate, can be coupled chemically to drive other reactions. When EF-Tu binds a molecule of GTP, the resulting complex has a high affinity for amino-acid–tRNA complex and binds to it.

When this new multipart complex, consisting of amino acid-tRNA and EF-Tu–GTP, arrives at the ribosome, GTP's trailing phosphate is removed, leaving behind a bound GDP. The EF-Tu–GDP form has much lower affinity for amino-acid–tRNA complex than does the EF-Tu–GTP form. As a result, the EF-Tu–GDP complex departs from the ribosome, leaving the amino acid-tRNA in the correct position to make the next peptide bond. In order to perform this function again, the EF-Tu has to exchange its GDP for a fresh molecule of GTP. That exchange reaction is promoted by EF-Ts.

The GDP form of EF-Tu was crystallized and its structure determined in 1985 in the laboratory of Jens Nyborg of the University of Copenhagen. The protein, from *E. coli,* could not be crystallized in its native form. In order to get crystals suitable for X-ray diffraction, Nyborg had to digest the EF-Tu with an enzyme called a protease, which removed a small, 17-amino-acid stretch of the protein. Good crystals were obtained, and the structure was solved

except for the missing part, which turned out to be the domain that binds to the ribosome.

Determining how GTP and GDP regulate the binding activity of EF-Tu required solving the structure of the EF-Tu–GTP complex as well. This enterprise was difficult because the complex loses a phosphate group even in the absence of ribosomes, converting itself into the inactive EF-Tu–GDP form. Fortunately, there is an analogue of GTP called GppNHp that is structurally similar to GTP but loses a phosphate only very slowly when complexed with EF-Tu. Use of this analogue was one innovation that made the structure determination possible. The other was the switch from *E. coli* as the source of the EF-Tu to a thermophilic bacterium called *Thermus thermophilus*. Thermophiles, bacteria that thrive in high-temperature environments, have been recognized as ideal sources of proteins for crystallographic studies. The EF-Tu of *T. thermophilus* had been studied extensively in the laboratory of Mathias Sprinzl of the University of Bayreuth, Germany, and crystallized there in 1991. The structure was solved to very high resolution in 1993 by Rolf Hilgenfeld and co-workers at the Hoechst Co., Frankfurt, Germany.

Comparison of the structures of the two forms of EF-Tu has provided insight into the mechanism by which the loss of a phosphate from the GTP form by hydrolysis is increased by binding to the ribosome and has shown why the GTP form, but not the GDP form, binds amino-acid–tRNA complex. In regard to the first point, recall that hydrolysis is a bond-breaking reaction in which the elements of a molecule of water are used to "patch" the ends of the broken bond. Hydrolysis of the bound GTP requires a water molecule located in a certain pocket defined by amino-acid side chains of the EF-Tu protein. The chemistry of that hydrolysis is improved greatly if the side chain of the amino acid histidine is nearby. There is a histidine poised to do the job, but it is prevented from doing so by another arm of the protein. When the complex consisting of amino acid-tRNA and EF-Tu–GTP binds to the ribosome, the latter arm slips out of the way, allowing the histidine to approach the water molecule to catalyze the hydrolysis of GTP.

Regarding the second point, the hydrolysis of GTP leads to a large change in structure of the EF-Tu protein, essentially closing the channel in which the bound tRNA molecule sits. Consequently, because the amino-acid–tRNA complex is firmly bound to the ribosome at this stage, the EF-Tu–GDP complex comes off. When the GDP is exchanged for a new molecule of GTP, the structure of EF-Tu reconfigures to its GTP form and is ready to ferry another amino acid-tRNA to the ribosome. While many years of biochemical studies were needed to define the roles of GTP and the T-type elongation factors in carrying tRNAs to the ribosome, the crystal structures have provided a remarkably detailed picture of how they actually do it.

A prostaglandin-synthesis enzyme. Another triumph in this banner year for X-ray crystallography was the determination of the structure of an enzyme, prostaglandin H_2 synthase, that catalyzes a key step in the synthesis of hormonelike compounds called prostaglandins. Unlike the steroid hormones, which are released into the bloodstream and can act on cells far removed from the site of synthesis, the prostaglandins are bound by surface receptors on the cell that make them or on nearby cells; their action is thus localized. Prostaglandins are involved in a wide variety of processes, including smooth-muscle contraction and blood-platelet aggregation. They also initiate the cellular responses that lead to inflammation. Aspirin reduces inflammation by chemically tying up prostaglandin H_2 synthase and so inhibiting prostaglandin synthesis.

The synthesis of prostaglandins, which are made in all mammalian tissues, begins with the action of a phospholipase enzyme on phospholipids, common components of the membranes of all mammalian cells. A phospholipid consists of a three-carbon-atom spine to which are attached two long-chain fatty acids and one phosphate group. The phospholipase cleaves a 20-carbon fatty acid called arachidonic acid from the phospholipid molecule. Prostaglandin H_2 synthase then converts arachidonic acid into prostaglandin H_2 by means of a reaction that involves the successive addition of two oxygen atoms. The synthase is located in the cell membrane; it is the first membrane protein other than those involved in photosynthesis to be solved.

The synthase structure was solved in 1993 by Daniel Picot, Patrick Loll, and Michael Garavito of the University of Chicago. The synthase was purified from sheep seminal vesicles, and the crystals used for X-ray crystallography were in the form of a complex of the enzyme with the anti-inflammatory drug flurbiprofen. Figure 3 shows a representation of a dimer (two-molecule unit) of the synthase inserted partially into a cell membrane. The structural elements are almost entirely α helices; there are almost no β sheets. Each enzyme monomer has three distinct folding domains: a small, compact domain held together by three disulfide (sulfur-sulfur) bonds, very similar to the structure of epidermal growth factor (EGF); a second domain consisting of four α helices that hold the enzyme in the phospholipid bilayer of the membrane; and then the bulk of the enzyme, 470 amino acids comprising the globular catalytic domain. Both the EGF-type domain, which probably functions to hold the enzyme together in its dimer form, and the catalytic domain are on the exterior of the cell.

The catalytic domain has a large lobe and a small lobe, between which is located a molecule of heme. Heme is a ring-shaped, iron-containing organic molecule that either can bind oxygen, as it does in the protein hemoglobin, or can participate as an electron donor or acceptor in oxidation-reduction reactions. In prostaglandin H_2 synthase, the heme functions as the active site for the enzyme's peroxidase activity, which involves the removal of hydrogen from an organic molecule by reaction with peroxide. The structure of this part of the enzyme turns out to be highly similar to that of other peroxidase enzymes whose crystal structures have been solved.

The synthase has two active sites, one the aforementioned peroxidase site and the other a cyclooxygenase site, which adds oxygen to arachidonic acid. The cyclooxygenase site consists of a long,

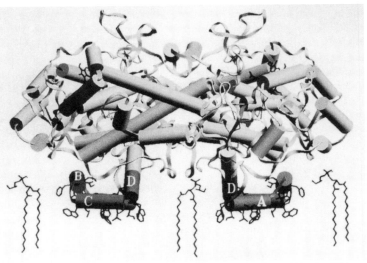

Figure 3: A dimer, or two-molecule unit, of prostaglandin H_2 synthase that is inserted partially into a cell membrane is shown in a schematic representation. Two domains (α helices labeled A–D), one from each monomer, serve to anchor the enzyme to the membrane; three phospholipid molecules belonging to the membrane are included for scale and placed near the domains. The remainder of the enzyme, including its catalytic domain, is on the cell exterior.

narrow channel running from the outer surface of the protein, near the membrane-binding domain, to the interior of the molecule. It is this channel that arachidonic acid must enter, and it is where anti-inflammatory drugs such as flurbiprofen and aspirin bind, preventing arachidonic acid from reaching the catalytic site. Thus, the enzyme's structure provides an explanation for the action of anti-inflammatory drugs and a rationale for the design of new ones.

—Robert Haselkorn

Zoology

New and exciting discoveries and observations continue to appear in the field of zoology. During the past year these included the discovery of a strange Cretaceous bird, recordings of the fastest animal movement, secretion of male-attracting pheromones by unmated female spiders, mariculture of endangered giant clams, the isolation of a potent antibiotic from shark stomachs, dimorphism in scale-eating cichlid fish, endothermic fish, cannibal amphibians, ultraviolet vision in lizards, the discovery of dwarf mammoths, the close relationship of sperm whales and blue whales, and the discovery of a new species of cow.

A strange bird? The discovery of an unusual specimen in Upper Cretaceous rocks (about 75 million years old) near Bugin Tsav, Mongolia, added to the complexity of bird evolution. A team of scientists—Perle Altangerel of the Mongolian Museum of Natural History in Ulan Bator and three colleagues, Mark A. Norell, Luis M. Chiappe, and James M. Clark of the American Museum of Natural History in New York City—described from two specimens a new species called *Mononychus olecranus*, which they believe is a primitive bird evolved from theropod dinosaurs and more closely related to modern birds than is the famous *Archaeopteryx* (around 150 million years old).

The find was particularly unusual since the remains were not crushed, as earlier discoveries had been, thus allowing a three-dimensional view of the bones. Although feather remains were not found, the turkey-sized *Mononychus* possessed several features resembling modern birds such as hollow bones, a keeled sternum, a birdlike pelvis with long legs, and a birdlike skull. The specimen also possessed dinosaur-like features, including a long tail, a long neck, and teeth. Although a primitive bird, this creature was not capable of flight; its forearms were short and powerful, and each ended in a single large claw that resembled a digging appendage. As suggested by the scientists, the flightless *Mononychus* either evolved from flying birds and lost its wings or evolved from a nonflying bird line. If the latter is true, then bird flight evolved once in the *Archaeopteryx* line and

Giant clams, which had become an endangered species in the South Pacific islands, are moved from artificial beds to a secret location on the outer Great Barrier Reef, where they can breed on their own.

once again in the modern bird line, a hypothesis that awaits more discoveries.

The fastest movement in the animal kingdom? The opened jaws of the South American trap jaw ant, *Odontomachus bauri*, were observed to snap together in 0.33 millisecond (ms), nearly twice as fast as any other recorded movements in the animal kingdom. This includes the release of jellyfish nematocysts (0.5 ms), the escape jumps of click beetles (0.6 ms), and the jumps of fleas (0.7–1.2 ms).

Three German scientists, Wulfila Gronenberg, Jürgen Tautz, and Bert Hölldobler of the Theodore Boveri Institute in Würzburg, observed the closing by using high-speed cinematography (3,000 frames per second) and photoelectric scanning. The jaws would snap close and then rebound after 0.66 ms of the initial snap. With the photoelectric scanning, the scientists observed that the jaws actually slowed down during the last third of the trajectory, presumably to keep the jaws from fragmenting if the prey escaped. In nature the trap jaw ant approaches a prey with its jaws opened, feels the prey with its antennae, and then surges toward it. As the jaws brush against the prey, trigger hairs stimulate the closing. The scientists examined the muscular and nervous mechanism and found a large muscle associated with the jaws but, amazingly, this muscle was not active during the closing. Further examination revealed that this muscle cocks the jaw open. The trigger hairs are mechanoreceptors (sensilla) that stimulate touch-sensitive nerve endings in the reflex

The spiny dogfish shark is notable for its ability to combat infections after injuries and surgery. Extracts obtained from the stomach of the shark were found to be potent killers of bacteria and to cause the disintegration of protozoa. The active compound in the extracts, squalamine, could serve as an antibiotic for many vertebrates.

system; these, in turn, rapidly stimulate a smaller muscle, causing the release of the cocked jaw.

Although the closing is not fully understood, the scientists determined that some highly elastic insect protein such as resilin stores mechanical energy in the jaws of the insect, similar to a spring. At the time of stimulation, this energy is released, snapping the jaw closed. The large jaw muscles then recock the system.

Spiders and sex. The female European linyphiid spider, *Linyphia triangularis,* spins a horizontal sheet web that is used to capture food and, under special conditions, to attract a mate. In the latter case, an unmated female presumably secretes a sex pheromone into her web. A male spider, attracted to the web by the volatile pheromone, cuts and rolls up the web into a ball in a predictable systematic manner. After completion of this process, the male undertakes the mating process, which may last five hours.

This male activity is called web-reduction behavior, and the web rolling presumably prevents the pheromone from attracting other male spiders that could interfere with the prolonged mating process. After mating, the female's next web lacks the pheromone and, as a result, does not elicit web-reduction behavior and mating in any approaching male.

In order to prove that the presence of a sex pheromone was stimulating the web-reduction behavior, two scientists, Siegfried Schultz of Germany and Søren Toft of Denmark, designed experiments to isolate and identify the compound. They collected webs produced by unmated females and by mated females, ascertained as such by whether males had performed the web-reduction behavior on each web. Using methylene chloride, methanol, or water, they made extracts from the webs of unmated females and sprayed them onto webs that had tested negatively for web-reduction behavior in males. After the spraying, males displayed web-reduction behavior on those webs. The compound was isolated and identified as an (R)-3-hydroxybutyric acid and its dimer, (R)-3-[(R)-3-hydroxybutyryloxy]-butyric acid. This was the first identification of a sex pheromone in a spider.

Mariculture of endangered clams. The giant clam, *Tridacna gigas,* has become an endangered species in the South Pacific islands because its shell is prized by poachers and its adductor muscle is an excellent protein source for the native islanders. In an attempt to aid the recovery of this species and also to benefit the islanders of Fiji, Tonga, and the Cook Islands, mariculture (cultivation of marine organisms) of the giant clams was carried out in experimental beds near Orpheus Island off the northeastern coast of Australia under the auspices of John Lucas of James Cook University in Townsville.

Lucas coordinated the clam studies, which involved artificial spawning, hatching, nursery, ocean nursery, and growth to maturity. As a result, during March 1993 some 3,000 clams raised by mariculture and weighing 18,200 kg (20 tons) were removed from artificial beds and transported to secret locations along the outer Great Barrier Reef by a landing craft of the Australian navy. Lucas concluded that under proper management clam farms could produce 7,300 kg (8 tons) of clam meat in 0.4 ha (one acre) of clear, warm offshore tidal waters.

New antibiotic from sharks. The spiny dogfish shark, *Squalus acanthias,* has a well-known ability to combat infections after injury and surgery. Believing that these sharks have a built-in antibiotic, Karen S. Moore of the Division of Human Genetics and Molecular Biology at Children's Hospital of Philadelphia, and several colleagues, prepared extracts from different organs of the shark and tested each for their effect on microbes. Stomach extracts proved to be potent killers of bacteria. The extracts also caused disintegration of protozoa.

The active compound in the extracts was isolated, identified, and named squalamine, a broad-spectrum steroidal antibiotic. Squalamine, an unusual steroid, represents a previously undescribed class of naturally occurring antibiotics of animal origin. The mechanism of squalamine involves attaching and punching holes in the membranes of microbes, which then leads to disruption of the cells. Since squalamine is not active on vertebrate tissue, it could serve as an antibiotic for numerous vertebrates. Furthermore, the compound has been synthesized in the laboratory, and so slaughter of dogfish sharks will not be necessary to obtain it.

Endothermic fish. The butterfly mackerel, tunas, and billfishes (swordfish and marlin), all members of the teleost suborder Scombroidei, have the ability to heat portions of their bodies to as much as 25° C (45° F) higher than the surrounding water. This process is called endothermy and is similar to systems found in mammals, birds, and some sharks. Other teleost fishes (including other scombroids) are ectodermic and can maintain a body temperature only within 1°–2° C (1.8°–3.6° F) of the surrounding water. Tunas warm their whole body, while the billfishes and butterfly mackerel warm only their brains and optical regions. Such endothermic functions give these fishes advantages over their cold-blooded competitors, such as the ability to descend to cold depths (billfishes and butterfly mackerel) and to migrate to cold waters (tunas), where prey are more plentiful.

In studies of the evolution of fishes, the question arises as to whether endothermy would evolve independently for all three groups or evolve only once. Barbara Block, John Finnerty, Alexandre Stewart, and Jessica Kidd of the department of organismal biology and anatomy at the University of Chicago pursued this question by comparing direct sequencing of a 600-base-pair portion of the mitochondrial cytochrome *b* gene from muscles of 32 species of fishes. These included 9 species of billfishes, 9 species of tunas, the butterfly mackerel, 10 species of ectodermic scombroids, and 3 species that were not teleosts. The results showed an independent origin for endothermy in all three groups. The scientists suggested that selective pressure for the fishes to expand their environmental niches, such as moving into colder water, was instrumental in the evolution of endothermy.

Dimorphic African fish. In Lake Tanganyika the scale-eating cichlid fish, *Perissodus microlepis*, has two forms; the direction of the mouth opening is either left-mouthed or right-mouthed. This fish attacks its common prey *Cyathopharynx furcifer* and tears off scales. Michio Hori of the department of biology at Wakayama (Japan) Medical College began studying these fish in 1982 and discovered that the population of both forms was stable and was maintained in a ratio of almost 1:1, implying that neither left-mouthed nor right-mouthed *P. microlepis* could gain an advantage on prey or each other.

Experiments were designed to determine if an individual *P. microlepis* could attack both sides of the prey and what role the prey plays in determining the ratio of the predator. Hori observed that the right-mouthed fish always attacked the left side of the prey and the left-mouthed fish always attacked the right side. Next, he observed that when one form was more common, the prey actually suffered more damage on the unexpected side because it would protect itself against the more common form and in so doing become a victim to the less common variety. Thus, the behavior of the prey in protecting its flank from the more common predator was benefiting the minority fish and, in the process, actually controlling the population balance of the two forms.

Cannibal salamanders. In nature the larvae of the Arizona tiger salamander, *Ambystoma tigrinum nebulosum*, consist of two different body types, one that feeds on invertebrates and one that feeds on larvae of its own species. The cannibal type is larger and has oral structures capable of consuming its kin. Whether the cannibal larvae prefer to consume their own siblings or more distant relatives was the subject of a series of experiments designed by David W. Pfennig of Cornell University, Ithaca, N.Y., and James P. Collins of Arizona State University.

The scientists were testing the inclusive fitness theory, which states that organisms can often increase their fitness (gene pool) by helping their kin. They reared related and unrelated tiger salamander larvae separately and mixed together. Larvae reared in mixed groups had a higher frequency of development of cannibal types (83–87%) than did larvae reared from the same batch (40%). However, in the related larval groups the cannibals appeared significantly later than in the unrelated groups, presumably allowing the cannibal to be less of a threat to its kin, which by that time would be more mobile and less likely to be nearby and a meal candidate. The scientists summarized that kinship environment has an influence on behavior and development and that perhaps chemical cues aid the organisms in protecting their own kin, thus increasing their own genetic pool and chance of survival.

Ultraviolet vision in lizards? Although ultraviolet vision has been described in some vertebrates, its function has remained unclear. In a recent discovery, however, scientists described what appears to be the use of ultraviolet vision for communication in lizards. Leo J. Fleishman of Union College, Schenectady, N.Y., Ellis R. Loew of Cornell University, and Manuel Leal of the University of Puerto Rico were examining the retina of anoline lizards in Puerto Rico for another purpose when they discovered ultraviolet photoreceptors, the first report of such an occurrence in any reptile. They then examined an ultraviolet reflection of the whole lizard and discovered that only the colorful expandable throat fan, or dewlap, reflected. The dewlap is expanded for communication and at other times is kept unexpanded. The scientists discovered that two species of *Anolis*—*A. krugi* and *A. cristatellus*—had an ultraviolet-bright dewlap reflection, while one species, *A. pulchellus*, had an ultraviolet-intermediate dewlap, and two species—*A. gundlachi* and *A. evermanni*—had an ultraviolet-dark dewlap reflection. The first three species live in or near sunlit areas, while the latter live in the understory of closed-canopy forests.

Fleishman concluded that ultraviolet reflection would serve for communication for lizards living in direct sunlight but would not aid visibility or communication for lizards in forests, where ultraviolet light would be greatly reduced. The presence of ultraviolet photoreceptors in forest species serves some other purpose, such as prey detection near sunlit areas.

Dwarf mammoths. In the northern and temperate latitudes of the Northern Hemisphere, the large woolly mammoth, *Mammuthus primigenius,* became extinct at the end of the Pleistocene Epoch, about 9,600–12,000 years ago. A recent discovery has provided evidence that some mammoths not only were present as recently as 4,000–7,000 years ago but also were small, only about half as large as their predecessors. Russian scientists Sergey L. Vartanyan, Vadim E. Garutt, and Andrey V. Sher examined teeth, tusks, and some bones from specimens of mammoths obtained from Wrangel Island, located in the Arctic Ocean some 200 km (125 mi) off the shore of northeastern Siberia. Interestingly, two sets of adult mammoth teeth were found, normal-sized teeth dating to 12,000 years ago and a smaller set dating to 4,000–7,000 years ago.

The scientists believe that the original population of woolly mammoths was trapped on the island when the ice started receding at the end of the Pleistocene, approximately 12,000 years ago. Since Wrangel Island maintained a high diversity of plant species common to a tundra meadow, the woolly mammoth was able to survive, but it became smaller. Thus, the scientists suggested that small size was the result of genetic isolation of a small population under nutritional pressure rather than an unusual event in evolution on an island.

Whale phylogeny. A recent study on whale evolution revealed a problem with the present taxonomic system. Living whales (order Cetacea) are presently divided into two suborders, the Odontoceti (the toothed form), consisting of sperm, bottlenose, beaked, killer, beluga, and pilot whales; dolphins; and porpoises; and the Mysticeti (the baleen whales), an example of which is the filter-feeding blue whale.

On the basis of past studies, these groups have traditionally been separated evolutionarily. However, Michel C. Milinkovitch of Yale University and two colleagues, Guillermo Orti and Axel Meyer of the State University of New York, demonstrated that the sperm whales are more closely related to the baleen whales than to the other toothed whales.

The scientists reached their conclusion after comparing DNA sequencing in two mitochondrial ribosomal gene segments between 16 species of cetaceans. This is a method particularly useful for studies when many closely related species are compared and is the first phylogeny (evolutionary history) for cetaceans based on explicit cladistic methods. (Cladistics is a system in which groups of animals and plants are defined by shared characteristics not found in ancestral groups). This close relationship of the sperm whales to the baleen whales suggests that they had a common ancestor that had teeth and possessed echolocation, both of which were lost by the baleen whales in the development of their large filtering apparatus.

A new large mammal. In the Vu Quang Nature Reserve located in the only extensive pristine forest in northern Vietnam, near the Laos-Vietnam border, a new species of living bovid, *Pseudoryx nghetinhensis,* was discovered and described, although none of the scientists involved in the study had examined a live one or had even seen a whole carcass. Vu Van Dung, Pham Mong Giao, Nguyen Ngoc Chinh, Do Tuoc, Peter Arctander, and John MacKinnon, all representing the Forest Inventory and Planning Institute of Vietnam's Ministry of Forestry, described the new species from partial specimens, including skins, skulls, and bones. In a re-creation of the animal from these fragments by a taxidermist, *Pseudoryx* resembles an antelope with long, smooth, almost straight, slender horns; it stands 80–90 cm (30–35 in) at the shoulder and weighs about 100 kg (220 lb).

On the basis of a study using the enzyme cytochrome *b* from DNA in organelles outside the nucleus of a cell, the animal was designated as a new species closely related to oxen. The species is from dark brown to reddish brown and has black and white markings on the face, neck, feet, and rump. It is believed to be the first large terrestrial mammal described in more than 50 years. After the discovery the Vietnamese government increased the Vu Quang Nature Reserve from 16,000 to 60,000 ha (39,500 to 148,200 ac) in order to protect *Pseudoryx* and other endangered species in the reserve.

—George G. Brown

See also Feature Articles: BORROWING THE BEST FROM NATURE; NO AND CO: THE BODY'S UNPRECEDENTED SIGNALING MOLECULES; SPECIES THAT NEED NO INTRODUCTION; ZOOPHARMACOGNOSY: ANIMALS HEALING THEMSELVES.

Materials sciences

Highlighting the past year in the materials sciences were significant improvements in the processing and properties of silicon nitride and zinc-coated steel. The former found applications in ceramic bearings, and the latter was an essential element in the production of corrosion-resistant automobiles.

Ceramics

Significant advances in silicon nitride technology resulted in increasing use of this material over the past year as rolling elements in precision bearings. Improvements in its processing and properties led to a range of bearing applications. The manufacturing firm SKF of Sweden estimated worldwide annual production of silicon nitride balls at 600,000, and this was expected to increase to several million per year during the next five years.

The recognition that silicon nitride offered significant advantages in wear applications is not new. Until recently, however, silicon nitride materials had not been specifically developed for bearing applications. Further, improved processing methods allowed rolling elements of the desired shape to be fabricated less expensively. These factors, combined with specialized needs that have been imposed on the bearings by new and more demanding applications, resulted in the increasing use of ceramic bearings. These applications ranged from high-speed machine tool spindles to dental drills to liquid rocket-engine turbopumps.

Bearing assemblies typically consist of inner and outer rings, termed races, between which the rolling elements are confined and rotate. To avoid contact between the elements, the races are often positioned within a ring-shaped structure called a separator or cage. The shape of the rolling elements can be spherical, cylindrical, or tapered cylindrical. For conventional bearings the races and rolling elements are made of hardenable steels. Cages are often metallic (steel, brass, aluminum), but nonmetallics such as phenolics and polyimides, sometimes fiber-reinforced, are frequently employed. Lubrication is necessary for successful metallic bearing operation. This is typically provided by grease, oil, a stream of air and oil, or a jet of oil.

Properties of silicon nitride. The properties of silicon nitride are well suited for bearings with reduced wear and extended life. In addition, silicon nitride's chemical inertness allows its use in environments that are highly degrading to steel. Silicon nitride is 40% less dense than bearing steels, which permits higher rotational speeds. Hardness is critical to good wear resistance, and silicon nitride is twice as hard as steel. As a result, wear life 10 times

greater than steel has been observed. The reduced loading for a given speed coupled with better friction characteristics reduces heat generation. This is important to the stability of both the bearing and the lubricant.

Silicon nitride is 50% stiffer than bearing steel. This results in higher contact stresses but also provides greater dimensional stability under load. Compressive strength is extremely high, and rolling-contact-fatigue resistance is excellent, superior to even the best bearing steels. When the ceramic fails, it does so by spallation (being gradually fladed away), as does steel. This noncatastrophic failure mode is essential for achieving reliable performance and is what sets silicon nitride apart from other ceramic-bearing-material candidates except zirconia, whose fatigue performance is unsatisfactory despite the nature of the failure.

Compared with steel, silicon nitride can survive far better under marginal lubrication conditions and is capable of operation at much higher temperatures. In addition, it is resistant to both corrosion and oxidation, and it is nonmagnetic and electrically insulating, all of which are important in a variety of specialty bearing applications.

Hybrids. Though the greatest advantages would accrue with all-ceramic bearing assemblies, most ceramic bearings in practice today are hybrid bearings. These employ ceramic rolling elements, most often spherical balls, in metallic races. This choice is influenced by the higher cost of the all-ceramic assemblies and the difficulties of attaching ceramic races to metallic shafts.

In addition, hybrid bearings can often be retrofitted directly to existing designs. When combined with appropriate selections of race, cage, and lubricant materials, hybrid bearings offer significant performance advantages over all-steel bearings.

Recent advances in silicon nitride formulations and processing have improved ceramic bearing performance and acceptability. The starting material is silicon nitride powder, to which yttria, alumina, and/or magnesia are added for densification. Powder formulations and quality have been greatly improved and have been tailored for bearing applications. Complete densification of the powder to final shape without porosity is critical to performance, and at one time the only method to achieve this was hot pressing (the application of temperature and pressure in graphite molds). This produced flat slabs or disks that were difficult and expensive to machine into ball blanks. More recently, hot isostatic pressing (HIP) has been successfully employed to make the blanks. The powder is mechanically compacted into porous balls, which are then encapsulated in glass. These are subjected to high temperature (about 1,700° C [3,092° F]) in a pressurized gaseous chamber. An

Used in such industries as machine tools and transportation equipment, bearing assemblies consist of rolling elements made of the ceramic silicon nitride and races made of bearing-grade steel. Twice as hard and 40% the density of bearing-grade steels, silicon nitride is well suited as a material for such components.

alternate method that eliminates encapsulation is to heat with low pressure to partially densify and seal the ball surface before applying higher pressure.

The resultant fully dense blanks must then be finished to ensure correct diameter, sphericity, and surface polish. Rough- and fine-finishing operations employ diamond abrasives owing to the hardness of the ceramic balls. Finally, the balls must be inspected to ensure that internal or surface flaws are not present. A variety of nondestructive evaluation techniques were being used, including computed tomography, microfocus X-ray, ultrasonics, thermal imaging, and fluorescent dye penetrants.

Applications. Perhaps the major use of hybrid ceramic bearings is for spindles in high-speed machine tools. Compared with steel, these bearings are stiffer, resulting in more precise machining; they also can run at higher speeds; generate less heat, noise, and vibration; and have longer lifetimes. Speed is desirable for enhanced productivity but leads to significant heat generation, which in turn degrades lubricants. Speed is rated by using the numerical quantity DN,

A liquid-cooled milling spindle, used in high-speed machine tools, contains hybrid ceramic bearings. Compared with steel bearings, the hybrid bearings are stiffer, which results in more precise machining.

Setco Sales Co., Cincinnati, Ohio

which is calculated by multiplying the bearing bore diameter, in millimeters, times the shaft speed, in revolutions per minute. Ingersoll Milling Machine Co. in the U.S. reported that hybrid ceramic bearings are essential in order to maintain lubricant integrity at DN above 750,000. In general, they observed that such bearings permit a 25% increase in speed and provide extended life at any speed. Costs are another important consideration. The higher price of the hybrids may be more than offset if the machine can be run with grease, as opposed to the expensive air-oil lubrication system required by steel bearings.

A new and expanding application for ceramic bearings is in lubrication-free dental drills. This has been motivated by the concern that communicable diseases, most notably AIDS, might be transmitted during dental procedures. As a result, some agencies have recommended that dental handpieces, in addition to drills and burrs, be heat-sterilized (autoclaved) after use on each patient. The handpiece is that part of the instrument held by the dentist and onto which the tool is mounted. It contains an air-driven turbine capable of operating at up to 500,-000 rpm. The steel turbine bearings are lubricated by periodic injections of copious amounts of an oil-lubricant mist about the assembly, most typically at the end of each day. Autoclaving after use on each patient requires repeated, time-consuming lubrication both before sterilization (to protect the bearings) and after (to replenish the lubricant). In addition, accumulated exposure to the autoclave environment will degrade the bearing components and the presence of substantial amounts of lubricant throughout the handpiece might interfere with complete sterilization and can contaminate the autoclave.

To overcome these concerns, the Star Dental Division of Den-Tal-Ez Inc. in the U.S. developed handpiece turbine bearings that use silicon nitride balls that do not need external lubrication. The instrument is capable of repeated sterilization procedures with reduced degradation and does not require intervening lubrication. The one-millimeter-diameter silicon nitride balls are packed in a few milligrams of grease that needs no replenishing. Races are grade 440C stainless steel. The current separator is phenolic, but this soon is to be replaced by a graphite-filled polyimide to achieve a longer lifetime. Since the drill does not employ oil mist for lubrication, it eliminates the possibility of residual lubricant's entering the oral cavity during burr rotation and thus provides a more pathogen-free environment.

In an exciting development, hybrid ceramic bearings were successfully tested under conditions simulating the operation of the high-pressure oxidizer turbopump of the space shuttle main engine. These new bearings employ silicon nitride balls, steel inner and outer races, and a self-lubricating polyimide composite separator. They displayed significantly greater durability than the metallic bearings currently used in the main engine. A continuing qualification program was expected to certify the hybrid bearings for mannned spaceflight in late 1995.

Additional applications of hybrid ceramic bearings include their use in equipment for manufacturing integrated circuits. These applications require operation at elevated temperature in high vacuum with minimal lubricant. As of mid-1994, at least four manufacturers were making vacuum pumps that employ hybrid bearings for long-term reliability and virtually oil-free ultrahigh vacuum generation.

Potential additional applications include computer disk drives, satellite and instrument gyroscopes, aircraft engine main shafts, undersea pumps, industrial blowers, and power generators. With expanded market penetration in mind, the Japanese firm Koyo Seiko Co., Ltd., projected its sales of ceramic bearings to total $30 million in 1995 alone, while estimates for the total U.S. market were as high as $300 million by the year 2000.

—Allan P. Katz

Metallurgy

Increasing demand for corrosion-resistant automobiles pushed the capacity for producing zinc-coated steels to new levels. Lack of process control, however, continued to prevent these materials from reaching their full potential. (Process control is the manipulation of conditions of a process in order to achieve desirable output characteristics.)

Steel is the dominant construction material for automobile body and frame components for a variety of reasons. It is inexpensive (11.4 cents per kilogram, or 25 cents per pound), is highly formable and weldable, and has outstanding mechanical proper-

ties (stiffness and strength). The major drawback of steel as a material for exterior applications, however, is its poor resistance to corrosion. When exposed to oxygen dissolved in water, the iron in steel spontaneously reacts to form iron hydroxide $Fe(OH)_3$, commonly called "rust." The rust is porous and does not adhere strongly to the steel, flaking off easily and exposing the underlying steel to continued corrosion.

Exposed steel is, therefore, usually protected with some type of surface coating. Organic-based paints are corrosion-resistant, are flexible, and come in many colors. Unfortunately, they can be chipped or scratched and degrade over time in sunlight. Rust blisters or complete perforations in body panels are common forms of damage to automobiles. Rusting of exposed structural members may lead to mechanical weakening or, in the worst case, unexpected failure.

The most successful metallurgical process for improving the corrosion resistance of steel has been "galvanization" of its surface with a thin coating of zinc metal. Methods of application are electroplating and dipping the steel in molten zinc. Unlike paint, which provides corrosion protection only if it physically covers the steel, zinc also provides electrochemical protection. If a scratch in the zinc coating exposes the steel, the zinc around it will corrode because zinc oxidizes more readily than iron, thereby protecting the exposed steel from oxidation. Galvanized steel is widely used in exterior applications such as roadway guard rails, light posts, roofing, and gutters. Only recently has it been more widely used in automobile manufacture. Market pressures for more corrosion-resistant vehicles have spurred zinc-coated-steel production to record levels. Three different coating processes are currently used to meet the growing demand.

Electrogalvanizing. Electrogalvanizing is essentially a continuous zinc electroplating process. The steel is cleaned and immersed directly into an acidic solution of zinc ions. Zinc metal is deposited on the steel surfaces by electrolysis, the passing of an electric current through the solution. Pure zinc coatings can be produced by this process, and coating thickness can be controlled with high precision.

Compared with the hot-dip processes discussed below, electrogalvanizing is more expensive. In addition, the pure zinc coating makes the product difficult to weld. Despite these drawbacks, several major auto manufacturers were firmly committed to using electrogalvanized sheet for outer body construction.

Hot-dip galvanizing. Hot-dip galvanizing is also done in a continuous process. After being cleaned, the steel strip is annealed. Annealing (heating at a particular temperature) recrystallizes the cold-rolled steel structure, thereby softening it and making it easier to form after being coated. Since the annealing time in a continuous process must be short (usually less than five minutes), the steel must be heated rapidly and accurately to a well-controlled temperature. A further complication in annealing is the need to protect the surface of the steel from oxidation. Protective atmospheres of reducing (deoxidizing) gases are needed to ensure that the annealed strip enters the zinc bath free of surface oxides.

The strip next passes through a bath of molten zinc at about 500° C (932° F). The zinc contains by weight 0.2% of aluminum, which acts as an inhibitor against reaction between the zinc and steel by forming a thin barrier layer of iron-aluminum compounds on the surface. As the strip is pulled vertically out of the zinc pot, the liquid zinc film adhering to the surface is "wiped" by blasts of nitrogen gas from specially designed nozzles positioned on both sides of the strip.

The coating thickness, typically 5 to 20 micrometers (millionths of a meter), is carefully controlled, as is the uniformity in thickness across the sheet. Special stabilizing rolls submerged in the pot reduce fluttering of the sheet as it passes the nozzles. Upon cooling, the zinc solidifies to form a metallurgically bonded coating.

One of the primary limitations of galvanized steel for automotive applications is that it welds poorly. Early attempts to overcome this problem included galvanizing the steel on one side only and galvanizing entire assemblies after welding. The results were not entirely successful, and so the "galvannealing" process was developed to produce weldable galvanized steel.

Galvannealing. Galvannealing follows essentially the same steps as hot-dip galvanizing, with an additional annealing step directly after application of the zinc. This step results in reaction between the zinc and steel to form a multilayer coating of zinc-iron intermetallic compounds. The increased iron content of the coating restores weldability without significantly sacrificing corrosion protection. The rapid rate of the zinc-iron reaction requires more stringent process controls in galvannealing as compared with standard hot-dip galvanizing. A variety of technological developments have improved process control, but several fundamental problems have prevented galvannealing from reaching its full potential.

In contrast to galvanizing, galvannealing requires reaction between the zinc and steel. Therefore, the aluminum content of the molten zinc bath is maintained at about 0.1% by weight, limiting the amount of iron-aluminum intermetallic compound that forms initially. Even more critical is the variability in aluminum concentration. Unfortunately, reliable instruments that can continuously monitor the aluminum concentration of the zinc bath are not yet available. The aluminum concentration is monitored by intermittent sampling and adjusted manually, resulting in cyclic variations.

The galvannealing treatment is conducted at temperatures in a narrow range around 500° C. At these temperatures the zinc is molten and diffuses rapidly into the surface of the solid steel. As the zinc content increases, the zinc-iron intermetallic compounds begin to form. Solid intermetallic crystals eventually push up through the surface of the molten zinc as it is consumed in the reaction. The thickness of the final coating is usually five to seven micrometers.

The first intermetallic compound to form is thought to be the zeta phase ($FeZn_{13}$). Adjacent layers of the delta phase ($FeZn_9$) and finally the gamma phase (Fe_3Zn_7) form beneath the zeta. The diffusion process is complex, and the sequence of reactions and resulting microstructure of the multilayer coating are not well understood.

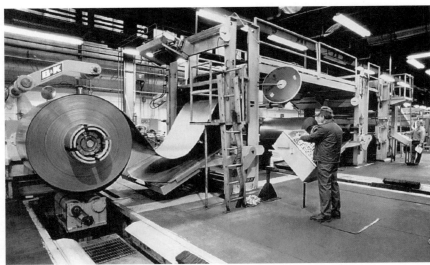

A production line at a steel coatings factory receives coils of steel weighing as much as 22,700 kg (50,000 lb) to be either coil coated or electrogalvanized. The increased demand for corrosion-resistant automobiles was causing some automakers to commit themselves to using pure-zinc electrogalvanized steels for the exterior panels of their cars.

Bethlehem Steel Corp./Inland Steel Co./Pre Finish Metals Inc.

The zinc-iron alloying reaction in galvannealing is complete in less than 30 seconds. The rate of alloying also depends strongly on temperature. Both time and temperature must thus be controlled accurately. Time can be controlled easily by adjustment of the strip velocity. Measurement of the process temperature, however, presents several fundamental problems.

Thermocouples cannot be used to measure the temperature of the strip since it is moving at a fast rate (1 to 2 m [3.3 to 6.6 ft] per second). A temperature-measurement technique that does not involve contact with the strip is necessary. Radiation pyrometry is the most widely used method under these circumstances. It is based on the fact that all bodies emit light in a continuous spectrum of wavelengths depending on their temperature (thermal radiation). Although at temperatures normally experienced such a small fraction of the thermal radiation is in the visible spectrum that humans cannot see it, the glow of hotter bodies such as coals in a fire and stars is visible. Regardless of the temperature of a body, it can be measured by radiation pyrometry provided certain conditions are met.

A special kind of body called a "blackbody" emits only thermal radiation. The rate of emission, called the emissive power, depends only on its temperature. The ratio of the emissive power of any body to that of a blackbody at the same temperature is defined as the "emissivity." If the emissivity of a body is known and its emissive power measured, its temperature can be determined.

In the case of galvannealing, the emissivity of the zinc coating on the steel changes from about 0.1 for the shiny, smooth liquid zinc surface just out of the bath to 0.7 to 0.8 for the gray, rough surface produced as the intermetallic crystals poke up through the liquid. This large change in emissivity during galvannealing hampers the use of radiation pyrometry for temperature measurement. Researchers were trying to quantify the structural and chemical processes responsible for the change in emissivity, as well as develop computer methods to compensate for its variability. Advanced pyrometer systems are capable of measuring temperatures in the galvannealing process to approximately $\pm 10°$ C (18° F). Many galvannealers were reluctant to use optical pyrometers and instead relied on furnace power settings or other indirect methods of controlling temperature.

The iron content of the galvannealed coating seems to correlate with the important quality characteristics of the product. At iron contents less than about 8% by weight, weldability is poor, as discussed above. At iron contents greater than about 12%, the coating tends to spall off in many small pieces or "powder" during forming operations. Powdering probably results from the fact that the zinc-iron inter-

metallic compounds are brittle. Stresses developed during bending and forming cause the coating to fracture. Small bits of coating left in the forming die may score the surface of subsequently formed parts.

Considering the brittleness of the intermetallics formed in the galvannealing process, powdering may ultimately be an intrinsic limitation. However, the addition of approximately one million tons per year of new galvannealing capacity in the U.S. and Canada in 1993 attests to the commitment of automobile manufacturers to galvannealing. As process-control continues to improve, more meaningful correlations of process parameters with coating microstructure and chemistry should emerge. Seldom does new process-control technology have as much potential for improving product consistency as in the case of galvannealing.

—Kevin P. Trumble

Mathematics

Mathematical discoveries during the past year included a new polyhedron that will fill space but only nonperiodically, an algorithm (step-by-step procedure) for envy-free fair division of resources, a breakthrough in the combinatorial designs known as Latin rectangles, and yet another new Mersenne prime. Nonetheless, all other events in the mathematical world were eclipsed by the unexpected announcement that the most famous unsolved problem in pure mathematics, Fermat's last theorem, had yielded at last. At the year's end, however, a gap was found in the proof of this result, and observers waited to see if the gap could be filled.

Fermat's last theorem. After seven years of secret work, Andrew Wiles of Princeton University surprised the world in June 1993 by announcing at the close of a series of lectures that the most famous outstanding problem in pure mathematics, the proof of Fermat's last theorem, followed as an easy consequence of Wiles's solution to another problem. His announcement created the greatest popular excitement in decades about mathematical research.

Pierre de Fermat (1601–65) stated that there are no solutions in positive integers to $a^n + b^n = c^n$ for $n > 2$. In other words, there is no cube that is the sum of two cubes, no fourth power that is the sum of two other fourth powers, etc. Fermat claimed to have a proof of this conjecture, which became known as "Fermat's last theorem" (FLT) despite the fact that no proof had ever been discovered. Fermat recorded the result in the margin of his copy of Diophantus' *Arithmetica*, with the note, "I have discovered a truly remarkable proof, but the margin is too small to contain it." Fermat never elaborated on his claim or mentioned it to others. Leonhard Euler

Andrew Wiles of Princeton University announced in June 1993 that he had discovered the proof of "Fermat's last theorem," the most famous unsolved problem in pure mathematics (see text). Though a gap in one detail of his proof was later discovered, Wiles expressed confidence that he could resolve that problem.

(1707–83) showed that there are no solutions for $n = 3$, and Ernst E. Kummer (1810–93) developed important ideas in abstract algebra in the process of proving that the conjecture is true for all n up to 100. Most mathematicians today, however, do not believe that Fermat had a valid proof. They consider his failure to say anything further on the matter as an indication that he later realized that his proposed proof would not work (though he did not cross out the marginal inscription).

It has been known since 1978 that any counterexample (an example that disproves a proposition or theory) to FLT, if one exists, must have $n > 125,000$. In 1992 J.P. Buhler of Reed College, Portland, Ore., and Richard E. Crandall of NeXT Computer Inc. raised this minimum to 4,000,000. Moreover, Gerd Faltings of Princeton University showed in 1983 that there can be at most a finite number of counterexamples.

FLT follows from a more general result obtained by Wiles about elliptic curves. Elliptic curves are part of algebraic geometry, a branch of mathematics that applies algebraic methods to geometric objects, such as curves and surfaces. An elliptic curve over the rational numbers consists of the points that satisfy an equation of the form

$$y^2 + axy + by = x^3 + cx^2 + dx + e,$$

where the coefficients a, b, c, d, and e are integers. The name is something of a misnomer, as an elliptic curve does not have the shape of an ellipse (Figure 1). Any elliptic curve can be simplified to a standard form

$$y^2 = x^3 + Ax^2 + Bx + C,$$

with A, B, and C integers.

In the 1960s Yves Hellegouarch realized that any counterexample to FLT, say with the equation $a^n + b^n = c^n$, has an accompanying special elliptic curve,

$$y^2 = x(x + a^n)(x - b^n).$$

This connection suggests that properties of elliptic curves could be translated back into facts about counterexamples to FLT.

One such property that plays a crucial role in Wiles's proof is modularity. An elliptic curve is *modular* if it can be obtained as a projection of another kind of curve, called a *modular curve*. André Weil of the Institute for Advanced Study observed in 1967 that work of Goro Shimura of Princeton University suggested that every elliptic curve is modular; Shimura noted that Yutaka Taniyama (1927–58) had made a smililar conjecture in the mid-1950s. On the other hand, in 1985 Gerhard Frey of the University of the Saarlands, Saarbrücken, Ger., conjectured that elliptic curves arising from counterexamples to FLT

The elliptic curve $y^2 = x(x + 9)(x - 16)$.

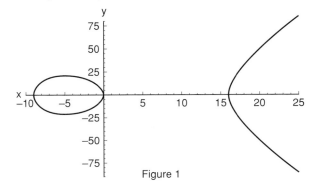

Figure 1

380

cannot be modular, and in 1986 Kenneth A. Ribet of the University of California at Berkeley proved that this is so. This result, combined with a proof of the Taniyama-Shimura-Weil conjecture, would imply that the elliptic curves arising from counterexamples to FLT would have to be both modular and not modular. Since there cannot be such a curve, there can be no counterexample to FLT, and Fermat's last theorem must be true.

Wiles's proof consists of showing that the Taniyama-Shimura-Weil conjecture is true for a special class of elliptic curves, the *semistable* ones, a class that includes any elliptic curves that may arise from the counterexamples to FLT. At the end of 1993, as colleagues were checking the 200-page proof by Wiles, a gap was discovered in one detail of the proof. However, Wiles expressed confidence that he could bridge the gap in the near future. This development recalled the case of Yoichi Miyaoka of Tokyo Metropolitan University, who claimed in 1988 to have a proof of Fermat's last theorem (from a totally different approach from Wiles's); his argument had a flaw that unfortunately turned out to be unfixable. However, even if Wiles's results fall short of a full proof of FLT, they mark a major advance on a new approach to the problem and an outstanding contribution to number theory.

Aperiodic space-filling polyhedron. It is easy to cover a plane with tiles all of which are the same size and shape, such as squares, triangles, or hexagons. The prints of Maurits C. Escher (1898–1972), however, provide marvelous illustrations of ways to tile a plane in a systematic way with irregularly shaped tiles. In 1966 Robert Berger discovered a set of 20,426 different tiles with the very strange property that copies of them can be used to cover the plane but only nonperiodically. That is, copies of these tiles can be arranged to cover the plane (without gaps or overlaps) but not in such a way that the tiles repeat regularly in some direction. Such a set of tiles that can cover the plane but never periodically is called *aperiodic*. In 1975 Roger Penrose, a mathematical physicist at the University of Oxford, devised the Penrose pieces—just two tiles—with the same property. No single tile is known to have this property.

A discovery a few years ago by Peter Schmitt of the University of Vienna showed that the situation is different when one moves from a plane to space. He described a single shape that would fill space only nonperiodically, but the shape is nonconvex. In a convex shape all points lying between two points in the figure also are part of the figure; in a nonconvex figure, such as an L shape, there are pairs of points for which this feature fails. In a sense, convex shapes are "nicer," and mathematicians were not completely surprised that a nonconvex shape could

be aperiodic. They were surprised in 1993, though, when John Horton Conway of Princeton University exhibited a convex aperiodic polyhedron.

Envy-free fair division. A traditional way to divide a piece of cake fairly between two competing children is to let one cut it and let the other choose from the two pieces. With some ingenuity one can extend this procedure to cover three or more children, so that each gets a piece that he or she regards as fair.

The mathematical study of fair division began with the Polish mathematician Hugo Steinhaus in the 1940s. It was not until 1967 that the cut-and-choose method was extended to more than three participants, by Harold W. Kuhn of Princeton University. Two of Steinhaus' students, however, Stefan Banach and Bronislaw Kastner, had earlier found a different procedure that also provides for this kind of fair division. Kastner had also observed that if the participants value pieces of the cake differently, then there is a division in which each gets what he or she regards as *more* than a fair share, and a procedure to implement this division was devised by Douglas R. Woodall of the University of Nottingham, England, in 1986.

In the case of two children, the cut-and-choose method ensures a certain stability for the division. If the child who cuts divides the piece of cake exactly in half, according to that child's perception, then that child is assured of getting exactly half, whichever piece the chooser elects. The chooser in turn gets at least half, according to the chooser's perception. Since each gets at least half (according to their respective perceptions), there should be no squabbling. This perhaps is the feature that has earned this method of division its place in family folklore. Mathematicians say that the method is *envy-free* because no participant prefers another's piece to his or her own.

Steinhaus had proved that for any number of participants, there is always an envy-free division. But his proof did not give an algorithm for performing the division, and none of the general methods of division invented during the intervening years was envy-free. Subsequent researchers produced complicated envy-free methods for the special case of three participants.

In 1993, however, Steven J. Brams, a political scientist at New York University, and Alan D. Taylor, a mathematician at Union College, Schenectady, N.Y., formulated an envy-free division procedure that works for any number of participants. Their method generalizes one that was invented by Conway and John Selfridge of Northern Illinois University. The generalization involves having one player cut the cake into more pieces than there are participants, after which the participants trim and choose the pieces.

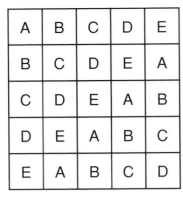

Figure 2

A Latin square of order 5 (number of rows/columns) follows an easy pattern.

The Brams-Taylor procedure can be applied to another family decision, the allocation of chores. Because the family is allocating something undesirable rather than something desirable (such as cake), the procedure calls not for trimming smaller and smaller pieces but for adding on smaller and smaller chores. The envy-free trimming procedure can also be adapted to the division of an estate that includes indivisible items (such as a house or car) provided there is enough liquidity supplied by many assets of small value or by the sale of one or more very large assets.

Latin rectangles. In 1779 Leonhard Euler proposed the problem of constructing what are now called Latin squares (so called because Euler labeled them with Latin letters). A Latin square is a square array of cells, each of which is occupied by a symbol, with each symbol appearing exactly once in each (horizontal) row and exactly once in each (vertical) column. Figure 2 shows a Latin square of order 5 (the number of rows/columns). For any order Latin squares are easy to construct. Trial and error can produce a Latin square cell by cell; each cell offers the choice from the same n different symbols, where n is the order of the square. Of course, choices made for previously determined cells in the same row or column forbid some of the options available.

Latin squares are important in the design of efficient experiments. For example, in an agricultural experiment the rows could correspond to plots of land, the columns to different hybrids of corn, and the symbols to different herbicides. In an industrial experiment the rows could correspond to particular machines, the columns to kinds of jobs, and the symbols to individual workers. Latin squares provide designs that can be analyzed by the statistical technique of analysis of variance.

Almost 200 years after Euler, in 1977 Jeff Dinitz, now at the University of Vermont, proposed a generalization of a Latin square, known as a partial Latin square. Like a Latin square, a partial Latin square cannot have the same symbol appear twice in any row or column. Also like a Latin square, for each cell there are n different symbols available to choose from. The difference is that different cells may offer different collections of n symbols, from a larger universe of symbols. Figure 3a shows the arrangement of constraints for one particular problem, and Figure 3b gives a partial Latin square that solves the problem. The question Dinitz asked is whether there is always a partial Latin square that fulfills a given set of constraints and, if so, how to find one.

Although it is easily solved for orders 2 and 3, Dinitz' problem is considerably more difficult than Euler's original problem of constructing Latin squares. In 1991 Noga Alon and Michael Tarsi at Tel Aviv (Israel) University solved Dinitz' problem for orders 4 and 6, but their method, which uses graph theory, cannot be applied to odd orders, not even 5.

In 1993 Jeannette C.M. Janssen, now at Concordia University, Quebec, made substantial progress on the problem for arbitrary order by solving a partial Latin rectangle problem. A partial Latin rectangle is a rectangular array of symbols, with no row or column having two of the same symbol. When the larger of the numbers of rows and columns of the rectangle is denoted by n, Janssen proved that if there are $n + 1$ choices available for each cell, then one can always construct a partial Latin rectangle.

Janssen's result almost solves the Dinitz problem. For a square of order n, one should think of the square as being embedded in a rectangle with one additional row. Janssen's result shows that for the resulting size of $(n + 1) \times n$, a partial Latin rectangle can be constructed provided there are $n + 1$ choices available for each cell. Removing the last row from

The possible symbols for each cell of a proposed partial Latin square (3a), and (3b) a partial Latin square that solves the problem in 3a.

A, B, or C	A, B, or D	A, B, or C
B, C, or D	A, C, or D	A, B, or D
B, C, or D	A, C, or D	A, B, or C

Figure 3a

A	B	C
B	A	D
D	C	A

Figure 3b

the completed partial Latin rectangle yields a partial Latin square. This approach does not quite solve the Dinitz problem, though, because it assumes that $n+1$ choices are available at each cell, instead of just n.

Janssen achieved her results by applying the methods of Alon and Tarsi. Whether further developments of that approach will permit solution of the partial Latin square problem, whether new techniques will be required, or whether in fact it may not be solvable remain as questions for further research.

New largest prime. At the beginning of 1994, computer scientists at Cray Research, Inc., announced the discovery of the largest-known prime number, found while conducting tests on a CRAY C90-series supercomputer. The new prime number, $2^{859,433}-1$, has 258,716 decimal digits. David Slowinski and Paul Gage of Cray Research developed the program that found the new prime number.

The largest Mersenne prime known previously, $2^{756,839}-1$, was discovered in February 1992 at AEA Technology's Harwell Laboratory in Didcot, England, by computer scientists who were also conducting a test of a Cray Research supercomputer. That number has (only) 227,832 digits.

Mersenne numbers, integers of the form $M_p=2^p-1$ with p a prime, are named after Marin Mersenne (1588–1648), a French monk who was an amateur mathematician. Although it is impossible to prove that a very large number is prime by trying all potential divisors, the special form of Mersenne numbers allows special methods to be applied. In particular, the Lucas-Lehmer test, devised by Édouard Lucas (1842–91) and Derrick H. Lehmer (1905–91), states that M_p is prime if and only if it divides S_{p-2}, a number in the sequence that starts with $S_0=4$ and has subsequent terms defined by $S_{n+1}=S_n^2-2$. For example, for $p=3$, $S_1=14$; because this quantity

is divisible by the Mersenne number $M_3=2^3-1=7$, $M_3=7$ must be prime.

The latest giant is the 33rd Mersenne number that is known to be prime. Other smaller ones may yet lie undiscovered in the unexplored gaps from $2^{370,000}$ to $2^{430,000}$ and from $2^{524,000}$ to $2^{750,000}$.

—Paul J. Campbell

Medical sciences

Physicians and medical researchers during the past year pushed the limits of reproductive science, cloning the first human embryos and enabling women in their 50s to give birth to healthy babies. Successes in pinpointing genetic bases of cancer, Alzheimer's disease, and many other disorders were leading researchers to new treatments. In the United States the number one medical issue for the year was that of health care reform.

General medicine.

AIDS and tuberculosis continued to spread despite progress in education, diagnosis, and treatment. In addition, other infectious agents were showing their mettle in unexpected ways, causing health officials to be concerned about a resurgence in infectious diseases.

AIDS. In Berlin at the Ninth Annual Conference on AIDS, scientists reported discouraging results concerning vaccines under development, the early use of zidovudine (azidothymidine, or AZT) to slow the onset of disease, and the use of drug combinations. But the scientists did suggest that they may have learned how to make the body's own immune system better able to fight infection. The scientists also stressed that other sexually transmitted diseases

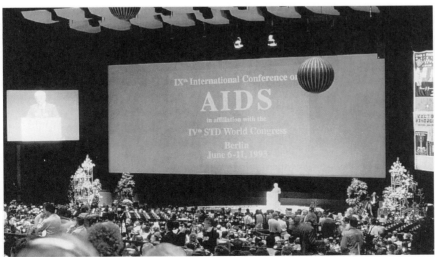

At the Ninth Annual Conference on AIDS, in Berlin in June 1993, researchers reported that they had not yet developed drugs that cure the disease or even contain it for long. They did suggest that they may have discovered how to improve the ability of the body's own immune system to fight infection.

© Rick Gerharter—Impact Visuals

make infection by HIV, the virus that causes AIDS, more likely.

In July 1993 the number of women infected with HIV through heterosexual contact exceeded the number of such women infected through intravenous drug use. Though more men than women had AIDS, the number of AIDS cases increased four times faster among women than among men in 1992, according to the U.S. Centers for Disease Control and Prevention in Atlanta, Ga.

Researchers from New Mexico and Georgia protected five of six macaque monkeys against vaginal transmission of the simian immunodeficiency virus by administering a vaccine consisting of killed virus encapsulated in microspheres. The May 1993 report indicated that oral vaccines were ineffective unless supplemented with inhaled or injected boosters.

In the U.S. molecular biologists were using gene therapy to fight AIDS. In California the strategy called for inserting the gene for a piece of RNA into HIV-infected T cells taken from people with AIDS. After growing many of these T cells, the scientists would return them to the body. The inserted genes prevented the virus from replicating (reproducing itself) in cells grown in test tubes. In Seattle, Wash., other scientists were trying to boost the numbers of another immune-system cell, which should seek out and destroy cells infected with HIV.

Laboratory studies revealed that HIV works even more deviously than previously thought and suggested that early intervention may be warranted. Virologists at the U.S. National Institutes of Health (NIH) showed that during the asymptomatic stages of AIDS, the virus invades the lymph nodes, the spleen, the tonsils, and the adenoids and actively replicates. The T cells that eventually become infected pick up the virus as they pass through the lymph nodes. In addition, Minnesota scientists discovered that even in these early stages of disease, about 100 billion T cells become infected. In June California immunologists discovered that HIV also destroys immature immune-system cells in fetal thymus tissue implanted into mice specially bred to lack an immune system of their own.

Other scientists showed that herpesvirus 6 may aid HIV by attacking white blood cells called natural killer cells and thereby making them vulnerable to HIV infection. HIV typically infects a different white cell, and so this herpesvirus may lead to more aggressive illness.

In February 1993 Nature magazine described results that indicated that HIV, when bombarded by multiple drugs, became weaker and eventually stopped replicating as it evolved resistance to treatment. Though they hailed their findings as a leap forward, the Harvard University researchers later discovered an error in their results, and British sci-

entists subsequently showed that HIV could remain viable even as it evolved this resistance. Even so, several groups throughout the world were testing the potential of using combinations of drugs to fight HIV.

In July a French scientist went to jail for failing to halt the distribution of HIV-contaminated blood-clotting factors to persons with hemophilia. In November charges of scientific misconduct lodged a year earlier against U.S. AIDS researcher Robert Gallo were dropped by the U.S. government. The adoption of a more restricted definition of misconduct would have required proof that Gallo was intentionally deceptive when he used a virus supplied by French scientists but did not give them credit.

Six reports in a February 1993 New England Journal of Medicine eased concerns about a new AIDS-like illness that had surfaced in 1992. Extensive reviews of these mysterious cases and other AIDS reports revealed no common link for this supposed syndrome, which was called idiopathic CD4 + T-lymphocytopenia.

Genetics. In Science magazine epidemiologists reported that a particular form of a molecule important for moving fatty molecules through the body was linked to an increased risk of Alzheimer's disease. However, scientists did not know the role of this molecule, Apo-E4, in the development of the dementia associated with Alzheimer's.

Two U.S. teams announced that they had identified the genetic defect underlying a common colorectal cancer. The gene, located on chromosome 2, normally directs the production of a protein that flags mistakes in newly replicated DNA and activates DNA repair mechanisms.

In March 1993 an international team of 31 scientists pinpointed the gene for the familiar form of amyotrophic lateral sclerosis (ALS). The defective gene, on chromosome 21, leads to an alteration in the enzyme superoxide dismutase so that it no longer helps the body get rid of potentially dangerous molecules called free radicals. The finding suggests potential treatments and provides clues about the cause of other forms of ALS.

A controversial study done by geneticists at the NIH found that inheriting one or more of as-yet-unidentified genes in a piece of the X chromosome may predispose some men to homosexuality. They derived these results after studying 114 families of homosexual men.

By studying genetically engineered mice, molecular biologists demonstrated that cancer genes may indeed be aberrant forms of genes critical in the growth of embryos. These Boston scientists discovered that the normal version of a gene blamed for the appearance of a pediatric kidney cancer called Wilms' tumor is essential in kidney development in the embryo.

The finding that the genetic defect leading to a neuromuscular disease called spinocerebellar ataxia 1 consists of a short bit of DNA that repeats 40 to 80 times bolstered the emerging notion that variability in these repetitions may underlie many genetic disorders. Scientists first determined these variable repeats as the defect in a hereditary form of mental retardation known as fragile-X syndrome. They also occur in myotonic dystrophy and spinobulbar muscular atrophy. In March scientists discovered that Huntington's disease also is characterized by variable repeats.

Other studies discovered that genetic material from people with different cancers was more likely to have increases in certain repeating DNA sections than genetic material from healthy people. One particular repeating section may account for one in 11 breast, colorectal, and bladder cancers, Boston scientists reported in the *New England Journal of Medicine*. The number of repeats can vary, but it tends to increase with each successive generation, leading geneticists to suggest that this may account for the variable course of some inherited diseases and the tendency for some disorders to become more severe in descendants.

Heart disease. A British and U.S. team discovered that the cholesterol-carrying molecule lipoprotein A, which was already associated with an increased risk of heart disease, stimulates the smooth muscle cells lining blood vessels to multiply more quickly than they would normally. This proliferation may speed the clogging of arteries.

The quest to control cholesterol to reduce the risk of heart disease was made more complicated when studies in genetically engineered mice showed that at least one type of the supposedly "good" fat-carrying molecules, the high-density lipoproteins, could increase the risk of arteries' becoming clogged if too abundant.

In the *New England Journal of Medicine,* Iowa scientists reported that during REM (rapid eye movement) sleep, at which time dreams occur, sympathetic nervous system activity more than doubles. This surge may help explain the high incidence of strokes and heart attacks in the predawn hours. The increased activity may make the platelets in the blood more likely to stick to blood vessel walls.

A five-year study of men by Dutch scientists found heart-protective benefit in diets rich in flavonoids. These men got these substances, which are often pigments in fruits and vegetables, mostly from apples, tea, and onions.

New Zealand and Canadian researchers demonstrated that consuming one's calories in nine meals a day, rather than in two or three, leads to a 6.5% fall in total cholesterol and an 8.1% fall in low-density lipoprotein (LDL) cholesterol, which translates into

a 13% reduction in heart-disease risk. Boston researchers analyzing data from two Harvard University studies, the long-term Nurses' Health Study and the Health Professionals Study, showed that middle-age adults who took vitamin E supplements every day reduced their heart disease risk by 40%.

Cancer. In February 1993 the Health Professionals Study, of 73,000 men, linked vasectomies to an increased risk of prostate cancer. This project tracked male health professionals, including dentists and veterinarians, and concluded that those undergoing vasectomy had a 66% greater risk of having prostate cancer than those who did not have this operation. The researchers' second study, the Nurses' Health Study, of husbands of nurses involved in a larger research project, found a 56% increased risk. Later that year data from those studies also revealed that men consuming high-fat diets rich in red meat or chicken with skin left on were more likely to develop more advanced stages of prostate cancer.

Other results from these two long-term studies supported the overall value of fruits and vegetables in the diet. Two nutrients, folate and methionine, help promote the addition of methyl groups to DNA, a reaction that helps keep cancer-causing genes inactive. Thus, diets that are rich in these nutrients seem to protect against the development of precancerous polyps in the colon and to lower the risk of colorectal cancer.

In addition, Chinese and U.S. scientists reported a 13% drop in death from cancer in a rural Chinese community that had generally consumed a poor diet. In those residents who took food supplements containing vitamin E, beta-carotene, and selenium over a five-year period, the researchers saw not only a decrease in cancers quite common there but also an improvement in the survival rate from many kinds of disease.

Ongoing studies by Italian epidemiologists suggested that a chemical spill in 1976 in Seveso, Italy, resulted in elevated cancer rates in people living near Milan. But the pattern of cancer seen thus far was unexpected. Those most heavily exposed to the airborne dioxin had not yet shown any increase in cancer, but women from a slightly less contaminated area had about five times the normal incidence of gallbladder and bile-duct cancers and men there had twice the incidence of those and liver cancers. Cancers in blood-forming tissues also doubled. In contrast, breast and uterine cancers declined, possibly because of dioxin's effect on estrogen metabolism.

Another epidemiological study, this one involving more than 1,000 participants, concluded that people suffering from on-the-job stress faced 5.5 times the risk of colorectal cancer as people who did not report having those problems. Animal studies supported this connection. Japanese researchers found

Phillip Taylor, M.D., National Cancer Institute; photo, The New York Times

In a rural community in China where diets are poor and the incidence of some cancers is high, residents wait to be screened as part of a five-year clinical trial to determine whether food supplements containing vitamin E, beta-carotene, and selenium could improve their health. The results, announced in 1993, showed a significant reduction in deaths from cancer as well as from other diseases.

that over several days rats that watched other rats subjected to electrical shocks suffered damage to their DNA. If not repaired, damaged DNA can lead to abnormal cell growth.

Scientists studying skin cancer discovered that aging may be a risk factor for cancer because each year people lose a little of their ability to repair damaged DNA. The researchers also found that some people inherit a poor ability to fix genes and consequently have the repair capacity of someone 30 years older. If they spend a lot of time exposed to sunlight, people with low repair capacity are five times more likely to develop skin cancer than are other people. In addition, women who received estrogen treatments after menopause retained more repair capacity than women who did not take the hormone.

Several studies strengthened the link between cancer and genomic instability, the tendency of DNA to get mixed up or to mutate and not be repaired. In particular, they tied the loss of normal tumor suppressor gene p53 to an increase in this instability and a slowing of DNA repair.

The elucidation of how p53 works improved the understanding of how cancer can represent growth gone awry. In November and December a half dozen research groups reporting in *Cell* and *Nature* magazines established links between p53 and the cell cycle. The protein encoded by the p53 gene activates a gene that makes a protein that in turn keeps cells in a resting, nondividing state.

During the spring, reports in *Cell, Nature,* and *Science* helped scientists piece together one way that cells transfer growth-regulating signals from their outer membranes to their nuclei. This growth-signaling pathway involves a protein, called Ras, that lies just under the cell membrane. It is encoded by a cancer-activating gene, or oncogene. Scientists from Britain, Canada, Australia, and the U.S. helped trace the steps involved in this signal transfer. The results should help in the development of anticancer treatments.

Scientists also furthered their understanding of the link between the skin cancer melanoma and sunlight. At the Brookhaven National Laboratory, Upton, N.Y., researchers discovered that a wide range of radiation, including ultraviolet and some visible light, may induce changes in melanin pigment and that those changes may in turn lead to DNA damage and, possibly, cancer. Another study, published in January 1994, showed that sunscreens do not protect mice from developing melanoma.

Japanese and U.S. scientists identified a faulty gene on chromosome 5 in many people with leukemia. The gene codes for a protein that helps regulate the production of interferon, an immune-system messenger.

Diabetes. Canadian and U.S. scientists at 29 medical centers saw surprising benefit in tightly controlling blood sugar levels in people with type I diabetes. The study of 1,441 people, half of whom took insulin twice a day and half of whom injected insulin three or more times daily and monitored their blood sugar four times daily, showed that the rigorous treatment can slow the development of complications arising from this disease. It slowed destruction of the retina by 76% and prevented or delayed kidney disease by 35% to 56%.

More than ever before, scientists were targeting molecular mechanisms for preventing diabetes. Two U.S. groups studying mice bred to develop diabetic symptoms believed that they pinpointed an enzyme that causes the body's white blood cells to attack the insulin-producing cells of the pancreas. The enzyme, glutamate decarboxylase, seems to set off an autoimmune response, which then escalates. By exposing newborn mice to this enzyme, they were able to prevent the development of diabetes in some mice.

In January diabetic mice that had been treated with a monoclonal antibody regained their ability to regulate their blood sugar, leading researchers to hope that a similar approach may one day eliminate insulin-dependent diabetes in humans. The monoclonal antibody homes in on the CD3 receptor molecule in T cells. This particular antibody, which is used to treat and prevent rejection in organ transplants, causes too many side effects in diabetes, but a fragment of it may one day prove useful as a human therapy.

Reproduction. Reproductive biologists pushed the limits of in vitro (outside the body) fertilization techniques to help women in their 50s give birth. In the medical journal *Lancet,* University of Southern California scientists described how 14 women who had already undergone menopause were treated with sex hormones to ready their uteri for implantation of eggs donated by younger women and fertilized by each of the 14 women's husbands. Eight became pregnant, and four had given birth to healthy babies at the time of the report.

Reproductive biologists stirred up an ethical beehive by "cloning" the first human embryos. The Washington, D.C., group split a very early embryo into individual cells and allowed those cells to multiply through the 32-cell stage of development. The scientists performed the experiment with abnormal embryos but hoped to one day use the technique to create multiple copies of normal embryos, possibly for use by infertile couples.

Other developments. Several important results emerged in studies concerning women. Even though type A behavior (marked by competitiveness, impatience, and hostility) increases the likelihood that a man who survives a heart attack will later die from heart disease, the opposite seems true for women. A Chicago study involving 83 women indicated that the women who died during the 10 years of the study tended not to have type A behavior and might have been vulnerable because they suppressed unpleasant emotions.

A Michigan study of about 100 women indicated that mothers who nurse infants more than six months may lose enough calcium from their bones to become susceptible to fractures later in life. Epidemiologists measured bone density two weeks after these women gave birth and then periodically thereafter. Nursing six months or more resulted in about 5% loss in bone density in the lower spine and the top of the leg bone. Women who stopped nursing within nine months recovered that lost density

within a year, but those who nursed longer did not. The researchers emphasized the need for women to get enough calcium to develop strong bones before they get pregnant. In January 1994 Australian scientists found that a variant of the gene that codes for the cell's docking site for vitamin D predisposes people to developing osteoporosis (decreased bone mass and density) earlier in life.

Swedish scientists evaluating data from 1,200 women who received radiation treatment for benign breast disease and from 1,874 women with that disease who did not undergo radiation treatment found a significantly increased risk of breast cancer in the first group. Scientists were also accumulating new evidence that estrogen-like substances in the environment, including pesticides, polycyclic aromatic hydrocarbons, and petroleum by-products, may increase a woman's risk of developing breast cancer.

A *New England Journal of Medicine* report questioned the benefit of aspirin for preventing high blood pressure during pregnancy because aspirin use increased the risk of the placenta's separating from the uterus, a life-threatening condition. Another study failed to confirm aspirin's supposed benefit in reducing the risk of colorectal cancer.

In early summer in the U.S. Southwest, the surprising deaths of 11 people from acute respiratory distress syndrome, often within hours of the first sign of symptoms, prompted a flurry of medical detective work to pinpoint the cause of "Four Corners disease," so named for the area where it first appeared. Investigators pinpointed a hantavirus carried by field mice and transmitted to humans via airborne dried urine or fecal matter. Since then, the virus and close relatives have been found in many parts of the U.S. and may have contributed to more deaths.

In research on tuberculosis (TB), immunologists from Rockefeller University, New York City, described how the bacterium that leads to TB hides from the immune system. Nebraska researchers incorporated the protein that lights up fireflies in a test that could quickly determine whether an individual with TB was infected with a resistant strain.

Neurobiologists in London and Virginia demonstrated that, like birds, mammals can grow new hair cells, a result that suggests it may be possible to recover hearing loss. These cells line the inner ear and contain bundles of tiny hairs that move in response to sound waves and head motion to make hearing and balance possible. Until those two reports, scientists did not think these cells could regenerate except during fetal development. However, bits of the balance organ of the inner ear from both guinea pigs and humans did produce new hair cells after the original ones were destroyed.

A six-year study involving 600 people suffering from an eye disorder called retinitis pigmentosa indi-

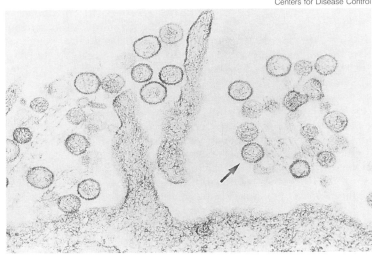

Electron micrograph reveals the hantavirus that killed 11 people in the U.S. Southwest in the early summer of 1993. Carried by field mice, it is transmitted to humans via airborne dried urine or fecal matter.

cated that high doses of vitamin A (15,000 international units per day) significantly slowed vision loss. The study also suggested that vitamin E supplements might speed up the degeneration of the retina.

French scientists came under fire—and, possibly, criminal charges—in July 1993 for treating children for dwarfism with contaminated human growth hormone taken from human cadavers. At least 24 of these children later developed Creutzfeldt-Jakob disease, a fatal neurodegenerative disorder.

Promising results boosted the prospect of new treatments for cystic fibrosis, a disease in which people produce a thick mucus and sustain damage to their lungs and other organs and die prematurely. Researchers in Iowa reported the successful transfer of a gene to correct the ion-channel defect that leads to this abnormal mucus. They tested the technique by inserting the gene into cells of the lining of noses of people with the disease. Other biologists demonstrated that a substance called uridine 5'-triphosphate helps people with cystic fibrosis clear the mucus by increasing fluid flow through cell membranes.

Researchers responded to a man's claim in January 1993 that portable phones contributed to the development of his wife's fatal brain cancer. However, they found no data to support a such a link.

Mental health. Studies provided additional clues about suicide, linking an increased risk of self-inflicted deaths to smoking among adult women nurses and to aggressive behavior in teenagers. Harvard University researchers surveyed 100,000 female registered nurses in 11 states every two years from 1976 to 1988 and obtained death certificates of those who died. Women who smoked up to 24 cigarettes a day were twice as likely to commit suicide as non-smokers, and those who smoked more than 24 were four times as likely to kill themselves. Most likely,

the smoking correlated with other factors that would incline one toward suicide, such as depression or cancer, the scientists suggested. Epidemiologists at the University of South Carolina questioned 3,700 high-school students. The 25% who attempted or considered suicide tended to include aggressive as well as depressed teenagers and heavy drinkers.

Data from a 50-year study of poor and privileged males in Massachusetts, presented at the June meeting of the American Psychiatric Association in Washington, D.C., showed that depressed people rarely become alcoholics but that alcoholics often become depressed. Poor city dwellers tended to become alcoholics in their 20s, while college-bound men waited until their 40s. By age 60, however, only one in five still drank too much.

An analysis of a 21-year study of 1,000 New Zealanders followed since birth suggested that many adolescents engage in delinquent acts but that only a few, often those with poor self-control and aggressive behavior, become career criminals. The rest engage in this behavior for lack of a better way to attempt to take on the responsibilities and privileges of adulthood. In girls, early puberty can contribute to the likelihood of engaging in delinquent behavior.

California epidemiologists found trends in the deaths of 28,000 Chinese-Americans in San Francisco that indicated that deeply held beliefs and attitudes can influence how well individuals survive major illnesses. According to Chinese lore, people are particularly susceptible to diseases associated with their birth years. Those who held this belief died one to five years sooner if stricken with a disease associated with their birth year than did nonbelievers of the same age and with the same illness. The California psychiatrists concluded that one's expectations could influence the course of a disease.

—Elizabeth Pennisi

Dentistry

Health care reform virtually dominated all discussions within the medical and dental community during 1993, and the American Dental Association (ADA) joined the chorus of professional associations in making its own recommendations known. At its annual session in San Francisco, the ADA adopted a resolution to maintain the advantages of the current dental care and benefits system for groups that were currently receiving regular dental care and thus did not require public-sector participation. The ADA also advocated that under any health system reform proposal, preventive services be provided for children of indigent families. "Oral health is an integral part of overall primary health care of an individual, with the dentist as the primary oral health care provider," said James H. Gaines of Greenville, S.C., ADA president.

High-tech dental surgery. Sometimes the better things in life are little known to the general population. A high-tech procedure called electrosurgery is one of them, according to William Trice of the University of Pittsburgh, Pa. Electrosurgery uses energy in the form of focused radio waves to cut, remove, or sculpt soft tissue. Because of its unique characteristics, electrosurgery has many advantages over other types of surgical techniques. It can be used to help make a diagnosis by securing a biopsy, improve the appearance of people who have a "gummy" smile, release soft tissue attachment when teeth are extracted, and, through use of a superheated steam, bleach teeth that have undergone a root canal.

"Many people think of a hot, cauterizing instrument when they hear the term electrosurgery, but it is a completely different technique," Trice explained. "The dentist exerts no more pressure with an electrode than an artist would with a brush on a palate." Cells next to the incision are not destroyed by heat as they are with cautery, and because the blood vessels are sealed as they are cut, the incision area remains free of blood. The dentist also has a clearer view of the surgical area than if a cold-steel blade was used.

Dental laser use. Although only a fraction of dentists were using lasers in their practices in 1994, a Chicago dentist predicted that by the year 2000, lasers would be used in more than 50% of all dental practices. "By the turn of this century, I genuinely believe we will see a new way that dental care will be delivered," Robert Pick told the Midwinter Meeting of the Chicago Dental Society. Various types of lasers cut tissues without using a scalpel. Lasers prevent bleeding during invasive procedure, and there is no need for sutures. They cause no swelling or scarring, and they reduce postoperative pain after surgery.

Lasers can also be used for other dental procedures, such as curing tooth-colored materials. Improvements in design continue to make them smaller and more portable so that they can easily be transported from one operation to the next, Pick concluded.

Paget's disease. Paget's disease, a condition that usually occurs after middle age and is more common in men than in women, has been diagnosed in 3% of the U.S. population. For affected persons the normal process of bone breaking down and then reforming is out of sequence, thus causing bone to regenerate erratically and sometimes resulting in extensive bone deformity and pain. Because the disease is asymptomatic in its early stages, most cases

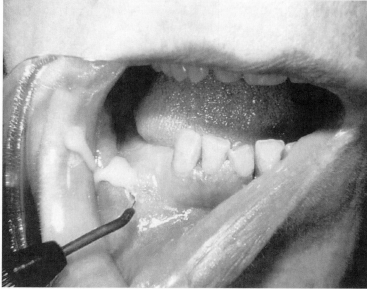

An abscess is incised and drained by means of electrosurgery, which uses focused radio waves to cut, remove, or sculpt soft tissue. The blood vessels are sealed as they are cut, so the area of the surgery remains free of blood.

William B. Trice, D.M.D.

are not detected until X-rays or bone scans are taken for other reasons. The most common body areas affected in this generally non-life-threatening disorder are the spine, pelvis, and skull, with the skull involved in more than one-fourth of all cases.

A study at the University of Florida found that a significant number of patients with Paget's disease whose condition involves the skull have a loss in the periodontal bone that supports teeth. In the study of 39 patients with the disease, Timothy Wheeler found that 83% of the patients with skull involvement had suffered periodontal bone loss. In contrast, only 33% of patients without skull involvement had such a loss. "Loss of periodontal bone may make it difficult for patients to clean their teeth and gums and eventually lead to tooth loss," he told the general session of the International Association for Dental Research in Chicago.

Chewing gum and tooth decay. Chewing gum containing the natural sweetener xylitol can reverse early tooth decay in children, and it may also help fight gum disease in adults, according to a University of Michigan dental researcher. A 40-month study of 1,227 10-year-olds in the Central American country of Belize found that xylitol-sweetened gum was highly effective in preventing cavities, according to Kauko Makinen. Another ongoing study at a Veterans Administration hospital in Ohio indicated that the sweetener may be useful treatment for periodontal (gum) disease. Children who regularly chewed gum sweetened with xylitol had half the number of new cavities as children who chewed gum sweetened with sorbitol and one-third the number of cavities as children who chewed sugar-sweetened gum, he said.

"We found cavities were prevented in existing teeth as well as in teeth that erupted during the study period. Xylitol-sweetened gum promoted the natural remineralization process that helps reverse cavities beginning to develop," Makinen explained. In addition, xylitol-sweetened chewing gum helps prevent the formation of plaque acid and plaque buildup. Unlike sorbitol and sugar, xylitol is not a source for plaque bacteria, which produce acids that attach to the teeth and cause decay. The gum comes in two shapes, pellet and stick. Pellet-shaped gum provided the greatest cavity-prevention benefits, Makinen said.

Germans and tooth loss. Only 25% of Germans over 65 years old wear dentures, while in the states of former East Germany 50% of the senior citizens do so, according to statistics from the German Dental Association. The reason is that beginning in the early 1970s insurance companies in West Germany paid for preventive and restorative treatment.

Only Switzerland and Sweden have a lower percentage of denture wearers, 24% and 20%, respectively. Statistics from other European countries convey a picture of a lack of preventive and restor-

ative dentistry, with the highest percentage of elderly denture wearers in Ireland (72%), Finland (65%), and Denmark (60%).

Saliva and the AIDS virus. Components of human saliva called mucins help it inhibit the AIDS virus, according to researchers at the State University of New York at Buffalo School of Dental Medicine and the University of Rochester, N.Y. The scientists found in laboratory studies that units of a strain of the human immunodeficiency virus (HIV) implicated in AIDS aggregate, or clump, with the two mucins found in human saliva. This naturally occurring mechanism in the human body facilitates removal of viruses from the oral cavity to the stomach, where they are destroyed by stomach acids. The role of the mucins in aggregation of the virus, he noted, helps explain why AIDS has not been shown to spread in saliva and should help allay fears that the disease can be transmitted through the exchange of saliva that may occur while kissing.

Aggregation may not be the only mechanism through which saliva hinders the AIDS virus. Researchers introduced human saliva, as well as purified mucins, to tissue cultures containing a known number of infectious units of HIV. Following incubation of the mixture, they passed it through a special filter that captures the infectious units. They found a reduction in the number of infectious units of the virus in the filtrates. In examination of the filters by electron microscopy, they also identified aggregates of virus particles. "This saliva aggregation of the

Human immunodeficiency virus (HIV) particles (arrowheads) bind to human saliva (S) collected on a nylon filter (F). This clumping mechanism facilitates the removal of viruses to the stomach, where they are destroyed by acids.

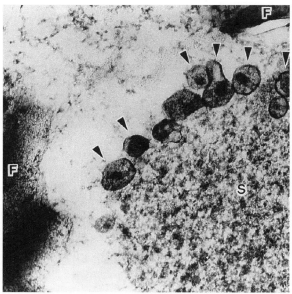

AIDS-related virus, combined with the small amount of the virus that is released into the oral cavity, are key reasons the disease is most likely not easily spread from the mouth," concluded E.J. Bergey of the State University of New York at Buffalo School of Dental Medicine.

Practical infection control. How safe is your dentist's office? It is one of the safest health care settings in the country today, according to John Molinari of the University of Detroit (Mich.) Mercy School of Dentistry. "Nevertheless, in light of recent publicity and legislative debate about HIV and other infectious diseases and health care providers, as dental consumer you have every right to ask that question," he said.

Molinari explained that universal precautions include wearing gloves, changing gloves and washing hands between patients, using some instruments and other items that can be thrown out after each use, cleaning and sterilizing dental instruments and disinfecting surfaces after each patient use, and properly disposing of waste and sharp items in special containers. An expert in infection control, Molinari stressed that dentistry has an "excellent record when it comes to these precautions and using infection control through the years. In fact, gloves were adopted in the 1970s by the profession, long before they were required by state and federal law."

—Lou Joseph

Veterinary medicine

Veterinary medicine achieved new heights during the year when a Colorado State University College of Veterinary Medicine and Biomedical Sciences professor of physiology, clinical sciences, and veterinary pathology became the first veterinarian in space. Martin J. Fettman participated in the Space Life Sciences 2 investigations during *Columbia*'s 14-day space mission in October 1993. These investigations were focused on improved understanding of how the body's various physiological systems adapt to the unique weightless or microgravity environment of space and then readapt to gravity upon returning to Earth. Since many of the adaptations occur very rapidly, it is necessary that they be studied as they occur. Both crew members and rats served as experimental subjects. Insights into the mechanisms of these adaptations could increase the understanding of how diseases affect body systems.

International veterinary medicine. Training of veterinary students at Washington State University's College of Veterinary Medicine was expanded to include a new global veterinary medical perspective. Termed the "DVM International Track," the new program was intended to increase students' knowledge and understanding of international veterinary

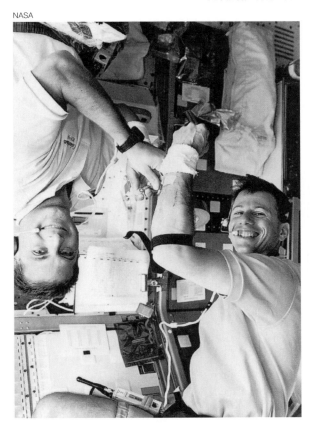

NASA

Inside the science module of the shuttle orbiter Columbia, *Martin J. Fettman (right), the first veterinarian in space, has his blood drawn by astronaut David Wolf. Blood samples from crew members were needed for several experiments.*

medical issues, foreign cultures, and various socioeconomic systems, enabling graduates to compete for jobs in the international arena. Opportunities for international field experiences were available as electives. Veterinary medical contributions in less developed countries had to focus on disease prevention because treatments could be too costly or simply not available. Often in those countries a single food animal could be critical to the survival of a family.

A unique program at the University of Edinburgh's Royal School of Veterinary Studies was that of the Centre for Tropical Veterinary Medicine, which was concerned with the training of veterinarians for work with animal health problems in the tropics. In 1993 this school celebrated the bicentenary of the birth of its founder, William Dick, who opened the school in 1823.

Emergency veterinary medicine. The loss of 85,-000 metric tons of North Sea light crude oil from the tanker *Braer*, which was wrecked on the coast of the Shetland Islands, presented Scottish veterinarians with new concerns for animal health. Previous major oil spills affected life in the sea and on

391

A staff member at the University of Edinburgh's Centre for Tropical Veterinary Medicine (CTVM) examines a water buffalo in northern India. The CTVM trains veterinarians for work with animal health problems in the tropics.

beaches but did not contaminate inland areas. The light nature of the *Braer*'s oil cargo aided cleanup in that about 50% was removed by evaporation, and the high seas created an emulsion of the oil that enhanced its dispersion. However, in combination with winds reaching 177 km/h (110 mph), sea spray droplets containing oil were carried some 5–6.5 km (3–4 mi) inland. Pasture contamination was severe, especially within the first 1.5 km (0.9 mi) inland, and prompted concern for the health of animals, including 10,000 sheep that were grazing the affected pastures or inhaling the vapors. Many seabirds died as a result of the spill, but only a small number of sheep were affected by the contamination, in large part because exposed sheep were moved to uncontaminated pastures or fed uncontaminated hay. While this unfortunate incident did not have a serious effect on food animal health, it did reveal the lack of information available to veterinarians and others regarding hazards associated with this type of wind-blown pollution.

The impact of Hurricane Andrew on animal and human health and well-being emphasized the need for a well-designed emergency preparedness plan for the coordinated involvement of veterinary medicine in disaster relief. The floods and fires of 1993 and past earthquake and tornado disasters further emphasized the need for such a plan. In response, the American Veterinary Medical Association (AVMA) introduced its Emergency Preparedness Plan at its mid-1993 annual meeting. This plan, which was approved by the U.S. Department of Health and Human Services, sought to expedite and coordinate delivery of vital veterinary relief services. Traditional disaster-relief plans and efforts of local, state, and federal agencies focused almost solely on human relief services.

During Hurricane Andrew some pet owners refused to evacuate their homes because emergency shelter arrangements were not available for care of their pets. Human relief shelters usually would not admit animals, primarily because of potential sanitation problems. Abandoned pets and livestock tended to become diseased, and carcasses of dead animals were a threat to public health and had to be disposed of properly, as noted in the AVMA plan. The plan also provided for the establishment of a specially trained reserve force of veterinarians and veterinary technicians that could be mobilized quickly when a disaster occurred.

New veterinary organizations. The American College of Veterinary Behaviorists was given provisional approval as a new veterinary specialty by AVMA. Five other specialties had provisional recognition, and 14 had full recognition. Attainment of full recognition could take up to 10 years. Several new associations held organizational meetings at the annual convention of AVMA. The American Association of Human-Animal Bond Veterinarians was organized to promote awareness and understanding of the human-animal bond. Establishment of the American Veterinary Medical Law Association reflected the growth of the field of veterinary law. A statement of the preliminary mission of this organization included promoting the legal well-being of the veterinary community, educating veterinarians and lawyers on legal issues that influence veterinary medicine, and encouraging career opportunities in veterinary law.

The International Sled Dog Veterinary Medical Association was organized to promote safety, health, and welfare for racing sled dogs, to provide leadership and education for those working with these dogs, and to encourage international cooperation between race organizations and uniformity of race standards.

Interim leaders included veterinarians involved in the Iditarod and Alpirod sled dog races.

Diseases. Equine viral arteritis (EVA) was diagnosed for the first time in the United Kingdom with the confirmation of 65 positive cases on several breeding farms. The disease is transmitted through the air and by sexual intercourse and is characterized by inflammation of the mucous membranes, fever, edema, and abortion. Infected stallions become permanent carriers and shedders of the virus. The only countries that remained free from EVA as of early 1994 were Ireland and Japan. Though a live virus vaccine for EVA was licensed in the U.S., it had not been licensed in the European Union.

Standardbred horses (pacers and trotters) are little affected by the virus, but other breeds of horses respond to the infection with serious illness. Because of the limited regulations governing interstate and international transport of horses or equine semen, the potential existed for a disastrous outbreak of EVA in the U.S., especially from imported carriers of the virus. Consequently, the American Association of Equine Practitioners developed guidelines to help prevent such an occurrence. Prompt attention to small EVA outbreaks at racetracks in Illinois, Kentucky, Nebraska, and Iowa during 1993 averted a major epidemic. Affected horses survived, but training and racing schedules were temporarily disrupted.

A severe epidemic of Venezuelan equine encephalomyelitis (VEE) in Venezuela and Colombia in 1962 was followed by the appearance of the disease in Texas in 1971. This viral disease is transmitted by mosquitoes and affects both horses and people. In July 1993 the disease was diagnosed in southern Mexico and resulted in a U.S. Department of Agriculture (USDA) ban of direct movement of horses, mules, and donkeys across the Mexican-U.S. border. These animals could be brought into the U.S. only after a seven-day quarantine in a USDA-approved, mosquito-proof facility. Mexican officials worked vigorously to stop the outbreak, but the USDA was not ready to end its import restrictions. Appearance of the disease in the U.S. would result in a minimum two-year ban on exporting horses to European Union countries.

As of 1994, fewer than 1% of the laboratory-confirmed cases of bovine spongiform encephalopathy (BSE), a disease of cattle that irreversibly damages the central nervous system, had occurred outside Great Britain. Since July 1989 the U.S. had banned importation of ruminant animals from countries with BSE. The source of infection was believed to have been the feeding of contaminated ruminant-derived meat and bone meal. Britain's banning of this practice in 1988 was just beginning to reduce the incidence of BSE because of the disease's prolonged incubation period (two to seven years).

The causative agent of BSE was unknown, but a prion was implicated. A prion is a small, proteinaceous particle. It is not a virus and is very resistant to treatments that normally kill pathogenic viruses. The disease is not transmitted between cattle but can be transmitted experimentally by special inoculation procedures. Increased concern for this disease recently emerged in the U.S. because of the laboratory-confirmed diagnosis of BSE in a five-year-old cow in Canada. The cow had been imported from Great Britain at six months of age. Since the causative agent for this disease produces no immune response, attempts to develop a standard diagnostic test for surveillance purposes were unsuccessful. The lack of such a test precluded identification of infected, clinically normal cattle prior to the onset of clinical signs of the disease.

Diagnostic methods and treatments. A researcher at Tufts University School of Veterinary Medicine in Medford, Mass., developed a heat-stable rinderpest vaccine for cattle. Undergoing its first major field trial in Somalia, where this disease was a significant problem, this vaccine did not require cold storage for at least 30 days, making it ideal for use in that hot African country. As of 1994 rinderpest had not occurred in cattle in the U.S.

A collaborative program termed PennHIP, concerned with reduction in the incidence of canine hip dysplasia (CHD), was initiated at the School of Veterinary Medicine at the University of Pennsylvania. The program involved veterinarians from many areas of the U.S. and Canada who had been trained in the use of a new radiographic technique to evaluate the laxity of hip joints in dogs. The new technique was much better than the standard hip-extended method in quantifying the laxity of the hip joint. An index scale varying from 0 to 1 was used, with an index near 0 indicating a tight hip joint and an index near 1 indicating an extremely lax joint. Three years of data collected through PennHIP showed that dogs with joint indexes of less than 0.3 continued to test negative for CHD. Selection of dogs for breeding that have indexes of less than 0.3 should reduce the occurrence of CHD.

Molecular genetics was gaining importance in veterinary medicine because of the growing need for reliable methods of diagnosis of genetic diseases. More than 400 genetic disorders had been reported in dogs, 70 in cats, and several in large domestic animals.

The Section of Medical Genetics at the University of Pennsylvania School of Veterinary Medicine developed a DNA test for identification of the mutation causing phosphofructokinase (PFK) deficiency in English springer spaniels. This was the first molecular genetic screening test for identification of healthy carriers of genes for an inherited disease in companion animals. The test required only a few drops of blood. Deficiency of PFK commonly results in acceleration of the normal process of destruction of red blood cells, which leads to anemia or jaundice. Affected dogs, particularly those used in field trials, show weakness, exercise intolerance, and poor performance, and some even refuse to move. The University of Pennsylvania group was exploring methods for gene replacement therapy, which would enable the removal of the disease-producing gene and replacement with a normal gene.

Genetic maps providing information on the relative order and placement of genes or DNA markers linked to disease genes on canine and bovine chromosomes were being developed. The maps were expected to greatly enhance progress in the development of new molecular and biochemical methods for detecting the carriers of mutant genes.

—John M. Bowen

Optical engineering

The past year was both a good and a bad one for optical engineering. The continuing cutback in defense expenditures caused a reduction in employment in most sectors of the business, but commercial applications of optics in data transmission, control, and communication expanded rapidly. Optical data storage and CD-ROM (compact disc read-only memory) systems finally appeared to have reached maturity. Development in visible and high-power diode lasers continued to dominate the laser market. The introduction of commercially available extreme ultraviolet and tunable short-pulse lasers opened new opportunities for lasers in product development and manufacturing.

The end of the Strategic Defense Initiative (SDI) programs brought an almost complete halt to interest in high-power lasers for use as weapons. The inevitable inertia of such defense programs did permit some continued funding for ground-based demonstrations of high-power chemical lasers. The concept of an airborne defensive laser was reintroduced as a demonstration project.

Large ground-based telescope development continued with the delivery of the largest-diameter mirror blank ever fabricated, from the Schott glass plant in Mainz, Germany, to the mirror-polishing facility near Paris. The segmented-primary-mirror Keck telescope became operational on Mauna Kea in Hawaii and achieved some successful first images. The second Keck telescope, adjacent to the first unit, was under construction. In space optics the most stunning development was the repair of the Hubble Space Telescope (HST) during a shuttle mission that took place in December.

Integration of optical and electronic data processing increased in several areas. Direct optical amplifiers for fiber communication systems became commercially available. Spectrometers fully integrated into an interface card for a personal computer (PC) entered the market, leading to simplified forms of industrial instrumentation. There were some minor advances in all optical digital computers, but any such computer with useful capacity remained far from early useful operation. Vertical cavity diode lasers, in which the light is emitted through a large area at the side of the laser rather than through a small area at the end of the laser, became available in visible wavelengths and at quite high powers. Blue lasers and solid-state ultraviolet lasers operating at wavelengths below 300 nm (nanometers; billionths of a meter) became widely available.

The use of optical data-storage devices greatly increased and seemed to have established a solid hold on parts of the computer market. Sales of CD-ROM discs and players boomed in response to a wide variety of new multimedia computer programs. In many cases the CD-ROM drive was being installed as a basic part of many PCs.

Applications of optics for storing large amounts of data on optical disks were significant. In some cases the effect upon the environment was striking. As one example, each month the U.S. government traditionally stored billing information for its telephone system in more than 10,000 boxes of computer paper. A full year's storage of data on the federal telephone system thus would occupy more than 100,000 boxes of computer paper each year. This amount of data could be stored on optical disks that occupied only about one meter (3.3 ft) of shelf space and weighed less than 2 kg (4.4 lb). The number of trees and volume of storage space that would be sacrificed to such an application would, therefore, be greatly decreased. The access to any information on the disks was greatly enhanced as well. Similar gains in storage density for many applications should be seen in the future.

Research interest in future optical data-storage devices centered on the use of blue-wavelength diode lasers. The size of a single bit of data that could be recorded on an optical disk was proportional to the wavelength used to write and read the information. Therefore, reduction of the wavelength from the infrared to the blue allowed more information to be written and read on optical disks. This permitted a gain that was at least fourfold in information density. IBM demonstrated an optical recorder that had an information density of 2.5 gigabits per square inch. (One gigabit equals one billion bits; one square inch is about 6.5 sq cm.) With this technology a disk that had a diameter of 13.34 cm (5.25 in) could hold the equivalent of 6,500 printed books of 250 pages each.

A staff scientist at an IBM Corp. research center operates a blue-wavelength diode laser optical recording system. Using blue wavelengths allows a greater amount of data to be written on optical disks.

Thus, a total personal library and data bank could be contained on only one computer disk.

Optical communications continued to dominate new long-distance communications installations. During the year Philips Industries demonstrated a link that would transmit 2.5 gigabits per second over 360 km (224 mi) without an amplifier. The tremendous information-carrying capacity of such long-distance optical fibers was being joined by the development of local fiber loops that would permit such high data rates to be available eventually at any home or office.

The potential for such high-speed data transfer had been the cornerstone of an initiative to develop an "information highway" that would link all computer owners and provide them with access to prodigious sources of information. Optical data-storage-and-transmission techniques formed the technical cornerstone of such a data highway, which would likely see some realization during the next year.

Digital optical computing as of 1994 had not demonstrated any such possibilities. The intrinsic parallelism, in which many data channels can be operated on simultaneously, of optical devices had not led to any significant gains in the construction of an all-optical digital computer, and one could safely predict that applications for optics would be restricted to data communication and storage for the next several years. (*See* Feature Article: COMPUTING WITH LIGHT.)

The demise of the SDI program caused some significant reductions in defense contracting. It did, however, leave a legacy of some possibly useful scientific technology. One example was large segmented optical components. The Large Active Mirror Program at the Itek division of Litton Industries Inc. resulted in the completion of a seven-segment primary mirror that was four meters in diameter. This mirror was produced on a faceplate only 17 mm (0.67 in) thick, with its surface shape being precisely maintained by 312 computer-controlled actuators. Itek also completed a demonstration single large pie-shaped segment for a 10-m-diameter demonstration mirror. This type of optical component, along with high-speed active deformable mirrors that correct for atmospheric turbulence or other optical deformations, could be the predecessor of future large optical components.

The repair of the HST provided a real-time public demonstration of elegant optical engineering. The Jet Propulsion Laboratory constructed a new wide-field/planetary camera with a new ultraviolet detector and small corrective optics that had been polished to compensate for the errors in the Hubble's primary mirror. Ball Research designed and constructed a set of corrective optical components called the COSTAR system that would correct the main telescope imagery for several other imaging sensors in the telescope. Extensive testing against an image error simulator indicated that both of these new optical systems should correct the large errors in the main Hubble telescope.

In December 1993 a team of seven astronauts was launched in the shuttle to install these corrective optical components into the HST. The repair, which required placing the new systems into the telescope to tolerances of a fraction of a millimeter, was extremely successful, and it appeared that the HST had been restored to the original intended operational capability.

Ground-based astronomy continued to progress with the operation of the first Keck telescope and the construction of the second. In April the first images from the completed telescope were recorded.

The status of the various ground-based telescope projects with apertures on the order of seven meters or larger remained generally unchanged. One of the four primary mirrors of the largest optical telescope, the Very Large Telescope of the European Southern

Optical engineering

Observatory, was in the early stages of fabrication. The Large Binocular Telescope of the University of Arizona and the Italian Arcetri Astrophysical Observatory was still in the initial stages of development. However, the 6.5-m-diameter Multiple Mirror Telescope replacement mirror for the Mt. Hopkins Observatory in Arizona was cast and was expected to be polished and ready for installation in 1995.

Both the Japanese "Subaru" eight-meter telescope and the multinational U.S.-based Gemini Telescopes were designed to use Corning ultra-low-expansion glass mirrors, the first of which was expected to be fabricated in 1994. One new proposed telescope was the 11-m-diameter spectroscopic telescope using 91 mirror segments being developed jointly by the University of Pennsylvania and the University of Texas. This new telescope would be equipped with a spherical segmented primary mirror that would contain a field corrector to obtain a small field of view for spectroscopic studies. The size and number of segments are likely to change in response to available funding.

Among smaller instruments, three new 3.5-m telescopes were proposed or under construction. In addition, the U.S. Air Force Phillips Laboratory planned to start operation of 3.5-m-aperture telescopes that were built specifically for demonstrating active atmospheric correction. These instruments, one nearing completion near Albuquerque, N.M., and one being

Originally designed for a space laser program, a seven-segment primary mirror four meters in diameter was completed at the Itek division of Litton Industries Inc.

Courtesy of Itek Division of Litton Industries

W.M. Keck Observatory; image by Keith Matthews and Gerry Neugebauer, Caltech

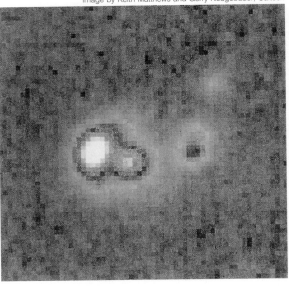

Among the first images obtained by the newly completed Keck telescope was that of the luminous galaxy FSC10214+4724. The Keck consists of a mosaic of 36 mirrors that acts as a single 10-m mirror.

planned for Mt. Haleakala, Hawaii, would be heavily instrumented and include a high-speed mirror for atmospheric correction. Both the Phillips Laboratory and Lawrence Livermore Laboratory were demonstrating new techniques for atmospheric correction in which an artificial guide star was generated by projection of a laser through the atmosphere to produce resonant fluorescence scattering from free sodium in the upper atmosphere. This reference source was collected by the telescope and used to produce a corrected wave front. This approach permitted observation of portions of the sky within which there was no reference star of adequate brightness to provide a feedback signal.

In areas more directly related to consumer products, the Center for Optical Manufacturing demonstrated a working version of its OPTICAM surface-generation-and-grinding machine, which was the first attempt to integrate computer-aided design and manufacturing of optical components. The surface finish on these components was said to show less subsurface crack damage than had been achieved by any previous finishing process and might provide great economic advantages in optical fabrication.

Other products of note included a new infrared video camera produced by Cincinnati (Ohio) Electronics Corp. Kodak introduced a 2,680 × 1,037-element color video camera, which approached the useful resolution of a film camera and might bring the reality of still electronic photography a bit closer once production costs had been lowered.

—Robert R. Shannon

Physics

The use of laser light to create "optical crystals" of atoms, additional evidence for the subatomic particle known as the top quark, and experimental confirmation of the prediction of a new, very hard solid material numbered among the achievements reported in physics during the past year. Researchers used a scanning tunneling microscope to confine electrons within a tiny two-dimensional "corral" of iron atoms and then image the quantum effects of the confinement. The quest continued in nuclear physics to create and study an extremely dense and energetic phase of matter called quark-gluon plasma.

General developments

Researchers during the past year provided striking demonstrations of the wave-particle duality of light and the subtle forces that arise out of "empty" space. They created structures of atoms held together by laser light instead of chemical bonds. They also demonstrated that the tilt in Earth's spin axis is highly stable, while the tilt associated with Mars is quite chaotic.

Young's double-slit experiment on an atomic scale. About 200 years ago the English physicist Thomas Young demonstrated the wavelike nature of light by shining light through a pair of closely spaced parallel slits (actually pinholes in the original experiments) and noting the interference patterns that appeared on a screen placed behind the slits. The patterns indicated that light, rather than acting like a particle passing through a single slit, had behaved like a water wave, breaking up when it hit the slits into two "wavelets" that combined behind the slits to create the pattern. Experimenters in 1991 passed atoms through slits and demonstrated the wavelike nature of atoms as well (see *1993 Yearbook of Science and the Future* Year in Review: PHYSICS: *General developments*).

More recently researchers at the U.S. National Institute of Standards and Technology (NIST), Boulder, Colo., performed Young's original experiment literally on an atomic scale—by shining light through a pair of atoms, which acted as the slits. Ulli Eichmann and his colleagues trapped a pair of ions (electrically charged atoms) of mercury in a Paul trap, a device that uses electric fields to keep ions in place. They then shone laser light on the ions. The light was scattered by the ions, generating wave fronts that interfered with each other to produce the familiar interference patterns. Patterns were recorded at three different ion separations, 3.7, 4.3, and 5.4 micrometers (millionths of a meter), and the observed patterns all agreed with basic theory. (A meter is about 40 in.)

What is unique about this version of Young's experiment is that it can demonstrate not only the wave nature of light but its particle nature as well, depending on how the experiment is observed. In the particle interpretation, light is treated as consisting of distinct packets of energy, called photons. As such, a photon of laser light that encounters the pair of ions in the experiment can interact with one or the other of the ions but not both. Because of the way that the experiment is designed, when a photon interacts with an ion it can scatter from the ion as one of two distinct forms of polarized light, called σ-polarized light and π-polarized light. If the ion scatters σ-polarized light after the interaction, it goes into an energy state different from that of its neighbor. Since this change, in principle, allows an experimenter to determine the path that the photon took as it passed through the ions, the scattered light takes on particle-like behavior, and the interference pattern does not appear. If, on the other hand, the ion scatters π-polarized light, it goes back into its original energy state and so makes it impossible for the experimenter to know which path the photon took; in that case the scattered light takes on wavelike behavior, and the interference pattern appears. Thus, when the experimenters set up their equipment to detect π-polarized light, they observed the light behaving as a wave; when they detected σ-polarized light, they observed the light behaving as a particle.

The experimental setup can also provide diagnostic information on the temperature of the ions in the traps or the spacing of the ions. Such information would be useful for the many experiments in modern physical research that employ trapped ions.

Detecting electromagnetic forces in "empty" space. One of the many surprises of modern physics is that "empty" space is not empty at all but filled with fluctuating electromagnetic fields and particles that pop in and out of existence. This interpretation arises as a result of the Heisenberg uncertainty principle, which states that the energy of a system, such as a vacuum, cannot be determined with perfect precision unless it is measured for an infinite time. Since the vacuum's energy cannot be determined to be perfectly zero over finite time intervals, it must have a slight spread of nonzero values. Since the 1940s physicists have predicted the existence of subtle forces that the vacuum would exert on particles.

One of the early predictions was that a neutral atom located between a pair of narrow metal plates would experience forces due to the vacuum. The reason is that the fleeting electromagnetic waves of the vacuum would be altered by the presence of the plates; wavelengths longer than the separation distance between the plates would not be able to exist. This would change the properties of the vacuum be-

NIST-7, the seventh generation of atomic clocks at the U.S. National Institute of Standards and Technology, Boulder, Colo., was unveiled in April 1993. It keeps time with an uncertainty of less than one second in a million years, a figure that is expected to be improved to less than one second in three million years. The clock is regulated by a precise frequency of microwave radiation needed to excite cesium atoms, which are maintained as an atomic beam, from their initial state to one of slightly higher energy.

tween the plates. In turn, the altered vacuum would create high- and low-energy regions for any atom traveling between the plates. Atoms would move toward those regions in which they would have the lowest energy. This effect was predicted in 1948 and was called the Casimir-Polder force after its discoverers.

In 1993 Charles I. Sukenik and his colleagues at Yale University reported experimentally detecting the Casimir-Polder force for the first time. In a technically difficult experiment they passed sodium atoms between a pair of gold plates that were separated about a micrometer apart and observed the deflection of the atoms by the vacuum. The force associated with the deflection agreed with the theoretical predictions made more than four decades earlier.

Holding atoms together with light. Researchers succeeded in creating structures of atoms held together by laser light. The structures, made in laboratories in France, Germany, and the U.S., not only will help scientists understand how matter interacts with light but also may lead to practical applications.

Natural crystals such as diamond are formed as a result of electrical forces. These forces organize a crystal's building blocks—carbon atoms in the case of diamond—into a repeating pattern called a lattice and hold them together in the form of chemical bonds. In the new experiments researchers created special laser-light patterns called optical lattices, which cause atoms to fall into a low-energy state at certain, regularly occurring spaces in the patterns. In their low-energy state the atoms become trapped at these spaces, forming so-called optical crystals.

Gilbert Grynberg and his colleagues at the École Normale Supérieure (ENS) in Paris first announced in 1992 that they had trapped cesium atoms in a one-dimensional pattern made with laser light having a wavelength of 852 nm (nanometers; billionths

of a meter). The pattern was designed to trap atoms at quarter-wavelengths of the laser light. This corresponds to a 213-nm spacing between traps for the atoms, which is hundreds of times farther apart than the spacings of typically less than one nanometer between atoms in natural crystals. The one-dimensional experiments were followed up by demonstrations in 1993 of two-dimensional and three-dimensional optical lattices by the ENS group and researchers at the University of Munich, Germany, and of three-dimensional experiments by researchers at NIST. Atoms in the three-dimensional structures occupy positions in a body-cubic-centered (bcc) lattice, a type of lattice found in natural crystals. In the bcc lattice the basic unit is a cube, and atoms can occupy the corners and center of the cube.

The atoms in these light-created patterns can be very precisely controlled. Experimenters are contemplating applications in which the atoms in the patterns can be stripped of most of their motion and thereby reduced to extremely low temperatures. Such low-temperature atoms have the potential to be used as the basis for a new, ultraprecise atomic clock. Another application, under development by Mara Prentiss of Harvard University and researchers at NIST, involves confining the atoms in their individual traps to a high degree and then depositing them onto silicon surfaces, making what perhaps can be used as atomic-scale circuit elements.

Earth's stability and the chaos of Mars. Scientists who study the orbital properties of planets in the solar system gained a new appreciation for the Moon in 1993. Jacques Laskar and his colleagues at the Bureau des Longitudes in Paris performed computer simulations revealing that the Earth's obliquity—the angle of tilt between its spin axis and the line perpendicular to the plane of its orbit around the Sun—stays relatively stable, varying by just 1.3° above or below a mean value of 23.3° over millions of years. The reason for the stability, Laskar and his colleagues found, is the presence of the Moon. Because of its gravitational influence, the Moon exerts a torque on the Earth, causing its spin axis to precess like a spinning top whose tilt slowly traces out circles. The precessional motion prevents gravitational tugs from other bodies in the solar system from destabilizing the Earth's obliquity. Without the presence of the Moon, the Earth at its present obliquity would tilt unpredictably, bringing about highly erratic variations in climate. So, in a sense, the Moon helps stabilize the Earth's climate.

On the other hand, Jack Wisdom and Jihad Touma of the Massachusetts Institute of Technology found that the obliquity of Mars fluctuates chaotically, meaning that its precise value, even if known now, becomes impossible to predict after a certain amount of time. Computer simulations performed by Touma and Wisdom revealed that the obliquity of Mars can vary somewhere between about 10° and 50° over millions of years. Such chaotic motion would bring about an inherently erratic climate on Mars; at high obliquity, for instance, the poles of Mars would receive increased radiation from the Sun, destabilizing whatever ice may have formed there.

—Ben P. Stein

High-energy physics

The year 1993 was not the best for elementary-particle physics. The focal point of the future of the field in the U.S., the construction of the Superconducting Super Collider (SSC), was terminated by the Department of Energy (DOE) after a successful bid to kill it in the House of Representatives. Cancellation of the project dislocated a large number of scientists and sent a clear message that Big Science had met a stone wall and would be facing an uncertain future of commitment by world governments.

The termination of the SSC reaches well beyond the discipline of particle physics. For a number of reasons the commitment of the U.S., as well as of other governments, to the funding of basic research is weakening. Among them are (1) the prolonged weakened world economy, felt acutely in recent years in the U.S. and broadly across the globe in Russia, Europe, and Japan; (2) the reduced military stance between East and West with the demise of the Cold War; (3) the growing popular misidentification of basic science as a threat to the global environment; and (4) the erosion of the quality and valuation of education in the U.S. Particle physics has no direct utilitarian applications, although it generates many significant technological developments in its demand for high-tech utilities (such as high-field magnets and large parallel-architecture computers). Applied,

as opposed to fundamental, science has been touted as a remedy for many of the ails of economy and society. The mood prevails, despite the fact that one can argue strongly that the esoteric discovery of quantum mechanics in the early 20th century now accounts for about two-thirds of the U.S. gross domestic product alone—about $4 trillion per year.

Search for the top quark. Despite the turmoil surrounding the termination of the SSC, elementary-particle physics made significant progress on several fronts in the past year. The most central question is to understand the origin of the masses of the elementary constituents of nature: the quarks, leptons, and gauge bosons. Science seeks ultimately a deep understanding that would allow one to compute the value of, say, the mass of the electron (a lepton) in terms of the mass of the charmed quark. This achievement would be on a par with the greatest scientific strides in history; e.g., Newton's establishing the universal law of gravitation or Einstein's connecting energy to mass and the speed of light.

The standard model of elementary-particle physics remains a successful description of all known particles and forces in terms of basic symmetry principles, called gauge symmetries. It is understood that the masses of all known elementary particles are tied to the so-called symmetry-breaking mechanism of the standard model. This mechanism elevates the gauge bosons that mediate the weak forces, the W boson and Z boson, to their lofty masses, separating them from the massless photon, the gauge boson that mediates electromagnetism. It is this difference in masses that causes electromagnetism to be the long-range force of everyday experience, and it also causes the weak forces to be weak. By means of additional indirect effects, the quarks and leptons "feel" this symmetry-breaking mechanism and acquire their masses as well. (The symmetries of the standard model dictate that the quarks and leptons must acquire their masses through this symbiosis; if the symmetry were unbroken, all of the quarks, leptons, and gauge bosons would be massless.) While physicists can describe these phenomena in the standard model, they do not understand the precise nature of the symmetry-breaking mechanism; the indirect effects that give the quarks and leptons their masses are even more mysterious. Thus, the standard model accommodates everything that is observed in the universe, but it does not explain very much of what is observed.

The particles currently observed in the standard model form a kind of "periodic table" of quarks, leptons, and gauge bosons, as shown in the Table on page 400. The quarks and leptons form three families, each family containing a negatively charged lepton (like the electron) and a neutral lepton (a neutrino); each family also contains three "colors"

"Periodic Table" of Quarks, Leptons, and Gauge Bosons

charge	colors	first family	second family	third family
			quarks	
$+2/3$	3	up (u)	charmed (c)	top (t)
$-1/3$	3	down (d)	strange (s)	bottom (b)
			leptons	
0	1	electron neutrino (ν_e)	muon neutrino (ν_μ)	tau neutrino (ν_τ)
-1	1	electron (e)	muon (μ)	tau (τ)

		gauge bosons
0	8	gluons (strong force)
$\pm1, 0$	1	$W^{\pm}$ and Z^0 bosons (weak forces)
0	1	photon (electromagnetism)
0	1	graviton (gravitation)

In the standard model the first-family quarks and leptons make up ordinary matter, and the gauge bosons give rise to the forces in nature. For the standard model to be complete, the existence of top quark is necessary.

of two kinds of quark—an up-type quark of electric charge $+2/3$ and a down-type quark of electric charge $-1/3$. Physicists do not fully understand why this pattern occurs in nature, although they do know that it is required for the mathematical consistency of the standard model. There may exist more than three families of quarks and leptons, but evidence against this possibility came in 1989 from experimental results at CERN (European Laboratory for Particle Physics), Geneva, that were consistent with the existence of only three light neutrino species. To date physicists have observed the six elementary leptons and five of the requisite six quarks. The top (t) quark has not officially been observed, yet it must exist because the bottom (b) quark has measured properties establishing that it requires a partner. In general, the pattern structure and consistency of the standard model are not complete without the top quark.

During 1993 experiments at the Tevatron, the highest energy particle accelerator in the world, located at the Fermi National Accelerator Laboratory (Fermilab), Batavia, Ill., made significant progress in the search for the top quark. The machine collides protons with antiprotons (the antimatter counterpart of protons) and has achieved a record luminosity of 9.2×10^{30} particles per square centimeter per second and a record energy of 900 GeV (billion electron volts). The results of the most recent Tevatron run from the D0 (Dee-Zero) collider experiment established that the mass of the top quark must be above 131 GeV/c^2 (in which c is the velocity of light). By comparison, the mass of the proton is approximately

1 GeV/c^2. Thus, the present lower limit on the top quark's mass implies that it is heavier than the nucleus of a xenon atom.

A proton contains quarks and an antiproton contains antiquarks; consequently, in proton-antiproton collisions at the Tevatron, a quark and its antiquark can collide, annihilating into a gluon, which then produces new particles such as a top quark and anti-top ($\bar{t}$) quark. Each quark in turn decays to a W boson and a bottom or an anti-bottom ($\bar{b}$) quark. The W can then decay to a charged lepton plus a neutrino or to a light quark and a light antiquark. The Feynman diagram for the process is shown in the Figure on the facing page.

The D0 and CDF (Collider Detector at Fermilab) experiments at the Tevatron found a total of three events containing both an electron and a muon, which are signs of possible t quark plus $\bar{t}$ quark decays. The CDF detected a handful of collision events containing the decay of a W boson into a charged lepton and four jets of particles. Jets are formed when at very high energies a quark or gluon is produced in a hadronic collision and then subsequently reforms into a collimated shower of hadrons owing to the strong confining force described by quantum chromodynamics (QCD), the theory of quark interactions mediated by gluons. (Hadrons are particles composed of quarks and gluons, such as protons, neutrons, and pions [pi mesons].) Some of these events may contain t and $\bar{t}$ quarks, but no claim of discovery for the top quark was made. It is clear that the t quark is very heavy, and a much longer run of the Tevatron—or its upgrade to a machine called the Main Injector, which presently is being planned—will be needed to ensure its discovery and to begin surveying the t quark's properties in detail. In April 1994 experimental evidence for the existence of the top quark was presented at Fermilab from the CDF experiment, implying a mass of 174 ± 17 GeV/c^2 for the particle.

Remarkably, even though it has not yet been officially observed, the top quark is providing possible new clues as to the origin of the symmetry-breaking mechanism of the standard model. This is due to the fact that the t quark is very massive. The t quark may prove to be a powerful probe of symmetry-breaking physics and a window on the origin of mass. In some theories the t quark forms a "vacuum condensate," much like a Cooper pair of electrons in a superconductor; this simultaneously causes the W and Z bosons to become heavy and elevates the t quark to a large mass. Thus, with a detailed understanding of the properties of the t quark, a full understanding of the masses of all particles may be at hand.

By means of the mathematical machinery of the standard model, various measurements made at different accelerators can be converted into predictions for the top quark's mass. The LEP (Large Electron-Positron) accelerator-collider results from CERN collected during the past few years have the highest statistical power and, when combined with the data from other laboratories, imply a mass of 166 ± 27 GeV/c^2 for the t quark. At the Stanford Linear Collider (SLC), Palo Alto, Calif., the weak mixing angle has been measured through observation of the left-right asymmetry. The measurement requires that electrons and positrons (the antimatter counterpart of electrons) whose spins have been aligned (polarized) collide to make polarized Z bosons, which then decay into muons with an asymmetric angular distribution. This yields detailed information about the weak interactions.

The polarization in the SLC was not well understood until recently, when consistent results were obtained before and after the electrons entered the circular arcs of the collider. The preliminary result obtained for the weak mixing angle (sin^2 Θ_W) is 0.2290 ± 0.001. The SLC result disagrees with the average of all measurements at the LEP machine at CERN, in which sin^2 Θ_W is 0.2321 ± 0.0006, even though the margins of error are comparable. If the SLC result is correct (and the LEP result is ignored), then the t quark mass is 240 ± 30 GeV/c^2. This higher value is also consistent with recent measurements in Fermilab neutrino experiments. The SLC result, however, is marginally inconsistent with the standard model for other reasons; if true, it would be a harbinger of a new physics beyond the standard model.

Only the Fermilab Tevatron can settle the issue by actually producing and measuring the mass of the t quark. The situation is tantalizing because particle physics may be on the verge of a new era in which the standard model begins to "self-destruct" and in which physicists' understanding of basic forces and matter will be increasingly challenged. For example, it is possible that new physics will begin to show itself in association with the t quark; $e.g.$, in the form of nonstandard production or decay modes of the t quark. The Tevatron and its upgrade to the Main Injector will produce a large statistical sample of t quarks for such studies and will be the highest energy particle accelerator into the first decade of the 21st century.

Bottom-quark physics. Also of intense interest in recent years has been the physics of the heavy quarks, such as charmed (c) quark and, especially, the bottom (b) quark (also dubbed the beauty quark). Heavy-quark physics allows physicists to map out the matrix of the weak decays of quarks in the standard model by means of the detailed studies of different decay modes. It allows testing of the standard model as a precise predictive theory and a way to better understand the relationships with other parts of the theory, such as the t quark.

The B$_s$ meson (consisting of an anti-bottom [$\bar{b}$] quark and a strange [s] quark) was discovered in 1993 at three of the LEP experiments and by the CDF experiment at the Tevatron. Also of great importance was the observation of the B**, an excited state, or resonance, of the B mesons, at the ALEPH experiment at LEP. Once produced, these resonances rapidly decay into the ground-state B meson and a charged pion. The charge of the pion "tags" the precise properties of a neutral B meson (B^0); $i.e.$, one can tell if the neutral B is a $\bar{B}^0$ (a $b\bar{d}$ quark combination) or a B^0 (a $d\bar{b}$ quark combination) at the instant it is created. This is important because one wants to know the difference in decay rates of the B^0 and the $\bar{B}^0$ into certain final states and must establish the identity of the decaying B meson precisely. These differences are measures of the violations of charge-parity (CP) conservation, the only interaction in nature that depends upon the direction of flow of time. The CP-violating interactions have been known

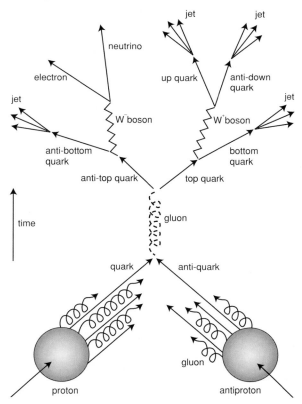

The production of top and anti-top quarks in a proton-antiproton collision is diagrammed. A quark and an antiquark within the colliding particles annihilate into a gluon, which then converts to top and anti-top quarks. Although the two quarks decay too quickly to be detected, their decay fragments are recorded. In the decay scheme shown the various quarks that are produced convert to observed jets of hadrons, and the electron is also observed.

The Collider Detector at Fermilab (CDF) was commissioned in the mid-1980s. The dark arches pulled to the sides contain modules of the central calorimeter, which were built by a collaboration of scientists from the U.S., Japan, and Italy. The modules surround the region in the CDF where collisions of protons and antiprotons take place. They contain photomultipliers and electronics used to measure the energies of particles produced in the collisions.

since the 1960s in the neutral K mesons (particles containing a $d\bar{s}$ or $s\bar{d}$ quark combination) but have yet to be observed in other systems. The neutral B mesons are prime candidates for the observation of CP violation in a system different from the neutral K mesons.

The CLEO experiment at the Cornell Electron Storage Ring (CESR), Cornell University, Ithaca, N.Y., and the ARGUS experiment at DESY, the German national accelerator laboratory in Hamburg, were spectacularly successful at establishing many of the properties of mesons containing the b quark and a lighter quark, either $\bar{u}$ or $\bar{d}$. The first observation of radiative decays of b quarks, $b \to s\gamma$ (a bottom quark decays into a strange quark and a gamma ray), occurred in 1993 at CLEO. The rate for the process places a severe constraint on hypothetical new physics beyond the standard model. Also, there were precise measurements of the weak mixing angles, the basic parameters of the standard model that control the rates of decays between quarks of different families, for example, involving $b \to c + \ldots$ and $b \to u + \ldots$, from ARGUS and CLEO.

The successes of these experiments and the theoretical developments in the arena of heavy-quark physics have created a great deal of enthusiasm for the construction of dedicated facilities, called B factories, to search for CP violation in the decays of B mesons and other heavy-quark physics. In October 1993 DOE recommended the construction at the Stanford Linear Accelerator Center (SLAC) of the Asymmetric e^+e^- B-Factory, which would collide electrons (e^-) and positrons (e^+). The CESR, which has already produced many significant results in B physics, will be upgraded as well. An e^+e^- B factory was also under construction at the KEK laboratory

in Tsukuba, Japan. All of these are electron-positron colliders that make the lightest B mesons ($\bar{b}u$ and $\bar{b}d$) and aim to find CP violation in a study of their decay modes.

On the other hand, the CDF experiment at the Tevatron proton-antiproton collider, with its high-resolution Silicon Vertex Detector (SVX), demonstrated that it is competitive with electron-positron collider experiments. Hadrons containing b quarks have a fortuitously long lifetime and therefore drift a resolvable distance away from the point of the collision in which they are produced before they decay. The typical displacement of a secondary decay vertex for a b-quark hadron is only about 400 μm (micrometers; millionths of a meter), while the SVX has demonstrated a resolution better than 15 μm. This "vertex separation" reduces unwanted backgrounds and significantly enhances the signal for detected b-quark hadrons. The technology evolved at Fermilab in the study of charmed mesons and has since become a significant tool in the arsenal of experimental high-energy physics. B physics in hadron colliders, and in detectors such as at CDF, is radically different from that in electron-positron machines because in hadron colliders all possible b-quark-containing particles are produced and because the production rates there are typically many orders of magnitude greater than at electron-positron colliders.

Eventually the world will require an even more powerful "microscope" for particle physics than the Tevatron and Main Injector. Perhaps the planned Large Hadron Collider (LHC) machine at CERN will be built within the existing LEP tunnel at one-third the SSC's energy but with a truly international collaboration. Beyond that, a more powerful supercollider with a lower cost through staged construction, using existing machines as injectors and magnets of much higher field strength than originally proposed for the SSC, may be considered. There remains, however, much physics to do in the next decade with the existing facilities and their modest upgrades.

—Christopher T. Hill

Nuclear physics

The search for a new form of matter and a key measurement concerning the creation of heavy elements in stars captured the attention of nuclear physicists during the past year.

High-density matter. Matter may take on a new form when compressed to the highest densities. In ordinary matter the densest material is the atomic nucleus, consisting of neutrons and protons—collectively called nucleons. Theorists have suggested that at higher density the nucleons would dissolve into smaller particles and a new phase of matter would be formed. According to the modern theory of elementary particles, nucleons are composed of quarks, which in turn are bound together by the gluon field. In the theory the interaction between quarks is so strong that they can never be seen in isolation. Thus, quarks are normally found bound together as protons, neutrons, or such other particles as pions.

Unfortunately, the equations governing the theory of quark interactions have been too difficult to solve precisely. Approximate solutions in the early 1980s predicted that when either the energy or the density of matter was increased beyond a certain point, the matter would undergo a phase change. In the new phase the quarks would not be bound in small groups but instead would be free to move about the entire volume occupied by the matter.

This phase has been given the name quark-gluon plasma in analogy with ordinary plasma gases, in which atoms are broken down into their constituent electrons and nuclei. If such a phase of matter exists, it may have played a significant role in the evolution of the universe. According to cosmologists' current understanding, the universe at its creation was very small and hot. As it cooled and expanded, it may have gone through the quark-gluon phase as an intermediate stage before subatomic particles condensed into ordinary matter.

To achieve higher densities than those found in ordinary nuclei, physicists use accelerators to give nuclei a high kinetic energy and to bombard other nuclei with them. The larger the nucleus and the higher the incident energy, the greater is the density that can be reached in the collision. Such experiments have been carried out at some of the world's largest accelerators, starting at the University of California at Berkeley in the 1970s and later at higher energies at Brookhaven National Laboratory, Upton, N.Y., and at CERN (European Laboratory for Particle Physics) in Geneva. From the early experiments it was clear that if the dense phase of matter exists at all, it is not stable. It breaks down into ordinary matter so fast that all one can observe is the debris of ordinary particles emerging from the collision.

In the CERN experiments, which have achieved the highest energies to date, several hundred secondary particles may be produced in the collisions. The apparatus to measure so many particles is quite elaborate, and the experiments have become progressively refined since they began in 1986. In 1993 many of the results were presented at a large conference, "Quark Matter 1993." Some of the major findings are summarized below.

One of the early questions about high-energy collisions between nuclei concerns whether the protons and neutrons interact strongly enough in a collision to slow each other down or whether at high energy they just punch through each other with only minor interactions. The possibility of forming the quark-gluon plasma depends on the answer to this important question. Only if the nucleons leave most of their energy behind in the collision would there be enough to make the plasma. Earlier experiments seemed quite promising because many more particles were produced than would be expected if protons and neutrons interacted only with a single partner in the collision. It was not known until the past year, however, whether the nucleons were actually slowed down substantially by the collisions. When a proton collides with another proton at high energy, it is hardly deflected by the interaction, although it typically loses half its energy.

The CERN experiments showed that in nucleus-nucleus collisions many of the nucleons are slowed essentially to a stop, making all of their energy available in a central zone. Since enough energy seems to be available to form a new phase of matter, the next question is whether there is anything different about the particles produced in the collision owing to their origin in a high-density medium. No striking differences were found among the particles that are composed of ordinary quarks; e.g., protons, neutrons, and pions. However, other, rarer particles that contain so-called strange and charmed quarks did show dramatic differences. Strange and charmed quarks are more difficult to produce than ordinary quarks in collisions, and the corresponding particles are not abundant in the products of proton collisions. If the quark-gluon plasma phase exists, the quarks inside it would collide repeatedly with each other, producing more and more strange quarks. Thus, nucleus-nucleus collisions would produce more strange mesons, a phenomenon that was actually observed in experiments at Brookhaven. Still, production of

Beams of heavy ions will collide at six points along the tunnel of the RHIC accelerator at Brookhaven National Laboratory when the facility opens in the late 1990s. In the high densities and temperatures achieved in the collisions, physicists hope to create a new phase of matter, the quark-gluon plasma.

strange mesons does not prove that a quark-gluon plasma has been made. The experiment did show that particles had collided repeatedly, implying that a region of dense matter had been created.

Another rare particle, called the J/psi, was studied in CERN experiments. This particle consists of a charmed quark bound together with its anti-quark counterpart. Whereas Brookhaven's experiments had shown that more strange mesons are produced in nucleus-nucleus collisions, at CERN it was discovered that nucleus-nucleus collisions produce relatively fewer J/psi particles than do proton-proton collisions. In the high-density environment of the nucleus-nucleus collision, the number of J/psi particles decreases because other nearby particles disturb the quark and antiquark in the J/psi and easily break them apart. The situation is analogous to an ordinary plasma, in which the hot environment ionizes atoms with bound electrons. Of course, after the matter has cooled, the charmed quarks would not be free but would be bound to some ordinary quarks in a different particle. Instead of the J/psi, one would see other particles that contain individual charmed quarks. Like the experiments measuring the increase of strange particles, the decrease in the number of J/psi particles shows that a hot, dense environment is produced, but it does not prove the existence of the quark-gluon plasma.

A more specific way to show that matter undergoes a phase transition to a different state would be to measure how long the matter stays in a state of high density. If the pions and other particles were produced immediately in the collision, one could infer that there had not been be enough time for a new phase to form. Conversely, if the colliding nuclei passed into a new phase, it would probably take some time to convert back to ordinary matter. Thus, the length of time the high-density matter lasts is an important clue to the existence of a phase transition.

Even a relatively long duration, however, would still be far too short to be measured directly; typically, a collision lasts about 10^{-24} seconds. Fortunately, there is an indirect method for inferring the relative emission times of mesons. The method uses the fact that mesons have wave properties just like those of light. The waves can interfere with each other, producing regions of high and low intensity. Just as the interference pattern of light coming from a distant star can be used to infer the diameter of the star, the interference of two meson waves produces information about the distribution of the meson source in space and time. The results of the 1993 measurements of meson source sizes are interesting. The numbers are about twice as large as would be expected if the high-density matter produced mesons immediately. Evidently the matter exists in some other form about twice as long as the collision lasts. But it is not possible from this measurement to say more specifically what form the matter has.

Plans are under way to produce even higher energies and densities both at CERN and at Brookhaven. At CERN the experiments will be repeated with beams of lead nuclei, which are about six times heavier then the present sulfur beams. Brookhaven is building a new accelerator that will use colliding beams to increase the available energy by a factor of 10. The accelerator is scheduled to start operation in the late 1990s.

Synthesis of elements in stars. An important measurement concerning the synthesis of elements in stars was carried out in 1993 by research groups at the TRIUMF Laboratory in Canada and at Yale University in the U.S. Most of the common elements on Earth are the direct by-products of nuclear fusion in ancient, exploded stars. Experimenters studied the fusion of carbon and helium nuclei, a reaction that produces oxygen and releases energy in the form of a gamma ray. The reaction $^{12}C + ^{4}He \rightarrow ^{16}O + \gamma$ is a key step in the chain leading to the creation of heavier elements, but it has been impossible to measure. Most stellar reactions occur at low energies and proceed at a pace that is too slow to be measured in the laboratory. Researchers get around the difficulty by measuring the reactions at higher energies, at which the reactions proceed more quickly, and then extrapolating the rates down to stellar energies. That procedure does not work for the oxygen-producing reaction, however. When the carbon and helium nuclei interact, they do not always produce a tightly bound oxygen nucleus immediately; instead, they sometimes first form an oxygen nucleus with loosely bound constituents; this energetically excited state then decays by emitting gamma rays. The intermediate step affects the overall reaction rate and makes the extrapolation unreliable.

Nevertheless, by using a rather complicated argument, physicists can deduce the influence of the loosely bound oxygen state. To treat the state they need to know how it couples to both the $^{12}C + {}^4He$ initial state and the $^{16}O + \gamma$ final state. They can measure the latter coupling easily, first by producing the loosely bound oxygen state and then by observing its gamma decay rate. However, the $^{12}C + {}^4He$ coupling has long been out of reach. The new experiments use a completely different reaction, the beta decay of nitrogen-16 to oxygen-16, to deduce the missing coupling. Part of the time the beta decay proceeds to the loosely bound oxygen state, yielding $^{12}C + {}^4He$ instead of ^{16}O. The energy spectrum of the ^4He is thus sensitive to the coupling of the loosely bound oxygen state. The new experiments measured this beta decay reaction. Because the energy of the ^4He is so low, the experiments were rather difficult to carry out. Both groups saw the influence of the loosely bound state and interpreted their results in terms of the basic nucleosynthetic reaction. The previously accepted rate for the reaction was 100, measured in units that include effects of the electrostatic repulsion between the nuclei. The new measurements give values in the range of 50–100 units.

Once a star runs out of ^4He and can no longer produce ^{16}O, the stage is set for later nucleosynthetic reactions that make heavier elements. If, prior to this time, the $^{12}C + {}^4He$ reaction was proceeding slowly, then the heavier elements are formed in a reaction chain that starts from carbon. On the other hand, if the ^{16}O-forming reaction was proceeding quickly, the heavier elements are formed from ^{16}O and at a higher temperature. Depending on these initial conditions, the mix of elements that will be expelled into the cosmos upon the star's explosive death can be quite different. In fact, their production depends so sensitively on the environment that the rate of the reaction $^{12}C + {}^4He \rightarrow {}^{16}O + \gamma$ has been inferred from the abundances of different elements observed in the solar system. That analysis yielded a rate of 170 units, which is higher than the new measure-

ments imply. Several uncertainties, however, may reconcile the apparent disagreement. In astrophysics the temperatures depend on somewhat uncertain assumptions about the heat transfer within the star. In nuclear physics additional states with differing quantum numbers might also contribute to the reaction. The additional states would increase the rate, possibly bringing it closer to the number inferred from the elemental abundances.

—George Bertsch and Sharon McGrayne

Condensed-matter physics

Scientists working in the area of atomic manipulation on surfaces scored a major success in 1993. Using the scanning tunneling microscope, they constructed atomic-size enclosures in which they were able to observe quantum confinement directly. Theoretical studies, combined with first-principles calculations, continued to play an important role in condensed-matter physics; the contribution of theory was highlighted by experimental confirmation of the prediction of a new, very hard solid. The changing world order produced a benefit in the form of increased availability of pure, stable isotopes from separation facilities in the former Soviet Union. As a result, isotopically controlled crystals were being grown that enabled a variety of elegant and exciting experiments. Researchers also reported incremental advances in so-called high-temperature superconductivity.

Quantum corrals. The scanning tunneling microscope (STM), invented by Gerd Binnig and Heinrich Rohrer at the IBM Zürich (Switz.) Research Laboratory in the early 1980s, already has had a tremendous impact on surface science. The instrument allows researchers to image the surface of conducting materials with atomic-scale resolution; in addition, the STM can be used for spectroscopy, probing the electronic structure of the surface on an atomic scale. These unprecedented achievements have been accomplished with an instrument that is, in essence, quite simple. It consists of a metal probe ending in a very sharp (atomic-size) tip; the tip is scanned over the surface of the sample by means of piezoelectric controls. A voltage is applied between tip and surface, and even though the tip is not in contact with the surface, a current flows because of the quantum-mechanical tunneling effect. The tip-surface separation is less than a nanometer (nm; a billionth of a meter); typical atoms are a few tenths of a nanometer in size. A feedback loop keeps the current constant while scanning, which usually translates into keeping the tip at a constant distance above the surface. Measuring the displacement perpendicular to the surface produces a map of the trajectory of the tip, reflecting both the topography and the electronic structure of the surface.

Recently surface scientists began to use the STM not just to analyze the surface but also to synthesize new structures. By setting the correct current and voltage conditions, one can select an individual atom that is absorbed on the surface, move it around, and place it in a specific location. Donald M. Eigler and co-workers at the IBM Almaden Research Center, San Jose, Calif., pioneered the technique in 1990, manipulating xenon atoms on a nickel surface. (See *1992 Yearbook of Science and the Future* Year in Review: PHYSICS: *General developments.*) In 1993 Eigler, Michael F. Crommie, and Christopher P. Lutz at the Almaden laboratory reported another breakthrough; they demonstrated that iron atoms can be manipulated and placed in specific locations on a copper surface. The whole operation had to be performed at very low temperature, requiring cooling by liquid helium at four degrees above absolute zero, in order to limit thermal motion of the atoms. One of the structures that the researchers constructed was a circle with a diameter of 14.3 nm. The same STM tip that was used to position the atoms was then scanned over the surface to obtain a picture of the location of the atoms. In addition, the STM provided information about the electronic wave functions on the surface.

Quantum mechanics predicts that a particle enclosed in a "box" of small dimensions exhibits quantized behavior. The energy of the particle can assume only discrete values, determined by the dimensions of the box. In addition, the probability of finding the particle in a certain location is not uniform throughout the box but oscillates in space. This behavior is related to particle-wave duality; the particle can be represented by a quantum-mechanical wave, which is reflected at the edges of the box, leading to interference and the formation of a standing-wave pattern. The amplitude of the wave corresponds to the probability of finding the particle in that location. In order for the interference effects to be produced, the size of the box should be comparable to the wavelength of the waves that correspond to elementary particles (electrons in the case of the IBM experiment), which is on the order of nanometers. The box in question actually need not be a three-dimensional object; a two-dimensional shape can be used to confine a particle in a plane. Nor does the box have to be rectangular; a circle works just as well, although the details of the interference pattern depend on the shape and size.

The circle of iron atoms constructed by Eigler and co-workers actually serves as a box in which electrons moving on the copper surface can be trapped. Tunneling spectroscopy indeed revealed the existence of discrete energies, consistent with quantization. The STM, however, made it possible to resolve the quantum states spatially as well as spectroscopically for the first time. The interference pattern produced by the electron wave corresponds to a variation in the local electron density, which is measurable with the STM. Ripples in the electron density indeed were observed, and they corresponded accurately to the quantum-mechanical predictions. The authors of the work referred to their circular enclosure for electrons as a "quantum corral."

The significance of the work goes far beyond the verification and elegant illustration of basic quantum mechanics. For instance, it now is feasible to

A quantum corral made of 48 iron atoms adsorbed on a copper surface encloses ripples in the local density of states of the surface electrons. The iron atoms were positioned with a scanning tunneling microscope (STM); the same STM was then used to make the image. The corral is about 14.3 nm in diameter, and the ripples closely match the quantum-mechanical predictions for a particle in a circular box.

study the properties of confined electrons in boxes with complicated shapes, such as polygons or stadia. Stadium-shaped boxes have attracted particular attention since they are known to lead to chaotic behavior. One also envisions studying the interaction of surface-state electrons with adsorbed atoms or molecules or with surface defects. Eigler and co-workers, for example, observed oscillations in the electron density in the neighborhood of point defects (associated with impurity atoms) and around step edges (which occur at the boundaries of terraces on the surface). In many respects the quantum corrals indicate that the vision of physicist Richard Feynman, outlined in 1959, has been realized—an era in which "the problems of chemistry and biology can be greatly helped if our ability to see what we are doing, and to do things on an atomic level, is ultimately developed."

New materials by design. First-principles calculations have made significant contributions to condensed-matter physics and materials science. *First principles* refers to the feature that no input from experiment enters the computations; only the atomic numbers and mass numbers of the atoms in the system are required. The computational approach then solves the quantum-mechanical equations for the system, producing information about the exact location of the atoms and the electronic wave functions, from which various properties of the system can be derived. The development of new algorithms and the availability of larger computing resources have enabled investigations of systems of increasing size and degree of complexity.

The role of first-principles calculations has often been a supporting one. When experimental observations indicated novel or unexpected behavior or properties, computations subsequently provided consistent and comprehensive explanations. Recently, however, computational physics has assumed a more active role by actually predicting new materials with useful properties. A prime example is supplied by the work of Marvin Cohen of the University of California at Berkeley.

Cohen originally developed an empirical model for the bulk modulus of covalent solids. In the absence of defects in the crystal structure, the bulk modulus determines the hardness of the solid. In turn, the bulk modulus depends on the nature of the chemical bonding. It was found that two properties are needed to achieve a large bulk modulus: low ionicity and short bond length. (The ionicity of a material increases with increasing difference in electronegativity between the constituent elements.) Both properties are present in diamond, which has the largest bulk modulus and is the hardest known solid. On the basis of the empirical model, however, it was suggested that a covalent solid formed of atoms

of carbon (C) and nitrogen (N) could have a larger bulk modulus than that of diamond, which is all carbon. The proposal was put on a stronger footing when Cohen and Amy Liu carried out first-principles calculations for a hypothetical covalent C-N solid, modeled after the known β-Si_3N_4 (silicon nitride) structure. The calculations showed that β-C_3N_4 is at least a metastable structure, with a moderately large cohesive energy and a bulk modulus comparable to that of diamond.

Stimulated by this prediction, Chumming Niu, Yuan Z. Lu, and Charles M. Lieber of Harvard University synthesized the material and verified the prediction about the hardness. Fragments from pulsed laser ablation of high-purity graphite and a beam of atomic nitrogen were used to form C-N films on a substrate. Electron diffraction data indicated the presence of β-C_3N_4 crystallites in the films, while photoelectron spectroscopy revealed that the C-N bond is covalent with relatively little charge transfer, in agreement with the theoretical predictions. While the bulk modulus and hardness of β-C_3N_4 remained to be measured, Niu and co-workers stated that their C-N films are "thermally robust and hard." The confirmation of theory implied by the experiments indicates that it is possible to use theory to design materials with predictable properties.

Isotopically controlled semiconductors. The elements in the periodic table are characterized by their atomic number, corresponding to the number of protons in the nucleus. For a given number of protons, the number of neutrons may vary, giving rise to isotopes with different masses. For instance, germanium (Ge), which has an atomic number of 32, has five stable isotopes: ^{70}Ge (20.5%), ^{72}Ge (27.4%), ^{73}Ge (7.8%), ^{74}Ge (36.5%), and ^{76}Ge (7.8%); the natural abundance of each isotope is indicated in parentheses. A germanium crystal would normally include a mixture of all these isotopes, in accordance with their natural abundance. Those properties of a solid that depend on the atomic mass therefore actually reflect some sort of average over these masses.

The advantages of being able to control the isotopic composition of a semiconductor have been known for some time. One example is the study of local vibrational modes (LVMs). When a light impurity is introduced in a semiconductor, vibrational modes appear that are localized on the impurity and that have specific frequencies, similar to molecular vibrations. Substituting with a different isotope of impurity atom leads to a predictable shift (inversely proportional to the mass of the impurity atoms) in the vibrational frequency and hence aids in the identification of the impurity. Isotope separation has traditionally been cumbersome and expensive, severely restricting the type and number of experiments that could be performed. Recently, however, isotopes for various elements became more readily available owing to the opening of markets in the former Soviet Union. Eugene Haller and co-workers at the University of California at Berkeley took advantage of this opportunity to grow isotopically controlled crystals (mostly germanium), which in turn allowed unprecedented experiments.

One type of investigation concerns the LVMs mentioned above but involves substituting different isotopes for the host atoms. The masses of the atoms surrounding the impurity atom affect the vibrational frequency. With host crystals made of isotopes occurring in their natural abundance, a large number of peaks in the vibrational spectrum may be produced. On the other hand, isotopically controlled crystals offer a tremendous simplification of the spectrum, allowing a detailed understanding of the origin of lines and a more straightforward identification of the location of the impurity in the crystal lattice.

The dependence of vibrational properties on atomic masses also affects the vibrational spectrum of the semiconductor; a group led by Manuel Cardona at the Max Planck Institute, Stuttgart, Germany, has been particularly active in this area. Various theoretical models, such as the coherent-potential approximation, have been used to take the distribution of atomic masses into account. The availability of isotopically controlled crystals now offers sensitive tests for such models. In germanium the mass differences are not large enough to produce localized modes, but resonances appear in the vibrational spectrum owing to the presence of specific isotopes.

Isotopic control can be applied not only to bulk solids but also to superlattice structures, artificial structures made of carefully controlled layers of atoms in which the atomic mass is varied from layer to layer. The periodic modulations of the isotopic mass in short-period superlattices can be used to investigate the vibrational properties of the bulk materials as well as the properties of the new, artificial structure. Such superlattices also allow the study of atomic motion through isotope disordering.

Isotopic control also leads to improved applications of neutron transmutation doping (NTD), a technique in which a semiconductor is bombarded with neutrons. Upon capturing a neutron, a nucleus may turn into another stable isotope of the same element or may be converted to another element, which can act as a dopant; i.e., an impurity that modifies the electrical characteristics of the semiconductor. The technique produces an extremely homogeneous dopant distribution, which is important for applications such as radiation detectors or high-power rectifiers. Combining NTD with the ability to grow isotope superlattices enables the realization of novel device structures with sharp boundaries between different regions.

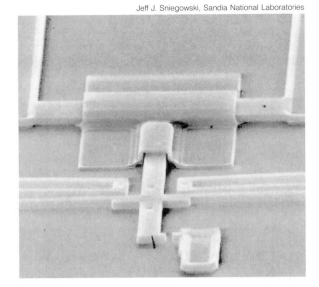

Jeff J. Sniegowski, Sandia National Laboratories

A microscopic steam engine built by physicists at Sandia National Laboratories, Albuquerque, N.M., is small enough to reside on a computer chip yet powerful enough to do useful work. Only micrometers in size, the engine consists of a piston that slides in and out of a silicon sleeve, propelled by a bubble of water vapor that expands on heating.

The availability of isotopes thus offers a wide range of scientific and technical opportunities. The increasing number of experiments carried out on "isotopically engineered" samples will continue to elucidate basic mechanisms as well as new physics.

High-temperature superconductivity. The record for the highest critical temperature in a superconductor, that is, the temperature below which the material loses all resistance to the flow of electricity, had been held by a thallium-bearing ceramic compound since 1988. That figure, 127 K (kelvins), was broken when a group from the Swiss Federal Institute of Technology, Zürich, reported a superconducting transition above 130 K in a compound of mercury, barium, calcium, copper, and oxygen. (To convert kelvins to degrees Celsius, subtract 273; thus, 127 K = −146° C. To convert Celsius to Fahrenheit, multiply by 1.8 and add 32.) In addition, the mercury-bearing material exhibits more favorable behavior in a magnetic field, and because of its simple structure it may offer some clues to the mechanism of superconductivity in the copper oxide ceramics, a consistent theoretical description of which is still lacking. A less firmly established result came from a group at the National Center for Scientific Research in Paris, who reported evidence for superconductivity at 250 K in a film containing copper and oxygen and built up layer by layer. Significantly more work will be needed to confirm this observation. (*See* Year in Review: CHEMISTRY: *Inorganic chemistry.*)

—Chris G. Van de Walle

Psychology

Researchers during the past year continued to report new findings and new facets to investigate in the complex set of phenomena collectively called "memory." Among these is the currently troublesome problem of determining the authenticity of so-called "repressed memories" and their apparent recovery, as in the much-publicized cases of childhood sexual abuse. Closely related is the problem of eyewitness identifications. Two approaches to the more effective use of memory are described below. Other subjects of importance include the increasingly widespread roles of clinical psychologists in hospitals and medical schools; the reactions to stress, as reflected in damage to the immune system; and the recently accelerated concern of psychologists with the development and utilization of moral principles and moral behavior as family structures deteriorate and violence spreads from the streets to the schools.

Repressed memories. The question of the authenticity of long-term memories, particularly those involving traumatic childhood events such as sexual abuse, has become one of the most difficult and most pressing problems for psychologists. The problem is especially acute when there has apparently been repression, or forgetting, and subsequent recovery of such memories, with attendant personal turmoil.

Though there is little solid experimental evidence for repression, it does seem that at least some of the allegedly recovered memories had in fact been repressed. Certainly many therapists think so and have acted accordingly. It also seems to be true that some of these "memories" were not genuine but rather were based on something other than actual events (although not necessarily deliberately fabricated).

Two major problems have arisen in this area. First, the basic difficulty is that there are at present no effective tests for authenticating the reports of such memories. Second, there are therapists who simply accept the emotional reports of their clients as genuine without recognizing the need for any critical evaluation. On the other hand, there are critics who seem to take the same kind of absolutist position on the other side of the fence—that is, they tend to regard the reports as not based on real events.

The issue has important practical as well as theoretical implications. There have been a rapidly increasing number of legal confrontations between family members based upon the alleged recovery of repressed memories of childhood sexual abuse. Perhaps the most sensational of these cases was the conviction for murder in 1990 of a 51-year-old California man as a result of reports by his daughter of the gradual recovery of memories after a 20-year interval. The daughter reported remembering that as an eight-year-old child she had witnessed her father first sexually assaulting and then killing one of her friends. The jury was so impressed by the confidence and vividness of her testimony that it found her father guilty after only one day of deliberation.

Eyewitness identifications. Closely related to the problem of authenticating the recovery of repressed memories is that of judging the reliability of eyewitness identifications. A comprehensive review of the current status of research on this problem was published during the past year by psychologist Gary Wells. Among his findings was the most reliable manner in which police lineups and photo spreads can be administered. Witnesses who are first shown a "blank" lineup (one that does not include the suspected culprit) and do not make any identification are more likely to detect the culprit in a later test. Also, sequential presentation of individuals results in fewer false identifications and equally accurate correct identifications of culprits, compared with the more commonly used simultaneous presentation of all of the lineup members.

Memory and problem solving. A new set of data was described during the year by psychologist Walter Kintsch, director of the Institute of Cognitive Science at the University of Colorado. A longtime leader in research and theory concerning the comprehension of discourse, Kintsch pointed out that the mere fact that people can remember things, from reading, for example, does not necessarily mean that they will be able to use that information effectively, as in the solving of problems. He called this kind of memory "inert knowledge." His research indicated that people who are not able to feed back the details of what they have read may nonetheless be able to use what they learned in adapting effectively to new situations. This distinction seems to be related to the important distinction between declarative or explicit memory, characterized by direct responses to questions about what was learned, and implicit or procedural memory, demonstrated by the learner's ability to behave in accordance with the demands of the task.

Kintsch and his colleagues developed some promising techniques designed to maximize the utility of learning. For example, when the order in which information was presented during the trials was varied, more effective implicit memory occurred. Kintsch explained this result on the basis of richer interconnections between mental representations of various parts of the text studied. Just the opposite result occurred when declarative rather than procedural tests were applied following such variations in order of presentation of materials; subjects were then much less able to reproduce the details of the text than when they studied the materials in the same order during the trials.

The implications of these results for instruction should be self-evident. Traditional practices, utilizing rote memory to produce exact replications of studied texts, do not achieve the kind of mental flexibility that is needed for effective problem solving.

Another attempt to bring the educational community into the 21st century was described by psychologist Nancy Vye of the Learning Technology Center at Vanderbilt University, Nashville, Tenn. In a talk on "Macrocontexts for Learning, Thinking, and Problem Solving," Vye reviewed a learning program called "anchored instruction." It used pretaped and live video programs intended to interest fifth- and sixth-grade students in active problem solving. The problems were sufficiently difficult to require collaboration between the students for solution. One story concerned a boy who was given the task of determining the best way to make money out of a project that centered on the use of a dunking machine for teachers at a school fair. Strategic thinking was required on such issues as the renting of a pool, the expense of filling the pool, etc.

The interactive learning embodied in these exercises went beyond the walls of the classrooms in which it started. Students from classrooms in Nashville participated in a live program called "The Big Challenge." They presented reports describing how earlier problems had been solved. The main objective was to demonstrate the ways in which general principles can be applied to concrete problems. According to Vye, the initial analyses of data produced promising results, with groups that had been given more training showing a "significant gain."

Psychologists in hospitals and medical schools. Psychologists in Iowa were able to overcome strenuous opposition from psychiatrists and others to achieve passage of legislation giving them hospital privileges. Iowa thus became the 10th state to enact such a law. Hospital privileges are especially important for clinical psychologists because managed-care organizations require them to have such credentials. Moreover, psychologists with hospital privileges are able to help formulate hospital policies on funding and research.

The role of psychologists in medical training was steadily increasing, and as of 1994 there were approximately 3,500 psychologists working in various capacities in medical schools in the U.S. and Canada. Although there were only six fully independent departments of psychology in the 126 U.S. medical schools, there were, on the average, 26 full-time psychologists in each medical school, scattered over a wide spectrum of different departments (such as pediatrics, medicine, neurology, and family practice and rehabilitation, in addition to the more traditional department of psychiatry).

The major result of this increasingly pervasive penetration of medical training was a marked weakening of the traditional predominance of the so-called "medical model," the tendency to consider all disorders to be based on physical disease. There was increasing recognition of alternative perspectives, notably the behavioral, and also of the importance of health-care professionals' being more closely attuned to the needs of their patients. The level of psychological sophistication in more recently trained physicians increased accordingly.

Reactions to stress. Differences between the sexes in their reactions to stress were intensively examined in the laboratory by Ohio State University psychologist Janice Kiecolt-Glaser, working in the department of psychiatry of the School of Medicine. She summarized her recent results in a National Institutes of Health symposium during the past year.

Sex differences, she found, were most clearly evident when the newlywed couples who were serving as subjects were more hostile and negative during the 30-minute interaction that was observed. Adverse immune-system reactions were greater in women than men. The adverse changes in immune function were indexed by the efficacy of the so-called natural killer cells in the bloodstream. Their function is to kill tumor cells and cells infected with viruses. The adverse changes were found to persist for at least 24 hours.

A high level of incidence and persistence of stress reactions in caregivers, even after the death of the ailing family member, was also reported during the year by Kiecolt-Glaser. In this study more than 200 caregivers, both spouses and offspring, were tested over several years and compared with more than 100 control subjects (noncaregivers). During the first five years of the study, consistently poorer immune-system scores and more infectious diseases were found in the caregivers, who were also more prone to depressive or anxiety disorder (55% incidence). Moreover, the weakening of the immune system persisted for two to four years after the end of the caregiving, a result that had not been anticipated by the researchers. A significant feature of the study was the relative absence of social support for the caregivers (that is, few comforting or sympathetic friends), which Kiecolt-Glaser said was "striking and sobering."

Morality. Although psychological examination of morality was by no means a new phenomenon, the apparent crumbling of moral standards within recent years lent a sense of urgency to such examination. In 1991 a landmark event was the publication of the three-volume *Handbook of Moral Behavior and Development,* edited by psychologists W.M. Kurtines and J.L. Gewirtz. Two years later a three-part review of these volumes appeared in *Psychological Science* (November 1993).

In the first commentary John Darley of Princeton University pointed out that "most individuals are susceptible to societization into morality . . . [an] issue [that] has received relatively little attention in the moral issues literature." He cited "ethnic cleansing" (as used by Serbs to justify their attacks upon Muslims in what was once Yugoslavia) as an example of this process. In the second commentary Jerome Kagan of Harvard University found "substantial progress" on the problem during the past several decades: "There is now explicit recognition of the role of emotion in morality, a richer appreciation of cultural diversity, and realization that the context of an act influences the judgment of both moral agents and observers."

The third commentary was by developmentalists Richard Schweder and Jonathon Haidt of the University of Chicago. They emphasized the distinction between moral justification, which, like most reasoning processes, is slow, and moral intuition (decision making), which tends to be fast. They used this distinction to account for the fact that some studies show moral development during the childhood years, while others do not. Those that do show such development were explained on the ground that moral reasoning, dependent upon the gradual growth of verbal and logical proficiency, was being tested. The studies that did not show developmental trends were said to test moral intuition. Studies using yes-or-no questions found little difference in moral standards between five-year-olds and adults, presumably because subjects at both age levels react to the questions in the same kind of emotionally based intuitive way.

—Melvin H. Marx

International developments. Many psychologists throughout the world have been increasingly concerned about finding ways to apply their knowledge of human behavior more effectively to the solution of such pressing global problems as hunger and the distribution of resources to those in need, environmental destruction, ethnic conflict, and the abuse of human rights. To address this problem, psychologists were being encouraged to recognize the limitations of working only in the traditional scientific and individualistic way, whereby the researcher values pure research and its publication in a high-quality scientific article as the primary indicator of accomplishment. Action research and interdisciplinary cooperation need to be encouraged as an alternative if psychologists are to influence policy formation. To this end the American Psychological Association was attempting to increase cooperation between psychologists from Canada, Mexico, and the U.S. to anticipate and prepare for the tremendous psychological consequences of the North American Free Trade Agreement. Implementing this pact will almost certainly involve some major relocation of industries and business with consequences for families and individuals. There will be new immigration patterns, increased multicultural emphasis in education, and, possibly, new cultural and ethnic conflicts. Similarly, in Europe four countries joined the 21 existing members of the European Federation of Professional Psychologists Associations (EFPPA), which was striving to achieve greater consistency in the patterns of training, ethical codes, and definition of professional roles among psychologists throughout the continent. Few European countries had laws regulating the practice of psychology or protecting the title "psychologist." The EFPPA began working to promote regulations in this area by means of lobbying efforts within the European Parliament and the European Council and through local initiatives within individual countries. One success was the passage in Denmark of a law regulating the practice of psychology.

Under the apartheid regime in South Africa, the discipline of psychology had developed along racial lines. The majority of the profession's resources were directed toward addressing the needs of the white members of the community, and 90% of all registered psychologists were white. In a historic move, as South Africa attempted to make the difficult transition to a postapartheid society, the membership of the Psychological Association of South Africa voted overwhelmingly to disband in favor of establishing a new association that would be more representative of all South African psychologists. The proposed new organization would be committed to broadening access to services and training for the country's disadvantaged population and to making available the resources of psychology to combat the consequences of a legacy of racism and sexism.

UNESCO also responded to the need to provide governmental policy makers with the knowledge from psychological and other social science research necessary for informed decision making. The Executive Board of UNESCO directed the agency's social sciences section to create from January 1994 a new international research program on Management of Social Transformations (MOST). Its goal was to ensure that information moved from the stage of scientific analysis to the national decision-making level, where it would be communicated in an appropriate and comprehensible form to policy makers, thus establishing a dialogue between the producers and users of social science research. The three proposed research areas under MOST were the management of change in multicultural and multiethnic societies, cities as arenas of accelerated social transformation, and local and regional economic, technological, and environmental transformations.

—Colin V. Newman

See also Feature Article: WHEN THE MIND GROWS OLDER: PERSPECTIVES ON COGNITIVE AGING.

Space exploration

Loss of the Mars Observer spacecraft and confusion in the U.S. space station program marred space activities in 1993. However, the U.S. National Aeronautics and Space Administration (NASA) ended the year on a high note as astronauts repaired the Hubble Space Telescope.

Manned flight

Space shuttle. The ambitious Hubble Space Telescope repair mission began on December 2 when a crew of seven veteran astronauts—commander Richard O. Covey, pilot Kenneth Bowersox, mission specialists Jeffrey Hoffman, Story Musgrave, Thomas D. Akers, and Kathryn C. Thornton, and Claude Nicollier (of Switzerland)—was launched in the shuttle *Endeavour*. The extravehicular activity (EVA) crew was made up of Hoffman and Musgrave, working on the first, third, and fifth space walks, and Akers and Thornton, on the second and fourth. Nicollier operated the robot arm. This alternating team schedule was developed because of the heavy workload and its physical demands on the astronauts. In addition, the crew's training time in underwater simulators was doubled to avoid the kinds of problems that had surprised other space repair missions.

The principal objectives of the mission were to correct Hubble's inability to focus properly and to replace key systems that were failing and threatening to leave the satellite a derelict regardless of its vision. About a month after launch in 1990, scientists had begun to realize that Hubble's 2.4-m (96-in) primary mirror was ground to the wrong figure. The result was a defect called spherical aberration, which causes fuzzy rather than sharp images. In addition, Hubble's solar arrays vibrated at sunrise and sunset as they adjusted to changes in temperature, gyroscopes that sensed position failed, and other mechanical and electronic problems occurred. Hubble had been designed for repair in orbit, so replacement of most of the equipment was relatively straightforward. However, correcting the primary mirror's problems required the designing and building of new optical systems.

A replacement for the Wide Field/Planetary Camera was built with parts of its own optical system reshaped to cancel the spherical aberration. A new device, COSTAR (Corrective Optics-Space Telescope Axial Replacement), was built as housing for corrective mirrors that were inserted into the light paths for three other science instruments (a fourth had to be removed to make room for COSTAR).

After its launch on December 2, *Endeavour* spent two days slowly catching up with Hubble and then captured it with the robot arm and berthed it on a special table in the payload bay. On the first day of the repairs, Musgrave and Hoffman replaced several electronics components and prepared the solar arrays for replacement. Both arrays were replaced, but only one could be rolled up for return to Earth.

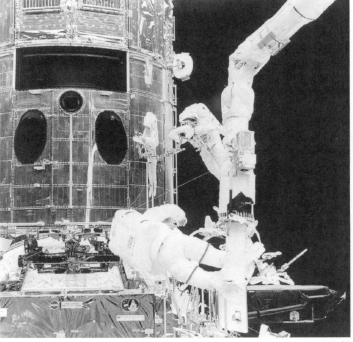

Astronaut Jeffrey Hoffman (foreground), anchored to the end of the Remote Manipulator System arm of the space shuttle Endeavour, *prepares to install a new Wide Field/Planetary Camera in the empty cavity (top left) of the Hubble Space Telescope. In the background Story Musgrave, his image reflected in the shiny surface of the Hubble, works with a portable foot restraint.*

Thornton released the other to decay from orbit in late 1994. On the third space walk, Musgrave and Hoffman installed the new Wide Field/Planetary Camera. As they placed new magnetometers over the existing ones, they discovered that the old casings were disintegrating; this posed a contamination hazard to the telescope. During the fourth EVA, Akers and Thornton installed COSTAR and an addition to the telescope's computer. Finally, on the last spacewalk, Musgrave and Hoffman installed new electronics and covered the magnetometers with shrouds made from Mylar tape and other materials in the crew's supplies. *Endeavour* then boosted Hubble to a higher orbit and, on the ninth day of the mission, released it. The crew returned in a night landing at the Kennedy Space Center on December 13.

The cost of the mission was estimated at $692 million, including $429 million for the flight and $160 million to design and build the corrective optics. In early January 1994, NASA announced that testing of the new systems was going well and that the new optics had fixed Hubble's vision.

Endeavour had started 1993 less dramatically by deploying in January the sixth Tracking and Data Relay Satellite (TDRS-6) and two-stage rocket to boost it to geostationary orbit. *Endeavour* also carried a diffuse X-ray spectrometer to scan the heavens in search of broad, faint X-ray sources. The crew consisted of commander John Casper, pilot Donald McGonagle, and mission specialists Gregory Harbaugh, Susan Helms, and Mario Runco, Jr. In preparation for operations aboard a space station, Harbaugh and Runco staged an EVA to test equipment for maneuvering and rescue. Inside, Runco and other crew members used toys to demonstrate physics principles as they talked with students at the elementary schools they had once attended.

Discovery in April carried the second in the Atmospheric Laboratory for Applications and Science (ATLAS) series to monitor yearly changes in 30 to 40 gases, including ozone, in the Earth's middle atmosphere. Members of the crew were commander Kenneth D. Cameron, pilot Stephen S. Oswald, and mission specialists Kenneth D. Cockrell, Michael Foale, and Ellen Ochoa (the first Hispanic woman in space). The crew also deployed and retrieved (April 11–13) the Spartan 201 satellite, which carried a coronascope and an ultraviolet telescope to study the Sun's outer atmosphere. ATLAS-3 was scheduled for launch in September 1994.

Columbia (April 26–May 6) carried Spacelab D-2 and brought the shuttle program's cumulative flight time to one year. The crew consisted of commander Steven Nagel, pilot Terence Henricks, flight engineer Charles Precourt, mission specialists Bernard Harris and Jerry Ross, and payload specialists Hans Schlegel and Ulrich Walter (both of Germany). Materials and

life sciences were the focus of the mission. Some 240 tadpoles and 240 fish larvae were flown to discover how their bodies adjusted to weightlessness; most died. In addition, the Galactic Ultrawide Angle Schmidt System (GAUSS) photographed swaths of the Milky Way. The crew spent two extra days in space, one for experiments and the second to wait out bad weather at the Kennedy Space Center.

The commercially developed Spacehab module was introduced by *Endeavour* (June 21–July 1). Crew members were commander Ronald J. Grabe, pilot Brian Duffy, flight engineer Nancy Sherlock, and mission specialists G. David Low, Janice Voss, and Peter ("Jeff") Wisoff. Spacehab added working space similar to that in the main cabin. *Endeavour* also captured the European Retrievable Carrier (EURECA), which had been deployed in August 1992 by *Atlantis*. EURECA carried automated materials experiments and an X-ray burst detector. Low and Wisoff tested techniques for the Hubble repair but had to devote part of their space walk to securing one of EURECA's antennae.

Two satellites were deployed and one retrieved by *Discovery* in late summer (September 12–22). The crew comprised commander Frank Culbertson, pilot William F. Readdy, flight engineer Daniel W. Bursch, and mission specialists James H. Newman, and Carl E. Walz. The Advanced Communications Technology Satellite was launched to test communications in the K-band of the radio spectrum. The crew released Germany's Shuttle Pallet Satellite (SPAS), which carried the Orbiting Retrievable Far and Extreme Ultraviolet Spectrometer and the Interstellar Medium Absorption Profile Spectrograph. SPAS operated independently for six days and then was retrieved for return to Earth. SPAS also carried a movie camera to film the shuttle in space. Newman and Walz tested Hubble repair techniques during an EVA.

Near the end of 1993 *Columbia* carried the second Space Life Sciences mission (October 18–November 1). Members of the crew were commander John E. Blaha, pilot Richard A. Searfoss, mission specialists Rhea Seddon, William S. McArthur, Jr., David A. Wolf, and Shannon W. Lucid, and payload specialist Martin J. Fettman (the first veterinarian in space). Most experiments measured the effects of space on the crew. One used bungee cords to pull a subject down while electrodes measured how the body's reflexes were changed by weightlessness. In another, a TV camera recorded how the eye compensates for perceived motion as a subject watched a rotating dome painted with dots. Wolf set a record for the fastest heart rate in space—196 beats per minute, versus an Earth peak of 244—as he pedaled on a bicycle ergometer. Other experiments used 48 rats to study space travel effects. During the flight, blood

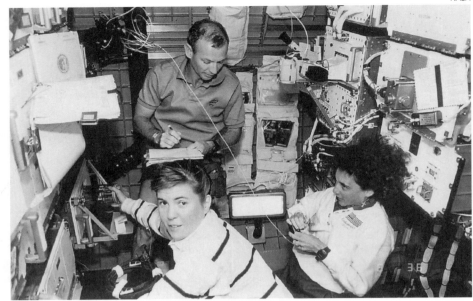

Inside the Spacehab module of the shuttle Endeavour, Janice Voss (foreground) works on an experiment with biomaterials products. Also engaged in Spacehab experiments are Brian Duffy and Nancy Sherlock.

and fluid samples were taken from 15, and several were injected with erythropoietin to stimulate the production of red blood cells. Six were sacrificed and dissected the day before landing to preserve subtle changes in their inner ears.

The two-week mission was the longest flown by a shuttle. The commander and pilot honed their landing skills with the first onboard simulator ever flown. The Portable In-flight Landing Operations Trainer (PILOT) combined a laptop computer with a real shuttle control stick and existing computer programs.

Russia's hopes for the first manned flight of its Buran shuttle faded (it flew once, unmanned, in 1988), and a Moscow newspaper reported that thieves had stripped equipment from Buran's launch facilities in Baikonur, effectively setting back any launch attempt by 18 months. Budget shortages forced the European Space Agency (ESA) to cancel plans to develop a small shuttlecraft in collaboration with Russia. Earlier, ESA had reduced its Hermes shuttlecraft program to smaller-scale projects, including an Apollo-style crew capsule.

At the pilot's station of the shuttle Columbia, Richard Searfoss takes part in the first tests of the Portable In-flight Landing Operations Trainer (PILOT), an onboard simulator that measures the effects of spaceflight on a pilot's proficiency.

Space stations. Russia continued to operate its *Mir 1* space station. On Feb. 4, 1993, cosmonauts released an aluminum-coated plastic film mirror that unfurled to a diameter of 20 m (66 ft.). Mirrors several kilometers wide were proposed to illuminate cities and increase daylight for crops. Cosmonauts Anatoly Solovyev and Sergey Abdeyev returned to Earth aboard Soyuz TM-15 on February 1 after having spent six months aboard *Mir* and performing a number of EVAs designed to rejuvenate the seven-year-old station. They had been replaced on January 26 by Gennady Manakov and Aleksandr Poleshchuk, who had been launched aboard Soyuz TM-16 on that same day.

On July 3, Soyuz TM-17 was launched to *Mir* with Vasily Tsibliyev, Aleksandr Serebrov, and French test pilot Jean-Pierre Haignere aboard. Tsibliyev and Serebrov stayed on *Mir,* and Manakov and Poleshchuk returned to Earth with Haignere on July 22. As they left *Mir,* the crew attached a docking target on the space station for U.S. shuttle crews to use starting in 1995. On September 16, 20, and 28, Tsibliyev and Serebrov conducted a series of EVAs outside *Mir.* On the first two they erected the Rapana experimental girder to test new materials for space structures. On the last they inspected the exterior of *Mir* for possible damage by the Perseid meteor shower and installed a space-exposure experiment. On Jan. 8, 1994, Tsibliyev and Serebrov were replaced by the Soyuz TM-18 crew; one member of the crew, Valery Polyakov, was slated to stay onboard for a record 427 days.

Russia's budget problems were highlighted by the sale of several pieces of hardware at an auction at

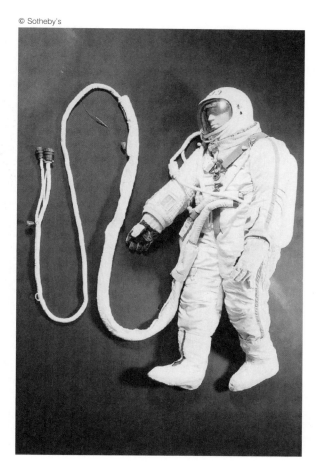

At Sotheby's in New York City in January, Russia sought to raise money by selling at auction equipment used in its space program. Above, the training suit worn by cosmonaut Aleksey Leonov, who in 1965 became the first person to walk in space, sold for $134,500. Bringing more than $1,650,000 was the Soyuz TM-10 capsule (left), which carried cosmonauts to and from the space station Mir 1 in 1990.

Sotheby's in New York City in January. The Soyuz TM-10 capsule fetched $1,650,000, and a space suit brought $134,500.

The efforts of the U.S. to build an international space station went through a final series of contortions that ended with the former adversary, Russia, signing on as a key partner in the venture. This capped nine years of development during which NASA spent more than the original $8 billion price tag without launching the first element of the station. The station even lost its original name, *Freedom*, and became *Alpha*. After Bill Clinton became U.S. president in January 1993, the future of the space station was uncertain, but he decided to continue the program if NASA could reduce its cost. In March a team of 45 people from NASA and its partners started work on new design options. On June 7 they submitted to an independent senior-level team a set of three options: (1) use existing, proven systems in a modular fashion, (2) use existing *Freedom* designs as much as possible, and (3) build the station as a single element launched by an unmanned shuttle. These were presented to President Clinton, who on June 17 selected a modified form of the first two options. The new design eliminated five of the major truss elements that served as the station's backbone and used a 14-m (46-ft)-long common module for laboratory, habitat, and docking. Russia's Soyuz TM spacecraft was to be used to ferry crew members to the station and back to the Earth.

On September 2—just five days before the new plans were submitted to the White House—U.S. Vice Pres. Al Gore and Russian Prime Minister Viktor Chernomyrdin signed an agreement that would link the U.S. and Russian space station programs. For $100 million a year, NASA would start using *Mir* and receive as much as two years of time for a crew of two and joint development of life-support and electrical power systems and a new space suit. The shuttle was scheduled to rendezvous with *Mir* 10 times during 1995–97 on missions to work out technical issues. Initial plans called for Russia's *Mir* 2, now under construction, to become a core module and habitat in the second phase of the project. Japanese, European, and Russian laboratory modules were to be added later. However, U.S. supporters objected to this plan, claiming that it made the project look "too Russian"; they wanted U.S.-built hardware launched first.

As described in November 1993, assembly of the international station was scheduled to start in May 1997 with the launch of a Russian space tug to boost the station's altitude, followed by the attachment of a docking module jointly developed by the U.S. and Russia, a U.S.-built node, and a Russian service module containing environmental systems. The station was to be placed in an orbit inclined 51.6° to the equator so that it could be reached by U.S. and Russian launch vehicles. Added during the next phase would be a Russian-U.S. mast with

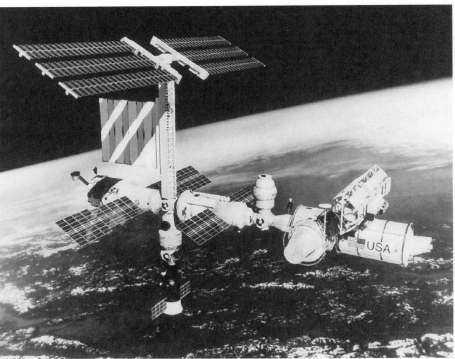

The planned international space station, shown in an artist's drawing, consists of components produced by the U.S. and Russia. On June 17, 1993, U.S. Pres. Bill Clinton approved a plan to use existing, proven systems and existing designs as much as possible.

NASA

solar arrays to power the station, the *Mir 2* module, a Canadian-built robot arm, a truss to serve as the keel for expansion, European and Japanese laboratory modules, and the U.S. habitat module. The last element, to be added in October 2001, would be a solar dynamic system using a parabolic mirror to focus sunlight on a turbogenerator that would supply additional electric power. Of the 31 launches needed to complete the station, 12 would be atop Russian booster rockets.

People. Donald K. ("Deke") Slayton died June 13 of a brain tumor, leaving five of the original seven Project Mercury astronauts selected in 1959 still alive (Virgil I. ["Gus"] Grissom was killed in 1967 in the Apollo 1 fire). Because of a heart arrhythmia detected in 1962, Slayton flew in space only once, on the Apollo-Soyuz Test Project in 1975. (*See* OBITUARIES.) Karl Henize, a mission specialist aboard the Spacelab 2 mission in 1985, died of heart failure during an attempt to climb Mt. Everest.

Space probes

Venus. The Magellan radar-mapping spacecraft was moved closer to Venus during the year for detailed surveys of the planet's gravitational field. Magellan was launched by the space shuttle in May 1989 and went into orbit around Venus on Aug. 10, 1990. Because Venus is covered with thick, permanent clouds of sulfuric acid, its surface is not visible from space. Radar is the only means by which the surface can be measured. In an orbit ranging from approximately 140 to 8,500 km (87 to 5,270 mi) above Venus, Magellan used a technique called synthetic aperture radar (SAR) to map the surface at high resolution.

During three radar-mapping cycles through September 1992, Magellan covered 98% of the planet's surface despite the loss of its primary transmitter modulator in January 1992 and increased noise that forced sparing use of the modulator's backup. The fourth science cycle was a gravitational survey that used slight changes in the spacecraft's radio signals to unmask the distribution of mass at and below the surface of Venus. Meanwhile, scientists planned a more daring close-up survey.

In late May Magellan's onboard thrusters lowered the orbit of the probe to 140 km (87 mi) so that it would pass within the upper reaches of Venus' atmosphere. At those times the probe was flown with the mapping antenna and solar arrays positioned to cause drag. This lasted until August 26, when the spacecraft was stabilized in a new orbit 197 by 540 km (122 by 336 mi) above the surface of the planet. In addition to changing Magellan's orbit to conserve fuel, the experiment also yielded some information on the density and structure of the upper atmosphere.

Mars. What was to be the year's premier planetary event became an embarrassing spell of silence as Mars Observer failed to check in after preparing to orbit Mars. The probe was launched in September 1992 to map the surface of Mars in great detail for a period of one Martian year (23 months). The spacecraft actually transmitted a few pictures of Mars on July 26 at a distance of 5.8 million km (3.6 million mi) as scientists started testing its instruments. The spacecraft's radio was shut down on August 21 to protect it while propellant tanks were pressurized for the burn to insert the craft into planetary orbit. Shortly thereafter the spacecraft failed to reestablish contact with controllers on Earth. NASA worked for five days to summon the spacecraft and then listened until August 30, hoping that the probe would go into the "safe mode" that had been programmed into it in case contact was lost. Nothing was ever heard.

An investigation by NASA was unable to reach a firm conclusion because there were no remains to be inspected. However, investigators decided that the most likely cause of the shutdown was a change in the way the propellant system was used. Originally the primary valves, by the main propellant tanks, were to be opened soon after launch. To reduce leakage, however, planners decided to leave them closed until shortly before orbital insertion. During the journey to Mars, traces of oxidizer might have leaked through the valves into the fuel lines. When fuel was released, it and the oxidizer ignited on contact and ruptured the fuel lines, causing uncontrolled jetting and tumbling the spacecraft out of control. Although a duplicate probe might have been prepared in time for a 1994 launch, NASA said that it had insufficient time to obtain funding for it. Instead, the agency was examining launching two missions in 1996.

On a lesser scale NASA and the Jet Propulsion Laboratory awarded two advanced study contracts for the Mars Surveyor program comprising a series of small, low-cost landers and miniature rovers that would be launched by low-cost Delta II rockets. The landers would use available technologies such as military ultra-high-frequency radios and automobile air bags. After a Pathfinder flight, a fleet of 16 probes would be sent to Mars. This would be followed by a more complex series of 7-kg (15-lb) rovers to study the surface in detail. Total cost was estimated at $1 billion plus launches.

Inflation and technical problems forced Russia to cancel the development of one of its three small Mars '94 landers and threatened the other two. Several U.S. instruments were to be aboard the canceled craft, forcing investigators to seek last-minute accommodations on the other two probes. In October Russia told its international partners that it needed $10 million to continue toward the late 1994 launch (a delay to 1996 also was discussed). The

Mars '94 spacecraft was to carry a compact disc containing recordings reflecting mankind's fascination with Mars.

Despite rumors of more cuts, Russia continued preparing a more ambitious space probe for launch in 1996. In addition to putting a rover on the surface of Mars, the craft would launch a balloon, housing several instruments, that would drift during the day and slowly descend at night.

Jupiter and beyond. Frustration continued with the Galileo spacecraft as it coasted on the final leg of its journey to Jupiter. Galileo's high-gain (most powerful) antenna had refused to open because dry lubricant had slipped away during the long prelaunch wait. In January 1993 engineers gave up attempts to free the antenna and started planning to retrieve pictures and data at much lower rates than planned. During October 4–8 the spacecraft made five thruster firings that comprised the first targeting maneuver for the final approach to Jupiter (arrival was scheduled to occur in December 1995).

Galileo flew past the Earth twice (in 1990 and 1992) in order to use the planet's gravity to power its trajectory outward toward Jupiter. In October 1993 Carl Sagan, W. Reid Thompson, and their colleagues reported in *Nature* magazine that, on the basis of data gathered by Galileo's sensors, Earth might harbor life. City lights and man-made artifacts were not detected, but methane was measured in quantities 30 times greater than an oxygen-laden atmosphere would otherwise allow (methane is produced by plants, animals, and bacteria as well as by human technology). The strongest indicator of intelligent life on Earth was the radio noise.

On June 9 the Ulysses solar polar probe passed 32° solar latitude, breaking Voyager 2's record, as it continued to arc below the plane of the ecliptic (the plane of the Earth's orbit around the Sun). The probe was scheduled to reach a heliocentric latitude of 80° in September 1994. Instruments indicated that already Ulysses was in the region dominated by the Sun's south pole. Ulysses detected signs of interstellar dust (a first) moving at a speed of about 30 km (18.6 mi) per second.

Development of the Cassini/Huygens mission to orbit Saturn continued, although budget pressures threatened it. The Jet Propulsion Laboratory also was studying a Pluto Fast Flyby mission that would send two 150-kg (331-lb) probes to the solar system's most distant planet.

Small bodies. On August 28 Galileo took about 150 images of asteroid 243 Ida as it zipped past at a distance of 2,400 km (1,491 mi) and a speed of 12.4 km (7.7 mi) per second. Ida turned out to be larger than expected—more than 50 km (31 mi) across instead of 30 to 35 km (18.6 to 21.7 mi)—and older. A large number of small craters indicated that it was some one billion years or more old. Galileo also

Asteroid 243 Ida (foreground), which circled the Sun between Mars and Jupiter, was revealed to have its own moon (right) in this picture obtained in August by the Galileo space probe. Ida is more than 50 km (31 mi) long, and the moon is about 1.5 km (1 mi) in diameter. This was the first conclusive evidence that natural satellites of asteroids exist.

revealed that Ida had its own moon, the first conclusive evidence that an asteroid has a natural satellite.

Gravitational maneuvers were cranking the trajectory of Japan's Sakigake (Pioneer) probe so that it would intercept Comet Honda-Mrkos-Pajdusakova in 1996. Sakigake was launched in 1985 as a forerunner of Japan's probe to Comet Halley. On June 14, 1994, Sakigake made the second of two annual Earth flybys.

An intriguing mission was to be launched in January by the Ballistic Missile Defense Organization (formerly the Strategic Defense Initiative Organization). The low-cost Clementine 1 probe would use miniature sensors to observe asteroid 1620 Geographos (named for the National Geographic Society). The mission was named Clementine because it would be "lost and gone forever" on its prospecting mission. After two months in lunar orbit, Clementine 1 would use an Earth-Moon flyby to sling itself onto a course to fly past Geographos on Aug. 31, 1994.

NASA also started planning for a Near Earth Asteroid Rendezvous mission that would launch a small Discovery probe to the 36-km (22-mi)-wide Eros asteroid in 1996. ESA was working on the Rosetta comet rendezvous mission for launch in 2003.

Future missions. In an effort to reduce the cost of exploring the planets, NASA began the Discovery program to develop planetary missions that could be launched just three years after their initiation and for less than $150 million. In addition to taking advantage of the last decade's advances in civilian and military electronics technologies, the program would also challenge managers to limit changes and tightly control budgets.

Robotic technologies for future space missions were tested at remote, hostile sites during the year. Perhaps the most engaging was the Teleoperated Robotic Vehicle (TROV), a small robot submarine operating below McMurdo Sound in Antarctica's Ross Sea. TROV carried a television camera equipped with special lenses to provide stereoscopic vision. The submarine was connected to the surface by a fiber-optic link and then, via satellite, to Ames Research Center in Mountain View, Calif. Engineers at Ames operated TROV through the satellite link and watched through virtual reality headsets to get a three-dimensional view. NASA also made the operation available for viewing at the U.S. National Air and Space Museum and involved students from several high schools.

A Russian Marsokhod model was driven a few meters across the rugged Kamchatka Peninsula in August by operators at McDonnell Douglas' Huntington Beach, Calif., facilities. The operators were linked to the vehicle by a communications satellite and used a virtual reality system to produce three-dimensional images of the terrain as they planned each move. The 682-kg (1,504-lb) titanium chassis rover was built by the same team that produced and operated the Soviet Union's two Lunokhod rovers in the 1970s. The Russian space agency hoped to launch Marsokhod in 1996 and possibly to equip it with a U.S.-supplied robot arm or to use U.S. virtual reality technology on Earth to help operate it.

Because of the delays involved in communicating with machines in deep space, such operations would appear painfully slow to the outside observer. Scientists would have to survey the terrain and calculate the next stage of each movement, which might be just a few meters, depending on surface conditions. Sending the new instructions would take several minutes, and the operators would have to wait as long for the return signal to provide them with the results. Thus, should the rover start to topple, the operators would be unable to steady it because the event would have ended several minutes before they found out about it.

—Dave Dooling

Transportation

The continuing competitive pressures in a slowly improving economic environment held down high-cost technological innovations in the field of transportation but proved a stimulus to the development and introduction of innovations that can provide short-term benefits in the form of lower operating costs and better transport services. In the operating area, all forms of transportation continued to utilize such high-tech developments as electronic data interchange (EDI), satellite and cellular communications, bar coding, and automated equipment identification.

A relatively new achievement was the ability to feed into a computer's software data that could predict with a high degree of accuracy, on the basis of the historical use of specific transport equipment, how well that equipment would perform. An area where the cost savings in transportation was significant was maintenance of aircraft, rail rolling stock, ships, and trucks. In this area, maintenance programs historically had been mandated on an equipment-use or time basis. With the use of such computers, equipment could be kept in good operating condition by the stressing of specific preventive maintenance without the performance of unneeded work or installation of new parts. Proponents of the innovation claimed it could cut maintenance costs by as much as 20%.

The rapid introduction and utilization of bar codes for electronic tracking of all types of transportation equipment and packages proved so successful that the use of bar codes became virtually universal. The

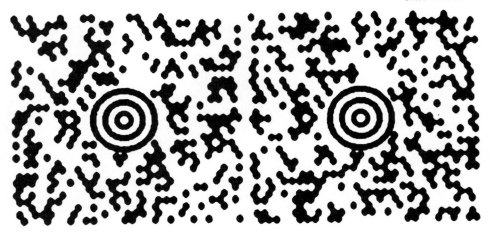

MaxiCode, a product code introduced by United Parcel Service, can be read up and down as well as back and forth. Thus, it can hold 100 characters of data in 6.45 sq cm (1 sq in), considerably more than can the standard bar codes.

problems in earlier use, such as accuracy in bar scanning, had been almost completely resolved, with users now claiming that current code scanning had an estimated error rate of only one for every 300 million characters scanned. The next step in this high-tech area was "two-dimensional symbology," which utilized labels only slightly larger than a postage stamp yet could provide many times the amount of information than the standard 40–80-character bar codes. The new MaxiCode, the two-dimensional symbology system being tested by United Parcel Service (UPS) at its hub in Grand Rapids, Mich., could provide, in addition to tracking data of a package, its postal code, country code, class of service, date of package pickup, and destination. Similar tests were under way at Consolidated Freightways, Inc., of Menlo Park, Calif., a major less-than-truckload carrier. That company predicted that the system would soon enable it to move its freight virtually without paper documents—further stimulating the use of EDI by the carrier's shippers.

The limited acceptance and use of RoadRailers, trailers with interchangeable rail and truck wheels that permit both rail and highway operations, could change because of several new developments. One was Conrail's purchase of a half interest in Triple Crown Services, the operator of RoadRailer services. Another was the steady improvement in the Road-Railers, such as the use of a detachable rail bogie (a platform equipped with railroad wheels) that allowed individual units to be removed from anywhere on the train without specialized lifting equipment and also eased highway operations by separating heavy rail wheels from the trailer.

The third development was the agreement with Schneider National, Inc., the nation's largest truck-load motor carrier, calling for extensive tests of RoadRailer operations on the Southern Pacific Rail-road's Los Angeles–Portland route. Through use of a special device called CouplerMate, the RoadRailers could be coupled very closely to provide a smoother ride. In addition, the resulting small space between the RoadRailers kept their doors from being fully opened, thus providing greater freight security from vandalism and theft. Triple Crown Services also claimed for RoadRailers a reduction of weight and progressively lower purchasing costs. Moreover, the start of ReeferRailer temperature-controlled service for North American Van Line services, Inc., in 1994 should open up a new market.

Air transport. Boeing Co. rolled out the first 747-400 freighter, using it as a backdrop for the visit by U.S. Pres. Bill Clinton to Boeing's complex at Everett, Wash. The huge air-freight transport was a hybrid of the earlier 747s but had longer wings, more advanced flight controls, and 2,565 sq m (27,610 sq ft) of cargo space for handling up to 122 tons of freight (20 tons more than a 747-200 freighter). It also was capable of operating nearly 8,000 km (5,000 mi) nonstop. In October the Federal Aviation Administration (FAA) certified the new transport for commercial operations, with similar action soon followed by European aviation authorities.

Air France took delivery of the first 747-400, but the first one to be placed in immediate service was sold to Cargolux Airlines International SA of Luxembourg, which planned to use it on its longest route, a polar flight between Luxembourg and the airline's U.S. West Coast hubs in Los Angeles, San Francisco, and Seattle, Wash. The price tag was $140 million. Cargolux cited the following reasons for choosing the 747-400 instead of used transport: smaller crews, lower fuel consumption, reduced maintenance, fewer overhauls, and lower noise levels. As of early 1994 Boeing had another 15 planes on order.

UPS, whose international air-cargo business continued to expand rapidly, reported an order for 30 of Boeing's new 767 twin-jet all-freight transports, which were designed for markets best served by a transport with medium-range and medium-payload capability. With this aircraft Boeing hoped to overcome the airlines' practice of buying older, cheaper passenger transports for conversion to freighters. Boeing claimed that such transports, while less expensive to purchase, were much less fuel-efficient and required more maintenance-related expenditures.

For its equally expanding U.S. air-freight service, UPS announced that it would spend $400 million over the next two years to equip its fleet of B-727-100 three-engine air freighters with new fuel-efficient and quiet Rolls-Royce Tay 651 engines. UPS said that six of these 727 Quiet Freighters already had begun flying in its U.S. network, and it claimed that the fuel savings should largely overcome the costs of reengineering, thus allowing the 727s to fly another 20 years.

Government-industry consortia in both Europe and the U.S. reported progress in their separate programs to develop a proposed high-speed civil transport (HSCT). Both groups were constrained financially because of continued poor economic conditions. The U.S. consortium (National Aeronautics and Space Administration [NASA], Pratt & Whitney, and General Electric) indicated that its choice of a power plant was a low-bypass turbojet and turbofan. The consortium reported that its detailed analysis revealed that the technological and environmental barriers to HSCT development were less intractable than originally thought. It claimed that steady gains had been made in the development of lightweight, low-noise engine inlets and nozzles and of low-emission combustors.

The European consortium (Rolls-Royce, Snecma, Motoren-und Turbinen-Union, and Fiat) announced that it favored a fan-propulsion system that would provide maximum power at takeoff, after which, as a result of fan adjustment, only 25% of the takeoff power would be required for maintaining cruise speed. An earlier concept permitted a similar power adjustment but required two power plants that were more complex and costly to operate in airline service.

For immediate use in business aircraft and later use by commercial air transports, Seattle Aviation Partners Inc. developed an advanced winglet, which it claimed would cut fuel consumption about 10% in cruise operations. (A winglet is a small nearly vertical airfoil at an airplane's wingtip that reduces drag by inhibiting turbulence.) The builder, which had spent more than $6 million for research and development on the program to date, said that winglets for 16 aircraft had been installed or ordered, the first set for the Gulfstream 2 business jet. The winglet had a constant radius and extended upward at the wingtip, to which it was easily bolted. A more ad-

vanced spiroid design for air transports was made of foam-filled fiberglass and weighed about 35 kg (80 lb) per wing. Flight tests on the Gulfstream 2 of both designs showed cruise fuel savings of 7% for the constant-radius design and more than 10% for the spiroid design, with both providing improved aircraft stability and climb performance. For the transport market, initial installations were aimed at retrofit aircraft such as Boeing 727s and 737s and McDonnell Douglas DC-9s.

During the year Boeing adopted a high-tech approach to minimizing maintenance costs and improving aircraft dispatch reliability for its upcoming 777 transport. The company's main focus in this regard was to assist the gate mechanic, who was responsible for having repairs made rapidly on incoming air transports in order to minimize delayed departures. This would be done by addition to the 777's onboard maintenance system (OMS) of computer software that included an "inbound faults" category. The gate mechanic was sent information developed by the computer's software that was based on historic and other information essential for fault diagnosis and corrective action; however, separate "nuisance fault" messages, which were a major cause of gate delays in the new-generation transports, would not be sent. The latter and more detailed engineering and maintenance data would be made available through other OMS operating modules.

Highway transport. The nation's trucking industry, in comments to the U.S. Senate Surface Transport Subcommittee, expressed continued support for recently passed legislation that authorized $659 million for IVHS (intelligent vehicle-highway system) by 1998, but it warned against overestimating the system's benefits and underestimating its costs. Industry spokesmen said that truly automated highways were still a thing of the future but also pointed out that innovations such as electronic toll collection, vehicle identification through use of "smart cards," vehicle tracking via bar codes and satellite communications, and collision-avoidance devices were already in use by commercial vehicles and should be encouraged aggressively. With the trucking industry's cooperation and assistance, the U.S. Federal Highway Administration started a project to develop automated roadside inspections of the nation's intercity trucks; in 1993 each inspection took an average of 35 to 45 minutes. The approach being used was to utilize onboard electronics and offboard diagnostic devices. Such devices could quickly check to see if brakes were properly adjusted and not running hot, if emissions were within legal limits, and if other safety-related components were working properly. The joint effort was being conducted by the Trucking Research Institute (a unit of the American Trucking Associations) and the Texas Transportation Institute.

Boeing 777 jetliner, the largest twin-engine plane ever built, nears completion at Everett, Wash. The Boeing Co. planned to equip the 777s with computer software that would inform gate mechanics of possible needed repairs on arriving planes.

J.B. Hunt Transport Co., the nation's second largest truckload motor carrier, announced that it had simplified the paperwork required for operating its 7,000-truck fleet by using software developed by Jetform Corp. of Waltham, Mass. Hunt said that its former process used five different data systems for tariffs and cargo contracts; these now would be consolidated into one database. The new system would be expanded to provide documents for the scheduling, hiring, and training of drivers, as well as creating letters to customers. Another benefit, Hunt said, would be the reduction from four days to four hours in the time needed each week to prepare operating data required to be submitted to the Interstate Commerce Commission.

General Motors Corp., while continuing to express reservations about consumer acceptance of electric automobiles, announced that it would begin testing a fleet of 50 electric cars in California, where strict air-pollution-emission standards were being mandated. GM said that its highly touted Impact electric car would be used and that it had filed an application with the California Air Resources Board to certify that the car was a zero-emission vehicle. GM also said that during the next two years it would provide 1,000 potential customers with vehicles for road testing and evaluation over a two-to-four-week period.

This California board certified the Dodge Caravan of the Chrysler Corp. as a candidate for meeting the board's upcoming zero-emission mandate. Costs and operating constraints clearly illustrated the remaining roadblocks to widespread use of such vehicles. Chrysler said that the electric van was powered by 30 six-volt batteries with a lifetime expectancy of 160,000 km (nearly 100,000 mi) and an operating range of up to 130 km (80 mi) between charges. The batteries accounted for about half the van's 2,680 kg (5,900 lb). The van was equipped with air-conditioning and heating systems, plus a braking system that helped recharge the batteries when the brakes were engaged. Its top speed was 105 km/h (65 mph), but it could accelerate from zero to 80 km/h (50 mph) in 27 seconds. It also could charge its batteries in only 30–45 minutes, compared with eight hours required for earlier electric vehicles. The major roadblock to the development of the van was its extremely high cost—$120,000 per vehicle. Even at that price, Chrysler said that it could not make much money on the model. (*See* Feature Article: The Rebirth of Electric Vehicles.)

UPS announced that, as part of a U.S. Department of Energy (DOE) demonstration project, it would start road tests in the Washington, D.C., area of 20 of its delivery trucks powered by compressed natural gas (CNG) engines. In contrast to similar tests earlier with trucks using gasoline engines converted to CNG use, the new engines, built by Thermo Power Corp. of Waltham, Mass., were manufactured for CNG operations. The project was part of DOE's alternative fuels program for heavy- and medium-duty commercial trucks. It was being run by the National Renewable Energy Laboratory in Golden, Colo., which would then evaluate data collected by the tests.

Con-Way Transportation Services, Inc., a provider of LTL (less-than-truckload) freight services throughout the U.S., announced that it had expanded its market to include shipments of refrigerated goods weighing from 0.45 to 900 kg (1 to 2,000 lb). This was made possible by the introduction of a midsize refrigerated shipping unit called a pallet reefer with a capacity of 2 cu m (72 cu ft) that is cooled with liquid carbon dioxide controlled by a built-in microprocessing unit capable of maintaining temperatures within 1.1° C (2° F) of a setting ranging from room temperature to −40° C (−40° F). The stainless steel pallet reefer could be kept cold for up to four days and could be moved by forklift. Con-Way said that the new pallet reefers, which cost $6,600 apiece, could be shipped by a regular LTL service, thus giving shippers more options than using only refrigerated carrier LTL service.

The 200 trucking companies that had established charge-card accounts with the Detroit & Canada Tunnel Corp. expressed strong approval of the innovation. The Detroit–Windsor tunnel served up to 20,000 vehicles each day. Truck drivers having the plastic charge cards found that passage through the toll booth took only about 15 seconds, compared with more than a minute under the old system. Use of the card automatically registered the trucking company's name and card number along with the date, time, truck weight, and, within seconds, the toll. The transaction entered the computer's memory and was printed out on the customer's monthly statement. As of 1994, the system was operating only on the U.S. side of the tunnel, but it was expected to be in use on the Canadian side later that year.

J.B. Hunt Transport Co. began installation of a new "smart communications system" that was designed to shave pennies off the cost of each digital communication between truck driver and dispatcher, currently done via satellite. The computerized onboard device was developed by IBM Corp. and cost $30 million, which Hunt predicted would be recovered within a year. Called RoadRider, the portable computer, mounted on the truck's dashboard, provided standard messages on any of 187 screens that could be selected by the driver. Hunt also claimed that RoadRider doubled the fleet managers' productivity and, by eliminating stops for making telephone calls, increased by 5% the time each truck was on the road.

Railroad transport. In 1993 competition among passenger-train builders to win orders from Amtrak for 26 complete trains (including locomotive and cars) for its Washington–Boston Northeast Corridor service increased sharply. Amtrak's plan called for approving contracts for those trains in late 1994, at an estimated cost of more than $400 million. Options for an additional 25 train sets were also planned, at a cost of an additional $400 million, to operate in other high-density U.S. corridors. A wide range of trains was under consideration since plans called for delivery of both electric- and turbine-powered units.

One candidate, Germany's InterCity Express (ICE) train, was tested on the Northeast Corridor. Weighing 562 tons and measuring 200 m (655 ft) in length, it featured a braking system that supplemented electric power consumption, electronic traction control, and a computerized diagnostic system. Its established European operations provided routine 255 km/h (160-mph) service. Another candidate was the Swedish X2000 tilt train, capable of high-speed operation around curves and thus well-suited for the many curves along the New York–Boston segment of the Northeast Corridor. It, too, completed a successful test.

Other candidates included the highly successful French TGV (Train à Grand Vitesse) passenger train, capable of regular-service speeds exceeding 320 km/h (200 mph), and the TM-1600, a modernized Amtrak train propelled by turbine engines and said to be capable of operating at routine-service speeds of 200 km/h (125 mph). The latter was awarded a $3 million U.S.-New York state grant to upgrade Amtrak's New York City–Albany service.

Freight-carrying railroads continued to express serious concerns about the safety of operating high-speed passenger trains along routes normally handling slower freight trains. At the same time, however, they recognized the impracticability and extremely high cost of building new rail lines specifically for the high-speed trains. One official said that such trains "don't make money anywhere in the world," and he added that "the full costs of high-speed rail passenger service, including liability, should be borne by those involved in such operations."

Despite the even higher costs of a high-speed, magnetically levitated (Maglev) passenger-train system, a U.S.-German corporate consortium promoting this high-tech innovation said, "Our Maglev technology is ready to serve customers around the world." Called Transrapid, the consortium stated that its assertion was "the result of a 15-year, $3 billion R&D effort."

Ford Motor Co. and the Burlington Northern Railroad selected the Autostack System developed by the Greenbrier Companies of Portland, Ore., for movement of the former's new automobiles between Midwest and Pacific Northwest routes. The Autostack System was designed to answer complaints by U.S. automobile manufacturers about damage to new cars while in transit to dealers. The new system was based on the use of a tubular steel frame that held up to six cars (three on a lower level and three on an upper level) that were securely positioned for loading into a standard container. To help minimize empty (frames only) backhauls and to stimulate return payloads, the frames of six-car units could be collapsed and fitted into a single container, freeing the other five containers for handling merchandise on the return trip.

The French TGV (Train à Grand Vitesse), capable of regular-service speeds exceeding 320 km/h (200 mph), was one of the many passenger trains being considered for service in the heavily traveled Washington, D.C.–Boston Northeast Corridor.

Despite huge potential benefits from an advanced train control system (ATCS) that would provide automated communications to maintain safe distances between trains, the huge cost—an estimated $8 billion to $16 billion—discouraged installation beyond the experimental stage, even though small-scale ATCS-type systems were tested and found to be operationally feasible. The National Transportation Safety Board was pressing for faster action and for a specific program of implementation but had no answer regarding costs. Because the slower freights were by far the most common trains, the train-separation problem was expected to worsen as more high-speed passenger trains went into service.

A major step toward automated traffic control was taken by the Burlington Northern Railroad with its announcement that it would spend more than $10 million for a consolidated-dispatching train-control system. It was scheduled to be installed in Fort Worth, Texas, by 1995. According to the railroad, computers would route and schedule trains, establishing the places where trains would meet and pass each other. The computers would also remotely control switches and signals. Dispatchers would assign priorities to trains, ensuring that the slower bulk-freight trains met and passed each other. The computers would also remotely control switches and signals. Dispatchers would assign priorities to trains, ensuring that the slower bulk-freight trains did not interfere with faster merchandise trains.

The Burlington Northern confirmed plans to acquire from General Motors' Electro-Motive Division 350 4,000-hp locomotives that offered a combination of AC (alternating current, as opposed to direct current) traction, a high-tech microprocessor, and an engine-control system. The builder claimed the locomotive "represents the most dramatic step forward in freight locomotive technology in decades" and said that three such units could replace up to five direct-current units, achieving greater fuel efficiency and less pollution.

The Norfolk Southern Railroad ordered from Electro-Motive 50 4,000-hp locomotives that employed special undercarriages to help the units bend around curves while maintaining better contact between the locomotives' wheels and the rail. Electro-Motive claimed that this improved tractive effort by 11%. The railroad said that the new locomotives, to be used primarily for coal trains, would use direct-current traction and were part of its program to convert from four-axle to six-axle power.

Union Pacific Railroad announced that it would begin tests, starting in January 1994, to determine the economic and social feasibility of using liquefied natural gas (LNG) as an alternative locomotive fuel. During the three-year test, six locomotives were to be powered by LNG rather than diesel oil. Two switch engines would operate in southern California, where the comparatively low noxious emissions of LNG would help the railroad meet that area's progressively tougher clean-air mandates. Two pairs of road locomotives were to operate throughout the railroad's 30,500-km (19,000-mi) system. The switch units were built by Morrison Knudsen Corp. of Boise, Idaho, while subsidiaries of General Motors and General Electric built the road units. Among the advantages of LNG cited by Union Pacific were its availability from domestic sources, its price stability in comparison with oil-based fuels, and its clean emissions. One major disadvantage was the need for special handling; to maintain its liquidity, LNG requires special tenders for carrying it under pressure at $-162°$ C ($-260°$ F).

The Burlington Northern Railroad, which had already successfully tested LNG as a locomotive fuel in its northern U.S. coal corridor, said that it would continue such tests, using engines that require diesel fuel for idle operations and to help boost LNG power. The railroad aimed to generate progressively higher percentages of LNG to a maximum 90% LNG-10% diesel mix at full power.

Water transport. The Federal Maritime Commission (FMC) claimed that its new automated tariff system, which went into operation in early 1993, operated on schedule without any major problems. Formally called the Automated Tariff Filing and Information System (AFTI), it had, through August, filed 900 ocean-carrier tariffs in its computer. The FMC issued many temporary filing exemptions during the year, mostly because of the complexities in converting from long-used paper tariffs to the electronic format that was required. A fee of 46 cents per minute for users of ATFI, in accord with a mandate by the U.S. Congress, was being imposed; users could, however, collect that fee from their customers or be exempt from nontariff data received from ATFI into their own computers. Because of the user fee, tariff service companies said that they would rely on FMC's data as little as possible and instead use tariff information that was supplied directly by shipping companies.

Crowley Maritime Corp. announced plans to spend about $100 million on a fleet of specialized tugs for escort and handling service for oil tankers and large barges working between Alaska and the west coast of the U.S. Crowley's plans called for purchasing, at a cost of $12 million each, eight so-called tractor tugs, which would be able to apply force in a variety of directions without repositioning—as opposed to the ability of conventional tugs to push only when going forward.

American President Companies (APC) reported that it planned to invest $15 million–20 million in automatic equipment identification (AEI) tags and readers during the next five years. It would install AEI tags on all its containers, chassis, tractors, railcars, and other equipment, along with scanner systems at 130 of its facilities throughout North America, Asia, and the Middle East. Its initial order for 100,000 AEI tags called for 1993 delivery. The AEI system consisted of tags on transport equipment that emitted special radio signals to scanners, which, in turn, passed along information such as equipment loca-

tion to the company's central computer for keeping shippers up to date on the status of their cargo. Besides this tracking function, AEI could help carriers with equipment inventory control and scheduling.

The U.S. Navy selected Marine Safety International, which operated a ship-handling training facility at Newport, R.I., to install and operate a similar center at the naval station in San Diego, Calif. The new facility, the first such center west of the Mississippi River, would be equipped with two computerized simulators to provide navy officers with ship-maneuvering and docking practice. A vertical view would be provided for close-up maneuvering at harbors and ports. Each simulator would also provide a horizontal scene to help officers upgrade their ship-handling capabilities for up to 40 different ships in dozens of ports and waterways and under different weather conditions.

The *Delaware Responder,* a 63-m (208-ft) oil-spill-response vessel, was commissioned during the year in Delaware City, Del., and set sail for intensive training of its crew of 17. The ship was one of 16 virtually identical vessels designed and built in response to the *Exxon Valdez* oil spill of 1989. They were to guard the major inland waterways of the Atlantic and Pacific oceans and the Gulf of Mexico, as well as territory up to 200 mi offshore. All the crews would be trained to operate on any of the vessels. Each ship contained a computer room that would be able to send and receive data from anywhere in the world, to communicate with oil-spill experts, and to make computer analyses of conditions relating to the nature or scope of the disaster. An onboard laboratory would analyze chemicals that could prove harmful to the crew; this chemical-analysis capability would also help the Coast Guard trace the ownership of a spilled chemical for the purpose of linking it to a specific ship for possible criminal prosecution.

The American Bureau of Shipping, which sets ship-design standards in the U.S., announced that it would replace its old written rules with a new computer software package. The major change, to increase tanker safety, would be in the distribution of steel in order to strengthen the hull. The bureau would do this by creating theoretical models of vessels and the stresses caused by strong winds and rough seas. The computerized standards would help determine where the steel was needed most.

—Frank A. Smith

U.S. science policy

Any change in administration brings with it a certain amount of upheaval in U.S. government policy circles. When the shift is from 12 years of Republican policies to a Democrat with radically different ideas about government's role in setting the country's scientific and technical agenda, the changes can seem cataclysmic, and if there was anything that Pres. Bill Clinton was determined to do with his administration, it was to make some changes.

The tone for the changes was set by the people the new president chose as his principal advisers. For example, in the Department of the Interior, where mining and logging interests once reigned supreme, the new secretary of the interior, Bruce Babbitt, was lobbying for an administration plan to limit logging in old-growth forests in order to protect the northern spotted owl. Later in the year Babbitt took on ranchers when he threatened to raise grazing fees on federal lands. In the Department of Health and Human Services, the new secretary, Donna Shalala, broke with her predecessors, who had fought to block federal spending on fetal tissue transplantation research. They had argued that it would encourage women to have abortions, but Shalala, former president of a major research university, assured

Congress that the administration was in favor of funding such research. When hamburgers tainted with a toxic bacterium caused the deaths of several young children in the Pacific Northwest, Secretary of Agriculture Mike Espy turned to consumer interest groups rather than the meat industry for advice on how to improve the federal meat-inspection system. At the Department of Commerce, where technology policy had scarcely been mentioned for a decade, Secretary Ron Brown emphasized the strategic role of the National Institute of Standards and Technology in helping the government keep U.S. high-tech industries competitive. This Cabinet was clearly heading in a different direction from the last one.

The new president pleased the scientific community by choosing John Gibbons to be his science adviser. Gibbons had been the director of the congressional Office of Technology Assessment before moving to the White House. He was among the first people to be named to the new president's team, suggesting that he would have an important role in the new administration. Indeed, Gibbons had been a

John Gibbons, a physicist and the director of the congressional Office of Technology Assessment since 1979, was chosen by U.S. Pres. Bill Clinton to be his science adviser.

particular favorite of Vice Pres. Al Gore when Gore was in the Senate. Despite Gibbons' auspicious start, however, his Office of Science and Technology Policy had only limited effectiveness in shaping policy. OSTP was asked to coordinate all federal science activities with a tiny staff of only a few dozen people, a nearly impossible task.

Health care and the NIH. The biggest policy shift proposed by the new administration had only an indirect effect on science policy. President Clinton had promised that health care reform would be a number one priority in his administration, and he made good on that promise. In September the president presented the nation with a comprehensive reform package to provide basic medical insurance for all Americans. Enthusiasm for the package was far from universal. Some leaders of industry proclaimed that health care reform would devastate the domestic pharmaceutical industry by eating into profits that have sustained the discovery and development of new drugs. But the administration sought to reassure nervous business executives, arguing that a favorable climate for research would be preserved. Others argued that paying for the reform package would require taking money from all other domestic programs, including biomedical research. The administration countered that its proposals would actually boost research spending. Indeed, the package presented to Congress included $500 million for prevention research, money that would go largely to the National Institutes of Health (NIH).

The question of what to do with the NIH presented the Clinton administration with one of its early policy challenges. Pres. George Bush had named cardiologist Bernadine Healy to head the agency in 1991. Healy proved to be a dynamo. Vowing to set the agency on a new course, she swept into the NIH and began charting a strategic plan for the $10 billion agency, with an emphasis on research to achieve national priorities. For this she earned the enmity of the scientific community, which feared that basic research would be abandoned. When President Bush lost his bid for reelection, Healy lobbied hard to retain her job, but the new administration decided that she had become a liability. She had angered several powerful Democratic congresswomen by fighting too hard for the Bush administration's moratorium on fetal tissue research.

President Clinton's choice of Harold Varmus to replace Healy brought smiles to researchers' faces throughout the country. Since winning the Nobel Prize in 1989 for his work on viruses and cancer, Varmus had taken an active interest in science policy issues and had become a champion for basic research. He argued that without the fundamental knowledge gained by such research, applied research would have nothing on which to build.

The choice of a basic researcher to head the NIH indicated that the Clinton administration was concerned about the health of basic research. Nevertheless, there were signs that basic researchers would be under increasing pressure to do something of immediate value even while pursuing fundamental questions in biology. While deciding against a large-scale effort to find a cure for AIDS, the president nonetheless indicated that there would be an increasing focus on certain areas of biomedical research. Breast cancer, childhood vaccines, and prevention research could expect more money in future budgets.

There was no question that the morale at the NIH changed with the election of Clinton. Many researchers had chafed under restrictions put in place by the Reagan and Bush administrations. One of Clinton's first acts as president was to end the moratorium on federal funding for fetal tissue transplantation research. Research in other countries and privately funded research in the U.S. had suggested that fetal tissue transplants could help patients with neurological disorders such as Parkinson's disease. By the end of the year, the NIH had announced that it would be supporting such research at the University of Colorado. The NIH also received congressional permission to start supporting research on test-tube babies, more properly known as in vitro fertilization.

During his campaign for president, Clinton promised to put AIDS higher on the national research agenda, and after his election he sought to do that. Early in 1993 Kristine M. Gebbie was named to be the federal AIDS "czar," a post intended to coordinate all federal AIDS programs. For the first time, the Centers for Disease Control and Prevention in Atlanta, Ga., was given permission to promote the use of condoms as a way to prevent the spread of AIDS. But there were some stumbles in AIDS research as well. During its first year in office, the administration was unable to recruit a director for the office of AIDS research at the NIH, and there were grumbles from AIDS activists that Gebbie was not strong enough to make the best use of her position as czar.

Environmental policy. The other major science policy shift resulting from the change in administrations was in environmental research. After years of refusing to go along with restrictions on greenhouse gas emissions or efforts to protect endangered species, suddenly the U.S. was looking like a team player, if not a global leader, on these issues.

Some of the changes were more symbolic than substantive. In June President Clinton signed the Convention on Biological Diversity. The Bush administration had refused to sign the treaty, aimed at protecting global genetic resources, arguing that it put unfair restrictions on U.S. companies that were seeking to make products by using genetic resources obtained from other countries. Although the administration reaped some political points from environmentalists for signing the convention, it was not clear exactly how the treaty would be implemented, so there was no real risk of offending industry by signing.

The president also vowed to make the Environmental Protection Agency a Cabinet-level department and appointed Carol Browner to head the agency. Browner had pleased environmentalists with her work as director of environmental protection for the state of Florida, and she came into the EPA full of energy. By the end of 1993, however, she had discovered how difficult it can be to move a federal bureaucracy. Congress never showed much enthusiasm for the Cabinet-level idea, and the president decided to spend his political capital in other areas.

The greatest change in environmental policy was at the Department of the Interior. Secretary Babbitt instituted a major reorganization of research at the department, emphasizing long-term studies. To do that, he proposed creating the National Biological Survey, moving scientists from the Fish and Wildlife Service and the National Park Service to work there. But even in this rearrangement, there were missteps. The administration proposed raising grazing fees as a way of limiting cattle damage to federal lands in the western U.S., but powerful western senators blocked the move. Babbitt's attempts to modify a Civil War-era mining law to include more environmental protections also failed to make it into law.

Defense. Defense-related research also faced difficult times during the past year. There was intense pressure on Department of Defense research agencies, such as the Defense Advanced Research Projects Agency and the Office of Naval Research, to cut their spending in the wake of the end of the Cold War. Several of these agencies scrambled to find potential civilian applications for their research. For example, the navy lent its underwater submarine surveillance system to marine biologists at Cornell University, Ithaca, N.Y., to study whale migrations.

The Department of Energy was having similar problems with its national laboratories. With no pressing need for a new generation of nuclear weapons, DOE labs in Los Alamos and Albuquerque, N.M., and Livermore, Calif., suddenly were without a clear mission. In the face of layoffs of hundreds of scientists, the labs sought to convert their high-tech weapons research to civilian applications. Their efforts resulted in a few small-scale successes; scientists at Los Alamos National Laboratory teamed up with General Motors Corp. to make ultrahard manufacturing tools by using equipment from a canceled nuclear fusion experiment. But such good matches with industry were the exception rather than the

rule. For laboratories steeped in a military culture, the change to a civilian mindset was not an easy task.

Space exploration. Optimists at the National Aeronautics and Space Administration (NASA) would look back on 1993 as a rather good year. The U.S. signed a new cooperative agreement with Russia to create a joint space station, the Galileo space probe sent back about 150 pictures of asteroid Ida as it passed by on its way to Jupiter, and the mission to repair the Hubble Space Telescope was successful. For pessimists, though, 1993 would be remembered as a year when yet another big NASA project flopped. Just days before it was supposed to arrive at Mars in August, the Mars Observer spacecraft stopped sending signals back to Earth.

Mars Observer was supposed to make the most detailed survey of the planet ever attempted. Data from the Mars Observer mission were considered crucial to future missions to land a probe on Mars and perhaps might even have paved the way for a manned flight to the planet. For a few frantic days, ground controllers tried desperately to signal the spacecraft to fire its engines and go into orbit. That might have happened, but ground controllers could not tell if it did. They heard nothing from the spacecraft, and the $900 million Mars mission was a total failure.

With no signal from the spacecraft, it was impossible to tell precisely what caused its demise. A review panel speculated that a poorly designed fuel system failed when the engines were being prepared for firing and laid the blame on NASA officials for poor management of the project.

Still, as with previous administrations, the Clinton administration remained steadfast in its support for NASA and its plans to build a permanently manned space station. The Clinton forces went to great lengths to protect the space station following a move to kill it in the House of Representatives. When he took office, President Clinton ordered a review of the space station project, and by summer a review panel chaired by Charles Vest, president of the Massachusetts Institute of Technology, was suggesting a scaled-down version of the station. The Vest panel also recommended trying to work out an agreement with Russia to share technology designed for the *Mir* space station. By autumn the administration had decided to do just that; the U.S. signed an agreement with Russia to collaborate on a joint space station.

This achieved two policy objectives for the administration. On the one hand, the U.S. stood to benefit from the vast fleet of Russian launch vehicles, providing a valuable backup for the shuttle and for the sparse fleet of unmanned U.S. rockets. At the same time, it also gave the Russians a ready-made market for their space technology so that they would not be tempted to sell their expertise to a less-friendly world power such as China.

Steve Kelley—Copley News Service

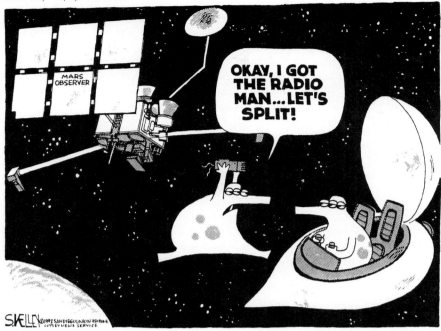

Super Collider. One major U.S. science project did not survive its annual congressional attack. In October Congress applied the coup de grâce to the Superconducting Super Collider. The SSC would have been the most powerful atom smasher ever built. An 87-km (54-mi)-long tunnel was being dug outside Dallas, Texas, to house the beam pipe through which protons would be accelerated to tremendous energies.

According to physicists who supported the project, the SSC was essential to further understanding of how our universe holds together, but to politicians the SSC had become a giant public works project for scientists. Because the discoveries the SSC was supposed to make were so obscure—such as the Higgs particle and the top quark—and because the cost of the project kept rising ($10 billion had become a conservative estimate), the SSC became an irresistible target for lawmakers anxious to seem to be doing something about the budget. Unlike its no-holds-barred support for the space station, the Clinton administration was only lukewarm in its support for the SSC. Although the Senate voted to restore funds the House had deleted for the project, the House prevailed, and the project was killed.

Human genome. The third of the Big Science projects that were begun in the 1980s was still going strong during the past year. The Human Genome Project was moving steadily forward as it attempted to determine a complete map of all the genes in the 23 pairs of human chromosomes. Tools developed for the genome project led during the year to the discovery of several genes associated with diseases. The most exciting was a gene associated with colon cancer. Armed with this knowledge, scientists should be able to develop a blood test that will be able to determine who is most likely to develop the cancer. Basic research scientists were particularly excited about the discovery because it underscored their argument that one cannot always predict how or when such research will find a practical application. Most of the fundamental knowledge about how this gene works came from research with yeast and bacteria.

The colon cancer gene pointed to a problem that was expected to arise with increasing frequency as the pace of genetic discoveries accelerated: what to do with the new information. In most cases the ability to diagnose a new genetic disease was far ahead of the ability to treat it. Scientists would have to grapple with the issue of when to start screening a population for a disease and what to do with the screening information once it was available. One of the biggest concerns was that insurance companies would use information from genetic testing to deny coverage for some people. Proponents of the Clinton health care plan maintained that the best way to avoid this problem was to mandate universal coverage so that all taxpayers would share the cost of treating genetic diseases.

Embryo cloning. Another event that brought ethical questions into the headlines in 1993 was the announcement in October that a team of scientists at George Washington University, Washington, D.C., had taken the first steps in cloning a human embryo. The scientists took fertilized human eggs from patients who were using in vitro fertilization to conceive a child, let each egg divide in the test tube, and then separated each embryo into two cells. In theory, each cell could develop into an identical baby, just like identical twins, although in practice the researcher carefully chose embryos that were damaged and incapable of developing.

When news of the experiment was reported in the media, it caused an uproar. Ethicists warned that the process could be used to select children for certain characteristics, creating multiple copies of the same baby by repeated separation of the embryo at an early stage of development. The NIH responded to the uproar by saying that it would not be funding any research like that done at George Washington until a new ethical review board had drawn up guidelines to determine ethically acceptable research. That panel's work was expected to be completed in mid-1994.

Ethics. Scientists themselves came in for some close ethical scrutiny during the past year. After a four-year investigation, the government dropped charges of scientific misconduct against Robert Gallo, a U.S. scientist who developed a blood test for the AIDS virus. Since 1984, when Gallo's lab first confirmed that a virus now called HIV (human immunodeficiency virus) was the cause of AIDS, Gallo had been embroiled in a controversy with French scientists over credit for the blood test. The French maintained that Gallo misused a sample of the AIDS virus that French scientists had sent him in 1983. Gallo responded that his work was based on his own samples of the virus. An investigation by the Office of Research Integrity (ORI), a part of the Department of Health and Human Services, rejected the French charges but reached a preliminary conclusion that Gallo was guilty of misconduct for a statement he made about his research in a 1984 scientific paper describing his work. Gallo appealed the finding, and the government dropped the case after an appeals panel dismissed similar charges against a Gallo associate, Mikulas Popovic.

The Gallo case was just one of several that the ORI either dropped or lost on appeal, raising questions about its effectiveness in proving true cases of misconduct. For years the scientific establishment has maintained that science is "99.999 percent pure" in the words of one journal editor, but a more careful examination suggests that this is not the case. In a poll of scientists taken by the Acadia Institute, Bar Harbor, Maine, some 9% claimed they had "direct knowledge" of a scientist who plagiarized, and 6% said that they had similar knowledge of a scientist who falsified data. An astonishing 50% of those interviewed said that they had direct knowledge of at least two instances of questionable practices on the part of their colleagues.

In addition to the collapse of cases against Gallo and Popovic, the Office of Research Integrity also lost cases that it had brought against researchers at Georgetown University, Washington, D.C., and the Cleveland (Ohio) Clinic Foundation. Following this embarrassing series of defeats, the government began yet another overhaul of its investigation procedures. By the year's end, it was not clear how the government would pursue misconduct cases in the future. What was clear was that universities were taking a far more aggressive stance in investigating such cases, and it appeared possible that the universities' action might forestall increasingly intrusive federal regulations.

The federal government also spent the year trying to balance two sometimes conflicting goals for science. On the one hand, since the mid-1980s the government has been trying to encourage scientists supported by the federal government to work to transfer promising new technology to industry, where it can be turned into goods and services, and thereby, in the words of President Clinton, "grow the economy." This applies both to researchers working directly for the government at a national laboratory and those being supported by the government by contracts or grants. At the same time, the government has been trying to eliminate issues of conflict of interest on the part of individual researchers, believing that scientists should not have a direct financial interest in the outcome of their research. Not only is there a legitimate concern that such an interest could affect the outcome of an experiment, but it also seemed unfair that an individual could reap a financial windfall from work done at the taxpayer's expense.

The first time the federal government tried to establish regulations regarding how much financial contact an individual scientist could have with a company, they were withdrawn following howls of indignation from the scientific community that the rules would eliminate any contact with industry. The government was still trying to pull together a policy as 1993 ended.

Nevertheless, a variation on this dilemma did reach a resolution during the year. Congress became interested in a deal made between the Scripps Research Institute and Sandoz Pharmaceuticals Corp. Scripps gave Sandoz an exclusive worldwide license to all Scripps research in exchange for $300 million in research support from the drug company. However, that agreement essentially gave Sandoz exclusive access to some $1 billion in federally funded research. Rep. Ron Wyden (Dem., Ore.) cried foul, and the deal had to be renegotiated, giving Sandoz exclusive access only to the research it paid for directly.

—Joseph Palca

Scientists of the Year

Honors and awards

The following article discusses recent awards and prizes in science and technology. In the first section the Nobel Prizes for 1993 are described in detail. The second section is a selective list of other honors.

Nobel Prize for Chemistry

The 1993 Nobel Prize for Chemistry was awarded to Kary B. Mullis, formerly of the Cetus Corp., and Michael Smith of the University of British Columbia. According to the Nobel committee, "The chemical methods that they have each developed for studying the DNA molecules of genetic material have further hastened the rapid development of genetic engineering. The two methods have greatly stimulated basic biochemical research and opened the way for new applications in medicine and biotechnology."

Mullis received the prize for his technique, called the polymerase chain reaction (PCR), of quickly making trillions of copies of a single fragment of DNA, the genetic material of living organisms. Mullis conceived of PCR, the idea for which he said came to him during a night drive in the California mountains, while employed at the biotech firm Cetus Corp. The technique was first published in 1985.

Before the development of PCR, obtaining a usable quantity of a specific DNA fragment from a large DNA molecule was a laborious, time-consuming process. Using Mullis' technique, however, scientists can multiply a tiny DNA segment from complicated genetic material millions of times in a few hours, generating from a trace fragment a quantity large enough to study. As a result, molecules that would otherwise be inaccessible can be studied and manipulated.

The PCR technique has become one of the most widespread methods of analyzing DNA. The method offers new possibilities in genome sequencing, the determination of the sequence of the individual molecules that are linked together to form genes, and also in the study of evolution. In its citation the Nobel committee stated, "Since it is possible with PCR to perform analyses on extremely small amounts of material, it is easy to determine genetic and evolutionary connections between different species. It is very probable the PCR combined with DNA sequencing is going to represent a revolutionary new instrument for studies of the systematics of plant and animal species."

The PCR method has made possible the ambitious Human Genome Project, which is undertaking to unravel the DNA code in the human genetic material. Also, forensic analysts can use the technique to make copies of tiny amounts of DNA in the fingerprints, blood, or hair left at crime scenes.

Using the PCR method on fossil remains, researchers can now mass produce DNA from animals that became extinct millions of years ago. Scientists have already succeeded in producing genetic material from insects that have been extinct for more than 20 million years by using the PCR method on DNA extracted from amber. It is this process that supplied the premise for the popular movie *Jurassic Park*, in which scientists use dinosaur DNA from the blood in a fossilized mosquito to re-create full-size dinosaurs. PCR has also been used to sequence DNA from a museum specimen of the quagga, an extinct species of zebra.

PCR has been applied to medical diagnostics as well. Now that it is possible to discover very small amounts of foreign DNA in an organism, viral and bacterial infections can be diagnosed without the time-consuming culture of microorganisms taken from patient sample. PCR is being used, for example, to detect the human immunodeficiency virus (HIV), the virus that causes AIDS. The method can also be exploited to localize the genetic alterations underlying hereditary diseases.

When the PCR technique is used for making copies of a short sequence of DNA, the two strands of the DNA's double helix containing the sequence are first separated by heat. Short segments of DNA called primers bind to the strands at each end of the target sequence. These primers transmit chemical signals to an enzyme called DNA polymerase, directing it to copy the segment between the primers. The polymerase copies the DNA segment alongside each original strand. In a few minutes the original sample of DNA is doubled and, because the new DNA strands can themselves reduplicate, repeating the cycle of heating and cooling leads to exponential growth in the number of DNA copies. Repeating the procedure 20 to 60 times can produce millions of DNA copies in just a few hours. The procedure is simple, requiring in theory only a test tube and some heat sources, and there are also commercial PCR apparatuses that manage the entire procedure automatically.

Michael Smith received the Nobel Prize for his development of the procedure known as site-directed mutagenesis (the generating of mutations) and his application of the procedure to the study of proteins. With Smith's method it is possible to reprogram the genetic code of a DNA molecule and, consequently, to construct proteins with new properties.

DNA occurs in cell nuclei and serves to encode genetic data. The giant molecules of DNA consist of two long strands, formed of smaller molecules called

431

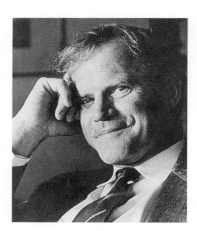

nucleotides, that are twisted around each other to form a double helix. A single molecule may contain many thousands of nucleotides, but there are only four different nucleotides: adenine (A), guanine (G), cytosine (C), and thymine (T). These nucleotides bond together in specific ways, and it is in the sequence of these bonds that genetic information is coded. This sequence provides the instructions for the synthesis of proteins in cells by determining the sequence of the amino acids composing proteins. Each amino acid is represented by a series of three nucleotides—CAG, ACT, or GCC, for example—which, considered as units, are called codons. There are 64 different possible codons, more than enough to form the approximately 20 amino acids that make up proteins.

When the genetic code is to be read off—for example, when proteins are being built in a cell—the two long strands of nucleotides are separated, and each codon is translated into one of the 20 amino acids that build up proteins. It is proteins that are responsible for the functions of living cells, including their ability to function as enzymes that maintain all the chemical reactions required for supporting life. The proteins' three-dimensional structure and, therefore, their function are determined by the order in which the various amino acids are linked together during protein synthesis.

The flow of genetic information proceeds from DNA via the translator molecule RNA into proteins. By reprogramming a codon of a DNA molecule—for example, by changing CAC to GAC—it is possible to obtain a protein in which one amino acid is replaced by another. In nature such misprogramming of the genetic material, called mutation, occurs randomly and is nearly always detrimental, or at best of no benefit, to the organism. In the laboratory biochemical researchers have long wanted to be able to alter a given codon in a DNA molecule so as to be able to study how the properties of the mutated protein differ from the natural one. Before Smith's development

of site-directed mutagenesis, researchers resorted to inducing random mutations in DNA by exposing cells to chemical mutagens or radiation. They then sorted through the mutated proteins to find those that could be of use in their research. Smith's process made it possible to produce specific mutations and thereby generate customized proteins.

Smith conceived of site-directed mutagenesis while working as a visiting researcher at the University of Cambridge in the early 1970s. His process uses short, single-stranded DNA fragments called oligonucleotides, which are synthesized chemically and then bound to a single-stranded virus DNA. Smith discovered that even if one of the nucleotides of the synthetic DNA fragment has been changed, the fragment is still able to bind at the correct site on the virus DNA. The virus DNA can then be inserted into a bacterium, which acts as a host organism in which the mutated DNA molecule is replicated. The mutated DNA then directs the synthesis of protein in the bacterium and so produces a modified protein.

In 1978 Smith and his co-workers succeeded in inducing a mutation in a bacteriophagic (bacteria-infecting) virus and then "curing" the mutation so that the virus regained its natural properties. Four years later Smith and his colleagues were able for the first time to produce and isolate large quantities of a mutated enzyme in which a predetermined amino acid had been exchanged for another.

Smith's method has created an entirely new means of studying in detail how proteins function, what determines their three-dimensional structure, and how they interact with other molecules inside the cell. According to the Nobel committee, "Site-directed mutagenesis has without doubt revolutionized basic research and entirely changed researchers' ways of performing their experiments." By systematically changing the amino acids in a protein, researchers can determine what role each amino acid plays in directing the protein's biological activity or maintaining the protein's three-dimensional structure.

The method is also widely used in biotechnology, where scientists are constructing altered proteins to produce variations that are more stable, more active, or more useful to medicine or industry than their natural counterparts. It is already possible to improve the stability of an enzyme that is an active component in detergents so that it can better resist the chemicals and high temperatures of wash water. Scientists are also trying to produce a mutated hemoglobin that may provide a new means of replacing blood. By mutating proteins in the immune system, researchers are hoping to construct antibodies that attack cancer cells. Researchers also hope that site-directed mutagenesis will have applications in gene therapy and make it possible to cure hereditary diseases by specifically correcting mutated codons in the genetic materials. Site-directed mutagenesis of plant proteins may make it possible to produce crops that grow faster by making more efficient use of atmospheric carbon dioxide during photosynthesis.

Kary Mullis was born in Lenoir, N.C., on Dec. 28, 1944. He received his Ph.D. in 1972 from the University of California at Berkeley. From 1973 through 1977 he held research posts at various universities in the U.S. He became a researcher at Cetus in Emeryville, Calif., in 1979. In 1988 he became director of Xytronyx Inc. in San Diego, Calif., and he later became a consultant based in La Jolla, Calif.

Michael Smith, now a Canadian citizen, was born in Blackpool, England, on April 26, 1932. He received a B.Sc. with honors from the University of Manchester in 1953 and, with the aid of a three-year state scholarship, he earned a Ph.D. from Manchester in 1956. From 1956 to 1960 he completed his postdoctoral fellowship at the British Columbia Research Council. For the next year he worked as a research associate at the University of Wisconsin. He then returned to Canada to head the chemistry division of the Vancouver (B.C.) Laboratory of the Fisheries Research Board of Canada.

He joined the faculty of the University of British Columbia in 1966 as an associate professor and became a full professor of biochemistry in 1970. In 1971 he worked for a year as a visiting researcher at MRC Laboratories in Cambridge, England, where he first conceived of the idea of site-directed mutagenesis. In 1987 he became director of the biotechnology laboratory at the University of British Columbia, where he also was a professor in the department of biochemistry and molecular biology.

The Protein Engineering Network of Centres of Excellence (PENCE) is headquartered at the university under the scientific leadership of Smith. PENCE is a collaborative research effort linking the Universities of British Columbia, Alberta, and Toronto with the National Research Council at Ottawa and Montreal; a forest-products industry-sponsored research laboratory, the Pulp and Paper Research Institute of Canada, Montreal; and research groups at Allelix Biopharmaceuticals, Connaught Laboratories, Syntex Canada, Synthetic Peptides, and Hypercube, a software-development company. As of 1994 five protein-engineering research projects involving more than 100 researchers and trainees were under way at PENCE.

Smith received numerous academic awards and distinctions. He was appointed a fellow of the Royal Society of Canada (1981) and a fellow of the Royal Society of London (1986). He received the gold medal of the Science Council of British Columbia (1984), the Gairdner Foundation International Award (1986), the Killam Research Prize, UBC (1986), the Award of Excellence of the Genetics Society of Canada (1988), the G. Malcolm Brown Award (1989), and the Flavelle Medal of the Royal Society of Canada (1992).

Nobel Prize for Physics

Two astrophysicists from Princeton University were awarded the 1993 Nobel Prize for Physics for their discovery of a new type of pulsar that "has opened up new possibilities for the study of gravitation," according to the Nobel committee. The prize went to Joseph H. Taylor, Jr., who conducted his prizewinning research while a professor at the University of Massachusetts at Amherst, and his graduate student at the time, Russell A. Hulse. In 1994 Taylor was a professor of physics at Princeton University, and Hulse conducted research at the Princeton Plasma Physics Laboratory.

Taylor and Hulse made their discovery in 1974 by using the 300-m-diameter radio telescope at Arecibo, P.R. The two researchers were conducting an extensive, systematic search for pulsars. Pulsars, short for pulsating radio stars, are a class of stars that emit extremely regular pulses of radio waves. A few are also known to give off short rhythmic bursts of visible light, X-rays, and gamma rays. Pulsars are thought to be rapidly spinning neutron stars, extremely dense stars composed almost entirely of neutrons and having a diameter of only 20 km (12 mi) or less. A neutron star is formed when the core of a violently exploding star called a supernova collapses inward and becomes compressed. Neutrons at the surface of the star decay into protons and electrons. As these charged particles are released from the surface, they enter an intense magnetic field that surrounds the star and rotates along with it. Accelerated to speeds approaching that of light, the particles give off electromagnetic radiation that is released as intense beams from the pulsar's magnetic poles.

These magnetic poles do not coincide with the rotational poles, and so the rotation of the pulsar

433

swings the radiation beams around. As the beams sweep regularly past the Earth with each complete rotation of the pulsar, an evenly spaced series of pulses is detected by ground-based telescopes. It is for these pulses of radiation that pulsars are named.

The first pulsar was discovered in 1967 by British astronomer Jocelyn Bell, who used a radio telescope at Cambridge that was specially designed to record very rapid fluctuations in radio sources. Anthony Hewish, Bell's doctoral thesis adviser and supervisor at Cambridge, won the Nobel Prize for her discovery in 1974.

That same year Taylor and Hulse, who had already discovered dozens of ordinary pulsars, found one with pulses that were not exactly regular. Thinking that the irregularity was due to some problem with their equipment, the scientists were at first disappointed. However, further observations revealed that the interval between pulses varied according to a definite pattern, decreasing and increasing over an eight-hour period. Taylor and Hulse concluded that the pulsar must be orbiting a companion body, causing its pulses to quicken during the part of the orbit in which the pulsar approached the Earth and slowing during the part of the orbit in which it receded from the Earth. From the behavior of the pulsar's signal, the scientists were also able to deduce that the companion was another neutron star, approximately as heavy as the pulsar and located at a distance corresponding to only a few times the distance between the Moon and the Earth. Both bodies have a radius of some 10 km (6 mi) and a mass comparable to that of the Sun.

The discovery by Hulse and Taylor of the first binary pulsar, called PSR 1913 + 16 (PSR stands for pulsar, and 1913 + 16 specifies the pulsar's position in the sky), "brought about a revolution in the field," according to the Nobel committee, because it provided a "space laboratory" in which researchers could test Einstein's general theory of relativity and alternative theories of gravity. This is possible in part because the pulse period of the binary pulsar, the time between two successive pulses (0.05903 second), proved to be extremely stable. In fact, the pulse period increases by less than 5% in one million years. Consequently, the pulsar can serve as a clock whose precision compares with the best atomic clocks—a feature that has proved very useful for studying the characteristics of the system.

Within a couple of weeks after their discovery of the pulsar, Taylor and Hulse came to believe that relativistic effects would be observable in the system. These effects include the increasing speed of two objects as they rotate around each other in orbits that have become tighter because the binary system is emitting energy in the form of gravitational waves. The scientists realized that the two stars' large,

Joseph H. Taylor, Jr.
Princeton University; photo, Robert Matthews

shifting gravitational fields could magnify relativistic effects to such an extent that the effects would be measurable and, because the stars are extremely dense, there would be no exchanges of gas or tidal shifting to interfere with those effects. In their 1975 article discussing their discovery, published in *Astrophysical Journal Letters,* Taylor and Hulse pointed out the potential for the pulsar to serve as "a nearly ideal relativity laboratory including an accurate clock in a high-speed, eccentric orbit and a strong gravitational field."

Einstein's general theory of relativity, presented in 1916, addresses the problem of gravity and that of nonuniform, or accelerated, motion. One example of accelerated motion is the motion of two bodies in orbit around each other, as is the case with the Taylor-Hulse binary pulsar. As a consequence of his general theory, Einstein proposed a geometric interpretation of gravitation that differed radically from the interpretation proposed by Isaac Newton in 1687. Newton held that every particle of matter in the universe attracts every other particle, and it is this force of attraction that is called gravitation. Newton's model was accepted as correct until the beginning of the 20th century, when the notion of instantaneous action at a distance, which it entailed, was recognized generally as unintelligible, particularly from Einstein's viewpoint of relativity.

In his general theory of relativity, Einstein developed a wholly new conception of gravitation. He proposed that the four-dimensional space-time continuum is curved by the presence of matter, producing a universe in which bodies travel in geodesics (shortest paths) that are the curved orbits interpreted by Newton as the result of some attractive force. Thus, in Einstein's interpretation, bodies follow curved paths because of the local curvature in space-time caused by the presence of mass, not because of the attractive force described by Newton. Einstein was able to construct a single equation describing the curvature of space at and the energy or mass of any point in space-time. With suitable simplifying assumptions, this equation reduces to Newton's law of gravitation, which can then be considered a special case of Einstein's theory for relatively slow speeds and weak gravitational fields.

The relativistic view of gravitation yielded predictions of several phenomena that violate Newtonian theory and that, to the limits of observational accuracy, have been confirmed. These include the reddening of light emitted by a very massive object and the slowing of a clock raised above the Earth relative to one remaining on the surface of the Earth. One of the theory's predictions, that a ray of light will be bent when it passes near a very massive object such as the Sun, was confirmed by the British astrophysicist Arthur Eddington during a solar eclipse in 1919. The theory also succeeded in accounting for an anomaly in the motion of the planet Mercury that had defied explanation by Newtonian theory.

In the 1960s the research of two U.S. scientists provided further support for Einstein's theory. Robert Dicke performed precise experiments in which the Sun's gravitational field on the Earth was used for verifying what is termed the equivalence principle, the identity between gravitational and inertial mass—one of the basic principles of the general theory of relativity and also of several alternative gravitation theories. (Inertial mass is mass determined in accordance with the law that the masses of bodies are inversely proportional to the velocities that a given force will impart to them in a given time.) I. Shapiro predicted and, by using radar echoes from Mercury, experimentally verified a new consequence of the general theory of relativity—a time-delay effect for electromagnetic signals passing through gravitational fields.

All these experiments, however, were confined to the solar system, where gravitational fields are very weak and consequently deviate little from Newtonian theory. Other predictions of Einstein's general theory that awaited confirmation in an arena outside the solar system included the existence of gravitational waves propagated by objects moving in a

gravitational field and of black holes formed by the collapse of massive stars into extremely small, dense objects whose gravitational fields are so intense that not even light can escape.

Thus, the discovery by Taylor and Hulse of a distant binary pulsar that could display measurable relativistic effects—including the existence of gravitational waves—sparked great excitement in the scientific world. Successive observations made by the two astrophysicists indicated that the pulsar's orbit was decaying slightly—that is, the system was losing energy, and the two stars were rotating faster and faster around each other in an increasingly tight orbit. The change, about 75 millionths of a second per year, is presumed to occur because the system is emitting energy in the form of gravitational waves, as predicted in Einstein's general theory. In fact, the rate at which the stars were spiraling together agreed with Einstein's prediction to an accuracy of better than 0.5%. This observation, reported in 1978, afforded the first experimental evidence for the existence of gravitational waves. The Taylor-Hulse binary pulsar also provided the test that distinguishes, better than any other, Einstein's theory as the correct variant among the host of theories that sought to improve on Newtonian mechanics.

Taylor and Hulse also detected several other effects predicted by general relativity, although the decay of the system's orbit was the most decisive confirmation of the theory. The scientists found that radio waves from the pulsar are bent when the pulsar passes behind its companion star and that there is a precession in the system's axis of rotation—both relativistic effects. (A precession is a comparatively slow rotation of the axis of a spinning body [or system] about a line intersecting the spin axis.)

The laureates' confirmation of the existence of gravitational waves fueled proposals for gravity-wave detectors—such as the proposed Laser Interferometer Gravitational Wave Observatory (LIGO) in the U.S. and the Franco-Italian detector Virgo—that would detect gravitational waves produced from astrophysical events. The gravitational waves emitted by the Taylor-Hulse binary pulsar are too weak to be measured on the Earth with existing techniques. However, the violent perturbations of matter that take place when two large astronomical bodies approach each other so closely that they fall into each other may give rise to gravitational waves that could be observed here.

Russell Hulse was born on Nov. 28, 1950, in New York City. He received his B.S. from the Cooper Union for the Advancement of Science and Art, New York City, in 1970 and his M.S. (1972) and Ph.D. (1975) degrees in physics from the University of Massachusetts. After working as a postdoctoral fellow at the National Radio Astronomy Observatory

Russell A. Hulse
Russell A. Hulse

in Charlottesville, Va., he changed fields from astrophysics to plasma physics and assumed a position at the Princeton Plasma Physics Laboratory in 1977. In the 1990s he worked on experiments associated with the Tokamak Fusion Test Reactor, an experimental facility devoted to the development of usable electrical power from controlled thermonuclear fusion.

Joseph Taylor, Jr., was born on March 14, 1941, in Philadelphia. He received his B.A. in physics from Haverford (Pa.) College in 1963 and his Ph.D. in astronomy from Harvard University in 1968. He joined the University of Massachusetts faculty as an assistant professor in 1969 and was promoted to associate professor in 1973 and to full professor in 1977. In 1980 he became a professor of physics at Princeton.

Since the mid-1970s Taylor has spent much of his time making the painstaking measurements that have provided experimental confirmation of general relativity theory by using the Taylor-Hulse binary pulsar and two others that his group subsequently discovered. In late 1985 Taylor and his group discovered a binary pulsar, cataloged as PSR 1855 + 09. Using the radio telescope near Arecibo, the scientists clocked the object's rotation at 186 times per second, making it the second most rapidly spinning pulsar known. Because of the speed and stability of its rotation, the pulsar and others like it could provide a better time standard than even the most accurate atomic clocks. Of the approximately 400 pulsars observed to date, only seven are known to be binary.

Taylor is a member of several professional organizations, including the National Academy of Sciences, the American Physical Society, the American Astronomical Society, and the International Union of Radio Science. He received the Dannie Heineman Prize of the American Astronomical Society and American Institute of Physics in 1980, a MacArthur fellowship in 1981, and the Wolf Prize in Physics in 1992.

Nobel Prize for Physiology or Medicine

The 1993 Nobel Prize for Physiology or Medicine was awarded to two molecular biologists—Richard Roberts, who performed his prizewinning research at the Cold Spring Harbor Laboratory on Long Island, N.Y., and Phillip Sharp of the Massachusetts Institute of Technology (MIT)—for their independent discovery that genes are often split, or discontinuous. Genes contain the coding for synthesizing proteins in cells.

Before the laureates' discovery, DNA research had focused primarily on bacterial cells, in which genes form continuous segments within long, double-stranded DNA molecules. By studying viral cells the laureates discovered that this model was not generally correct. In 1977 Roberts and Sharp demonstrated that individual genes are often interrupted by long sections of DNA, since dubbed introns, or more popularly called nonsense DNA, that do not encode protein structure—that is, genes can be present in DNA in the form of well-separated segments.

According to the Nobel citation, "Roberts' and Sharp's discovery has changed our view on how genes in higher organisms develop during evolution. The discovery also led to the prediction of a new genetic process, namely that of splicing, which is essential for expressing the genetic information. The discovery of split genes has been of fundamental importance for today's basic research in biology, as well as for more medically oriented research concerning the development of cancer and other diseases."

Bacterial studies conducted before 1977 showed that when a gene is activated, its double-stranded DNA is copied into a single-stranded RNA molecule, called messenger RNA. The messenger RNA is then immediately translated into the protein for which the original gene was coded. However, bacterial cells are not typical of all cells. They are very simple in structure, having no nucleus and, as it turned out, generally having no introns in their DNA.

On the other hand, viral cells, although they likewise have no nucleus, can infect other cells—including the nucleated cells of higher organisms—and use the mechanisms of the host cells to produce new viruses. Thus, both Roberts and Sharp reasoned that by studying the process of protein synthesis in viral cells, they could learn about protein synthesis in the nucleated cells that the viruses infected. Both laureates studied the genetic material in a common cold-causing virus, called adenovirus, the genes of which have many properties resembling those of its higher host cells. At the same time, the genetic material, or genome, of adenovirus has a simple structure—it consists of a single long DNA molecule. The scientists' aim was to determine where in the genome different genes were located.

In their experiments Roberts and Sharp found that one end of the adenovirus messenger RNA did not behave as expected. One possible explanation was that the gene segment corresponding to this end was not located in the expected position on the DNA molecule. When the researchers used electron microscopy to determine where this segment was, they found that a single adenovirus messenger RNA molecule corresponded to not one but four well-separated segments on the DNA molecule.

Roberts and his colleagues at Cold Spring Harbor and Sharp and his MIT team presented their findings at a meeting at the Cold Spring Harbor Laboratory in June 1977. The announcement sparked intensive research by other scientists in the following months to discover whether this discontinuous gene structure is found in other viruses and in ordinary cells.

Richard Roberts
© David Comb

Soon several researchers had shown that split genes are common—in fact, they are now known to be the most common type of gene structure in higher organisms, including humans.

The laureates' discovery changed the model for understanding how proteins are synthesized from genes. Because in the nucleated cells of higher organisms and in the viruses that infect them the genes are usually split, the messenger RNA that directs protein synthesis cannot be copied directly from the discontinuous gene. Scientists now understand that the messenger RNA is first assembled as a large precursor molecule with the nonsense segments from the DNA included. These surplus segments must then be selectively removed and, in a process called splicing, the remaining meaningful segments, called exons, must be recombined in the correct order before the messenger RNA can be translated into a protein. After their initial discovery, the laureates were able to duplicate this snipping-and-splicing process in the laboratory without relying on living cells.

Subsequent research revealed that it is not always the same gene segments that are identified as exons and included in the final messenger RNA molecule. In different tissues or developmental stages, different exon combinations may be used to produce the final RNA molecule. Thus, the same DNA region can determine the structure of many different proteins. The process is called alternative splicing and represents a fundamentally new principle; the genetic message, which gives rise to a particular product, is not definitely established at the stage when the RNA is first synthesized. Instead, it is the splicing pattern that determines the nature of the final product.

The discovery of gene splicing radically changed scientists' view of how the genetic material developed during the course of evolution. It had long been considered likely that evolution takes place as the result of the accumulation of mutations—minor alterations in the genetic material—that cause a gradual change in the overall organism. But the fact that genes are often split suggests that higher organisms, in addition to undergoing mutations, may also use another mechanism to speed up evolution: the rearrangement of gene segments into new functional units. This hypothesis gained increased favor after further research found several individual gene segments that correspond to building modules in proteins, so-called domains, to which specific functions can be attributed. A gene segment would thus correspond to a particular subfunction in the protein, and the rearrangement of segments could result in a new combination of subfunctions. This kind of process could drive evolution by rearranging modules with specific functions.

The laureates' studies and those of other researchers also suggested that, in contrast to the dominant view in evolutionary theory, higher organisms may not have evolved from present-day bacteria. Instead, both bacteria and higher organisms may have evolved from some now-extinct organism. Studies of how genes change during evolution indicate that some nonsense segments have persisted for a billion years even though they do not carry hereditary information.

Some scientists believe that by separating and recombining the hereditary message, DNA with nonsense segments may safeguard genetic coding better than can unbroken genes, which could be damaged more easily. In fact, in the cells of mammals there is sometimes more nonsense material than working gene units. Sharp and others argued that the efficiency of bacterial genes—those without the nonsense material—may have come at the expense of making adaptation more difficult. In this view, "inefficient" mammalian genes, with all their nonsense subunits, are probably more flexible in an evolutionary sense.

Recent research also suggested that introns are something more than simply surplus DNA. They appear to serve some sort of regulatory function since engineered genes from which the introns have been removed often fail to produce protein.

Phillip Sharp
© The Nobel Foundation

The process of protein production from gene snipping and splicing is an astonishingly precise process with many opportunities for error. Splicing mistakes have been shown to result in a number of disorders, including the blood disorder beta-thalassemia and chronic myelogenous leukemia. Beta-thalassemia, a form of anemia, is characterized by a deficiency of hemoglobin, the blood molecule that transports oxygen to the tissues. The disease is due to abnormal functioning of a protein called betaglobin, which forms part of the hemoglobin. Scientists have found small defects in the genetic material of several beta-thalassemia patients. These genetic defects result in errors in the splicing process and consequently in the synthesis of poorly functioning betaglobin.

Chronic myelogenous leukemia, a type of cancer of the blood, is characterized by the presence in the tumor cells of a special, shortened chromosome called the Philadelphia chromosome, named after the city in which it was discovered. A chromosome is an array of many linked genes. In the Philadelphia chromosome, two chromosomes have fused in such a way that a cancer gene is joined to a normal gene. The two genes are then copied into a single messenger RNA molecule. During the splicing process, exons from the two genes are linked to form an RNA molecule that specifies the synthesis of a new protein, a so-called fusion protein. The action of this protein gives rise to leukemia.

Richard Roberts was born on Sept. 6, 1943, in Derby, England. He obtained a B.Sc. in chemistry (1965) and a Ph.D. in organic chemistry (1968) from the University of Sheffield, England. He completed three years of postdoctoral research at Harvard University, where he studied the transfer RNAs that are involved in the synthesis of bacterial cell walls.

In 1972, at the invitation of 1962 Nobel laureate James Watson, Roberts became a senior staff investigator at the Cold Spring Harbor Laboratory. In 1986 he became the lab's assistant director for research. He began work on a newly discovered class of restriction enzymes, proteins that cleave DNA molecules at specific regions, and under his direction more than 100 such enzymes were discovered and characterized. His laboratory also pioneered the use of computers for determining DNA sequencing and analysis.

Roberts remained at Cold Spring Harbor until 1992. He then became director of eukaryotic research at New England Biolabs, Beverly, Mass.

Roberts is a member of the American Society of Biological Chemistry, the American Chemical Society, the American Society for Microbiology, and the American Association for the Advancement of Science. He served on the editorial boards of *Nucleic Acids Research* (1977–87) and the *Journal of Biological Chemistry* (1979–84).

Phillip Sharp was born on June 6, 1944, in Falmouth, Ky., on a small farm on which his parents raised tobacco and corn. He first developed an interest in science while in high school. His parents encouraged him to save for college, and to help him they gave him a piece of tobacco land. Sharp used the earnings from that land to pay for part of his education at Union College, Barbourville, Ky. He holds a B.A. (1966) in chemistry and mathematics from Union College and a Ph.D. (1969) in chemistry from the University of Illinois at Urbana-Champaign. He worked for two years as a postdoctoral fellow at the California Institute of Technology, and from 1971 to 1972 he worked at the Cold Spring Harbor Laboratory with James Watson. From 1972 to 1974 he was a senior research investigator there.

Sharp joined the faculty of MIT in 1974 as an associate professor of biology and a research scientist in the MIT Center for Cancer Research. He was promoted to professor in 1979. He became associate director of the Center for Cancer Research in 1982 and served as director from 1985 to 1991, when he was appointed to head MIT's Department of Biology. Although in 1990 Sharp accepted the position of president of MIT, he withdrew his acceptance to continue his work in science. His research focused on the molecular biology of tumor viruses and the mechanisms of RNA splicing. In 1992 Sharp became the first Salvador E. Luria professor, a chair established by MIT in honor of Luria, who won the Nobel Prize in 1969 for research on viruses that infect bacteria. From 1987 to 1992 Sharp also held the John D. MacArthur professorship at MIT.

Sharp's numerous scientific awards include the 1990 Dickson Prize of the University of Pittsburgh, Pa., the 1988 Albert Lasker Basic Medical Research Award, the 1988 Louisa Gross Horwitz Prize of Columbia University, New York City, the 1986 Alfred P. Sloan Prize of the General Motors Cancer Research Foundation, the 1986 New York Academy of Sciences Award in Biological and Medical Sciences, the 1986 Gairdner Foundation International Award, the 1985 Howard Ricketts Award of the University of Chicago, the 1980 Eli Lilly Award in Biological Chemistry, and the 1980 National Academy of Sciences—U.S. Steel Foundation Award in Molecular Biology.

The author of more than 240 articles in scientific journals and books, Sharp served on the editorial board of the scientific journal *Cell* and formerly was on the editorial boards of the *Journal of Virology, Virology,* and *Molecular & Cellular Biology.* He was also a cofounder and member of the board of directors of Biogen, Inc., of Cambridge, Mass., which uses genetic engineering techniques to produce human interferon.

—Carolyn Hemenway

AWARD	WINNER	AFFILIATION
ARCHITECTURE AND CIVIL ENGINEERING		
Izaak Walton Killam Memorial Prize	Alan G. Davenport	University of Western Ontario, London
Outstanding Civil Engineering Achievement Award	Colorado Department of Engineering	Denver, Colo.
Pritzker Architecture Prize	Fumihiko Maki	Tokyo
ASTRONOMY		
Annenberg Foundation Award	Dorrit Hoffleit	Yale University, New Haven, Conn.
Annenberg Foundation Award	Carl Sagan	Cornell University, Ithaca, N.Y.
Arctowski Medal	John A. Simpson	University of Chicago
Beatrice M. Tinsley Prize	Robert H. Dicke	Princeton University, Princeton, N.J.
C.W. Bruce Award	Martin Rees	University of Cambridge, England
Dirk Brouwer Award	Stanton Peale	University of California, Santa Barbara
Gold Medal of the British Royal Astronomical Society	Eugene Parker	University of Chicago
Helen B. Warner Prize	Edmund Bertschinger	Massachusetts Institute of Technology, Cambridge
Helen B. Warner Prize	John F. Hawley	University of Virginia, Charlottesville
Henry Draper Medal	Ralph A. Alpher	Union College, Schenectady, N.Y.
	Robert Herman	University of Texas, Austin
Henry Norris Russell Lecture	Lawrence H. Aller	University of California, Los Angeles
Henry Norris Russell Lecture	P. James E. Peebles	Princeton University, Princeton, N.J.
James B. Macelwane Medal	David J. McComas	Los Alamos National Laboratory, Los Alamos, N.M.
John Adam Fleming Medal	Alexander J. Dessler	Rice University, Houston, Texas, and Marshall Space Flight Center, Huntsville, Ala.
Klumpke-Roberts Award	David Morrison	Ames Research Center, Sunnyvale, Calif.
NASA Medal for Exceptional Scientific Achievement	Carl Sagan	Cornell University, Ithaca, N.Y.
National Medal of Science	Vera C. Rubin	Carnegie Institution of Washington, D.C.
Newton Lacy Pierce Prize	Arlin P.S. Crotts	Columbia University, New York City
Newton Lacy Pierce Prize	Alexei V. Fillipenko	University of California, Berkeley
Public Understanding of Science Award	Carl Sagan	Cornell University, Ithaca, N.Y.
CHEMISTRY		
Alan E. Pierce Award	Victor J. Hruby	University of Arizona, Tucson
Applied Polymer Science Award	James E. Mark	University of Cincinnati, Ohio
Bower Award and Prize in Science	Isabella L. Karle	Naval Research Laboratory, Washington, D.C.
Buck-Whitney Award	Peter B. Armentrout	University of Utah, Salt Lake City
Chemical Sciences Award	Richard H. Holm	Harvard University, Cambridge, Mass.

AWARD	WINNER	AFFILIATION
Chemistry in Service to Society Award	Harold S. Johnston	University of California, Berkeley
Chromatography Award	William H. Pirkle	University of Illinois, Urbana-Champaign
Coblentz Award	Peter Felker	University of California, Los Angeles
Computers in Chemistry Award	Michael J.S. Dewar (Emeritus)	University of Florida, Gainesville
Creative Work in Fluorine Chemistry Award	Oskar Glemser (Emeritus)	University of Göttingen, Germany
David C. Grahame Award	Arthur T. Hubbard	University of Cincinnati, Ohio
Distinguished Service Award	Howard A. Smith	Condux Inc., Newark, Del.
Distinguished Service in Advancement of Polymer Science Award	Leo Mandelkern	Florida State University, Tallahassee
Earle B. Barnes Award	Jerry A. Cogan, Jr.	Milliken Research Corp.
Earle K. Plyler Prize	Ahmed H. Zewail	California Institute of Technology, Pasadena
Eric Bruell Distinguished Service Award	Fred W. Stone	Firmenich, Inc., Princeton, N.J.
Francis P. Garvan-John M. Olin Medal	Barbara J. Garrison	Pennsylvania State University, State College
Gold Medal of the American Institute of Chemists	Fred Basolo	Northwestern University, Evanston, Ill.
Harry & Carol Mosher Award	Carl R. Johnson	Wayne State University, Detroit, Mich.
Havinga Medal	William H. Okamura	University of California, Riverside
Herman F. Mark Award	Edwin J. Vandenberg	Arizona State University, Tempe
Herbert P. Broida Prize	Curt Wittig	University of Southern California, Los Angeles
Hewlett-Packard Award	Jonathan S. Lindsey	Carnegie Mellon University, Pittsburgh, Pa.
Inorganic Chemistry Award	Tobin J. Marks	Northwestern University, Evanston, Ill.
International Award	Donald R. Paul	University of Texas, Austin
Irving Langmuir Prize in Chemical Physics	Robert G. Parr	University of North Carolina, Chapel Hill
John Scott Award	Richard E. Smalley	Rice University, Houston, Texas
John W. Hyatt Award	Thomas R. Tice	Southern Research Institute, Birmingham, Ala.
Joseph O. Hirschfelder Prize	Rudolph A. Marcus	California Institute of Technology, Pasadena
Justin L. Powers Research Achievement Award	James T. Stewart	University of Georgia, Athens
Kaj Lingstrøm-Lang Prize	Harry B. Gray	California Institute of Technology, Pasadena
Linus Pauling Award	Richard Zare	Stanford University Stanford, Calif.
MacArthur Fellow	Stephen Lee	University of Michigan, Ann Arbor
Nobel Laureate Signature Award	Mark W. Grinstaff	California Institute of Technology, Pasadena
Nuclear Chemistry Award	E. Kenneth Hulet	Lawrence Livermore National Laboratory

AWARD	WINNER	AFFILIATION
Outstanding Achievement in Plastics Research Award	Ronald K. Eby	University of Akron, Ohio
Organometallic Chemistry Award	John A. Gladysz	University of Utah, Salt Lake City
Perkin Medal	Lubomyr T. Romankiw	IBM Corp.
Polymer Chemistry Award	Helmut Ringsdorf	University of Mainz, Germany
Priestley Medal	Howard E. Simmons, Jr. (Retired)	E.I. DuPont De Nemours & Co.
Pure Chemistry Award	Gerard F.R. Parkin	Columbia University, New York City
Ralph K. Iler Award	Michael L. Hair	Xerox Corp.
Research Award in Mass Spectrometry	Susan Graul	Carnegie Mellon University, Pittsburgh, Pa.
Richtmyer Memorial Lecture	Richard E. Smalley	Rice University, Houston, Texas
Robert A. Welch Award	Gilbert Stork (Emeritus)	Columbia University, New York City
Technical Award	John R. Dunn (Retired)	Polysar Rubber Corp.
Theoretical Chemistry Award	William H. Miller	University of California, Berkeley
William H. Nichols Medal	Richard E. Smalley	Rice University, Houston, Texas
Winthrop-Sears Medal	Emerson Kampen	Great Lakes Chemical Corp.
Wolf Prize	Ahmed H. Zewail	California Institute of Technology, Pasadena

EARTH SCIENCES

AWARD	WINNER	AFFILIATION
Arthur L. Day Prize	Hiroo Kanamori	California Institute of Technology, Pasadena
Charles A. Whitten Medal	Kurt Lambeck	Australian National University, Canberra
E.O. Lawrence Award	James G. Anderson	Harvard University, Cambridge, Mass.
Francis J. Pettijohn Medal	Charles V. Campbell	Exxon Production Research Co., Florence, Mont.
Francis J. Pettijohn Medal	Gerard V. Middleton	McMaster University, Hamilton, Ont.
Francis P. Shepard Medal	Maria Bianca Cita	University of Milan, Italy
Francis P. Shepard Medal	William B.F. Ryan	Lamont Doherty Geological Observatory, Palisades, N.Y.
Gold Medal of the British Royal Astronomical Society	Dan McKenzie	University of Cambridge, England
Groundwater Science Award	Richard C. Berg	Illinois State Geological Survey
Henry Draper Medal	Ralph A. Alpher	Union College, Schenectady, N.Y.
	Robert Herman	University of Texas, Austin
Ian Campbell Medal	Peter T. Flawn	University of Texas, Austin
James B. Macelwane Medal	Michael Gurnis	University of Michigan, Ann Arbor
Japan Prize	Frank Press	National Academy of Sciences, Washington, D.C.
Lomonosov Medal	Joseph O. Fletcher (Retired)	National Oceanic and Atmospheric Administration
MacArthur Fellow	Maria L. Crawford	Bryn Mawr College, Bryn Mawr, Pa.
National Award of the Geological Society of London	Alister Burnett	Florida Atlantic University, Boca Raton
Public Service Award	Virgil E. Barnes	Bureau of Economic Geology, College Station, Texas
Public Service Award	Charles W. Spencer	U.S. Geological Survey
Raymond C. Moore Medal	Robert W. Frey	University of Georgia, Athens

AWARD	WINNER	AFFILIATION
Raymond C. Moore Medal	Reuben J. Ross	Colorado School of Mines, Boulder
Roger Revelle Medal	Syukuro Manabe	National Oceanic and Atmospheric Administration
Sidney Powers Memorial Award	Robert R. Berg	Texas A&M University, College Station
Vetlesen Prize	Walter H. Munk	Scripps Institution of Oceanography
V.M. Goldschmidt Award	Stanley Hart	Woods Hole Oceanographic Institution, Woods Hole, Mass.
William H. Twenhofel Medal	Robert H. Dott	University of Wisconsin, Madison
William H. Twenhofel Medal	Harold G. Reading	University of Oxford, England

ELECTRONICS AND INFORMATION SCIENCES

Charles Stark Draper Prize	John Backus (Retired)	IBM Corp.
Industrial Application of Science Award	Nick Holonyak, Jr.	University of Illinois, Urbana-Champaign
International Prize for New Materials	Gordon C. Osbourn	Sandia National Laboratories
Kyoto Prize	Jack St. Clair Kilby	Texas Instruments, Inc.
National Medal of Science	Alfred Y. Cho	AT&T Bell Laboratories

ENERGY

Frank M. Tiller Award	Chiang Shiao-Hung	University of Pittsburgh, Pa.
Henry H. Storch Award	Gary R. Dyrkacz	Argonne National Laboratory, Argonne, Ill.
MacArthur Fellow	Amory Lovins	Rocky Mountain Institute, Snowmass, Colo.
MacArthur Fellow	Robert Williams	Princeton University, Princeton, N.J.

ENVIRONMENT

Chemistry in Service to Society Award	Harold S. Johnston	University of California, Berkeley
Chuck Yeager Award	David Frederick	U.S. Fish and Wildlife Service
Corporate Award	Tampa Bay Electric Co.	Tampa Bay, Fla.
Distinguished Service Citation	Paul G. Risser	Miami University, Oxford, Ohio
Earth Day Award	Gaylord Nelson	Wilderness Society, Washington, D.C.
Earth Day Award	Robert Rauschenberg	New York City
Eminent Ecologist Award	Margaret Bryan Davis	University of Minnesota, Minneapolis
Environmental Science & Technology Award	Steven J. Eisenreich	University of Minnesota, Minneapolis
Excellence in Environmental Health Research Award	Arthur C. Upton (Retired)	New York University
Hugh Hammond Bennett Award	George W. Langdale	U.S. Department of Agriculture
John Wesley Powell Award	James Pankow	Oregon Graduate Institute of Science and Engineering, Portland
MacArthur Award	Peter M. Vitousek	Stanford University, Stanford, Calif.
Robertson Memorial Lecture	F. Sherwood Rowland	University of California, Irvine
Sol Feinstone Award	Charles and Nina Bradley	Leopold Memorial Reserve, Wisconsin
Sol Feinstone Award	Vivian Menaker	Haines, Alaska

AWARD	WINNER	AFFILIATION
Sol Feinstone Award	Peter J. Russo	Lyndhurst, N.J.
Sol Feinstone Award	Dale Shields	Sarasota, Fla.
Sol Feinstone Award	Richard S. Weinstein	Palm Beach, Fla.
Tyler Prize for Environmental Achievement	F. Herbert Bormann (Emeritus)	Yale University, New Haven, Conn.
	Gene E. Likens	Institute of Ecosystem Studies, Millbrook, N.Y.
Volvo Environment Prize	Norman Myers	University of Oxford, England
	Peter H. Raven	Washington University, St. Louis, Mo.

FOOD AND AGRICULTURE

Alexander von Humboldt Award	Charles M. Rick	University of California, Davis
Harvey W. Wiley Award	James Pestka	Michigan State University, East Lansing
International Service in Agronomy Award	Pedro Sanchez	International Centre for Research in Agroforestry, Nairobi, Kenya
International Soil Science Award	Pedro Sanchez	International Centre for Research in Agroforestry, Nairobi, Kenya
Kenneth A. Spencer Award	Clarence A. Ryan, Jr.	Washington State University, Pullman
Wolf Prize	John Casida	University of California, Berkeley

LIFE SCIENCES

Alan T. Waterman Award	Deborah L. Penry	University of California, Berkeley
Alfred Bader Award	Kenneth N. Raymond	University of California, Berkeley
American Cyanamid Award	Ian H. Mather	University of Maryland, College Park
Career Achievement Award	Edwin Carstensen	University of Rochester, N.Y.
Cecil H. Green Award	Stanley W. Watson	Woods Hole Oceanographic Institution, Woods Hole, Mass.
Crafoord Prize	Seymour Benzer	California Institute of Technology, Pasadena
	Richard Hamilton	University of Oxford, England
Creative Work in Synthetic Organic Chemistry	Stuart L. Schreiber	Harvard University, Cambridge, Mass.
David Perlman Memorial Lecture	Michael C. Flickinger	University of Minnesota, Minneapolis
Distinguished Service Award	John A. Moore (Emeritus)	University of California, Riverside
E.B. Wilson Award	Shinya Inoué	Marine Biological Laboratory, Woods Hole, Mass.
Ernest Guenther Award	Paul J. Scheuer (Emeritus)	University of Hawaii, Honolulu
Gregor J. Mendel Medal	Lawrence I. Gilbert	University of North Carolina, Chapel Hill
Helmut Horten Prize	Herbert W. Boyer	University of California San Francisco
	Stanley N. Cohen	Stanford University, Stanford, Calif.
Izaak Walton Killam Memorial Prize	Peter W. Hochachka	University of British Columbia, Vancouver
Izaak Walton Killam Memorial Prize	André Roch Lecours	University of Montreal
Japan's Order of the Sacred Treasure	William Schull	University of Texas, Houston

443

AWARD	WINNER	AFFILIATION
Life Sciences Award	H. Ronald Kaback	Howard Hughes Medical Institute, New York City, and University of California, Los Angeles
	Peter C. Nowell	University of Pennsylvania, Philadelphia
MacArthur Fellow	Victoria Foe	University of Washington, Seattle
MacArthur Fellow	Jane Lubchenco	Oregon State University, Corvallis
MacArthur Fellow	Margie Profet	University of California, Berkeley
MacArthur Fellow	Heather Williams	Williams College, Williamstown, Mass.
Marvin J. Johnson Award	T. Kent Kirk	University of Wisconsin, Madison
Max Planck Research Award	Manfred Fahle	University of Tübingen, Germany
	Tomaso A. Poggio	Massachusetts Institute of Technology, Cambridge
Paul Dawson Biotechnology Award	John P.N. Rosazza	University of Iowa, Iowa City
Richard and Minnie Windler Award	Warren F. Lamboy	Cornell University, Ithaca, N.Y.
Richard Evans Schultes Award	Calvin R. Sperling	U.S. Department of Agriculture
Russell and Burch Award	Charles E. Branch	Auburn University, Auburn, Ala.
Willard Gibbs Medal	Peter B. Dervan	California Institute of Technology, Pasadena

MATERIALS SCIENCES

AWARD	WINNER	AFFILIATION
E.O. Lawrence Award	Alan R. Bishop	Los Alamos National Laboratory, Los Alamos, N.M.
National Medal of Technology	William D. Manly (Retired)	Oak Ridge National Laboratories, Oak Ridge, Tenn.

MATHEMATICS

AWARD	WINNER	AFFILIATION
Cole Prize	Karl Rubin	Ohio State University, Columbus
Cole Prize	Paul Vojya	University of California, Berkeley
MacArthur Fellow	Demetrios Christodoulou	Princeton University, Princeton, N.J.
National Medal of Science	Martin D. Kruskal	Rutgers University, New Brunswick, N.J.
Steele Prize	Jacques Dixmier	Paris
	James G. Glimm	State University of New York, Stony Brook
	Peter D. Lax	New York University
Steele Prize	Eugene B. Dynkin	Cornell University, Ithaca, N.Y.
	George D. Mostow	Yale University, New Haven, Conn.
	Walter Rudin	University of Wisconsin, Madison
Wiener Prize	Michael Aizenman	Princeton University, Princeton, N.J.
	Jerrold Marsden	University of California, Berkeley
Wolf Prize	Mikhael Gromov	Institut des Hautes Etudes Scientifiques, Bure-sur-Yevette, France
	Jacques Tits	Collège de France, Paris

AWARD	WINNER	AFFILIATION

MEDICAL SCIENCES

AWARD	WINNER	AFFILIATION
Albert Lasker Basic Medical Research Award	Günter Blobel	Rockefeller University and Howard Hughes Medical Institute, New York City
Albert Lasker Clinical Medical Research Award	Donald Metcalf	Walter and Eliza Hall Institute of Medical Research, Melbourne, Australia
Albert Lasker Public Service Award	Paul G. Rogers	Former U.S. Representative
	Nancy S. Wexler	Columbia University, New York City
Benjamin Rush Award	James A. Kaufmann	Atlanta, Ga.
	Gerold L. Schiebler	Gainsville, Fla.
Charles A. Dana Award	Anders Bjorklund	University of Lund, Sweden
	Fred H. Gage	University of California, San Diego
Distinguished Service Award of the American Medical Association	Henry P. Pendergrass	Nashville, Tenn.
Excellence in Science Award	Susan E. Leeman	Boston University
Harvey W. Wiley Award	P. Frank Ross	U.S. Department of Agriculture
Health Education Award	Jerome P. Kassirer	Boston
Industrial Chemistry Award	Marion D. Francis	Procter & Gamble Co.
Japan Prize	Arvid Carlsson (Emeritus)	Göteborg University, Göteborg, Sweden
John Scott Award	Carlo M. Croce	Thomas Jefferson University, Philadelphia
Joseph B. Goldberger Award	Laurence Finberg	Brooklyn, N.Y.
King Faisal International Prize for Medicine	Françoise Barré-Sinoussi	National Institute of Health and Medical Research, Marseilles, France
	Jean-Claude Chermann	National Institute of Health and Medical Research, Marseilles, France
	Luc Montagnier	Pasteur Institute, Paris
MacArthur Fellow	Paul E. Farmer	Harvard University, Cambridge, Mass.
MacArthur Fellow	Ellen Silbergeld	University of Maryland, College Park
National Medal of Science	Howard M. Temin	University of Wisconsin, Madison
Scientific Achievement Award	William H. Beierwaltes	Grosse Pointe Park, Mich.
Service to the Public Citation	Massachusetts Medical Society and Massachusetts Medical Society Alliance	Boston
Silvio O. Conte Award	Carla J. Shatz	University of Calfironia, Berkeley
William Beaumont Award	John R. Delfs	Boston

OPTICAL ENGINEERING

AWARD	WINNER	AFFILIATION
Robert M. Burley Prize	Erwin G. Loewen (Retired)	Milton Roy Co.

PHYSICS

AWARD	WINNER	AFFILIATION
Achievement in Asia Award	Ou-Yang Zhongcan	Chinese Academy of Sciences
Albert A. Michelson Medal	Serge Haroche	Ecole Normale Supérieure, Paris
	Herbert Walther	Max Planck Institute
Aneesur Rahman Prize	Kenneth G. Wilson	Ohio State University, Columbus
Compton Award	Victor Weisskopf (Emeritus)	Massachusetts Institute of Technology, Cambridge

Scientists of the Year

AWARD	WINNER	AFFILIATION
Comstock Prize	Erwin L. Hahn (Emeritus)	University of California, Berkeley
	Charles P. Slichter	University of Illinois, Urbana-Champaign
E.O. Lawrence Award	Carl E. Wieman	University of Colorado, Boulder
Fermi Award	Leon M. Lederman	Fermi National Accelerator Laboratory, Batavia, Ill.
Frederic Ives Medal	Leonard Mandel	University of Rochester, N.Y.
Fritz London Memorial Award	Dennis S. Greywall	AT&T Bell Laboratories
	Horst Meyer	Duke University, Durham, N.C.
	Albert Schmid	University of Karlsruhe, Germany
Gold Medal of the Acoustical Society of America	David T. Blackstock	University of Texas, Austin
Gustav Hertz Prize	Dieter Wintgen	University of Freiburg, Germany
I.I. Rabi Prize	Timothy E. Chupp	University of Michigan, Ann Arbor
J.J. Sakurai Prize	Mary K. Gaillard	University of California, Berkeley
John T. Tate International Award	Roald Z. Sagdeev	University of Maryland, College Park
Julius Edgar Lilienfeld Prize	David N. Schramm	University of Chicago
King Faisal International Prize for Science	Steven Chu	Stanford University, Stanford, Calif.
	Herbert Walther	Max Planck Institute
Max Planck Medal	Kurt Binder	University of Mainz, Germany
National Medal of Science	Val Fitch	Princeton University, Princeton, N.J.
National Medal of Technology	Hans W. Liepmann (Emeritus)	California Institute of Technology, Pasadena
Max Born Medal	David Hanna	University of Southampton, England
Outstanding Research Award	Terence Hwa	Harvard University, Cambridge, Mass.
Outstanding Research Award	Shen Zhixun	Stanford University, Stanford, Calif.
Prix Des Sciences Physiques et Mathématique	Cécile DeWitt-Morette	University of Texas, Austin
Pupin Medal	Norman F. Ramsey	Harvard University, Cambridge, Mass.
Robert R. Wilson Prize	John P. Blewett (Retired)	University of Maryland, College Park
Robert Wichard Wohl Prize	Bruno Lüthi	University of Frankfurt, Germany
Roy W. Tess Award	Larry F. Thompson	AT&T Bell Laboratories
Shock Compression Science Award	Robert A. Graham	Sandia National Laboratories
Silver Medal in Engineering Acoustics	Alan Powell	University of Houston, Texas
Silver Medal in Musical Acoustics	Thomas D. Rossing	Northern Illinois University, De Kalb
Silver Medal in Noise	George C. Maling, Jr. (Retired)	IBM Corp.
Silver Medal in Underwater and Engineering Acoustics	Victor C. Anderson (Retired)	University of California, San Diego
Stern-Gerlach Medal	Klaus Winter	CERN (European Laboratory for Particle Physics)
Stuart Ballantine Medal	Leroy L. Chang	Hong Kong University of Science and Technology
Walter Schottky Prize	Gertrud Zwicknagl	Max Planck Institute
Wolf Prize	Benoit B. Mandelbrot	IBM Corp.

AWARD	WINNER	AFFILIATION

SPACE EXPLORATION

Bruno Rossi Prize	Gerald H. Share	Naval Research Laboratory
Daniel Heineman Prize in Astrophysics	John C. Mather	Goddard Space Flight Center, Greenbelt, Md.
Japan Prize	William H. Pickering (Emeritus)	California Institute of Technology, Pasadena

TRANSPORTATION

Edward Warner Award	Arnold Kean (Retired)	U.K. Civil Aviation Authority
Excellence in Pilot Training Award	Sierra Academy of Aeronautics	
Ground Testing Award	Raymond J. Stalker	University of Queensland, St. Lucia, Australia
Robert E. Gross Award	Jeff Cramer	Lockheed Aeronautical Systems Co.
Service Technician Award	James Anderson	Anderson Aircraft, Fairbanks, Alaska
William A. Ong Memorial Award	Thomas Davis (Retired)	Piedmont Aviation

SCIENCE WRITING

Aviation Journalism Award	Greg Napert	*Aircraft Technician*
Children's Science Writing Award	Gail Gibbons	Corinth, Vermont
Science Writing Award for Journalists	Malcolm W. Browne	*New York Times*
Science Writing Award for Journalists	Billy Goodman	Upper Montclair, N.J.
Science Writing Award for Professionals	Thomas M. Georges	National Oceanic and Atmospheric Administration
Science Writing Prize	David C. Cassily	Germany
Walter Sullivan Award	John McPhee	*The New Yorker*

OTHER AWARDS

Benjamin Harrison Medallion	Gilbert Gordon	Miami University, Oxford, Ohio
E.O. Lawrence Award	John W. Shaner	Los Alamos National Laboratory, Los Alamos, N.M.
Esther Hoffman Beller Award	Robert Greenler	University of Wisconsin, Milwaukee
Fermi Award	Harold Brown	Center for Strategic and International Studies, Washington, D.C.
	John S. Foster, Jr.	Tilkington Aerospace, Garden Grove, Calif.
Hall of Honor Award	Peter T. Flawn (Emeritus)	University of Texas, Austin
Harry C. Rowsell Award	Harry C. Rowsell (Retired)	Canadian Council on Animal Care
James Bryant Conant Award	Lee Marek	Naperville North High School, Naperville, Ill.
James Flack Norris Award	Arthur C. Breyer	Beaver College, Glenside, Pa.
Kavaler Award	Vincent A. Sarni	PPG Industries
Lewis Thomas Prize	Lewis Thomas (Emeritus)	Sloan-Kettering Cancer Center
MacArthur Fellow	Nancy Cartwright	London School of Economics and Political Science
MacArthur Fellow	Frank von Hippel	Princeton University, Princeton, N.J.
Melba Newell Phillips Award	Anthony P. French	Massachusetts Institute of Technology, Cambridge

Scientists of the Year

AWARD	WINNER	AFFILIATION
Preservation of Natural History Collections Award	Mary Lou Florian (Retired)	Royal British Columbia Museum, Canada
Public Welfare Medal	Jerome B. Wiesner (Emeritus)	Massachusetts Institute of Technology, Cambridge
National Medal of Science	Norman Hackerman	Robert A. Welch Foundation, Houston, Texas
National Medal of Science	Maxine Frank Singer (Emerita)	National Institutes of Health and Carnegie Institution, Washington, D.C.
National Medal of Technology	Merck & Co., Inc.	Whitehouse Station, N.J.
National Medal of Technology	Walter L. Robb (Retired)	General Electric Co.
Technologist/Inventor Award	Robert Astheimer	Edo Corp., Shelton, Conn.
Westinghouse Science Talent Search	1. Forrest N. Anderson	Helena High School, Helena, Mont.
	2. Jennifer Lin	Hunter College High School, New York, N.Y.
	3. John L. Staub	Sisseton High School, Sisseton, S.D.
	4. Robert C. Sarvis	Thomas Jefferson High School for Science and Technology, Alexandria, Va.
	5. Steven D. Sherman	Winona Senior High School, Winona, Minn.
	6. Flora Tartakovsky	Bronx High School of Science, Bronx, N.Y.
	7. Janos Zahajszky	Canton High School, Canton, Mass.
	8. Jennifer M. Kalish	Bryn Mawr School, Baltimore, Md.
	9. Margaret C. Bothner	Falmouth High School, Falmouth, Mass.
	10. Jamel L. Oeser-Sweat	Martin Luther King Jr. High School, New York, N.Y.

Obituaries

Belluschi, Pietro (Aug. 18, 1899—Feb. 14, 1994), Italian-born architect, designed the Equitable Life Assurance Building (1944–48), Portland, Ore., a sleek office tower of aluminum and glass that served as one of the finest and earliest examples of the International Style of architecture, but later became most closely identified as the premier regional designer of the Pacific Northwest with a series of magnificent domestic and religious structures that relied on the use of indigenous materials, notably wood. Before going to the U.S. as an exchange student in 1923, Belluschi studied engineering at the University of Rome. He attended Cornell University, Ithaca, N.Y., before settling in Portland and working for Albert E. Doyle, a prominent architect there. After Doyle's death Belluschi emerged (1928) as the firm's chief designer. In 1943 he purchased the company and renamed it after himself. In Portland he created additions to the Portland Art Museum (1930–38) and such prized structures as the Sutor House (1938), St. Thomas More Chapel (1939–41), and Zion Lutheran Church (1950). From 1951 to 1965 Belluschi headed the School of Architecture and Planning at the Massachusetts Institute of Technology, and he continued to collaborate with leading architectural firms. He codesigned such New York City landmarks as the Juilliard School of Music, Lincoln Center, and the Pan Am (now Met Life) Building and such San Francisco buildings as the Bank of America World Headquarters and St. Mary's Cathedral. In 1972 Belluschi was the recipient of the Gold Medal of the American Institute of Architects, and in 1991 he was awarded the National Medal of the Arts.

Bolton, John Gatenby (June 5, 1922—July 6, 1993), British-born Australian astronomer, was a pioneer in the field of radio astronomy and director (1961–71) of the Australian National Radio Astronomy Observatory, where the 64-m (210-ft) Parkes radio telescope played a crucial role in the U.S. Apollo space program. Bolton studied mathematics and physics at Trinity College, Cambridge, and then served as a radar officer in the British Royal Navy (1942–46). He immigrated to Australia in 1946 and joined the staff of the Radiophysics Laboratory of the Council for Scientific and Industrial Research in Sydney. In 1948 Bolton's team identified the first known radio galaxies, or "radio stars," external galaxies that can be traced by the strong signals they emit at radio wavelengths. He established the Owens Valley Radio Observatory during a six-year stint teaching physics and astronomy at the California Institute of Technology (1955–61), but in 1961 he returned to Australia to oversee construction of the Parkes dish. In 1962–63, under Bolton's direc-

tion, this radio telescope played a key role in the discovery of the prototype of a family of very distant and luminous objects called quasars. Bolton later used it to pinpoint more than 8,000 extragalactic radio sources, including hundreds of quasars. In 1969 the instrument became the ear of the world when it received the radio signals transmitted by Apollo 11 from the Moon. Bolton was made Commander of the Order of the British Empire in 1981.

Burkitt, Denis Parsons (Feb. 28, 1911—March 23, 1993), Irish physician, recognized the significance of varying climatic conditions and eating habits in the incidence of cancer and certain other diseases. His most significant medical achievement was in the painstaking study of the cause of and treatment for Burkitt's lymphoma, a lethal cancer of the lymphatic system that had a high incidence among children in tropical Africa. Outside of medical circles, however, he was best known for his well-publicized theories on nutrition and the importance of a high-fiber diet. Burkitt graduated from Trinity College, Dublin (B.A., 1933; M.D., 1946) and served as an army doctor during World War II. In 1946 he joined the colonial service in Uganda, where he was a government surgeon, a lecturer in surgery at Makerere University Medical School, and senior surgeon to the Ministry of Health. In the late 1950s he sent out hundreds of questionnaires to physicians and traveled some 16,000 km (10,000 mi) across Africa to study hospital records concerning a form of malignant facial tumor found mainly in boys under 12. His research demonstrated that Burkitt's lymphoma (as it came to be called) was endemic only in mosquito-ridden equatorial Africa and led to the discovery that the cancer was linked to the presence of the Epstein-Barr virus (the cause of acute infectious mononucleosis) in children whose immune system was depressed by chronic malaria. He later helped develop an effective chemotherapy treatment for the lym-

Denis Burkitt
AP/Wide World

phoma. Burkitt joined the Medical Research Council (MRC) in Uganda in 1964, and two years later he transferred to the London MRC center. In the late 1960s he turned his attention to the apparent link between dietary fiber and colon cancer. His subsequent publications, including the popular book *Don't Forget Fibre in Your Diet* (1979), triggered a new interest in nutrition and a greater emphasis on fiber in the Western diet.

Gimbutas, Marija (Jan. 23, 1921—Feb. 2, 1994), Lithuanian-born U.S. archaeologist, was an expert on prehistoric societies and was renowned for studies that tracked the influence of Indo-European-speaking people into Europe during that period. Gimbutas formulated a controversial theory that held that a peaceful Stone Age existed during which societies revered goddesses and focused on women. She maintained, however, that some 6,000 years ago a harmonious European culture was destroyed when patriarchal invaders shattered the conviviality between the sexes and fostered the worship of warlike gods. Her interdisciplinary investigations helped usher in a new field, archaeomythology. Gimbutas was also the leading proponent of the theory that held that such languages as English, French, German, and Iranian were all related. She held that warlike groups speaking a tongue ancestral to all Indo-European languages forced their language on those they conquered. Gimbutas, who studied at Vilnius (Lithuania) University (1938–42) and the University of Vienna (1944), earned a Ph.D. in archaeology from the University of Tübingen, Germany. She directed important Neolithic archaeological excavations in Yugoslavia and Greece and served from 1955 as research fellow of the Peabody Museum at Harvard University. From 1963 to 1990 she was professor of European archaeology at the University of California at Los Angeles. Gimbutas was the author of more than 200 scholarly articles on European prehistory and folklore and of 20 books, notably *Goddesses and Gods of Old Europe* (1974), *The Language of the Goddess* (1989), and *The Civilization of the Goddess* (1991).

Hafstad, Lawrence Randolph (June 18, 1904—Oct. 12, 1993), U.S. physicist, while conducting research on a one million-volt vacuum tube at the Carnegie Institution, Washington, D.C., became (1939) the first American to duplicate (with equipment he designed with colleagues Richard Roberts and Merle Tuve) a feat first accomplished by German scientists in the late 1930s—the successful splitting of the nucleus of the uranium atom. Hafstad, who received a B.S. (1926) in electrical engineering from the University of Minnesota, earned a Ph.D. (1933) from Johns Hopkins University, Baltimore, Md. He worked at Carnegie (1928–42) before moving to the Applied Physics Laboratory of Johns Hopkins, where he directed a project to create a variable-time radio-proximity fuse, a device credited with aiding the Allied victory in the Battle of the Bulge. Hafstad spent much of his career in military ordnance. He was involved in the development of ramjet engines, missiles and their guidance mechanisms, nuclear-bomb detection, nuclear power for submarines, and nuclear reactors for the generation of power. In 1946 Hafstad was elevated to director of research at Johns Hopkins, but he left its laboratory the following year to become (1948) the first director of reactor development for the U.S. Atomic Energy Commission. He spent much of the remainder of his professional career (1955–69) at General Motors Corp., where he served as chief of its research laboratories. From 1969 to 1972 he served as head of the Committee on Undersea Warfare for the National Academy of Sciences.

Hirst, George Keble (March 2, 1909—Jan. 22, 1994), U.S. virologist, was a pathfinder who was instrumental in discovering the footprints of viruses; in 1941 he found that influenza virus grown in the tissues of the chicken embryo could be detected because red blood cells adhere to one another when mixed with influenza viruses. He then developed the hemagglutination assay, a method used both to estimate the amount of virus present in a sample and to determine the amount of antibody in a person's blood serum. Hirst received both his B.S. (1930) and M.D. (1933) from Yale University and during the late 1940s and early '50s was one of the first to conduct work on the genetics of animal viruses. During his association (1940–46) with the Rockefeller Foundation's International Health Division, he studied influenza and its prevention by vaccination. He joined (1946) the Public Health Research Institute in New York City, where he served as director from 1956 to 1980.

Hogg-Priestly, Helen Battles Sawyer (Aug. 1, 1905—Jan. 28, 1993), U.S.-born Canadian astronomer, was an internationally recognized expert in the field of variable stars within globular star clusters, and she spent her entire professional career cataloging these stars of changing brightness in the International Astronomical Almanac. Hogg-Priestly received an undergraduate degree (1926) from Mount Holyoke College, South Hadley, Mass., before earning a Ph.D. (1931) from Radcliffe College, Cambridge, Mass., where she became interested in star clusters. In 1935 she and her first husband, Frank Hogg, became affiliated with the University of Toronto. She served as a volunteer for a year before becoming a lecturer and research assistant there in 1936, spending much of her time at the David Dunlap Observatory at Richmond Hill, Ont. She became a professor of astronomy in 1957, a post she held until her retirement in 1976, when she was named professor emerita. Besides her many scholarly writings, including *The Stars Belong to Everyone* (1976), Hogg-Priestly popularized her subject for the general public in "The Stars," a weekly column she wrote for the *Toronto Daily Star* from 1951 to 1981 (the column had been written by her husband from 1941 until his death in 1951). In 1985 she married Francis E.L. Priestly, who died in 1988. For her work Hogg-Priestly was awarded the Annie J. Cannon Prize of the American Astronomical Society (1950), the Rittenhouse Silver Medal (1967), and the Companion of the Order of Canada (1976). In 1984 Asteroid 2917, which had been discovered in 1980, was renamed Asteroid Sawyer Hogg.

Holley, Robert William (Jan. 28, 1922—Feb. 11, 1993), U.S. biochemist, shared the 1968 Nobel Prize for Physiology or Medicine with H. Gobind Khorana and Marshall W. Nirenberg; the three scientists independently conducted research that helped to decipher the genetic code and explain how the genetic information stored in the DNA of a cell controls the synthesis of proteins, the building blocks of cells. Holley, who began his painstaking work in 1956 while at the U.S. Department of Agriculture's Plant, Soil and Nutrition Laboratory at Cornell University, Ithaca, N.Y., determined the structure of alanine transfer RNA by purifying small amounts of the RNA isolated from more than 135 kg (300 lb) of baker's yeast. In 1965 Holley reported that "the complete nucleotide sequence of an alanine transfer RNA, isolated from yeast, has been determined. This is the first nucleic acid for which the structure is known." After earning a Ph.D. in organic chemistry (1947) from Cornell, Holley became associated with the university's state and federal agricultural stations and taught biochemistry and molecular biology (1962–66), serving as chairman of the biochemistry department from 1965 to 1966. In 1968 he became a resident fellow at the Salk Institute for Biological Studies in La Jolla, Calif., where he remained until his death. There he studied both the normal and the abnormal functions of the growth of cells in mammals, primarily focusing on the timing of cell division. The latter was crucial to the understanding of the growth of cancer and aided in the diagnosis and treatment of that disease and others. Holley was also the recipient of the prestigious Lasker Award (1965) and of an award for molecular biology (1967) from the National Academy of Sciences.

Hollows, Frederick Cossom (April 9, 1929—Feb. 10, 1993), New Zealand-born Australian physician, was a leader in the campaign to combat eye diseases (especially trachoma) among Aboriginal peoples and was cofounder of the Aboriginal Medical Service (AMS), which established a system of community clinics. Hollows was educated in New Zealand and at the Royal College of Ophthalmology in London. In 1965 he immigrated to Australia, where he accepted a professorship at the University of New South Wales. He soon learned that thousands of Aborigines were going blind from trachoma, a treatable eye disease brought on by poor hygiene and inferior sanitation. Despite official opposition, he developed an efficient, inexpensive cure for the disease, trained a team of specialists to take the treatment to those in need, and thus restored eye health to some 30,000 affected Aborigines. In 1971 Hollows was brought in as a consultant for the first AMS clinic in Sydney. He later set up similar programs in Nepal, Vietnam, and Eritrea (then part of Ethiopia). Hollows was named Australian of the Year in 1990 and was made an Officer of the Order of Australia the following year. The Hollows Foundation was established in 1992.

Hungerford, David Alden (May 7, 1927—Nov. 3, 1993), U.S. cytogeneticist, was a codiscoverer (1959) of the Philadelphia chromosome, an aberrant, short-armed chromosome that was the first chromosomal abnormality linked consistently to cancer in humans. Hungerford earned a B.A. (1951) from Temple University, Philadelphia, and was a graduate student working as a research fellow with Peter C. Nowell of the University of Pennsylvania at the Institute for Cancer Research at Fox Chase Cancer Center when he found that chronic granulocytic leukemia was linked to a defect (shortened arm) on one chromosome. Though he initially identified chromosome 21 as the one involved, other researchers proved that chromosome 22 held the defect. The Philadelphia chromosome, named for the city of its discovery, was later linked to eight types of cancer, tumors of the brain and soft tissue, mental retardation, and various familial congenital heart defects, notably a fatal heart arrhythmia known as long QT syndrome. Hungerford's work also provided the foundation for the identification of oncogenes (tumor genes). In 1961 he received a Ph.D. in zoology from the University of Pennsylvania. From 1951 he was associated with the Fox Chase Cancer Center, and he retired as a senior member in 1982, when multiple sclerosis reduced his activities.

Kerst, Donald William (Nov. 1, 1911—Aug. 19, 1993), U.S. physicist, designed particle accelerators, devices that are used to reveal the structure and properties of the atomic nucleus and the interactions of subatomic particles. During World War II he invented the betatron, an accelerator in which electrons are propelled by means of a rapidly varying magnetic field. The betatron achieved energies of up to about 300 million electron volts, a significant accomplishment at the time. After earning a Ph.D. from the University of Wisconsin in 1937, Kerst became a professor at the University of Illinois. He worked during World War II on the Manhattan Project, which developed the atomic bomb. After the war he was the technical director of the Midwest University Research Association and conducted research for the General Dynamics Corp. before serving as a professor of physics at the University of Wisconsin from 1962 until his retirement in 1980.

Kopal, Zdenek (April 4, 1914—June 23, 1993), Czech-born astronomer, directed an international project, financed by the U.S. Air Force, to photograph and map the entire surface of the Moon by using the refracting telescope at the Pic du Midi Observatory in southern France. He also made important discoveries concerning the transfer of matter between close binary stars. Kopal matriculated at Charles University in Prague (B.S., 1934; D.Sc., 1937) and received fellowships to the University of Cambridge and Harvard University. He taught astronomy at Harvard (1940–48) and at the Massachusetts Institute of Technology (1947–51). In 1951 he was invited to England to head the new astronomy department at the University of Manchester. In 1958 Kopal took charge of the lunar-mapping project, which increased scientific understanding of the Moon and paved the way for the National Aeronautics and Space Administration's (NASA's) Apollo lunar missions. He also worked as a special consultant to NASA, the U.S. Army, the space science division of the Jet Propulsion Laboratory in Pasadena, Calif., and private industry. Kopal was founding editor of three journals—*Icarus*, *Astrophysics and Space Science*, and *Moon* (later renamed *Earth, Moon and Planets*). His published works include *Numerical Analysis* (1955), *Close Binary Systems* (1959), *Physics and Astronomy of the Moon* (1962), *Mapping of the Moon* (1974), *Dynamics of Close Binary Systems* (1978), and *Mathematical Theory of Stellar Eclipses* (1990). He retired from the University of Manchester in 1981.

Kusch, Polykarp (Jan. 26, 1911—March 20, 1993), German-born U.S. physicist, was awarded the 1955 Nobel Prize for Physics for his precise work in measuring the electron's magnetic moment, a vital determination that led to revised theories about the interactions of electrons with electromagnetic radiation and to new scientific principles as a basis for quantum electrodynamics; he shared the prize with Willis E. Lamb, Jr., who independently performed related experiments on the hyperfine structure of the hydrogen atom. Kusch emigrated from Germany to the U.S. with his family in 1912 and became a citizen in 1922. He graduated (1931) from Case Institute of Technology, Cleveland, Ohio, before earning an M.A. (1933) and a Ph.D. (1936) from the University of Illinois at Urbana-Champaign, where he taught physics from 1931 to 1936. He joined the faculty of Columbia University, New York City, in 1937, and there, with physicist Isidor I. Rabi, he conducted studies of the effects of magnetic fields on beams of atoms. Kusch remained associated with Columbia until 1972 except for a time during World War II, when he engaged in military research on the applications of vacuum tubes and microwave generators at Westinghouse Electric Corp. (1941–42) and Bell Telephone Laboratories (1944–46). At Columbia he served as chairman of the physics department (1949–52 and 1960–63), director of the radiation laboratory (1952–60), and academic vice president and provost (1969–72). From 1972 until his retirement in 1982, he taught at the University of Texas at Dallas.

Langmuir, Alexander (Sept. 12, 1910—Nov. 22, 1993), U.S. epidemiologist, created and led the Epidemic Intelligence Service (EIS) for the U.S. government and was credited with saving thousands of lives with his revolutionary work. Langmuir received his medical degree at Cornell University, Ithaca, N.Y., in 1935. He joined the United States Public Health Service in 1949, becoming the chief epidemiologist for the Communicable Disease Center (the forerunner of the Centers for Disease Control and Prevention [CDC]). In 1951 he created and headed the EIS, which was established to study and track the transmission of disease. Langmuir's vigorous training and high standards proved critical for his group's effectiveness, and the service gained renown for its "shoe-leather" detective work in the field. Langmuir served at the CDC until 1970, when he retired from public service, and taught at Harvard University until 1977. In later years he criticized the CDC's tracking of the spread of AIDS.

Moore, Charles (Oct. 31, 1925—Dec. 16, 1993), U.S. architect, was one of the most important and prolific advocates of the eclectic style known as Postmodernism; he was influential as an architect, educator, and author. Moore graduated from the University of Michigan in 1947 and received his Ph.D. from Princeton University in 1957. He achieved prominence in the 1960s as a member of the partnership that came to be known as MLTW/Moore Turnbull. In 1966 Moore gained acclaim for his Sea Ranch condominium project in California. The resort featured a style that seemed to reflect its dramatic cliffside location and one that became popular for many suburban developments. Other important projects included the Piazza d'Italia in New Orleans, La. (1978), and the Alumni Center at the University of California at Irvine (1983–85). Moore taught at numerous universities and served as the chairman of the architecture departments at the University of California at Berkeley (1962–65) and Yale University (1965–69); from 1985 he held the O'Neil Ford chair in architecture at the University of Texas at Austin. He wrote or co-wrote 11 books, notably *Body, Memory and Architecture* (1978; with Kent Bloomer), and won the prestigious 1991 Gold Medal of the American Institute of Architects.

Niederland, William Guglielmo (Aug. 29, 1904—July 30, 1993), German-born U.S. psychoanalyst, was the first to formulate (1961) a "survivor syndrome," which he defined as a feeling of self-reproach and severe guilt among survivors of Nazi death camps, natural disasters, and automobile accidents and which was manifested by symptoms of insomnia, nightmares, personality changes, chronic depression, anxiety, disturbances of memory, and psychosomatic illnesses. Niederland himself was a refugee from Nazi Germany, was interned in Britain as an enemy alien, and was able to assimilate some of his own experiences into his work. He had received M.D.'s from the Universities of Würzburg, Germany, and Genoa, Italy, before obtaining another from the New York Institute of Psychoanalysis. Niederland practiced medicine in Milan and served as a ship's doctor in the Philippines before arriving in New York in 1940. In his private practice he treated more than 800 persons who had been subjected to massive cumulative trauma, and from these sessions he coined the term *survivor syndrome.* Niederland taught at the University of Tampa, Fla., served as a staff psychiatrist at Mount Sinai Medical Center in New York City, and from 1952 to 1974 was in private practice while also teaching. He was intrigued with studying the psychological motives of explorers, including Columbus, and what he termed the "dark roots of creativity," an unconscious factor such as a defect or malformation that could result in "heightened bodily sensation" and spark genius. He was the author of some 200 articles and such books as *Man-Made Plague: A Primer on Neurosis* (1948), *Psychic Traumatization* (1971), and *The Schreber Case: Psychoanalytic Profile of a Paranoid Personality* (1974), one of his most famous studies.

Ochoa, Severo (Sept. 24, 1905—Nov. 1, 1993), Spanish-born molecular biologist, was co-winner of the 1959 Nobel Prize for Physiology or Medicine for his work in artificially synthesizing RNA, genetic material essential to the translation into protein of the hereditary information contained in genes. He shared the prize with Arthur Kornberg, who had synthesized DNA. Ochoa graduated from the University of Málaga, Spain, at the age of 16 and entered the University of Madrid's medical school at age 17. After earning an M.D. degree in 1929, he worked for two years at the laboratory of Nobel Prize-winning biochemist Otto Meyerhof. He briefly served (1935–36) as head of the physiology research division at the medical school of the University of Madrid but left that post because he felt that research opportunities in Spain would be hindered by the civil war. He worked at various European universities before immigrating to the U.S. in 1941. Ochoa joined the staff of New York University in 1942, becoming chairman of the biochemistry department in 1954. While

Severo Ochoa
© The Nobel Foundation

conducting research on high-energy phosphates in 1955, he made an accidental discovery. He found that the bacterial enzyme that he called polynucleotide phosphorylase was able to synthesize RNA from its chemical building blocks instead of breaking down the molecule as expected; he was then able to create molecules of artificial RNA. It was for this groundbreaking work that Ochoa received the Nobel Prize. As research continued, it was confirmed that the enzyme Ochoa discovered did indeed break down RNA except under specific laboratory conditions, when the enzyme's natural reaction ran in reverse. From the early 1970s he was associated with the Autonomous University of Madrid and, after leaving New York University in 1974, with the Roche Institute of Molecular Biology in Nutley, N.J.(1974–85).

Paul, Wolfgang (Aug. 10, 1913—Dec. 6/7, 1993), German physicist, developed the Paul trap, an electromagnetic device that captures ions and holds them long enough for study and precise measurement of their properties. For his work he shared the 1989 Nobel Prize for Physics with Hans G. Dehmelt and Norman F. Ramsey. Paul studied physics and engineering at technological institutes in Munich and Berlin, receiving (1939) a doctoral degree from the Technical University in Berlin. During World War II he was part of a group researching a method of producing material to be used in atomic bombs, though he later opposed the possession of nuclear weapons by the German military. In 1944 he became a lecturer at the University of Göttingen, and from 1950 he was a full professor there. In 1952 he also became director of the Physics Institute at the University of Bonn. In addition, Paul was involved in the development of the European Organization for Nuclear Research (CERN) in Geneva, was president of the Alexander von Humboldt Foundation (1979–89), and received a number of honorary degrees.

Pontecorvo, Bruno (Aug. 22, 1913—Sept. 25, 1993), Italian-born British physicist, was a distinguished scientist who defected to the Soviet Union to study the peaceful uses of nuclear power. Pontecorvo was one of eight children born to a Jewish textile merchant. He received his doctorate from the University of Rome, where in the early 1930s he worked with Enrico Fermi. After Mussolini's government passed a series of race laws, Pontecorvo fled to Paris to continue his research. When Paris was invaded by the Germans in 1940, he made his way to the U.S. In 1943 Pontecorvo joined the Anglo-Canadian nuclear research team at Chalk River, Ont. He became a British citizen in 1948, and the following year he joined the Atomic Energy Authority research station at Harwell, England, where classified research was being conducted. While on vacation in Italy in 1950, Pontecorvo, his wife, and their three children abruptly left for Stockholm. They then went to Helsinki, Fin., and were not heard from until 1955, when Pontecorvo appeared at a press conference in Moscow to promote the peaceful use of nuclear power. His disappearance had followed revelations that some highly placed scientists (including Klaus Fuchs, one of Pontecorvo's colleagues at Harwell) had given secrets to the Soviet Union and raised fears about how seriously these scientists had endangered the free world. Pontecorvo denied ever having worked on nuclear weapons research. While in the Soviet Union, he worked at the Joint Institute for Nuclear Research outside Moscow. He received numerous awards from the state, including the Lenin Prize (1963) and the Order of Lenin (1983).

Sabin, Albert Bruce (Aug. 26, 1906—March 3, 1993), Polish-born U.S. physician and microbiologist, was a towering figure in medical research and the developer in 1955 of the first oral vaccine for polio, which was administered to millions of children in Europe, Africa, and the Americas beginning in the late 1950s. His live, weakened (attenuated) vaccine, which was dispensed on a sugar cube or in liquid, was easier to administer and provided longer protection than the killed, injected vaccine developed by Jonas Salk a year earlier. Both vaccines, however, were credited with virtually eradicating the crippling and sometimes fatal effects of poliomyelitis, or infantile paralysis, a scourge that, at its peak in 1952, paralyzed 21,000 Americans and killed 3,100. With his family, Sabin immigrated to the U.S. in 1921, and two cousins taught him enough English to make it possible for him to enter high school. Ten years later he earned an M.D. degree from New York University. He served two years as house physician at Bellevue Hospital in New York City before attending the Lister Institute of Preventive Medicine in London. After returning to New York City in 1935, he joined the staff of the Rockefeller Institute for Medical Research, where he was the first to demonstrate the growth of poliovirus in human nervous tissue outside the body. After becoming (1939) associate professor of pediatrics at the University of

Albert Sabin
AP/Wide World

Cincinnati (Ohio) College of Medicine, he served as chief of the college's division of infectious diseases at the Children's Hospital Research Foundation (1939–43). During World War II he interrupted his polio research to work with the U.S. Army Medical Corps. Sabin isolated the virus that caused sandfly fever, which was epidemic among U.S. troops in Africa, and he later developed vaccines against dengue fever and Japanese encephalitis. After the war he returned to the University of Cincinnati and served as professor of research pediatrics (1946–60) and distinguished service professor (1960–71) before becoming professor emeritus in 1971. Sabin was also associated with the University of South Carolina at Charleston, the Weizmann Institute of Science in Rehovot, Israel, and the National Institutes of Health in Bethesda, Md. Though he was paralyzed (1983) with polyneuritis, an inflammation of the nerve cells, he made almost a full recovery and continued working on a measles vaccine before retiring in 1988. Sabin was elected to the National Academy of Sciences in 1951 and was the recipient of the U.S. Medals of Science (1970), Freedom (1986), and Liberty (1986).

Schaefer, Vincent Joseph (July 4, 1906—July 25, 1993), U.S. chemist, was conducting atmospheric research at the General Electric (GE) Research Laboratory in Schenectady, N.Y., when in 1946 he undertook the first systematic series of experiments to investigate the physics of precipitation. Schaefer, who struck upon a method to create a snowstorm in the laboratory, proved that he could accomplish the same feat with supercooled clouds in the free atmosphere. From an aircraft over Massachusetts, he seeded clouds with pellets of dry ice (solidified carbon dioxide) and successfully produced snow. His initiative launched the science of experimental meteorology and weather control. Schaefer dropped out of school at the age of 16 but later graduated (1928) from the Davey Institute of Tree Surgery, Kent, Ohio. After joining GE he became the protégé of Nobel laureate Irving Langmuir. The two worked on studies of surface chemistry (1931–40) before undertaking defense work during World War II. They invented several useful devices to aid the military, notably gas mask filters, submarine detectors, and a machine for making smoke clouds to conceal aircraft maneuvers. After leaving GE in 1954, Schaefer served as research director of the Munitalp Foundation until 1958, when he resigned to devote his time to research and education. He joined the faculty of the State University of New York at Albany in 1959, and the following year he became a founder of the Atmospheric Sciences Research Center, which he directed from 1966 to 1976. Schaefer was the author of some 300 scientific papers and books and in 1976 received a special citation from the American Meteorological Society.

Slayton, Donald Kent ("DEKE") (March 1, 1924—June 13, 1993), U.S. astronaut, was selected in 1959 by the National Aeronautics and Space Administration (NASA) as one of the original Mercury Seven astronauts, the highly touted aviators who made solo spaceflights during the infancy of the U.S. space program. Slayton's flight, however, was delayed for 16 years (he had been scheduled to become the second in orbit, after John Glenn) because he was found to have an irregular heartbeat. In 1975, after the ailment unaccountably disappeared, he served as pilot of the Apollo docking module in the historic Apollo-Soyuz mission, in which U.S. and Soviet spacecraft linked in space. Slayton, who joined the Army Air Forces in 1942, flew 56 combat missions during World War II. After the war he earned a B.A. in aeronautical engineering (1949) from the University of Minnesota and worked for Boeing Aircraft Co. in Seattle, Wash., before being recalled to active duty in the Minnesota Air National Guard. He became a test pilot at Edwards Air Force Base in California after attending school there. When Slayton's dream

Donald K. ("Deke") Slayton
NASA

of spaceflight as a Mercury Seven astronaut was crushed, he proved instrumental as chief of flight operations at the Johnson Space Center, where he directed astronaut training and chose crews for nearly all Gemini and Apollo missions. He was determined, however, to regain his health. Slayton quit smoking and started exercising and dieting. After participating in the last Apollo mission, he returned to NASA in a managerial capacity, directing early tests of the space shuttle until his 1982 retirement. He then founded and directed Space Services Inc., a pioneering company that launched small satellites.

Temin, Howard Martin (Dec. 10, 1934—Feb. 9, 1994), U.S. virologist, shared the 1975 Nobel Prize for Physiology or Medicine with Renato Dulbecco and David Baltimore for his role in discovering reverse transcriptase, an enzyme that transcribes nucleotide sequences in RNA into nucleotide sequences in DNA. While conducting research on a virus that causes cancer in chickens, Temin identified the enzyme. Baltimore independently found the enzyme in a virus that causes cancer in mice. Temin's groundbreaking finding dramatically illustrated the exception to one of the fundamental tenets of molecular biology—that information flows uniquely from DNA to RNA to protein. Temin's studies helped scientists detect that reverse transcriptase also has a role in such viruses as hepatitis B, cauliflower mosaic (a plant virus), and human immunodeficiency virus, which causes AIDS. Temin's original 1964 theory that RNA could make DNA was derided in the scientific community, but he persevered for six years before proving his hypothesis. Temin graduated from Swarthmore (Pa.) College and earned a Ph.D. (1959) at the California Institute of Technology. There, working under the tutelage of Dulbecco, he began his investigations into viruses and their role in animal cancers. Temin contended, however, that viruses probably did not play a central role in cancers in humans. An antismoking crusader, he felt that the incidence of cancer could be reduced by the elimination of smoking. In 1960 Temin joined the faculty of the University of Wisconsin, where he successively served as associate professor, full professor, Wisconsin Alumni Research Foundation professor of cancer research, and American Cancer Society professor of viral oncology and cell biology. Temin succumbed to a type of lung cancer not associated with smoking.

Thomas, Lewis (Nov. 25, 1913—Dec. 3, 1993), U.S. physician and author, translated his passionate interest in and wonder at the intricate mystery of the Earth's biology into a series of finely crafted, award-winning essays that reached a wide audience. Thomas was the son of a doctor and a nurse. He graduated from Princeton University at age 19 and earned his medical degree from Harvard Medical School at 23. He went on to work at various universi-

ties, serving as researcher, educator, and administrator as well as pathologist, pediatrician, bacteriologist, and epidemiologist. He joined the staff of New York University in 1954, and in 1966 he became dean of the School of Medicine there. In 1969 Thomas moved to Yale University, where in 1972 he became dean of the School of Medicine. From 1971 to 1980 he wrote a column for the *New England Journal of Medicine* entitled "Notes of a Biology Watcher"; some of these essays were collected into a book, *The Lives of a Cell* (1974), which won the National Book Award in the arts and letters category in 1975. From 1973 to 1980 he served as president of the Memorial Sloan-Kettering Cancer Center in New York City. Other works include *The Medusa and the Snail* (1979), *Late Night Thoughts on Listening to Mahler's Ninth Symphony* (1983), and *The Fragile Species* (1992).

Wilson, J(ohn) Tuzo (Oct. 24, 1908—April 15, 1993), Canadian geophysicist, helped rekindle the concept of plate tectonics with his important 1965 paper *A New Class of Faults and Their Bearing on Continental Drift,* which introduced his theory of an entirely new class of geologic faults, transform faults (boundaries of plates that slide past each other), as a third type of movement in addition to convergent plates (those moving closer together) and divergent plates (those moving apart). His theory, devised to help explain continental drift, became almost universally accepted, and he was credited with coining the term *plate* in reference to the rigid portions into which the Earth's crust is divided. Wilson's mother, Henrietta Tuzo, was an explorer and mountaineer, and her name was given to British Columbia's Mt. Tuzo in the Canadian Rockies. By the time he was out of high school, Wilson had participated in geologic field expeditions into the Canadian wilderness. When he graduated (1930) from Trinity College, University of Toronto, he was the first person at any Canadian university to have earned a degree in geophysical studies. He later attended St. John's College, Cambridge (B.A., 1932), Princeton University (Ph.D., 1936), and the University of Cambridge (M.A., 1940; Sc.D., 1958). Known as an adventurer, Wilson was the first to climb the 4,000-m (12,000-ft) Mt. Hague in Montana, and he visited each continent at least once. After working with the Geological Survey of Canada (1936–39) and serving with the Royal Canadian Engineers during World War II, he became professor of geophysics at the University of Toronto, where he remained until 1974. That year he became director general of the Ontario Science Centre, which he turned into a fascinating interactive environment for children, who were encouraged by posted signs to "please touch." As director of the Science Centre until 1985, he introduced working models, innovative demonstrations, and traveling exhibits to help make scientific study enjoyable. He published *One Chinese Moon* (1959), *IGY: Year of the New Moons* (1961), *A Revolution in Earth Science* (1967), and *Continents Adrift and Continents Aground* (1977). The Wilson mountain range in Antarctica was named in his honor.

Zuckerman of Burnham Thorpe, Solly Zuckerman, BARON (May 30, 1904—April 1, 1993), British scientist, made an improbable transition from his beginnings as a research anatomist with the London Zoological Society (1928–32) to being a trusted scientific adviser and military strategist with the British Defense Ministry (1939–46; 1960–66) and finally to his position as chief scientific adviser to the British government (1964–71). Zuckerman matriculated at the University of Cape Town and University College Hospital, London, eventually receiving doctorates in science and medicine. At the Zoological Society he studied primate physiology and wrote his groundbreaking first books, *The Social Life of Monkeys and Apes* (1931) and *Functional Affinities of Man, Monkeys, and Apes* (1933). In 1934 he switched his focus to human anatomy, which he taught at the Universities of Oxford (1934–45), Birmingham (1946–68), and East Anglia (1969–74). During World War II Zuckerman was called on to determine the effects on the body of the shock waves from bomb blasts. He quickly became an invaluable government adviser, with strong views on everything from saturation bombing (which he opposed) to nuclear disarmament (which he endorsed) to environmental pollution. These diverse interests were reflected in his later books, notably *Scientists and War* (1966) and *Great Zoos of the World* (1980), and in his two volumes of memoirs, *From Apes to Warlords* (1978) and *Monkeys, Men, and Missiles* (1988). Zuckerman remained with the Zoological Society throughout his career, serving as secretary (1955–77) and president (1977–84). He was knighted in 1964, awarded the Order of Merit in 1968, and elevated to a life peerage in 1971, shortly after he retired from public service.

Contributors to the Science Year in Review

Paul Bradley Addis *Food and agriculture: Nutrition.* Professor of Nutrition and Dietetics, and Food Science and Technology, University of Minnesota, St. Paul.

George F. Bertsch *Physics: Nuclear physics* (in part). Professor of Physics, University of Washington, Seattle.

Harold Borko *Electronics and information sciences: Information systems and services.* Professor, Graduate School of Library and Information Science, University of California, Los Angeles.

John M. Bowen *Medical sciences: Veterinary medicine.* Associate Dean for Research and Graduate Affairs and Professor of Pharmacology and Toxicology, College of Veterinary Medicine, University of Georgia, Athens.

George G. Brown *Life sciences: Zoology.* Professor of Zoology and Genetics, Iowa State University, Ames.

Paul J. Campbell *Mathematics.* Professor of Mathematics and Computer Science, Beloit College, Beloit, Wis.

Douglas E. Comer *Electronics and information sciences: Computers and computer science.* Professor of Computer Science, Purdue University, West Lafayette, Ind.

Dave Dooling *Space exploration.* D² Associates, Freelance Science Writing and Aerospace Consulting, Huntsville, Ala.

F.C. Durant III *Electronics and information sciences: Satellite systems* (in part). Aerospace Historian and Consultant, Chevy Chase, Md.

David Guise *Architecture and civil engineering.* Professor Emeritus of Architecture, City College of New York, and private practice of architecture, New York City.

R. Cargill Hall *Electronics and information sciences: Satellite systems* (in part). Aerospace Historian, Center for Air Force History, Bolling Air Force Base, Washington, D.C.

Robert Haselkorn *Life sciences: Molecular biology.* F.L. Pritzker Distinguished Service Professor, Department of Molecular Genetics and Cell Biology, University of Chicago.

Carolyn Hemenway *Scientists of the Year: Nobel Prizes.* Freelance Writer and Editor, Oakland, Ore.

Myrl C. Hendershott *Earth sciences: Oceanography.* Professor of Oceanography, Scripps Institution of Oceanography, La Jolla, Calif.

Christopher T. Hill *Physics: High-energy physics.* Scientist II, Fermi National Accelerator Laboratory, Batavia, Ill.

John Patrick Jordan *Food and agriculture: Agriculture* (in part). Administrator, Cooperative State Research Service, U.S. Department of Agriculture, Washington, D.C.

Lou Joseph *Medical sciences: Dentistry.* Science Writer, Des Plaines, Ill.

Ronald H. Kaitchuck *Astronomy.* Associate Professor of Physics and Astronomy, Ball State University, Muncie, Ind.

Allan P. Katz *Materials sciences: Ceramics.* Technical Manager for Structural Ceramics, Wright Laboratory, Materials Directorate, Wright-Patterson Air Force Base, Ohio.

George B. Kauffman *Chemistry: Applied chemistry.* Professor of Chemistry, California State University, Fresno.

David B. Kitts *Earth sciences: Geology and geochemistry.* Professor Emeritus of the History of Science, University of Oklahoma, Norman.

Patricia Brazeel Lewis *Food and agriculture: Agriculture* (in part). Public Relations Consultant, New Jersey Agricultural Experiment Station, Rutgers University, New Brunswick, N.J.

Melvin H. Marx *Psychology* (in part). Professor of Psychology, Western Carolina University, Cullowhee, N.C., and Professor Emeritus of Psychology, University of Missouri, Columbia.

Sharon McGrayne *Physics: Nuclear physics* (in part) Freelance Science Writer, Seattle, Wash.

John E. McMurry *Chemistry: Organic chemistry.* Professor of Chemistry, Cornell University, Ithaca, N.Y.

Franz J. Monssen *Electronics and information sciences: Electronics.* Instructor, Department of Electronic and Computer Engineering Technology, Queensborough Community College, New York City.

John A. Morrison *Chemistry: Inorganic chemistry.* Professor of Chemistry, University of Illinois at Chicago.

Charles S. Mueller *Earth sciences: Geophysics.* Geophysicist, U.S. Geological Survey, Menlo Park, Calif.

Larry L. Naylor *Anthropology.* Chair, Anthropology, Institute of Anthropology, University of North Texas, Denton.

Colin V. Newman *Psychology* (in part). Executive Secretary, British Psychological Society, Leicester, England.

Joseph Palca *U.S. science policy.* Science Correspondent, National Public Radio, Washington, D.C.

Elizabeth Pennisi *Medical sciences: General medicine.* Editor, *Science News,* Washington, D.C.

Roger A. Pielke *Earth sciences: Atmospheric sciences.* Professor of Atmospheric Science, Colorado State University, Fort Collins.

John Rhea *Defense research.* Freelance Science Writer, Woodstock, Va.

Robin K. Roy *Energy.* Project Director, Office of Technology Assessment, Congress of the United States, Washington, D.C.

Robert R. Shannon *Optical engineering.* Professor Emeritus and Past Director, Optical Sciences Center, University of Arizona, Tucson.

Lawrence J. Shimkets *Life sciences: Microbiology.* Professor of Microbiology, University of Georgia, Athens.

Albert J. Smith *Life sciences: Botany.* Professor of Biology, Wheaton College, Wheaton, Ill.

Frank A. Smith *Transportation.* Executive Consultant, Eno Transportation Foundation, Leesburg, Va.

Leslie Smith *Earth sciences: Hydrology.* Professor of Geological Sciences, University of British Columbia, Vancouver.

Ben P. Stein *Physics: General developments.* Science Writer, American Institute of Physics, College Park. Md.

Robert E. Stoffels *Electronics and information sciences: Communications systems.* Editor, *Telephone Engineer & Management* magazine, Chicago.

Kevin P. Trumble *Materials sciences: Metallurgy.* Assistant Professor of Materials Engineering, Purdue University, West Lafayette, Ind.

Chris G. Van de Walle *Physics: Condensed-matter physics.* Research Scientist, Xerox Palo Alto Research Center, Palo Alto, Calif.

Philip R. Watson *Chemistry: Physical chemistry.* Professor of Chemistry, Oregon State University, Corvallis.

Kenneth E.F. Watt *Environment.* Professor of Ecology and Evolution, University of California, Davis.

James D. Wilde *Archaeology.* Director, Office of Public Archaeology, Brigham Young University, Provo, Utah.

Contributors to the Encyclopædia Britannica Science Update

R. Stephen Berry *Matter* (in part). James Franck Distinguished Service Professor of Chemistry, University of Chicago. Coauthor of *Physical Chemistry* and others.

Donald M. Ginsberg *Matter* (in part). Professor of Physics, University of Illinois at Urbana-Champaign. Editor of *Physical Properties of High Temperature Superconductors.*

Robert M. Hazen *Matter* (in part). Staff Scientist, Geophysical Laboratory, Carnegie Institution of Washington, D.C., and Clarence Robinson Professor of Earth Science, George Mason University, Fairfax, Va. Author of *The New Alchemists: Breaking Through the Barriers of High Pressure* and others.

Michael C. Kelley *Matter* (in part). Professor of Electrical Engineering, Cornell University, Ithaca, N.Y. Author of *The Earth's Ionosphere: Plasma Physics and Electrodynamics.*

Anthony J. Leggett *Matter* (in part). John D. and Catherine T. MacArthur Professor of Physics, Center for Advanced Study, and Professor of Physics, University of Illinois at Urbana-Champaign. Author of *The Problems of Physics.*

Bruce S. Liley *Matter* (in part). Professor of Physics, University of Waikato, Hamilton, N.Z.

Michael Widom *Matter* (in part). Associate Professor of Physics, Carnegie Mellon University, Pittsburgh, Pa. Author of *Renormalization Group Analysis of Quasi-Periodicity in Analytic Maps.*

A Science
Classic

Charles Darwin

On the Origin of Species by Means of Natural Selection

Charles Darwin (1809–82) revolutionized biology with the publication in 1859 of On the Origin of Species by Means of Natural Selection. *Though the idea of the evolution of organisms did not originate with him, Darwin was the first to present a mechanism—natural selection—and persuasive evidence for the process. Excerpts from this landmark volume are reprinted below.*

Introduction

When on board H.M.S. *Beagle* as naturalist, I was much struck with certain facts in the distribution of the organic beings inhabiting South America, and in the geological relations of the present to the past inhabitants of that continent. These facts, as will be seen in the latter chapters of this volume, seemed to throw some light on the origin of species—that mystery of mysteries, as it has been called by one of our greatest philosophers. On my return home, it occurred to me, in 1837, that something might perhaps be made out on this question by patiently accumulating and reflecting on all sorts of facts which could possibly have any bearing on it. After five years' work I allowed myself to speculate on the subject, and drew up some short notes; these I enlarged in 1844 into a sketch of the conclusions, which then seemed to me probable: from that period to the present day I have steadily pursued the same object. I hope that I may be excused for entering on these personal details, as I give them to show that I have not been hasty in coming to a decision.

My work is now (1859) nearly finished; but as it will take me many more years to complete it, and as my health is far from strong, I have been urged to publish this abstract. I have more especially been induced to do this, as Mr. Wallace, who is now studying the natural history of the Malay Archipelago, has arrived at almost exactly the same general conclusions that I have on the origin of species. In 1858 he sent me a memoir on this subject, with a request that I would forward it to Sir Charles Lyell, who sent it to the Linnean Society, and it is published in the third volume of the *Journal* of that society. Sir C. Lyell and Dr. Hooker, who both knew of my work—the latter having read my sketch of 1844—honoured me by thinking it advisable to publish, with Mr. Wallace's excellent memoir, some brief extracts from my manuscripts.

This abstract, which I now publish, must necessarily be imperfect. I cannot here give references and authorities for my several statements; and I must trust to the reader reposing some confidence in my accuracy. No doubt errors will have crept in, though I hope I have always been cautious in trusting to good authorities alone. I can here give only the general conclusions at which I have arrived, with a few facts in illustration, but which, I hope, in most cases will suffice. No one can feel more sensible than I do of the necessity of hereafter publishing in detail all the facts, with references, on which my conclusions have been grounded, and I hope in a future work to do this. For I am well aware that scarcely a single point is discussed in this volume on which facts cannot be adduced, often apparently leading to conclusions directly opposite to those at which I have arrived. A fair result can be obtained only by fully stating and balancing the facts and arguments on both sides of each question; and this is here impossible.

I much regret that want of space prevents my having the satisfaction of acknowledging the generous

Courtesy, National Portrait Gallery, London; oil painting by John Collier

Charles Darwin

assistance which I have received from very many naturalists, some of them personally unknown to me. I cannot, however, let this opportunity pass without expressing my deep obligations to Dr. Hooker, who, for the last fifteen years, has aided me in every possible way by his large stores of knowledge and his excellent judgment.

In considering the Origin of Species, it is quite conceivable that a naturalist, reflecting on the mutual affinities of organic beings, on their embryological relations, their geographical distribution, geological succession, and other such facts, might come to the conclusion that species had not been independently created, but had descended, like varieties, from other species. Nevertheless, such a conclusion, even if well founded, would be unsatisfactory, until it could be shown how the innumerable species inhabiting this world have been modified, so as to acquire that perfection of structure and coadaptation which justly excites our admiration. Naturalists continually refer to external conditions, such as climate, food, &c., as the only possible cause of variation. In one limited sense, as we shall hereafter see, this may be true; but it is preposterous to attribute to mere eternal conditions, the structure, for instance, of the woodpecker, with its feet, tail, beak, and tongue, so admirably adapted to catch insects under the bark of trees. In the case of the mistletoe, which draws its nourishment from certain trees, which has seeds that must be transported by certain birds, and which has flowers with separate sexes absolutely requiring the agency of certain insects to bring pollen from one flower to the other, it is equally preposterous to account for the structure of this parasite, with its relations to several distinct organic beings, by the effects of external conditions, or of habit, or of the volition of the plant itself.

It is, therefore, of the highest importance to gain a clear insight into the means of modification and coadaptation. At the commencement of my observations it seemed to me probable that a careful study of domesticated animals and of cultivated plants would offer the best chance of making out this obscure problem. Nor have I been disappointed; in this and in all other perplexing cases I have invariably found that our knowledge, imperfect though it be, of variation under domestication, afforded the best and safest clue. I may venture to express my conviction of the high value of such studies, although they have been very commonly neglected by naturalists.

From these considerations, I shall devote the first chapter of this Abstract to Variation under Domestication. We shall thus see that a large amount of hereditary modification is at least possible; and, what is equally or more important, we shall see how great is the power of man in accumulating by his Selection successive slight variations. I will then pass on to the variability of species in a state of nature; but I shall, unfortunately, be compelled to treat this subject far too briefly, as it can be treated properly only by giving long catalogues of facts. We shall, however, be enabled to discuss what circumstances are most favourable to variation. In the next chapter the Struggle for Existence amongst all organic beings throughout the world, which inevitably follows from the high geometrical ratio of their increase, will be considered. This is the doctrine of Malthus, applied to the whole animal and vegetable kingdoms. As many more individuals of each species are born than can possibly survive; and as, consequently, there is a frequently recurring struggle for existence, it follows that any being, if it vary however slightly in any manner profitable to itself, under the complex and sometimes varying conditions of life, will have a better chance of surviving, and thus be *naturally selected*. From the strong principle of inheritance, any selected variety will tend to propagate its new and modified form.

This fundamental subject of Natural Selection will be treated at some length in the fourth chapter; and we shall then see how Natural Selection almost inevitably causes much Extinction of the less improved forms of life, and leads to what I have called Divergence of Character. In the next chapter I shall discuss the complex and little known laws of variation.

In the five succeeding chapters, the most apparent and gravest difficulties in accepting the theory will be given: namely, first, the difficulties of transitions, or how a simple being or a simple organ can be changed and perfected into a highly developed being or into an elaborately constructed organ; secondly, the subject of Instinct, or the mental powers of animals; thirdly, Hybridism, or the infertility of species and the fertility of varieties when intercrossed; and fourthly, the imperfection of the Geological Record. In the next chapter I shall consider the geological succession of organic beings throughout time; in the twelfth and thirteenth, their geographical distribution throughout space; in the fourteenth, their classification or mutual affinities, both when mature and in an embryonic condition. In the last chapter I shall give a brief recapitulation of the whole work, and a few concluding remarks.

No one ought to feel surprise at much remaining as yet unexplained in regard to the origin of species and varieties, if he make due allowance for our profound ignorance in regard to the mutual relations of the many beings which live around us. Who can explain why one species ranges widely and is very numerous, and why another allied species has a narrow range and is rare? Yet these relations are of the highest importance, for they determine the present welfare and, as I believe, the future success and modification of every inhabitant of this world. Still less do we know of the mutual relations of the innumerable inhabitants of the world during the many past geological epochs in its history. Although much remains obscure, and will long remain obscure, I can entertain no doubt, after the most deliberate study and dispassionate judgment of which I am capable, that the view which most naturalists until recently entertained, and which I formerly entertained— namely, that each species has been independently created—is erroneous. I am fully convinced that species are not immutable; but that those belonging to what are called the same genera are lineal descendants of some other and generally extinct species, in the same manner as the acknowledged varieties of any one species are the descendants of that species. Furthermore, I am convinced that Natural Selection has been the most important, but not the exclusive, means of modification.

Chapter IV

Natural Selection; or the Survival of the Fittest

How will the struggle for existence, briefly discussed in the last chapter, act in regard to variation? Can the principle of selection, which we have seen is so potent in the hands of man, apply under nature? I think we shall see that it can act most efficiently. Let the endless number of slight variations and individual differences occurring in our domestic productions, and, in a lesser degree, in those under nature, be borne in mind; as well as the strength of the hereditary tendency. Under domestication, it may be truly said that the whole organisation becomes in some degree plastic. But the variability, which we almost universally meet with in our domestic productions, is not directly produced, as Hooker and Asa Gray have well remarked, by man; he can neither originate varieties, nor prevent their occurrence; he can preserve and accumulate such as do occur. Unintentionally he exposes organic beings to new and changing conditions of life, and variability ensues; but similar changes of conditions might and do occur under nature. Let it also be borne in mind how infinitely complex and close-fitting are the mutual relations of all organic beings to each other and to their physical conditions of life; and consequently what infinitely varied diversities of structure might be of use to each being under changing conditions of life. Can it, then, be thought improbable, seeing that variations useful to man have undoubtedly occurred, that other variations useful in some way to each being in the great and complex battle of life, should occur in the course of many successive generations? If such do occur, can we doubt (remembering that many more individuals are born than can possibly survive) that individuals having any advantage, however slight, over others, would have the best chance of surviving and of procreating their kind? On the other hand, we may feel sure that any variation in the least degree injurious would be rigidly destroyed. This preservation of favourable individual differences and variations, and the destruction of those which are injurious, I have called Natural Selection, or the Survival of the Fittest. Variations neither useful nor injurious would not be affected by natural selection, and would be left either a fluctuating element, as perhaps we see in certain polymorphic species, or would ultimately become fixed, owing to the nature of the organism and the nature of the conditions.

Several writers have misapprehended or objected to the term Natural Selection. Some have even imagined that natural selection induces variability, whereas it implies only the preservation of such variations as arise and are beneficial to the being under its conditions of life. No one objects to agriculturists speaking of the potent effects of man's selection; and in this case the individual differences given by nature, which man for some object selects, must of necessity first occur. Others have objected that the term selection implies conscious choice in the animals which become modified; and it has even been urged that, as plants have no volition, natural selection is not applicable to them! In the literal sense of the word, no doubt, natural selection is a false term; but who ever objected to chemists speaking of the elective affinities of the various elements?—and yet an acid cannot strictly be said to elect the base with which it in preference combines. It has been said that I speak of natural selection as an active power or Deity; but who objects to an author speaking of the attraction of gravity as ruling the movements of the planets? Every one knows what is meant and is implied by such metaphorical expressions; and they are almost necessary for brevity. So again it is difficult to avoid personifying the word Nature; but I mean by Nature, only the aggregate action and product of many natural laws, and by laws the sequence of events as ascertained by us. With a little familiarity such superficial objections will be forgotten.

We shall best understand the probable course of natural selection by taking the case of a country undergoing some slight physical change, for instance, of climate. The proportional numbers of its inhabitants will almost immediately undergo a change, and some species will probably become extinct. We may conclude, from what we have seen of the intimate and complex manner in which the inhabitants of each country are bound together, that any change in the numerical proportions of the inhabitants, independently of the change of climate itself, would seriously affect the others. If the country were open on its borders, new forms would certainly immigrate, and this would likewise seriously disturb the relations of some of the former inhabitants. Let it be remembered how powerful the influence of a single introduced tree or mammal has been shown to be. But in the case of an island, or of a country partly surrounded by barriers, into which new and better adapted forms could not freely enter, we should then have places in the economy of nature which would assuredly be better filled up, if some of the original inhabitants were in some manner modified; for, had the area been open to immigration, these same places would have been seized on by intruders. In such cases, slight modifications, which in any way favoured the individuals of any species, by better adapting them to their altered conditions, would tend to be preserved; and natural selection would have free scope for the work of improvement.

We have good reason to believe, as shown in the first chapter, that changes in the conditions of life give a tendency to increased variability; and in the foregoing cases the conditions have changed, and this would manifestly be favourable to natural selection, by affording a better chance of the occurrence of profitable variations. Unless such occur, natural selection can do nothing. Under the term of "variations," it must never be forgotten that mere individual differences are included. As man can produce a great result with his domestic animals and plants by adding up in any given direction individual differences, so could natural selection, but far more easily from having incomparably longer time for action. Nor do I believe that any great physical change, as of climate, or any unusual degree of isolation to check immigration, is necessary in order that new and unoccupied places should be left, for natural selection to fill up by improving some of the varying inhabitants. For as all the inhabitants of each country are struggling together with nicely balanced forces, extremely slight modifications in the structure or habits of one species would often give it an advantage over others; and still further modifications of the same kind would often still further increase the advantage, as long as the species continued under the same conditions of life and profited by similar means of subsistence and defence. No country can be named in which all the native inhabitants are now so perfectly adapted to each other and to the physical conditions under which they live, that none of them could be still better adapted or improved; for in all countries, the natives have been so far conquered by naturalised productions, that they have allowed some foreigners to take firm possession of the land. And as foreigners have thus in every country beaten some of the natives, we may safely conclude that the natives might have been modified with advantage, so as to have better resisted the intruders.

As man can produce, and certainly has produced, a great result by his methodical and unconscious means of selection, what may not natural selection effect? Man can act only on external and visible characters: Nature, if I may be allowed to personify the natural preservation or survival of the fittest, cares nothing for appearances, except in so far as they are useful to any being. She can act on every internal organ, on every shade of constitutional difference, on the whole machinery of life. Man selects only for his own good: Nature only for that of the being which she tends. Every selected character is fully exercised by her, as is implied by the fact of their selection. Man keeps the natives of many climates in the same country; he seldom exercises each selected character in some peculiar and fitting manner; he feeds a long and a short beaked pigeon on the same food; he does not exercise a long-backed or long-legged quadruped in any peculiar manner; he exposes sheep with long and short wool to the same climate. He does not allow the most vigorous males to struggle for the females. He does not rigidly destroy all inferior animals, but protects during each varying season, as far as lies in his power, all his productions. He often begins his selection by some half-monstrous form; or at least by some modification prominent enough to catch the eye or to be plainly useful to him. Under nature, the slightest differences of structure or constitution may well turn the nicely balanced scale in the struggle for life, and so be preserved. How fleeting are the wishes and efforts of man! how short his time! and consequently how poor will be his results, compared with those accumulated by Nature during whole geological periods! Can we wonder, then, that Nature's productions should be far "truer" in character than man's productions; that they should be infinitely better adapted to the most complex conditions of life, and should plainly bear the stamp of far higher workmanship?

It may metaphorically be said that natural selection is daily and hourly scrutinising, throughout the world, the slightest variations; rejecting those that are bad, preserving and adding up all that are good; silently and insensibly working, *whenever and wherever opportunity offers,* at the improvement of each organic being in relation to its organic and inorganic conditions of life. We see nothing of these slow changes in progress, until the hand of time has marked the lapse of ages, and then so imperfect is our view into long-past geological ages, that we see only that the forms of life are now different from what they formerly were.

In order that any great amount of modification should be effected in a species, a variety when once formed must again, perhaps after a long interval of time, vary or present individual differences of the same favourable nature as before; and these must be again preserved, and so onwards step by step. Seeing that individual differences of the same kind perpetually recur, this can hardly be considered as an unwarrantable assumption. But whether it is true, we can judge only by seeing how far the hypothesis accords with and explains the general phenomena of nature. On the other hand, the ordinary belief that the amount of possible variation is a strictly limited quantity is likewise a simple assumption.

Although natural selection can act only through and for the good of each being, yet characters and structures, which we are apt to consider as of very trifling importance, may thus be acted on. When we see leaf-eating insects green, and bark-feeders mottled-grey; the alpine ptarmigan white in winter, the red grouse the colour of heather, we must believe that these tints are of service to these birds and insects in preserving them from danger. Grouse, if not destroyed at some period of their lives, would increase in countless numbers; they are known to suffer largely from birds of prey; and hawks are guided by eyesight to their prey—so much so, that on parts of the Continent persons are warned not to keep white pigeons, as being the most liable to destruction. Hence natural selection might be effective in giving the proper colour to each kind of grouse, and in keeping that colour, when once acquired, true and constant. Nor ought we to think that the

occasional destruction of an animal of any particular colour would produce little effect: we should remember how essential it is in a flock of white sheep to destroy a lamb with the faintest trace of black. We have seen how the colour of the hogs, which feed on the "paint-root" in Virginia, determines whether they shall live or die. In plants, the down on the fruit and the colour of the flesh are considered by botanists as characters of the most trifling importance; yet we hear from an excellent horticulturist, Downing, that in the United States, smooth-skinned fruits suffer far more from a beetle, a Curculio, than those with down; that purple plums suffer far more from a certain disease than yellow plums; whereas another disease attacks yellow-fleshed peaches far more than those with other coloured flesh. If, with all the aids of art, these slight differences make a great difference in cultivating the several varieties, assuredly, in a state of nature, where the trees would have to struggle with other trees, and with a host of enemies, such differences would effectually settle which variety, whether a smooth or downy, a yellow or purple fleshed fruit, should succeed.

In looking at many small points of difference between species, which, as far as our ignorance permits us to judge, seem quite unimportant, we must not forget that climate, food, &c., have no doubt produced some direct effect. It is also necessary to bear in mind that, owing to the law of correlation, when one part varies, and the variations are accumulated through natural selection, other modifications, often of the most unexpected nature, will ensue.

As we see that those variations which, under domestication, appear at any particular period of life, tend to reappear in the offspring at the same period;—for instance, in the shape, size, and flavour of the seeds of the many varieties of our culinary and agricultural plants; in the caterpillar and cocoon stages of the varieties of the silk-worm; in the eggs of poultry, and in the colour of the down of their chickens; in the horns of our sheep and cattle when nearly adult;—so in a state of nature natural selection will be enabled to act on and modify organic beings at any age, by the accumulation of variations profitable at that age, and by their inheritance at a corresponding age. If it profit a plant to have its seeds more and more widely disseminated by the wind, I can see no greater difficulty in this being effected through natural selection, than in the cotton-planter increasing and improving by selection the down in the pods on his cotton-trees. Natural selection may modify and adapt the larva of an insect to a score of contingencies, wholly different from those which concern the mature insect; and these modifications may affect, through correlation, the structure of the adult. So, conversely, modifications in the adult may affect the structure of the larva; but in all cases natural selection will ensure that they shall not be injurious: for if they were so, the species would become extinct.

Natural selection will modify the structure of the young in relation to the parent, and of the parent in relation to the young. In social animals it will adapt the structure of each individual for the benefit of the whole community, if the community profits by the selected change. What natural selection cannot do, is to modify the structure of one species, without giving it any advantage, for the good of another species; and though statements to this effect may be found in works in natural history, I cannot find one case which will bear investigation. A structure used only once in an animal's life, if of high importance to it, might be modified to any extent by natural selection; for instance, the great jaws possessed by certain insects, used exclusively for opening the cocoon—or the hard tip to the beak of unhatched birds, used for breaking the egg. It has been asserted, that of the best short-beaked tumbler-pigeons a greater number perish in the egg than are able to get out of it; so that fanciers assist in the act of hatching. Now if nature had to make the beak of a full-grown pigeon very short for the bird's own advantage, the process of modification would be very slow, and there would be simultaneously the most rigorous selection of all the young birds within the egg, which had the most powerful and hardest beaks, for all with weak beaks would inevitably perish; or, more delicate and more easily broken shells might be selected, the thickness of the shell being known to vary like every other structure.

It may be well here to remark that with all beings there must be much fortuitous destruction, which can have little or no influence on the course of natural selection. For instance a vast number of eggs or seeds are annually devoured, and these could be modified through natural selection only if they varied in some manner which protected them from their enemies. Yet many of these eggs or seeds would perhaps, if not destroyed, have yielded individuals better adapted to their conditions of life than any of these which happened to survive. So again a vast number of mature animals and plants, whether or not they be the best adapted to their conditions, must be annually destroyed by accidental causes, which would not be in the least degree mitigated by certain changes of structure or constitution which would in other ways be beneficial to the species. But let the destruction of the adults be ever so heavy, if the number which can exist in any district be not wholly kept down by such causes,—or again let the destruction of eggs or seeds be so great that only a hundredth or a thousandth part are developed,—yet of those which do survive, the best adapted individuals, supposing that there is any variability in a favourable direction, will tend to propagate their kind in larger numbers than the less well adapted. If the numbers be wholly kept down by the causes just indicated, as will often have been the case, natural selection will be powerless in certain beneficial directions; but this is no valid objection to its efficiency at other times and in other ways; for we are far from having any reason to suppose that many species ever undergo modification and improvement at the same time in the same area.

Sexual Selection

Inasmuch as peculiarities often appear under domestication in one sex and become hereditarily attached to that sex, so no doubt it will be under nature. Thus it is rendered possible for the two sexes to be modified through natural selection in relation to different habits of life, as is sometimes the case; or for one sex to be modified in relation to the other sex, as commonly occurs. This leads me to say a few words on what I have called Sexual Selection. This form of selection depends, not on a struggle for existence in relation to other organic beings or to external conditions, but on a struggle between the individuals of one sex, generally the males, for the possession of the other sex. The result is not death to the unsuccessful competitor, but few or no offspring. Sexual selection is, therefore, less rigorous than natural selection. Generally, the most vigorous males, those which are best fitted for their places in nature, will leave most progeny. But in many cases, victory depends not so much on general vigor, as on having special weapons, confined to the male sex. A hornless stag or spurless cock would have a poor chance of leaving numerous offspring. Sexual selection, by always allowing the victor to breed, might surely give indomitable courage, length to the spur, and strength to the wing to strike in the spurred leg, in nearly the same manner as does the brutal cockfighter by the careful selection of his best cocks. How low in the scale of nature the law of battle descends, I know not; male alligators have been described as fighting, bellowing, and whirling round, like Indians in a war-dance, for the possession of the females; male salmons have been observed fighting all day long; male stag beetles sometimes bear wounds from the huge mandibles of other males; the males of certain hymenopterous insects have been frequently seen by that inimitable observer M. Fabre, fighting for a particular female who sits by, an apparently unconcerned beholder of the struggle, and then retires with the conqueror. The war is, perhaps, severest between the males of polygamous animals, and these seem oftenest provided with special weapons. The males of carnivorous animals are already well armed; though to them and to others, special means of defence may be given through means of sexual selection, as the mane of the lion, and the hooked jaw to the male salmon; for the shield may be as important for victory, as the sword or spear.

Amongst birds, the contest is often of a more peaceful character. All those who have attended to the subject, believe that there is the severest rivalry between the males of many species to attract, by singing, the females. The rock-thrush of Guiana, birds of paradise, and some others, congregate; and successive males display with the most elaborate care, and show off in the best manner, their gorgeous plumage; they likewise perform strange antics before the females, which, standing by as spectators, at last choose the most attractive partner. Those who have closely attended to birds in confinement well know that they often take individual preferences and dislikes: thus Sir R. Heron has described how a pied peacock was eminently attractive to all his hen birds. I cannot here enter on the necessary details; but if man can in a short time give beauty and an elegant carriage to his bantams, according to his standard of beauty, I can see no good reason to doubt that female birds, by selecting, during thousands of generations, the most melodious or beautiful males, according to their standard of beauty, might produce a marked effect. Some well-known laws, with respect to the plumage of male and female birds, in comparison with the plumage of the young, can partly be explained through the action of sexual selection on variations occurring at different ages, and transmitted to the males alone or to both sexes at corresponding ages; but I have not space here to enter on this subject.

Thus it is, as I believe, that when the males and females of any animal have the same general habits of life, but differ in structure, colour, or ornament, such differences have been mainly caused by sexual selection: that is, by individual males having had, in successive generations, some slight advantage over other males, in their weapons, means of defence, or charms, which they have transmitted to their male offspring alone. Yet, I would not wish to attribute all sexual differences to this agency: for we see in our domestic animals peculiarities arising and becoming attached to the male sex, which apparently have not been augmented through selection by man. The tuft of hair on the breast of the wild turkey-cock cannot be of any use, and it is doubtful whether it can be ornamental in the eyes of the female bird;—indeed, had the tuft appeared under domestication, it would have been called a monstrosity.

Illustrations of the Action of Natural Selection, or the Survival of the Fittest

In order to make it clear how, as I believe, natural selection acts, I must beg permission to give one or two imaginary illustrations. Let us take the case of a wolf, which preys on various animals, securing some by craft, some by strength, and some by fleetness; and let us suppose that the fleetest prey, a deer for instance, had from any change in the country increased in numbers, or that other prey had decreased in numbers, during that season of the year when the wolf was hardest pressed for food. Under such circumstances the swiftest and slimmest wolves would have the best chance of surviving and so be preserved or selected,—provided always that they retained strength to master their prey at this or some other period of the year, when they were compelled to prey on other animals. I can see no more reason to doubt that this would be the result, than that man should be able to improve the fleetness of his greyhounds by careful and methodical selection, or by that kind of unconscious selection which follows from each man trying to keep the best dogs without any thought of modifying the breed. I may add, that, according to Mr. Pierce, there are two varieties of the wolf inhabiting the Catskill Mountains, in the United States, one with a light greyhound-like form, which pursues deer, and the other more bulky, with shorter legs which more frequently attacks the shepherd's flocks.

It should be observed that, in the above illustration, I speak of the slimmest individual wolves; and not of any single strongly-marked variation having been preserved. In former editions of this work I sometimes spoke as if this latter alternative had frequently occurred. I saw the great importance of individual differences, and this led me fully to discuss the results of unconscious selection by man, which depends on the preservation of all the more or less valuable individuals, and on the destruction of the worst. I saw, also, that the preservation in a state of nature of any occasional deviation of structure, such as a monstrosity, would be a rare event; and that, if at first preserved, it would generally be lost by subsequent intercrossing with ordinary individuals. Nevertheless, until reading an able and valuable article in the *North British Review* (1867), I did not appreciate how rarely single variations, whether slight or strongly-marked, could be perpetuated. The author takes the case of a pair of animals, producing during their lifetime two hundred offspring, of which, from various causes of destruction, only two on an average survive to procreate their kind. This is rather an extreme estimate for most of the higher animals, but by no means so for many of the lower organisms. He then shows that if a single individual were born, which varied in some manner, giving it twice as good a chance of life as that of the other individuals, yet the chances would be strongly against its survival. Supposing it to survive and to breed, and that half its young inherited the favourable variation; still, as the reviewer goes on to show, the young would have only a slightly better chance of surviving and breeding; and this chance would go on decreasing in the succeeding generations. The justice of these remarks cannot, I think, be disputed. If, for instance, a bird of some kind could procure its food more easily by having its beak curved, and if one were born with its beak strongly curved, and which consequently flourished, nevertheless there would be a very poor chance of this one individual perpetuating its kind to the exclusion of the common form; but there can hardly be a doubt, judging by what we see taking place under domestication, that this result would follow from the preservation during many generations of a large number of individuals with more or less strongly curved beaks, and from the destruction of a still larger number with the straightest beaks.

It should not, however, be overlooked that certain rather strongly marked variations, which no one would rank as mere individual differences, frequently recur owing to a similar organisation being similarly acted on—of which fact numerous instances could be given with our domestic productions. In such cases, if the varying individual did not actually transmit to its offspring its newly-acquired character, it would undoubtedly transmit to them, as long as the existing conditions remained the same, a still stronger tendency to vary in the same manner. There can also be little doubt that the tendency to vary in the same manner has often been so strong that all the individuals of the same species have been similarly modified without the aid of any form of selection. Or only a third, fifth, or tenth part of the individuals may have been thus affected, of which fact several instances could be given. Thus Graba estimates that about one-fifth of the guillemots in the Faroe Islands consist of a variety so well marked, that it was formerly ranked as a distinct species under the name of *Uria lacrymans*. In cases of this kind, if the variation were of a beneficial nature, the original form would soon be supplanted by the modified form, through the survival of the fittest.

To the effects of intercrossing in eliminating variations of all kinds, I shall have to recur; but it may be here remarked that most animals and plants keep to their proper homes, and do not needlessly wander about; we see this even with migratory birds, which almost always return to the same spot. Consequently each newly-formed variety would generally be at first local, as seems to be the common rule with varieties in a state of nature; so that similarly modified individuals would soon exist in a small body together, and would often breed together. If the new variety were successful in its battle for life, it would slowly spread from a central district, competing with and conquering the unchanged individuals on the margins of an ever-increasing circle.

It may be worth while to give another and more complex illustration of the action of natural selection. Certain plants excrete sweet juice, apparently for the sake of eliminating something injurious from the sap: this is effected, for instance, by glands at the base of the stipules in some Leguminosæ, and at the backs of the leaves of the common laurel. This juice, though small in quantity, is greedily sought by insects; but their visits do not in any way benefit the plant. Now, let us suppose that the juice or nectar was excreted from the inside of the flowers of a certain number of plants of any species. Insects in seeking the nectar would get dusted with pollen, and would often transport it from one flower to another. The flowers of two distinct individuals of the same species would thus get crossed; and the act of crossing, as can be fully proved, gives rise to vigorous seedlings which consequently would have the best chance of flourishing and surviving. The plants which produced flowers with the largest glands or nectaries, excreting most nectar, would oftenest be visited by insects, and would oftenest be crossed; and so in the long run would gain the upper hand and form a local variety. The flowers, also, which had their stamens and pistils placed, in relation to the size and habits of the particular insects which visited them, so as to favour in any degree the transportal of the pollen, would likewise be favoured. We might have taken the case of insects visiting flowers for the sake of collecting pollen instead of nectar; and as pollen is formed for the sole purpose of fertilisation, its destruction appears to be a simple loss to the plant; yet if a little pollen were carried, at first occasionally and then habitually, by the pollen-devouring insects from flower to flower, and a cross thus effected, although nine-tenths of the pollen were destroyed it might still be a great gain to the plant to be thus robbed; and the individuals which produced more and more pollen, and had larger anthers, would be selected.

When our plant, by the above process long continued, had been rendered highly attractive to insects, they would, unintentionally on their part, regularly carry pollen from flower to flower; and that they do this effectually, I could easily show by many striking facts. I will give only one, as likewise illustrating one step in the separation of the sexes of plants. Some holly-trees bear only male flowers, which have four stamens producing a rather small quantity of pollen, and a rudimentary pistil; other holly-trees bear only female flowers; these have a full-sized pistil, and four stamens with shrivelled anthers, in which not a grain of pollen can be detected. Having found a female tree exactly sixty yards from a male tree, I put the stigmas of twenty flowers, taken from different branches, under the microscope, and on all, without exception, there were a few pollen-grains, and on some a profusion. As the wind had set for several days from the female to the male tree, the pollen could not thus have been carried. The weather had been cold and boisterous, and therefore not favourable to the bees, nevertheless every female flower which I examined had been effectually fertilised by the bees, which had flown from tree to tree in search of nectar. But to return to our imaginary case: as soon as the plant had been rendered so highly attractive to insects that pollen was regularly carried from flower to flower, another process might commence. No naturalist doubts the advantage of what has been called the "physiological division of labour"; hence we may believe that it would be advantageous to a plant to produce stamens alone in one flower or on one whole plant, and pistils alone in another flower or on another plant. In plants under culture and placed under new conditions of life, sometimes the male organs and sometimes the female organs become more or less impotent; now if we suppose this to occur in ever so slight a degree under nature, then, as pollen is already carried regularly from flower to flower, and as a more complete separation of the sexes of our plant would be advantageous on the principle of the division of labour, individuals with this tendency more and more increased, would be continually favoured or selected, until at last a complete separation of the sexes might be effected. It would take up too much space to show the various steps, through dimorphism and other means, by which the separation of the sexes in plants of various kinds is apparently now in progress; but I may add that some of the species of holly in North America, are, according to Asa Gray, in an exactly intermediate condition, or, as he expresses it, are more or less diœciously polygamous.

Let us now turn to the nectar-feeding insects; we may suppose the plant, of which we have been slowly increasing the nectar by continued selection, to be a common plant; and that certain insects depended in main part on its nectar for food. I could give many facts showing how anxious bees are to save time: for instance, their habit of cutting holes and sucking the nectar at the bases of certain flowers, which, with a very little more trouble, they can enter by the mouth. Bearing such facts in mind, it may be believed that under certain circumstances individual differences in the curvature or length of the proboscis, &c., too slight to be appreciated by us, might profit a bee or other insect, so that certain individuals would be able to obtain their food more quickly than others; and thus the communities to which they belonged would flourish and throw off many swarms inheriting the same peculiarities. The tubes of the corolla of the common red and incarnate clovers (*Trifolium pratense* and *incarnatum*) do not on a hasty glance appear to differ in length; yet the hive-bee can easily suck the nectar out of the incarnate clover, but not out of the common red clover, which is visited by humble-bees alone; so that whole fields of red clover offer in vain an abundant supply of precious nectar to the hive-bee. That this nectar is much liked by the hive-bee is certain; for I have repeatedly seen, but only in the autumn, many hive-bees sucking the flowers through holes bitten in the base of the tube by humble-bees. The difference in the length of the corolla in the two kinds of clover, which determines the visits of the hive-bee, must be very trifling; for I have been assured that when red clover has been mown, the flowers of the second crop are somewhat smaller, and that these are visited by many hive-bees. I do not know whether this statement is accurate; nor whether another published statement can be trusted, namely, that the Ligurian bee which is generally considered a mere variety of the common hive-bee, and which freely crosses with it, is able to reach and suck the nectar of the red clover. Thus, in a country where this kind of clover abounded, it might be a great advantage to the hive-bee to have a slightly longer or differently constructed proboscis. On the other hand, as the fertility of this clover absolutely depends on bees visiting the flowers, if humble-bees were to become rare in any country, it might be a great advantage to the plant to have a shorter or more deeply divided corolla, so that the hive-bees should be enabled to suck its flowers. Thus I can understand how a flower and a bee might slowly become, either simultaneously or one after the other, modified and adapted to each other in the most perfect manner, by the continued preservation of all the individuals which presented slight deviations of structure mutually favourable to each other.

I am well aware that this doctrine of natural selection, exemplified in the above imaginary instances, is open to the same objections which were first urged against Sir Charles Lyell's noble views on "the modern changes of the earth, as illustrative of geology"; but we now seldom hear the agencies which we see still at work, spoken of as trifling or insignificant, when used in explaining the excavation of the deepest valleys or the formation of long lines of inland cliffs. Natural selection acts only by the preservation and accumulation of small inherited modifications, each profitable to the preserved being; and as modern geology has almost banished such views as the excavation of a great valley by a single diluvial wave, so will natural selection banish the belief of the continued creation of new organic beings, or of any great and sudden modification in their structure.

Institutions
of
Science

CSIRO
Australia's Science Powerhouse

by John W. Stocker

Early in the 20th century Australia's leaders envisioned a national laboratory that would benefit the country's economic mainstays of agriculture, pastoralism, and mining. The organization that they created has since grown into the largest, most wide-ranging research establishment in Australia.

In 1916 Australia's Prime Minister William M. Hughes spoke of using science to make the deserts of Australia bloom. In that year he convened a conference to establish a national laboratory. Some mark the date as the foundation of the Commonwealth Scientific and Industrial Research Organisation (CSIRO), which today is the largest scientific research institution in Australia. Nevertheless, another decade would pass before anything like the current organization began to emerge.

Rather than immediately creating a research laboratory, the conference decided to establish a Bureau of Information in Melbourne. W.B. Alexander, a biologist with the Western Australian Museum, became its first employee, bearing the official title of science abstractor. Alexander's primary job was to be a scientific librarian, but by 1919 the bureau had been authorized by Australia's minister for trade and customs to answer queries and give advice. Some of the inquiries that are listed in the bureau's 1919 report give a flavor of the times; others are almost prophetic. Information had been requested about, among other things, the manufacture of small-bore tubes for water, gas, and steam; analysis and manufacturing processes of sheep-dips; an electrical method for prospecting for mineral ores; the supply, demand, and uses of magnesite, an industrially important magnesium-containing mineral; and, far in advance of its time, the use and applications of solar energy as they had been observed in Egypt.

In 1920 an act was passed establishing a permanent scientific institute, and in 1925 the Australian government convened a further conference of scientific and industrial leaders to advise on how best the institute should be organized and its activities extended.

Foundation and early work

As a result of the Science and Industry Research Act of 1926, the Bureau of Information became the Council for Scientific and Industrial Research (CSIR). The first chairman of CSIR was George Julius, a consulting engineer. Just before he was appointed, he delivered the presidential address to the Institution of Engineers in Hobart, Tasmania. His subject was "Australian made," and his speech was a strongly put argument for improving the linkages between Australian science, technology, and industry.

Although CSIR's early years were marked by fluctuating political and financial support, a number of scientific successes were recorded. A.C.D. Rivett, a chemist, was appointed permanent chief executive officer, and under his guidance CSIR devoted most of its resources during the years before World War II to agricultural and veterinary science in support of Australia's primary industry.

An important CSIR campaign, for both scientific and political reasons, was the eradication of prickly pear, an American cactus of the genus *Opuntia*. The plants had been introduced deliberately to Australia in the early 19th century by pastoralists as a form of hedging. Unfortunately, the prickly pear thrived in Australia, where it enjoyed a suitable climate and no natural enemies. Large tracts of New South Wales and Queensland, as much as 23.5 million hectares (58 million acres), became dominated by the pest. A variety of uses for the cactus were proposed—a fermentation base for alcohol manufacture, a source of pulp for paper manufacture, stock feed—but none was successful. Also unsuccessful were attempts to eradicate the plant by mechanical or chemical means.

After a long-running program of research, first in Texas (where it was observed that the cactus was controlled naturally by indigenous insect predators) and then in quarantine laboratories in Brisbane, several

472

Investigators from CSIR's Division of Plant Industry (top) gather data for the control of skeleton weed, a pest of pastures and wheat crops, at Cowra, New South Wales, in the 1930s. At that time CSIR initiated a program of research into noxious weeds, most of which had been introduced into Australia. Some plants had been carried into the country on clothing, on the coats and feet of livestock, or in commercial seed mixes; others were "escapees" from domestic gardens. In modern times CSIRO has achieved some control of skeleton weed with the introduction of a rust fungus. The control of introduced rabbits (bottom), whose numbers had reached plague proportions by the early 1900s, was a major target of CSIR and CSIRO research in the 1930s and '40s. A series of trials with myxoma virus, which is deadly to rabbits, culminated in the induction of a widespread myxomatosis epidemic in the wild rabbit population.

species of insect were identified that showed potential for controlling the cactus. Finally, in 1926, larvae from 3,000 eggs of the cactus moth (*Cactoblastis cactorum*) were released on Australian land. Within 18 months it was clear that the operation was a success; in some cases the rapidly spreading insect population destroyed areas of prickly pear even before owners of the land had received their own consignments of cactus moth eggs. Although CSIR scientists were aware that prickly pear had presented them with a unique opportunity to demonstrate biological control techniques and that similar successes might be hard to repeat, the cactus moth story established the idea of biological control in Australia's popular culture as well as in the more cautious culture of Australian scientists.

Beginning in the late 1700s, rabbits were introduced into Australia with the first European settlers (who also went to great pains to re-create their homeland by releasing larks, sparrows, and foxes). At first, rabbits were regarded as a minor pest, and at times they even provided certain benefits; during the Great Depression of the 1930s, for example, they served as a source of income for trappers, the skins being in great demand for fur felt, and as a source of food for impoverished rural families, who called the flesh "underground mutton." Increasingly during the early 20th century, however, rabbits became recognized as a plague in Australia. In many places not a blade of grass survived, bushes were stripped of leaves, and livestock were unable to find fodder.

Experiments on the biological control of rabbits were carried out with the myxoma virus in England in 1934, with inconclusive results, and again in 1936 in Australia. Although it was demonstrated that myxomatosis, the disease caused by the virus, was deadly to rabbits, the necessary vector to spread the disease did not seem to be available. In 1949 Francis Ratcliffe of the Wildlife Survey Section of the newly formed CSIRO, the successor to CSIR, decided that further trials were necessary, and he was enthusiastically supported by the new CSIRO chairman, Ian Clunies Ross. After more inconclusive results—outbreaks

CSIR's Plant Pathology Laboratory, pictured two years after its opening in 1930 at the Division of Plant Industry, Canberra, undertook research into such crops as tobacco, apples, tomatoes, wheat, and bananas. Today CSIRO's Division of Plant Industry is a world leader in the field of plant genetic engineering.

475

The animal on the left is afflicted with coast disease, a wasting illness of sheep that long resisted the efforts of veterinarians to understand its cause. In the 1930s CSIR brought the expertise of a wide variety of scientists to bear on the problem. A CSIR chemist's discovery of the cause of the disease, a cobalt deficiency of the soil, led to an important period of research into the role of trace elements in animal health and nutrition.

(Opposite page) An early radar device developed by CSIR's Division of Radiophysics was the Light Weight Air Warning (LW/AW) Mark I (top). The equipment was first set up in a Sydney suburb in September 1942 and was dispatched for World War II service to New Guinea the following month. The LW/AW radar gave Australian and U.S. forces in the southern Pacific theater of operations a decided advantage over the Japanese, who did not possess radar until very late in the war. The MV Warreen (bottom) was the first research vessel of CSIR's Division of Fisheries. Used variously for exploratory fishing, oceanography, hydrology, and plankton studies, it also served the Royal Australian Navy during World War II and was involved in British atomic bomb tests off the coast of Australia in the early 1950s.

of myxomatosis remained local and then died out—a release of the virus in the Murray River Valley in the Victoria-New South Wales border area near Albury suddenly blossomed into an epidemic of myxomatosis. Within two months the Melbourne *Argus* carried the headline "Farmers' New Ally Kills 90% of Rabbits."

Public acceptance is a necessity for public science. By an unfortunate coincidence the myxoma virus releases were accompanied by an outbreak of a serious disease of humans called Murray Valley encephalitis. The idea spread that the encephalitis was related to myxomatosis and that people were being infected by diseased rabbits. Something had to be done to persuade people that rabbits could be controlled without risk to humans. Three prominent scientists—CSIRO's Clunies Ross, microbiologist F.J. Fenner of the Australian National University, Canberra, and medical scientist Frank Macfarlane Burnet of the Walter and Eliza Hall Institute of Medical Research, Melbourne—allowed themselves publicly to be injected with doses of myxoma virus sufficient to kill 100–1,000 rabbits each. It was an effective demonstration of the safety of the virus for humans.

Today rabbits are kept to manageable numbers by the disease, which has become endemic. There is concern that strains of rabbit with immunity to myxomatosis may become dominant, and research is continuing into a variety of biological control mechanisms. It has also been recognized that the control of rabbits implies the need to control foxes, because a reduction in the population of one without that of the other could have disastrous consequences. A shortage of rabbits could drive foxes to destroy more poultry and native animals than they do now, while a drop in the numbers of foxes could inadvertently cause a rabbit population explosion.

Not all of CSIR's early research involved the control of pests. A notable success was the treatment and cure of coast disease, a wasting disease of sheep that had baffled veterinarians since the early days of settlement in

South Australia. Coast disease was common along a large strip of coastal country stretching through Victoria and part of South Australia, where it was especially serious because of the relatively small amount of well-watered grazing land in that state. It had been noticed that sick animals that were moved to disease-free country quickly recovered. Various suggestions were offered, including infestation with worms or a mineral deficiency, but no cause was determined.

In 1930 CSIR started its own investigation in South Australia and, unlike the state veterinarians, it was able to call on a wide variety of scientists: biochemists, soil scientists, geologists, and agrostologists (botanists who specialize in grasses) in addition to veterinarians. Even then it took a piece of inspired deduction by a chemist from the Division of Animal Nutrition, Dick Thomas, to determine that the cause of coast disease was cobalt deficiency of the soil. This discovery pointed the way to a cure—cobalt pellets given orally to the animals by means of an applicator. It also led to an important period of research into the importance of trace elements, with major economic consequences for Australia, as areas previously considered poor could be opened up for agriculture or grazing.

Industry and war

By 1936 CSIR had begun to become involved in secondary industry and in a proposal for a national standards laboratory. Many Australian scientists and industrialists were becoming acutely aware of the country's degree of dependence on imports of machinery and equipment. To some extent this situation had been stimulated by World War I, and the political uncertainties of the 1930s added to the momentum. A number of experiences, particularly in the manufacture of small arms, demonstrated that Australia's industry had no choice but to ensure that national standards of measurement conformed exactly with those of Great Britain, Europe, and the United States. To better understand the requirements and

Mining operations at Kunwarara, Queensland, site of the largest known deposit of magnesite, are shown in an aerial view. Two divisions of the Institute of Minerals, Energy and Construction are involved in a national project to aid Australia's magnesite industry, which will soon benefit from a new magnesium-extraction process developed with CSIRO contributions.

operation of a national standards institute, CSIR scientists spent time at the National Physical Laboratory in England and the U.S. National Bureau of Standards. The Australian National Standards Laboratory was then approved, to be situated in the grounds of the University of Sydney. The laboratory building was completed and occupied in 1940, and of necessity the facility operated almost entirely for defense production in its first years.

Meanwhile, CSIR became involved in urgent wartime technological research. Much of it was aimed at enabling Australia to produce aircraft and aircraft engines, and important work was done on lubricants and bearings.

The development of radar, in particular, played a key role in the history of Australian science. In 1939 the British government approached Australia's Prime Minister Joseph Lyons with an offer to provide details of a secret defense project. David Martyn, a physicist, was chosen to receive the information because he had been doing research into the upper atmosphere for CSIR's Radio Research Board and had been in continuous correspondence with colleagues in England, including Edward Appleton and, until his death in 1937, Ernest Rutherford. He returned from England to Australia by sea, carrying secret documents and a number of electron tubes in a lead-lined trunk.

478

CSIR's Division of Radiophysics was formed (the name being deliberately vague) and attached to the National Standards Laboratory in Sydney. Whereas the British by this time had developed radar to the point of being able to locate a moving aircraft at a distance of 160 kilometers (100 miles), the CSIR laboratory was charged with the development of equipment suitable for Australia's conditions. Starting at Dover Heights in Sydney, the first Australian installation was built. By the end of 1940 the technical success of this early equipment had convinced the Australian army that the coastal defense system should be extended to cover the main northern ports and approaches. Eventually 37 sets of radar equipment were installed in northern Australia, with others at Port Moresby and Rabaul in Papua New Guinea. Because the equipment continued to be regarded as top secret, radar scientists sometimes ran into difficulty communicating its potential to a skeptical military without divulging too many details.

Overall, the Division of Radiophysics contributed a large number of technological innovations to the war effort and, in the years that followed, it pioneered applications of the principles of radar to radio astronomy and aircraft navigation. The latter category includes a microwave-based approach-and-landing system for aircraft, Interscan, which the International Civil Aviation Organization recognizes as the standard.

This water-treatment plant, which supplies clean water for Sheffield, England, uses the Sirofloc process developed by a CSIRO research team. Sirofloc exploits the electrical and magnetic properties of particles of magnesite, a form of iron oxide, to aggregate and remove organic substances from polluted water.

479

Postwar highlights

CSIR was reconstituted in 1949 by the Science and Industry Research Act as the Commonwealth Scientific and Industrial Research Organisation. The new organization gave up defense work to concentrate its full effort on its peacetime program, which had expanded to include such areas of research as meteorology, metallurgy, building materials, coal, and textiles in addition to agriculture and pastoralism.

One of CSIRO's major postwar developments can be traced to a day in 1952 when Alan Walsh, a Lancashire-born physicist, was tending his garden in Melbourne. As he worked, his mind was fixed on a problem that had baffled scientists for a century: how to measure small concentrations of metallic elements by using spectroscopy. All previous attempts to solve the problem had involved measuring radiative emissions after vaporizing a sample, but suddenly Walsh saw that the best results could be obtained from a measurement of light absorption. Within a few hours Walsh constructed an experimental prototype of his absorption spectrometer. Nevertheless, it took him years of work to refine his invention and to convince other scientists of its value. Today the atomic absorption spectrometer is a standard item of hospital equipment and is used in factories and laboratories around the world for measuring traces of metallic elements.

Scientists in many CSIRO divisions historically have been involved with improving Australia's sheep and wool industry. Sirospun, for example, is a technique developed over 15 years in the 1970s and early '80s to improve wool spinning. In combining the traditional processes of spinning and twisting into one operation and doubling the quantity of twofold yarn produced from a given number of spindles, Sirospun cuts the cost of spinning by 56%. The technique also makes possible the fine wool used for Cool Wool, a lightweight, "transseasonal" clothing fabric. Over the years CSIRO researchers also have found a variety of innovative uses for wool based on the fiber's excellent insulation characteristics. They

Infestation of cotton bolls by caterpillars (below) is expected to be substantially reduced in cotton plants genetically engineered by CSIRO scientists to produce their own biological insecticide against the cotton bollworm. The insecticide is harmless to humans, other mammals, and beneficial arthropods such as spiders. An array of rail-mounted, movable dish antennas (opposite page, top), located at Culgoora, New South Wales, serves as the core of the Australia Telescope, a radio telescope facility operated by the Division of Radiophysics. To gain greater resolution and sensitivity, the array can be linked with other antennas nearby and scattered across the Australian continent. The A4 chip (opposite page, bottom), a microchip designed by the Division of Radiophysics for home and automobile sound systems, derives from technology developed for radio astronomy.

include protective clothing for people who work long hours in extreme temperatures, space-age tents for harsh conditions, wool-filled quilts, and even insulation for buildings in extreme-temperature environments. Yet another development has been so-called self-shearing sheep, or biological wool harvesting, which involves injecting sheep with a natural protein, epidermal growth factor. The injection temporarily interrupts hair growth, causing a weak spot to develop in each strand of wool. In about a month the whole fleece can be removed easily by hand.

Today's science

Australia's science and technology have always been determined by the realities of the Australian continent: vast distances, little water, and shallow topsoil. Consequently, the country has developed characteristic areas of expertise: transport and communications, remote sensing, soil and water management, and arid-zone farming, as well as the exploitation of minerals and petrochemicals. Some examples of current CSIRO research give an idea of the range of projects that are undertaken.

The world's largest known deposit of magnesite is at Kunwarara in central Queensland. Atypical of Australian mining areas, the site has excellent access to a major highway, National Highway 1, and to the cities of Rockhampton and Gladstone, the latter an important seaport. Two divisions from CSIRO's Institute of Minerals, Energy and Construction are closely involved in the Australian Magnesium Research and Development Project. The $A 50 million project is funded by the federal and

481

Queensland governments in conjunction with Queensland Metals Corp., M.I.M. Holdings of Brisbane, and Ube Industries Ltd. of Japan.

Excellent progress has been made in the first 18 months of the project. An electrolytic process for extracting magnesium in the form of high-purity anhydrous magnesium chloride from magnesite has been substantially developed with contributions from CSIRO, M.I.M., and Ube scientists. A final pilot-plant design is expected in mid-1994. The long-term future for the magnesite industry in Australia thus seems assured, with applications ranging from effluent treatment, lightweight metal parts for the automotive industry, improved linings for steelmaking furnaces, and magnesium-based cements and building products.

In 1977 a CSIRO research team devised a water-purification technique based on the fact that particles of magnetite, a magnetic form of iron oxide, develop a positive electrical surface charge in acidic chemical environments. When magnetite particles are added to a batch of polluted water, which is naturally acidic, their positive charge attracts negatively charged organic pollutants present in the water. Exposing this mixture to a magnetic field temporarily magnetizes the magnetite particles, which clump together and sink, carrying along the attached pollutants to form a sludge. The purified water then can be drawn off the top, while the magnetite particles can be separated from the sludge and reused. Subsequent research and development resulted in a practical process that CSIRO dubbed Sirofloc, and in 1983 the first commercial Sirofloc plant was built at Bell Bay in Tasmania. Two plants were ordered by the

A Japanese woman (above) evaluates an Australian breakfast cereal at CSIRO's Sensory Research Centre in an experiment designed to examine the effects of different sweetness levels on the product preferences of Japanese and Australian consumers. Noninvasive imaging (right) maps different patterns of cellular activity in the nose when different odors stimulate the olfactory receptors. The investigation is part of the Sensory Research Centre's efforts to develop a better understanding of how the nose works.

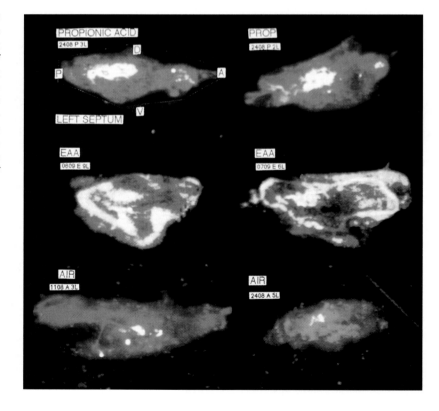

Yorkshire (England) Water Authority to provide clean water, the bigger of the two providing drinking water to 55,000 people in Sheffield.

In 1993 the first Sirofloc plant designed for sewage treatment opened at Malabar near Sydney, the result of a collaboration between CSIRO, the Sydney Water Board, and a Melbourne-based engineering firm, Davy John Brown. The performance of the plant has been remarkable, the rate of raw-sewage clarification being far in excess of that achieved by treatment plants based on other advanced physical and chemical processes or conventional biological processes. Sirofloc can remove 85% of suspended matter and 90% of oils and greases from sewage within 15 minutes. By contrast, it would take 10 hours to obtain the same results from a conventional plant. Whereas the Malabar pilot plant is adequate for a population of 20,000 people, Sirofloc collaborators are negotiating commercial contracts for much larger populations and expect to attract an international market.

Cotton production in Australia historically has relied on very heavy insecticide use to control the crop's major pest, cotton bollworms, which are caterpillars of *Heliothis* moths. Computer-based integrated-pest-management packages have been developed by CSIRO to reduce the amount of chemicals used by the industry, but an additional problem has been the bollworm's increasing resistance to conventional insecticides. The Division of Entomology has taken a number of approaches to the control of *Heliothis*. For example, studies of the genetic basis of resistance to pesticides are showing how resistance develops and what strategies need to be adopted. Meanwhile, the Division of Plant Industry is developing new varieties of cotton that are less attractive to insect pests. In 1992 the division conducted field trials to test genetically engineered plants that produce their own biological insecticide, which kills the bollworm within 24 hours. The insecticide, a natural protein product of a bacterium, does

CSIRO's head office is located at Parkville in Melbourne. The organization comprises more than 100 sites around Australia that together employ over 7,000 people.

483

not harm humans, other mammals, or natural predators such as spiders. It is activated only in the gut of the pest caterpillar.

A new way of delivering therapeutic drugs and vaccines, nicknamed the Trojan bullet, is being developed by CSIRO's Division of Tropical Animal Production in Brisbane. Although the technology was originally intended for treating diseases of livestock, researchers plan to use it against diseases of humans as well. Initially the focus will be on vaccines against the Epstein-Barr virus, which is the agent of infectious mononucleosis, or glandular fever, and the papillomavirus, which causes cervical cancer. The Trojan bullet is a synthetic virus particle that has been constructed so that it cannot reproduce or cause disease. Instead, the particle makes use of the natural infective ability of viruses in order to target and penetrate cells of diseased or infected tissue. Once inside the cell, it releases genes that carry the code for a specific protein product, for example, a therapeutic drug or a substance that stimulates the body's immune system. The effectiveness of the system was demonstrated when the CSIRO research team, with colleagues in Paris, developed the world's first synthetic rabies virus particle.

The A4 chip, a microchip designed by CSIRO's Division of Radiophysics for home and automobile applications, can make an ordinary stereo system sound like a concert hall. The technology for the A4 chip derives from radio astronomy and astronomical signal processing. Intended to be a very low-cost component, the device provides sound equalization and generates spatial effects that can simulate conditions in a concert hall or other acoustic environment.

In 1992 CSIRO's chairman, Adrienne Clarke, opened the new Sensory Research Centre in Sydney as an addition to the organization's Food Research Laboratory. One recent undertaking for the research center, called the Japan Project, is an innovative research effort aimed at determining the food preferences of Japanese consumers, their sensory responses to Australian products, and the factors underlying these responses. Initiated in 1990, the project has two main objectives: to provide scientific data on the taste preferences of the Japanese and to provide a service to Australian food companies that wish to market their products in Japan. The project selects consumers from Japan and Australia to participate in "blind" evaluations of food products. The Sensory Research Centre also carries out sophisticated chemosensory research into the basic mechanisms of olfaction, taste, and oral and nasal pungency. In addition, it is conducting a program to develop chemical sensors, based on an understanding of how the nose functions, that will be applied to improving quality and efficiency in food production.

The Southern Ocean Cloud Experiment (SOCEX), organized by the CSIRO Division of Atmospheric Research, is designed to find out more about the likely effect of human activity on clouds and global temperatures. Industrialization, especially in the Northern Hemisphere, is increasing the concentration of particulate matter in the atmosphere. The particles act as nuclei for the condensation of water droplets and thus affect the distribution and composition of clouds. The amount of

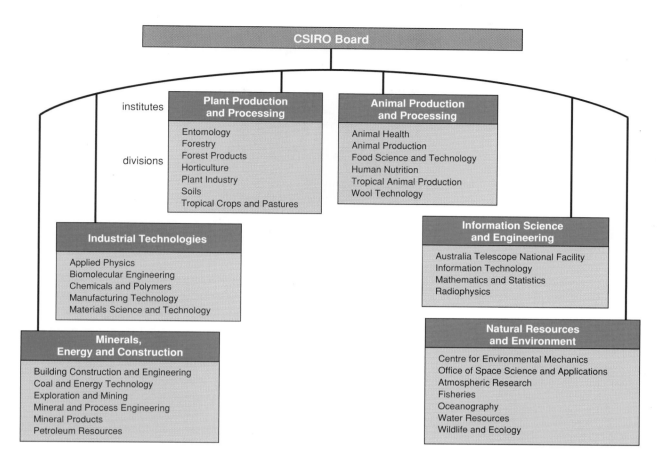

CSIRO Board

institutes

divisions

Plant Production and Processing
Entomology
Forestry
Forest Products
Horticulture
Plant Industry
Soils
Tropical Crops and Pastures

Animal Production and Processing
Animal Health
Animal Production
Food Science and Technology
Human Nutrition
Tropical Animal Production
Wool Technology

Industrial Technologies
Applied Physics
Biomolecular Engineering
Chemicals and Polymers
Manufacturing Technology
Materials Science and Technology

Information Science and Engineering
Australia Telescope National Facility
Information Technology
Mathematics and Statistics
Radiophysics

Minerals, Energy and Construction
Building Construction and Engineering
Coal and Energy Technology
Exploration and Mining
Mineral and Process Engineering
Mineral Products
Petroleum Resources

Natural Resources and Environment
Centre for Environmental Mechanics
Office of Space Science and Applications
Atmospheric Research
Fisheries
Oceanography
Water Resources
Wildlife and Ecology

solar energy absorbed and reflected by the clouds may change and, in turn, affect global temperatures.

The future global climate will depend very much on the composition of clouds. Ocean plankton, the collection of microscopic and near-microscopic organisms that live at or near the sea surface, release sulfur-containing gases, which generate natural cloud nuclei. In winter cloud nuclei concentrations are low. In summer, when plankton are more active, there are far more cloud nuclei in the atmosphere. By making measurements in winter and then again in summer, SOCEX scientists are working to determine how increased levels of cloud nuclei change cloud properties.

Organization

In the mid-1990s CSIRO employed more than 7,000 people at more than 100 sites around Australia. The head office is situated at Parkville in Melbourne. The organization is divided into six institutes that broadly target the main sectors of industry; together the institutes comprise 35 divisions (*see* Figure). There is considerable crossover among the various divisions and areas of expertise, and it is one of the major strengths of CSIRO as an organization that it can summon up a very powerful interdisciplinary team to approach and solve real-life problems as they occur.

485

For example, Australia has been plagued in recent summers by potentially toxic blooms, or sudden population explosions, of cyanobacteria (blue-green algae) in the main waterways. These blooms have had serious effects on rural life and production along the length of the waterways, and in response water authorities have been able to attack the problem by calling upon CSIRO water scientists, soil scientists, specialists in sediment tracing, remote-sensing experts, waste-management technologists, and the whole range of scientific skills available throughout the organization.

CSIRO is a statutory authority, established in its present form by legislation passed in 1986. Policy is determined by a 10-member board, although the organization is ultimately answerable to Australia's minister for science. The board includes a chief executive, presently John Stocker, who is responsible for the organization's activities, and a board chairman, Adrienne Clarke. The principal source of funds for CSIRO is the Australian taxpayer, through government allocation. Nevertheless, CSIRO must also heed a government-imposed requirement for the organization to earn at least 30% of its funds from "external," that is, commercial, sources.

Setting priorities

Clearly, in an organization as large and diverse as CSIRO, aims must be constantly kept in view and held up against the needs and imperatives of the time. Priority decisions for the whole of CSIRO are made every three years. By the terms of the present legislation, the minister for science may direct that certain research be undertaken and may argue a case for or against particular funding items in Cabinet, but the major strategic decisions are made by CSIRO's board on the basis of recommendations made by an executive committee comprising the chief executive and the directors of institutes. The most recent triennium funding decision, announced in March 1993, was for priority to be given to research in the areas of mineral resources, manufacturing industries, and information and communication industries and for funding to be maintained at the

486

previous level for environmental knowledge and environmental aspects of economic development.

Decisions are based on a systematic assessment of research priorities throughout CSIRO. The executive committee meets and considers in turn various research areas. This is done not in a random way but by means of a sophisticated priority-setting procedure that involves careful analysis of such sectors as agriculture, mining, and energy resources while including some unusual additional sectors, highly relevant to CSIRO, such as environmental knowledge.

CSIRO's board has the final say on priority areas, which are identified during a process of debate, discussion, and actual voting by members of the executive committee. The various sectors are allocated positions on a graph whose axes are "attractiveness" and "feasibility." When this system was first devised, the axis "attractiveness" was more simply labeled "benefits." It was a CSIRO modification to the system to add the notion of "capturability" of the benefits.

The final graph from the March 1993 priority-setting workshop, labeled "Return to Australia," is the basis for the executive committee's recommendations to the board. In a summation of the workshop, the committee stated:

Our examination of Australia's future needs and CSIRO's capacity to contribute has identified: the growing importance and impact of multi-Divisional and multi-disciplinary projects and programs in CSIRO; the importance of marketing research capability to State and Federal Government agencies; the need to encourage Rural Industry R & D Corporation funding of large research programs; [and] the importance of Federal Government financial stimulus for small and emerging companies in their quest for growth through innovation.

Systematic assessment of priority areas for research at CSIRO is carried out with the aid of a graph having "attractiveness" and "feasibility" as axes. Various programs for consideration are allocated positions on the graph, a process that helps in visualizing the merits of each relative to the others.

CSIRO's future

CSIRO has as its mission the carrying out of scientific research to assist Australian industry, to benefit the Australian community, and to encourage the application of the results of scientific research. Since its founding the organization has maintained a close relationship with the traditional suppliers of Australia's wealth: the mining and minerals industry, agriculture, and the pastoral industry.

CSIRO will continue to maintain its traditional strengths in these sectors but will also expand into other fields. Its latest priority assessment is taking it into the manufacturing sector and the information-and-communication sector, where Australian industry is posting significant growth. CSIRO is also taking keen note of the emerging importance of smaller businesses in world trade. A study in 1992 by the international consultants McKinsey & Co., New York City, found that the most innovative and export-oriented sector of Australia's economy was a group of about 700 small to medium-sized enterprises, quickly dubbed the Magnificent Seven Hundred by the media.

The way in which some small and medium-sized firms operate reflects certain underlying changes in the way that work is undertaken in today's information age. An individual with a personal computer, a phone, and a facsimile machine can now play a powerful international business role. CSIRO is recognizing that this capability has major implications for the commercialization of technology. This is especially so in the transfer of research results from the public to the private sector, which, after all, is in essence an information transfer. CSIRO has established a team to look into the issue and come up with long-term strategies for strengthening the links between CSIRO and small to medium-sized business enterprises.

CSIRO's outreach to these enterprises is symbolic of the need to reach into all sectors of Australia's society. For CSIRO to be effective, the society that it serves must be willing to support government funding of research and development and be prepared to embrace the changes in work and lifestyle that technological advances bring and that the conservation of the environment demands. In her introduction to CSIRO's Strategic Plan 1992–1996, Chairman Clarke wrote:

Australian science, effectively applied and made attractive to our young people as a career, lies at the heart of Australia's future. With the commitment and dedication of CSIRO to research that benefits the nation and with matching support from the government and community, I am confident that the goals we have set for the next five years and beyond will be achieved.

FOR ADDITIONAL READING

George Currie and John Graham, *The Origins of CSIRO: Science and the Commonwealth Government 1901–1926* (CSIRO, 1966).

Andrew McKay, *Surprise and Enterprise: Fifty Years of Science for Australia* (CSIRO, 1976).

C.B. Schedvin, *Shaping Science and Industry: A History of Australia's Council for Scientific and Industrial Research 1926–1949* (Allen & Unwin, 1987).

Index

This is a three-year cumulative index. Index entries for review articles in this and previous editions of the *Yearbook of Science and the Future* are set in boldface type, *e.g.,* **Archaeology.** Feature articles appear under the article title and are identified as such. Entries to other subjects are set in lightface type, *e.g.,* radiation. Additional information on any of these subjects is identified with a subheading and indented under the entry heading. Subheadings in quotes refer to feature articles on that topic. The numbers following headings and subheadings indicate the year (boldface) of the edition and the page number (lightface) on which the information appears. The abbreviation "*il.*" indicates an illustration.

Archaeology 95–286; **94**–286; **93**–281
    cats **94**–166
    "Dead Men's molecules" **94**–122
    "In Search of the First Americans" **93**–10

All entry headings are alphabetized word by word. Hyphenated words and words separated by dashes or slashes are treated as two words. When one word differs from another only by the presence of additional characters at the end, the shorter precedes the longer. In inverted names, the words following the comma are considered only after the preceding part of the name has been alphabetized. Names beginning with "Mc" and "Mac" are alphabetized as "Mac"; "St." is alphabetized as "Saint." Examples:

    Lake
    Lake, Simon
    Lake Placid
    Lakeland

a

a-life: *see* artificial life
A300-600F (air freighter) **93**–418, *il.* 419
A4 chip (microchip) **95**–484, *il.* 481
AAAS: *see* American Association for the Advancement of Science
AAEP: *see* American Association of Equine Practitioners
AAUW: *see* American Association of University Women
ab initio quantum mechanical calculation: *see* first-principles quantum mechanical calculation
Abbe, Ernst **94**–106
ABE: *see* Autonomous Benthic Explorer
Abegg, Martin, Jr. **93**–276
abortion
  fetal tissue in transplantation research **94**–429
  genetic research **94**–387
abstraction
  biomimetics **95**–182
AC: *see* alternating current
AC 114
  extragalactic astronomy **94**–297, *il.* 298
AC induction motor, *or* AC asynchronous motor
  electric vehicles **95**–157
AC synchronous motor: *see* permanent magnet DC brushless motor
Acanthodactylus dumerili: *see* desert lizard
Acanthostega **93**–369
accelerator mass spectrometry, *or* AMS **93**–21, 22
accident and safety
  electric vehicles **95**–164
  environmental disasters **93**–349
  lecture guidelines **95**–235
  truck accidents **93**–420
  see also disaster
accretion disk
  extragalactic astronomy **94**–296
accumulator ring
  antimatter **94**–38
ACE: *see* Advanced Computing Environment
ACE inhibitor: *see* angiotensin converting enzyme inhibitor
acetogenesis **94**–364
acid deposition
  energy **95**–345
acid rain **93**–54
Acinonyx jubatus: *see* cheetah
Acosta, José de **93**–10
acoustic cavitation **93**–396
acoustic cycle **94**–142
acquired immune deficiency syndrome: *see* AIDS
actin **94**–364
active galaxy **95**–61
active-matrix liquid crystal display, *or* active-matrix LCD **94**–314; **93**–197, *il.* 198

active oxygen species, *or* AOS
  nutrition **95**–358
acute respiratory distress syndrome, *or* Four Corners disease **95**–387
ADA: *see* American Dental Association
ADA deficiency: *see* adenosine deaminase deficiency
adagen, *or* PEG-ADA **95**–128
ADAMHA (U.S.): *see* Alcohol, Drug Abuse, and Mental Health Administration
add-with-carry (math.) **93**–381, *il.* 382
additive **93**–307
adenosine deaminase deficiency, *or* ADA deficiency **93**–126, *il.* 130
adenosine diphosphate: *see* ADP
adenosine triphosphate: *see* ATP
adobe
  earthquake damage **94**–322
ADP, *or* adenosine diphosphate **93**–368
Adriano, Domy **94**–478
ADSL, *or* asymmetrical digital subscriber line
  communications **95**–330
Advanced Communications Technology Satellite **94**–343
Advanced Computing Environment, *or* ACE **93**–330
Advanced Electronics System, *or* ARES
  automatic train control **94**–425
Advanced Mobile Phone Service **93**–326
Advanced Networks and Services, *or* ANS **94**–336
Advanced Research Projects Agency, *or* ARPA
  defense research **95**–312
Advanced Satellite for Cosmology and Astrophysics, *or* ASCA
  stars **95**–295
Advanced Technology Program, *or* ATP **94**–313
Advanced Traffic Management Systems **94**–180, *il.* 181
advanced train control system, *or* ATCS
  railroad transport **95**–424
Advanced Traveler Information Systems **94**–183
Advanced Turbine Technology Applications Project, *or* ATTAP **94**–375
Advanced Vehicle Control Systems **94**–187
Advanced Weather Interactive Processing System **95**–315
AEC: *see* Atomic Energy Commission
Aedes albopictus: *see* Asian tiger mosquito
AEI: *see* Automatic Equipment-Identification System
aerogel **94**–310
aerosol **94**–316; **93**–313
aerospace industry
  defense research **94**–315
  navigation satellites **94**–345
Africa
  AIDS and tuberculosis **94**–383; **93**–347, 363
  cats **94**–167
  environmental factors **94**–350

human origin **95**–283; **94**–284, *il.* 285; **93**–284
molecular archaeology **94**–134
Project SIDA **93**–383
silver ants **94**–372
African sleeping sickness **93**–373
aftershock (geophysics) **95**–322; **94**–323
AFTI: *see* Automated Tariff Filing and Information System
aggregate
  oceanography **94**–329
aggression **94**–355
  environment **95**–351
aging **95**–103
  glutathione treatment **95**–357
agriculture: *see* Food and agriculture
Agriculture, U.S. Department of, *or* USDA
  food and agriculture **95**–355; **94**–358
  veterinary medicine **95**–393
AIDS, *or* acquired immune deficiency syndrome
  computer-aided drug design **94**–98, *il.*
  dementia **95**–92
  dentistry **95**–390
  environment **94**–355
  epidemiology **93**–347
  gene therapy **93**–134
  medical microbiology **95**–365
  medical research **95**–383; **94**–384; **93**–383
  organic chemistry **95**–304
  U.S. science policy **95**–427; **94**–429; **93**–427
air pollution: *see* pollution
air pump **95**–223
air-traffic control: *see* aviation
air transport: *see* aviation
Airbus Industrie of France **94**–422; **93**–418
aircraft: *see* aviation
airport
  architecture **94**–292, *il.*; **93**–285
  transportation **94**–422
Airy disk **94**–113
Akers, Thomas D. **94**–414
  Hubble Telescope repair **95**–412
ALA: *see* American Library Association
Alamillo Bridge **94**–414
Alan Guttmacher Institute
  AIDS research **94**–355
Alaska **93**–17, 343
Alcock, Charles **95**–296
Alcohol, Drug Abuse, and Mental Health Administration, *or* ADAMHA (U.S.) **94**–429
alcoholism
  depression **95**–388
Alexander, James Waddell **93**–80
Alexander polynomial **93**–80
algae **94**–363
  farm-raised catfish **95**–357
  Lake Baikal **94**–217
  see also individual genera and species by name
algal bloom, *or* water bloom **93**–323
  microbiology **94**–363
Ali-Scout
  traveler information system *il.* **94**–186
alien
  "Imagining Aliens" **94**–68, *ils.* 69–85
"Alien" (motion picture) **94**–68
all-trans-retinoic acid **94**–368
allergy **94**–387
Allosaurus fragilis *ils.* **93**–33, 36
alloy **94**–379; **93**–307
Allseas Marine Services **94**–424
Almaz SAR **94**–344; **93**–325, 339
"Alpha" (proposed space station): *see* "Freedom"
Alpha chip
  computers **94**–334
  electronics **94**–337
ALS: *see* amyotrophic lateral sclerosis
alternating current, *or* AC
  locomotive traction **95**–424; **94**–426
alumina **93**–375
aluminum
  batteries **95**–309
  corrosion resistance **95**–378
aluminum gallium arsenide **94**–408
Alvarez, Luis Walter **93**–314
  "The Search for the KT Crater" **93**–90
"Alvin" (submersible) **95**–11, *il.*; **94**–330
Alyea, Hubert Newcombe **95**–232, *il.*
Alzheimer's disease **95**–384; **94**–386; **93**–384
  aging **95**–106
amalgam tooth filling **93**–390
  mercury contamination **95**–364
Amazon River region (S.Am.)
  indigenous peoples **94**–284
amber
  ancient DNA preserved **95**–360; **94**–370
Ambystoma tigrinum neblosum: *see* tiger salamander
American Anthropological Association **94**–283; **93**–279
"American Anthropologist" (Am. journ.)
  archaeology **94**–286

American Association for the Advancement of Science, *or* AAAS
  history of science **93**–240
  molecule of the year **94**–299
  psychology **94**–411
American Association of Casualty and Surety Companies **93**–212, 217
American Association of Equine Practitioners, *or* AAEP **93**–393
American Association of University Women, *or* AAUW **93**–409
American Bureau of Shipping
  computerized standards **95**–425
American cactus: *see* prickly pear
American Canine Sports Medicine Association **93**–391
American Chemical Society **95**–235; **94**–312
American chestnut, *or* Castanea dentata **95**–214; **94**–362
American College of Veterinary Behaviorists **95**–392
American Dental Association, *or* ADA **95**–389; **94**–389; **93**–389
American Dietetic Association **93**–356
American Flywheel Systems Inc.
  electronics **95**–338
American Indian, *or* Native American
  anthropology **95**–285; **93**–279
  archaeology **94**–286
  earliest Americans **93**–10
  molecular archaeology **94**–126, 131
American Institute of Architects **94**–291
American Library Association, *or* ALA **93**–335
American literature
  information systems and services **95**–341
American Mobile Satellite Corp.
  communications satellites **95**–342
American Physical Society, *or* APS **93**–427
American President Companies
  automatic equipment identification **95**–425
American Psychoanalytic Association **94**–413
American Psychological Association, *or* APA **95**–411; **94**–410; **93**–408
  information systems and services **95**–340
"American Scientist" (journ.)
  cold fusion **94**–309
American Society of Civil Engineers **94**–293
American Telephone & Telegraph Company, *or* AT&T **94**–331; **93**–419
  high-definition television **94**–337
  voice encryption **95**–336
American Veterinary Medical Association, *or* AVMA **95**–392; **94**–392
American Veterinary Medical Law Association **95**–392
Americas, the **93**–10, 91
AMIGOS Bibliographic Council (U.S.) **93**–337
amino acid **95**–126, 366; **94**–89; **93**–283, 364
ammonia **93**–405
amnesia **94**–413
amorphous iron
  sonochemistry **94**–153
amorphous metal **93**–396, *il.*
  sonochemistry **94**–153
AMP: *see* cyclic adenosine monophosphate
amphibian
  decline **94**–355
  Savannah River Ecology Laboratory **94**–483
amphipod *il.* **94**–330
  Lake Baikal **94**–218, *il.* 221
AMR Corp.
  automated shipping **94**–421
AMS: *see* accelerator mass spectrometry
Amtrak **95**–423; **94**–425; **93**–422
amyotrophic lateral sclerosis, *or* ALS **95**–384; **93**–386
analog microscope **94**–111
analog transmission, *or* analog scheme **94**–332; **93**–326
Anatomist
  CD-ROM data bases **94**–340
anatomy **95**–224
"Anatomy Lesson of Dr. Nicolaes Tulp, The" (Rembrandt) **95**–224, *il.*
anchored instruction (psychol.) **95**–410
anchovy **93**–324
Aneilema aequinectiale
  zoopharmacognosy **95**–198
anemia **95**–120
Andersen Bjornstad Kane Jacobs
  civil engineering **94**–293
Anderson, Carl David **94**–33, *il.*
Anderson, Thomas Foxen **93**–443
Anderson, W. French
  "Gene Therapy: A New Frontier in Medicine" **93**–126
Andrew, Hurricane: *see* hurricane
androgen **93**–143
Angara River (Russ.) **94**–212
angiotensin converting enzyme inhibitor, *or* ACE inhibitor
  heart disease **94**–385

Acknowledgments

6   (Top to bottom) Atlantis Submarines International; Giraudon/
    Art Resource; © Fawcett, Heuser, and Reese—Science Source/
    Photo Researchers, Inc.; AT&T Bell Laboratories

7   (Top to bottom) David Woodfall—NHPA; © London Scientific
    Films—OSF; Terry Chambers; CSIRO

54, 62   Illustrations by John L. Draves

88–101   Illustrations by Steven Kapusta

106, 109, 110   Illustrations by Stephanie Motz

137–146   Illustrations by Kathryn Diffley

155, 159, 162   Illustrations by Jon Hensley

212   (Left) adapted from *The Ecology of Invasions by Animals and
      Plants* (1958) by C.S. Elton, Methuen, London; (right) adapted
      from "Measuring the Rate of Spread of Early Farming in
      Europe," A.J. Ammerman and L.L. Cavalli-Sforza, *Man,* vol. 6,
      pp. 674–688, 1971

300   From "Capillarity-induced Filling of Carbon Nanotubes," P.M.
      Ajayan and Sumio Iijima, reprinted by permission of *Nature,* vol.
      361, no. 6410, cover and pp. 333–334, January 28, 1993,
      © Macmillan Magazines Ltd.

306   From "Pattern Formation by Interacting Chemical Fronts,"
      Kyoung J. Lee, W.D. McCormick, Qi Ouyang, Harry L. Swinney,
      Science, vol. 261, no. 5118, pp. 192–194, July 9, 1993, © 1993
      AAAS

367   From "Crystal Structure of Bacteriophage T7 RNA Polymerase at
      3.3 Å Resolution," Rui Sousa, Yong Je Chung, John P. Rose, and
      Bi-Cheng Wang, reprinted by permission of *Nature,* vol. 364,
      no. 6438, pp. 593–599, August 12, 1993, © 1993 Macmillan
      Magazines Ltd.

370   From "The X-ray Crystal Structure of the Membrane Protein
      Prostaglandin H_2 Synthase-1," Daniel Picot, Patrick J. Loll, and
      R. Michael Gravito, reprinted by permission of *Nature,* vol. 367,
      no. 6460, pp. 243–249, January 20, 1994, © 1994 Macmillan
      Magazines Ltd.

390   From "Interaction of the Human Immunodeficiency Virus
      Type-1 with Human Salivary Mucins," E. James Bergey, *et al.,*
      Journal of Acquired Immune Deficiency Syndromes (in press),
      reproduced with permission of Raven Press, Ltd.

406   From "Confinement of Electrons to Quantum Corrals on a Metal
      Surface," M.F. Crommie, C.P. Lutz, and D.M. Eigler, *Science,*
      vol. 262, no. 5131, pp. 218–220, October 8, 1993, © 1993
      AAAS